OXFORD
UNIVERSITY PRESS

ASPIRE
SUCCEED
PROGRESS

Complete Mathematics for Cambridge IGCSE®

Fifth Edition

Core

David Rayner
Ian Bettison
Mathew Taylor

Oxford excellence for Cambridge IGCSE®

OXFORD
UNIVERSITY PRESS

Great Clarendon Street, Oxford, OX2 6DP, United Kingdom

Oxford University Press is a department of the University of Oxford.
It furthers the University's objective of excellence in research, scholarship, and education by publishing worldwide. Oxford is a registered trade mark of Oxford University Press in the UK and in certain other countries

First published in 2018

British Library Cataloguing in Publication Data
Data available

978-0-19-842504-5

3 5 7 9 10 8 6 4

Paper used in the production of this book is a natural, recyclable product made from wood grown in sustainable forests. The manufacturing process conforms to the environmental regulations of the country of origin.

Printed and bound by CPI Group (UK) Ltd, Croydon, CR0 4YY

Acknowledgements
The publishers would like to thank the following for permissions to use copyright material:

® IGCSE is the registered trademark of Cambridge Assessment International Education.

Past paper examination material reproduced by permission of Cambridge Assessment International Education.

Cambridge Assessment International Education bears no responsibility for the example answers to questions taken from its past question papers which are contained in this publication.

p72: Dreamcreation/Shutterstock; **p76:** Mariontxa/Shutterstock; **p79:** Hadrian/Shutterstock; **p89:** sizov/Shutterstock; **p90:** Clara/Shutterstock; **p92:** Quang Ho/Shutterstock; **p93:** FrameAngel/Shutterstock; **p97:** sandar Todorovic/Shutterstock; **p98:** Dado Photos/Shutterstock; **p100:** Supertrooper/Shutterstock; **p103:** Tarikdiz/Shutterstock; **p106:** acceptphoto/Shutterstock; **p107:** OlegSam/Shutterstock; **p109:** Eric Isselee/Shutterstock; **p111:** Gallinago_media/Shutterstock; **p116:** MarijaPiliponyte/Shutterstock; **p119:** Robert Gubbins/Shutterstock; **p120:** Ken Browning/Shutterstock; **p124:** Tomacco/Shutterstock; **p151:** MuchMania/Shutterstock; **p151:** DNY59/iStock; **p151:** Radoman Durkovic/Shutterstock; **p153:** Alexandr79/Shutterstock; **p154:** nexus 7/Shutterstock; **p177:** Blend Images/Shutterstock; **p250:** John T Takai/Shutterstock; **p250:** baitong333/Shutterstock; **p255:** Regissercom/Dreamstime.com; **p259:** Aphelleon/Shutterstock; **p260:** ChiccoDodiFC/Shutterstock; **p262:** kotiss/Shutterstock; **p264:** alphaspirit/Shutterstock; **p267:** philophoto/Shutterstock; **p268:** kovop58/Shutterstock; **p277:** DimaChe/Getty Images; **p280:** Panda Vector/Shutterstock; **p282:** M. Cornelius/Shutterstock; **p282:** Memo Angeles/Shutterstock; **p290:** mahfud21/Shutterstock; **p292:** Claudio Divizia/Shutterstock; **p342:** Q2A Media

Cover image: Shutterstock

Although we have made every effort to trace and contact all copyright holders before publication this has not been possible in all cases. If notified, the publisher will rectify any errors or omissions at the earliest opportunity.

Links to third party websites are provided by Oxford in good faith and for information only. Oxford disclaims any responsibility for the materials contained in any third party website referenced in this work.

Contents

Access your support website for extra homework questions and exam revision material
www.oxfordsecondary.com/9780198425045

Cambridge IGCSE® Mathematics 0580: Core

Syllabus topic		Page numbers in student book
C1: Number		
C1.1	Identify and use natural numbers, integers (positive, negative and zero), prime numbers, square numbers, common factors and common multiples, rational and irrational numbers (e.g. π, $\sqrt{2}$), real numbers, reciprocals.	72–74, 88–92
C1.2	Understand notation of Venn diagrams. Definition of sets e.g. $A = \{x: x \text{ is a natural number}\}$, $B = \{a, b, c, \ldots\}$	301–302
C1.3	Calculate squares, square roots, cubes and cube roots of numbers.	328–333
C1.4	Use directed numbers in practical situations.	339–343
C1.5	Use the language and notation of simple vulgar and decimal fractions and percentages in appropriate contexts. Recognise equivalence and convert between these forms.	102–103, 257–258
C1.6	Order quantities by magnitude and demonstrate familiarity with the symbols $=, \neq, >, <, \geqslant, \leqslant$	78, 92–94, 337
C1.7	Understand the meaning and rules of indices (fractional, negative and zero) and use the rules of indices. Use the standard form $A \times 10^n$ where n is a positive or negative integer, and $1 \leqslant A < 10$.	331–336
C1.8	Use the four rules for calculations with whole numbers, decimals and vulgar (including mixed numbers and improper fractions), including correct ordering of operations and use of brackets.	74–77, 80–88, 97–100, 275–276, 336–338
C1.9	Make estimates of numbers, quantities and lengths, give approximations to specified numbers of significant figures and decimal places and round off answers to reasonable accuracy in the context of a given problem.	118–120, 259–260
C1.10	Give appropriate upper and lower bounds for data given to a specified accuracy.	263–264
C1.11	Demonstrate an understanding of ratio and proportion. Calculate average speed. Use common measures of rate.	107–114, 115–118
C1.12	Calculate a given percentage of a quantity. Express one quantity as a percentage of another. Calculate percentage increase or decrease.	101–104, 253–256
C1.13	Use a calculator efficiently. Apply appropriate checks of accuracy.	276–278
C1.14	Calculate times in terms of the 24-hour and 12-hour clock. Read clocks, dials and timetables.	94–97

C1.15	Calculate using money and convert from one currency to another.	114–115
C1.16	Use given data to solve problems on personal and household finance involving earnings, simple interest and compound interest. Extract data from tables and charts.	104–106
C2: Algebra and graphs		
C2.1	Use letters to express generalised numbers and express basic arithmetic processes algebraically. Substitute numbers for words and letters in formulae. Transform simple formulae. Construct simple expressions and set up simple equations.	49–57, 243–245, 343–346
C2.2	Manipulate directed numbers. Use brackets and extract common factors. Expand products of algebraic expressions.	241–242
C2.4	Use and interpret positive, negative and zero indices. Use the rules of indices.	331–333
C2.5	Derive and solve simple linear equations in one unknown. Derive and solve simultaneous linear equations in two unknowns.	226–232
C2.7	Continue a given number sequence. Recognise patterns in sequences including the term-to-term rule and relationships between different sequences. Find the *n*th term of sequences.	47–49, 221–226
C2.10	Interpret and use graphs in practical situations including travel graphs and conversion graphs. Draw graphs from given data.	57–60, 150–151, 232–240
C2.11	Construct tables of values for functions of the form $ax + b$, $\pm x^2 + ax + b$, $\frac{a}{x}$ $(x \neq 0)$, where a and b are integral constants. Draw and interpret these graphs. Solve linear and quadratic equations approximately, including finding and interpreting roots by graphical methods. Recognise, sketch and interpret graphs of functions.	65–67
C3: Coordinate geometry		
C3.1	Demonstrate familiarity with Cartesian coordinates in two dimensions.	61–65, 196–198
C3.2	Find the gradient of a straight line.	61–62
C3.4	Interpret and obtain the equation of a straight-line graph in the form $y = mx + c$.	62–65
C3.5	Determine the equation of a straight line parallel to a given line.	65
C4: Geometry		
C4.1	Use and interpret the geometrical terms: point, line, parallel, bearing, right angle, acute, obtuse and reflex angles, perpendicular, similarity and congruence. Use and interpret vocabulary of triangles, quadrilaterals, circles, polygons and simple solid figures including nets.	4–5
C4.2	Measure and draw lines and angles. Construct a triangle given the three sides using ruler and pair of compasses only.	1–3

C4.3	Read and make scale drawings.	37–39
C4.4	Calculate lengths of similar figures.	312–315
C4.5	Recognise congruent shapes.	315–316
C4.6	Recognise rotational and line symmetry (including order of rotational symmetry) in two dimensions.	14–16
C4.7	Calculate unknown angles using the following geometrical properties: • angles at a point • angles at a point on a straight line and intersecting straight lines • angles formed within parallel lines • angle properties of triangles and quadrilaterals • angle properties of regular polygons • angle in a semicircle • angle between tangent and radius of a circle.	5–14
C3.7	Use the following loci and the method of intersecting loci for sets of points in two dimensions which are: • at a given distance from a given point • at a given distance from a given straight line • equidistant from two given points • equidistant from two given intersecting straight lines.	200–203
C5: Mensuration		
C5.1	Use current units of mass, length, area, volume and capacity in practical situations and express quantities in terms of larger or smaller units.	121–123
C5.2	Carry out calculations involving the perimeter and area of a rectangle, triangle, parallelogram and trapezium and compound shapes derived from these.	26–29
C5.3	Carry out calculations involving the circumference and area of a circle. Solve problems involving the arc length and sector area as fractions of the circumference and area of a circle.	16–26
C5.4	Carry out calculations involving the surface area and volume of a cuboid, prism and cylinder. Carry out calculations involving the surface area and volume of a sphere, pyramid and cone.	31–36
C5.5	Carry out calculations involving the areas and volumes of compound shapes.	17, 20, 21, 27, 32, 35
C6: Trigonometry		
C6.1	Interpret and use three-figure bearings.	203–208
C6.2	Apply Pythagoras' theorem and the sine, cosine and tangent ratios for acute angles to the calculation of a side or of an angle of a right-angled triangle.	209–211, 316–322

C7: Vectors and transformations		
C7.1	Describe a translation by using a vector represented by e.g. $\begin{pmatrix} x \\ y \end{pmatrix}$, $\overrightarrow{AB}$ or **a.** Add and subtract vectors. Multiply a vector by a scalar.	193–195
C7.2	Reflect simple plane figures in horizontal or vertical lines. Rotate simple plane figures about the origin, vertices or midpoints of edges of the figures, through multiples of 90°. Construct given translations and enlargements of simple plane figures. Recognise and describe reflections, rotations, translations and enlargements.	179–193
C8: Probability		
C8.1	Calculate the probability of a single event as either a fraction, decimal or percentage.	293–307
C8.2	Understand and use the probability scale from 0 to 1.	292–293
C8.3	Understand that the probability of an event occurring = 1 – the probability of the event not occurring.	293–307
C8.4	Understand relative frequency as an estimate of probability. Expected frequency of occurrences.	296–297, 299–300
C8.5	Calculate the probability of simple combined events, using possibility diagrams, tree diagrams and Venn diagrams.	294–307
C9: Statistics		
C9.1	Collect, classify and tabulate statistical data.	138–150, 153–154
C9.2	Read, interpret and draw simple inferences from tables and statistical diagrams. Compare sets of data using tables, graphs and statistical measures. Appreciate restrictions on drawing conclusions from given data.	138–150
C9.3	Construct and interpret bar charts, pie charts, pictograms, stem-and-leaf diagrams, simple frequency distributions, histograms with equal intervals and scatter diagrams.	138–150, 169–173
C9.4	Calculate the mean, median, mode and range for individual and discrete data and distinguish between the purposes for which they are used.	165–168
C9.7	Understand what is meant by positive, negative and zero correlation with reference to a scatter diagram.	151–154
C9.8	Draw, interpret and use lines of best fit by eye.	155–156

Introduction

About this book

This revised 5th edition is designed to provide the best preparation for your Cambridge IGCSE examination, and has been completely updated for the latest Mathematics 0580 and 0980 Core syllabus.

Finding your way around

To get the most out of this book when studying or revising, use the:

- **Contents list** to help you find the appropriate units.
- **Index** to find any key concept straight away.

Exercises and exam-style questions

There are thousands of questions in this book, providing ample opportunities to practise the skills and techniques required in the exam.

- **Worked examples and comprehensive exercises** are one of the main features of the book. The examples show you the important skills and techniques required. The exercises are carefully graded, starting from the basics and going up to exam standard, allowing you to practise the skills and techniques.
- **Revision exercises** at the end of each unit allow you to bring together all your knowledge on a particular topic.
- **Examination-style exercises** at the end of each unit consist of questions from past Cambridge IGCSE papers.
- **Examination-style papers:** there are two papers, corresponding to the papers you will take at the end of your course: Paper 1 and Paper 3. They give you the opportunity to practise for the real thing.
- **Revision section:** Unit 12 contains multiple-choice questions to provide an extra opportunity to revise.
- **Answers to numerical problems** are at the end of the book so you can check your progress.

Investigations

Unit 11 provides many opportunities for you to explore the world of mathematical problem-solving through investigations, puzzles and games.

Links to curriculum content

At the start of each unit you will find a list of objectives that are covered in the unit. These objectives are drawn from the Core sections of the Cambridge IGCSE syllabus.

What's on the website?

The support website contains a wealth of material to help solidify your understanding of the Cambridge IGCSE Mathematics course, and to aid revision for your examinations.

All this material can be found online, at www.oxfordsecondary.com/9780198425045

1 Shape and Space 1

C4.1 Use and interpret the geometrical terms: point, line, parallel, bearing, right angle, acute, obtuse and reflex angles, perpendicular, similarity and congruence. Use and interpret vocabulary of triangles, quadrilaterals, circles, polygons and simple solid figures including nets.

C4.2 Measure and draw lines and angles. Construct a triangle given the three sides using ruler and pair of compasses only.

C4.3 Read and make scale drawings.

C4.6 Recognise rotational and line symmetry (including order of rotational symmetry) in two dimensions.

C4.7 Calculate unknown angles using the following geometrical properties:

- angles at a point
- angles at a point on a straight line and intersecting straight lines
- angles formed within parallel lines
- angle properties of triangles and quadrilaterals
- angle properties of regular polygons
- angle in a semicircle
- angle between tangent and radius of a circle.

C5.2 Carry out calculations involving the perimeter and area of a rectangle, triangle, parallelogram and trapezium and compound shapes derived from these.

C5.3 Carry out calculations involving the circumference and area of a circle. Solve simple problems involving the arc length and sector area as fractions of the circumference and area of a circle.

C5.4 Carry out calculations involving the surface area and volume of a cuboid, prism and cylinder. Carry out calculations involving the surface area and volume of a sphere, pyramid and cone.

C5.5 Carry out calculations involving the areas and volumes of compound shapes.

1.1 Accurate drawing

Some questions involving bearings or irregular shapes are easy to solve by drawing an accurate diagram.

Navigators on ships use scale drawings to work out their position or their course.

To improve the accuracy of your work, follow these guidelines.

- Use a *sharp* HB pencil.
- Don't press too hard.
- If drawing an *acute* angle make sure your angle is less than 90°.
- If you use a pair of compasses make sure they are fairly stiff so the radius does not change accidently.

Example

Draw the triangle ABC full size and measure the length x.

a) Draw a base line *longer than* 8.5 *cm*.

b) Put the centre of the protractor on A and measure an angle 64°. Draw line AP.

c) Similarly draw line BQ at an angle 40° to AB.

d) The triangle is formed.
Measure $x = 5.6$ cm.

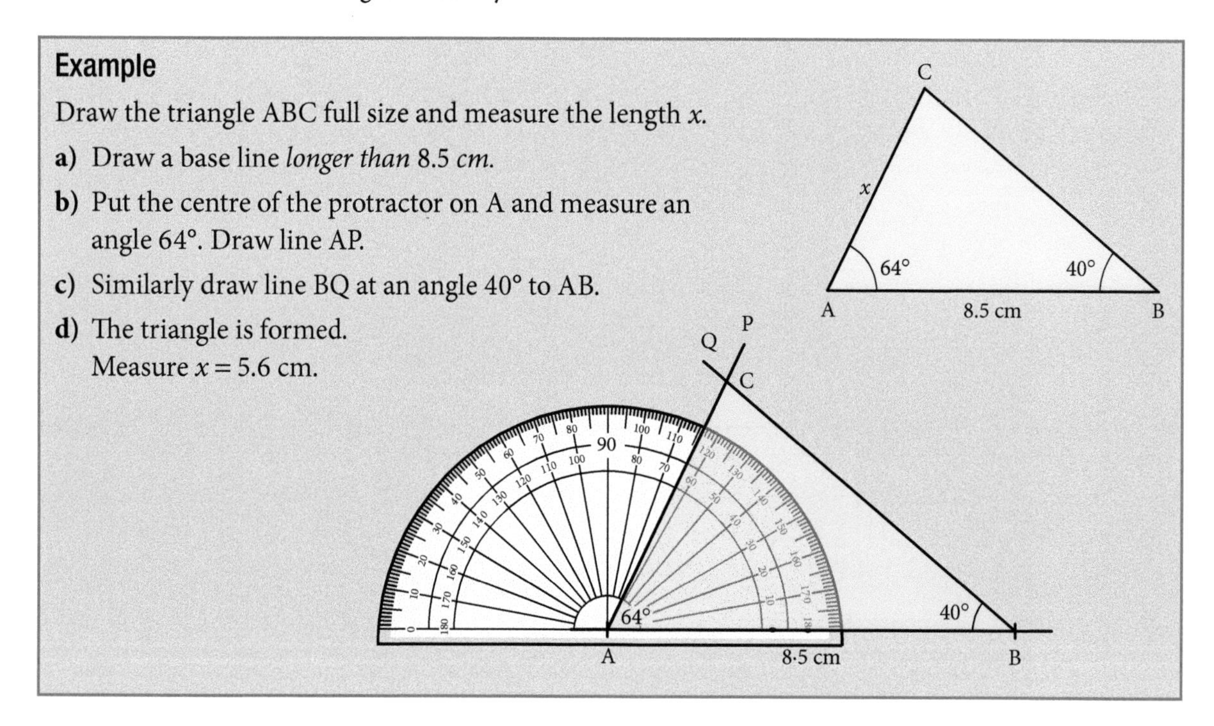

Exercise 1

Use a protractor and ruler to draw full size diagrams and measure the sides marked with letters.

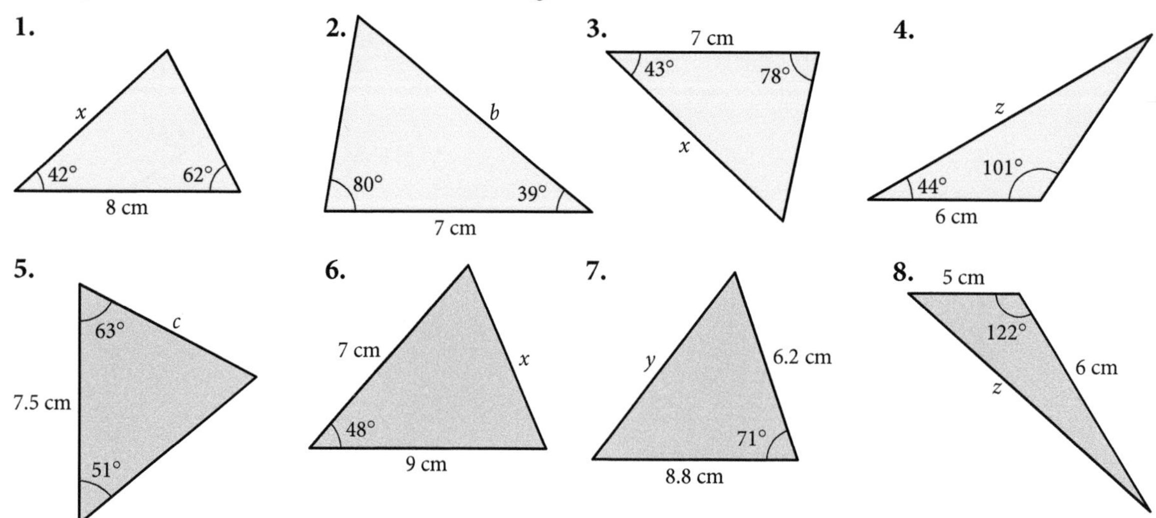

9.

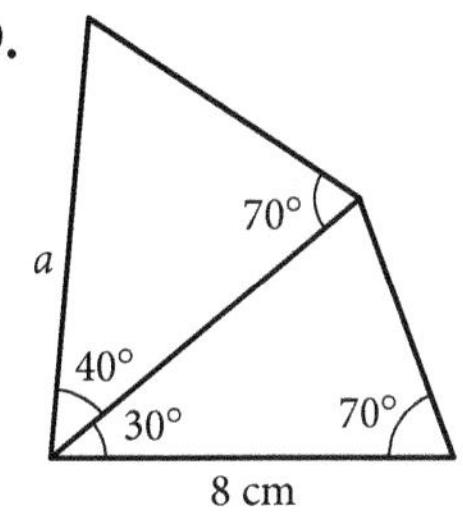

10.

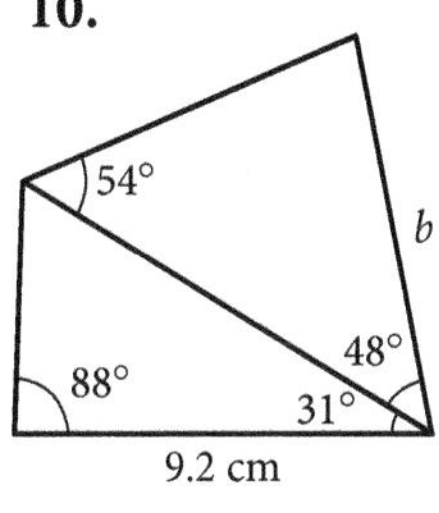

11.

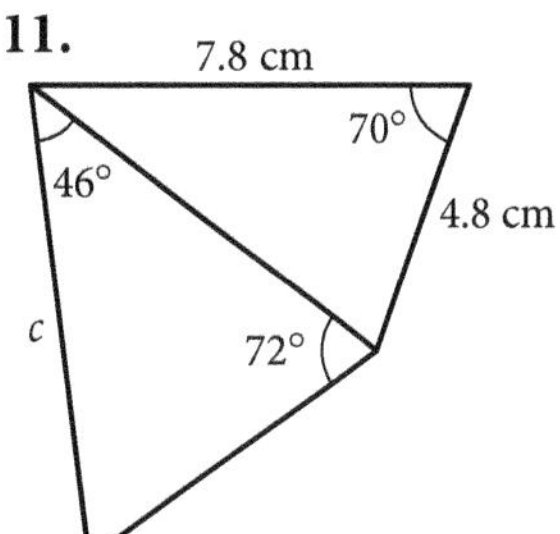

12.

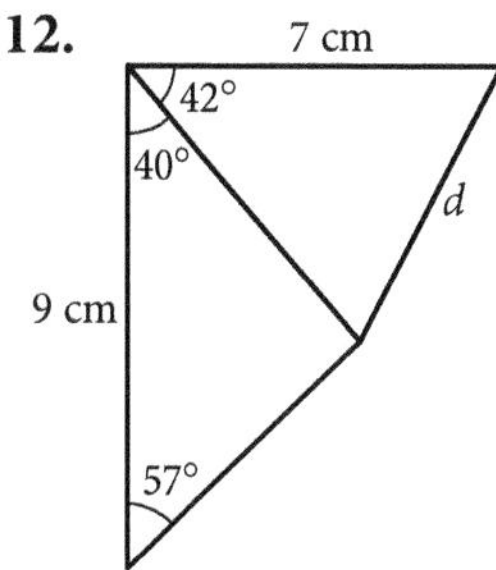

Example

Draw the triangle ABC full size and measure the angle x.

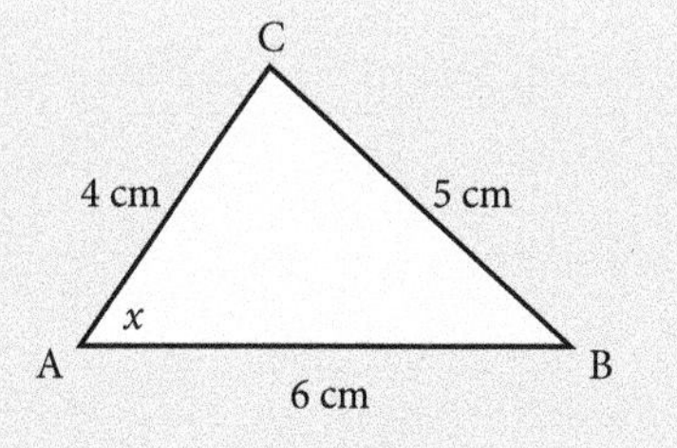

a) Draw a base line AB exactly 6 cm long.

b) Set a pair of compasses to 4 cm and draw an arc centred on A above the base line.

c) Similarly, set a pair of compasses to 5 cm and draw another arc centred on B intersecting the first.

d) Join this crossing point to A and B. The triangle is formed.

e) Measure the angle marked $x = 56°$.

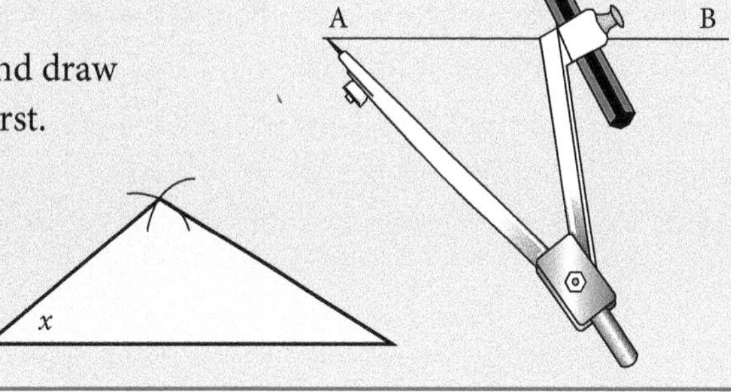

Exercise 2

Use a ruler and pair of compasses to make accurate drawings of these triangles and measure the angles marked with x.

1.

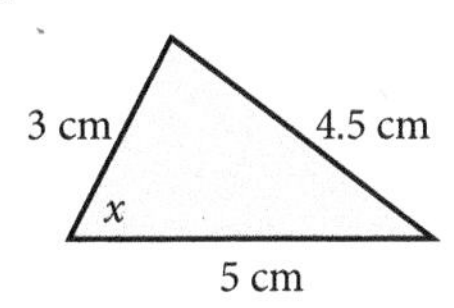

2.

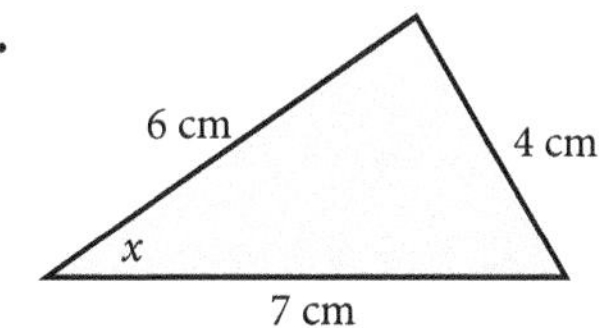

3.

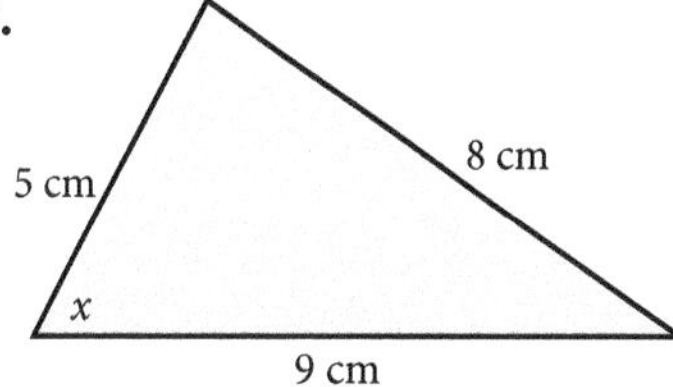

4.

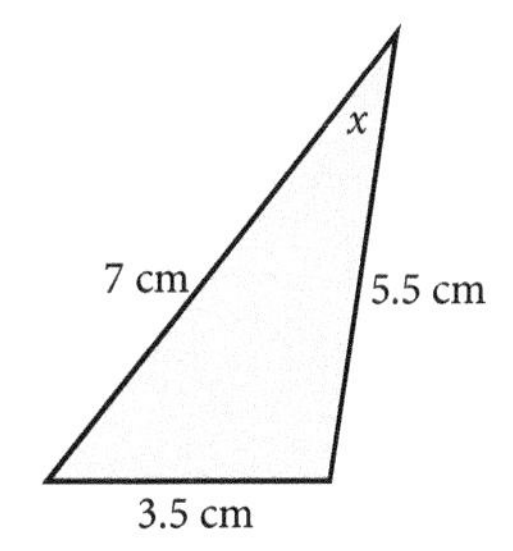

5.

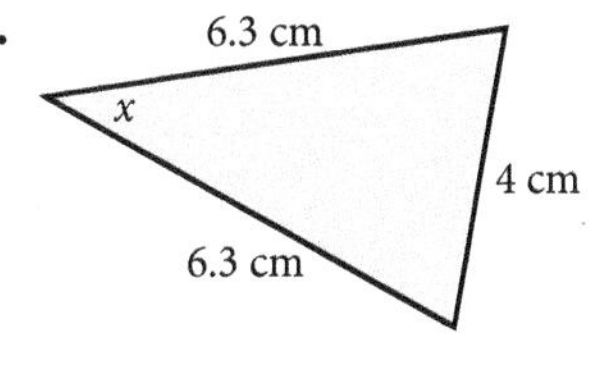

6.

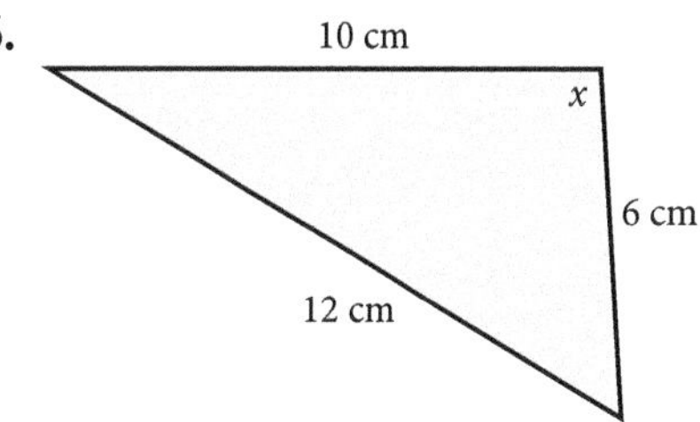

Nets

If the cube here was made of cardboard, and you cut along some of the edges and laid it out flat, you would have the *net* of the cube.

Here is the net for a square-based pyramid.

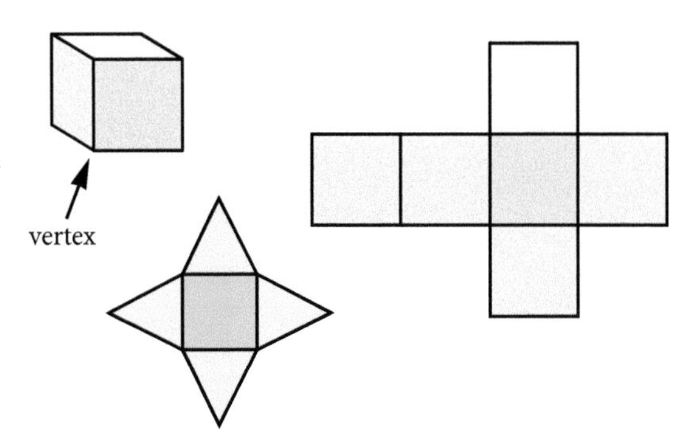

Exercise 3

1. Which of the nets below can be used to make a cube?

a) **b)** **c)** **d)**

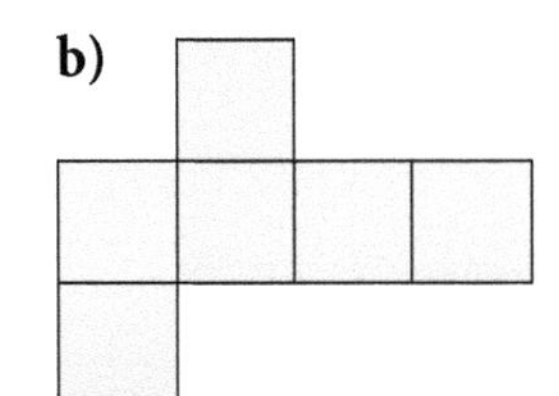

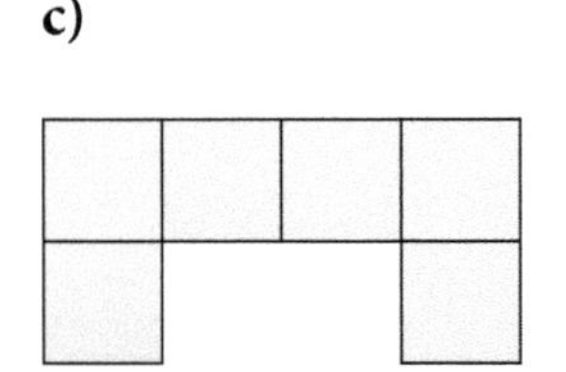

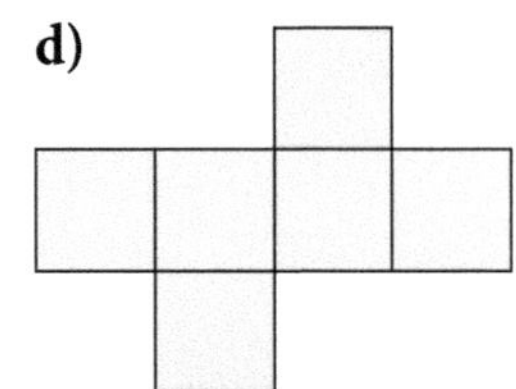

2. The numbers on opposite faces of a dice add up to 7. Take one of the possible nets for a cube from Question **1** and show the number of dots on each face.

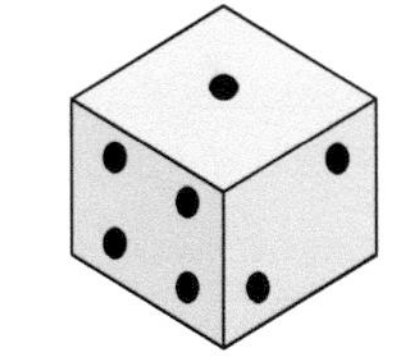

3. Here we have started to draw the net of a cuboid (a closed rectangular box) measuring 4 cm × 3 cm × 1 cm.
Copy and then complete the net.

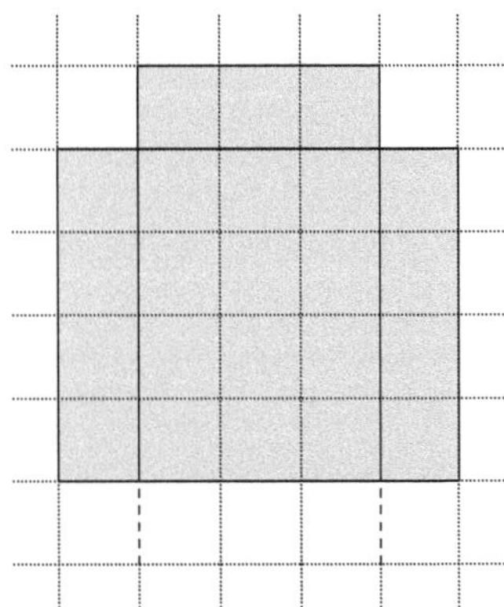

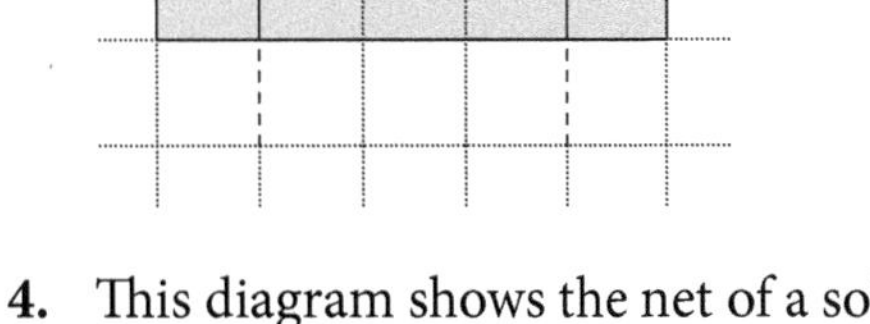

4. This diagram shows the net of a solid.

a) Use a ruler and pair of compasses to draw the net accurately on paper or card.

b) Draw on some flaps.

c) Cut out the net, fold and glue it to make the solid.

d) What is the name of the solid?

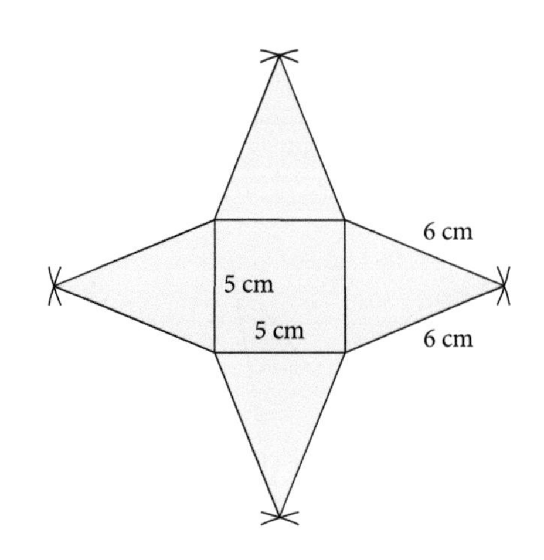

5. A cube can be made from three equal pyramids.

Make three solids from the net shown and fit them together to make a cube. All lengths are in cm.

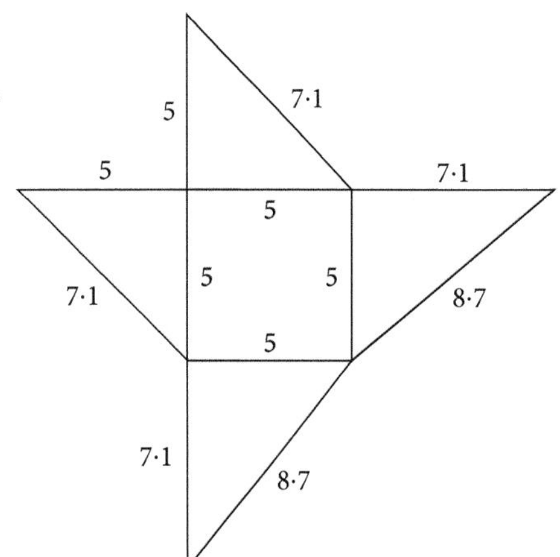

6. Sketch a possible net for each of the following:

a) a cuboid measuring 5 cm by 2 cm by 8 cm

b) a cuboid with sides 3 cm, 4 cm and 5 cm.

1.2 Angle facts

- The angles at a point add up to 360°.
- The angles on a straight line add up to 180°.
- An angle of 90° is called a **right angle**.
- An **acute** angle is less than 90°.
- An **obtuse** angle is between 90° and 180°.
- A **reflex** angle is greater than 180°.

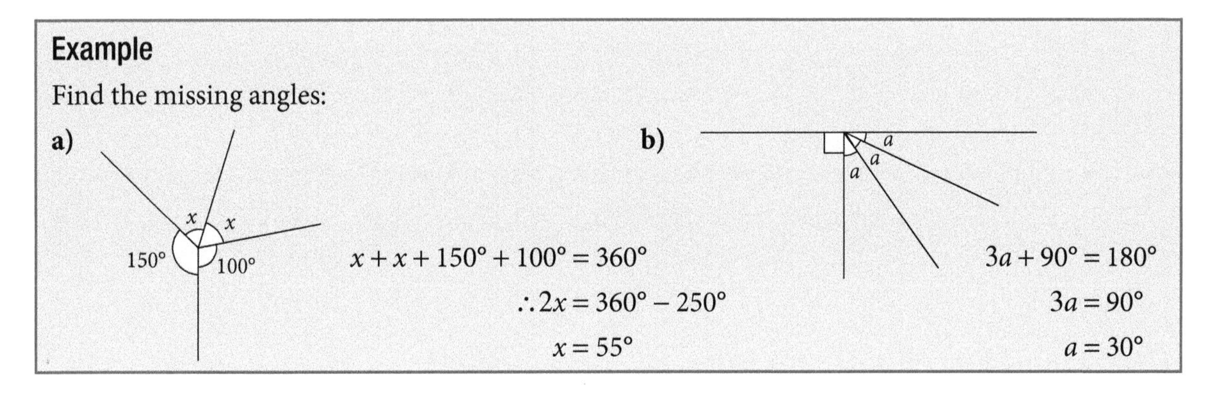

Exercise 4

Find the angles marked with letters. The lines AB and CD are straight.

1. c, 150°, 140°

2.

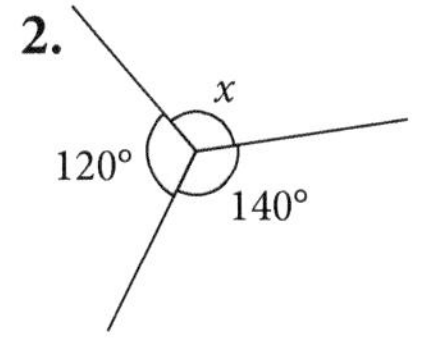

3.

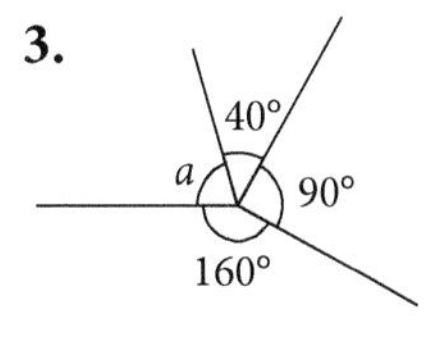

4.

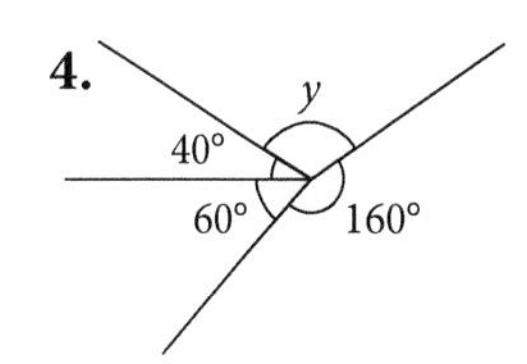

5. A, B, 71°, 65°, y

6.

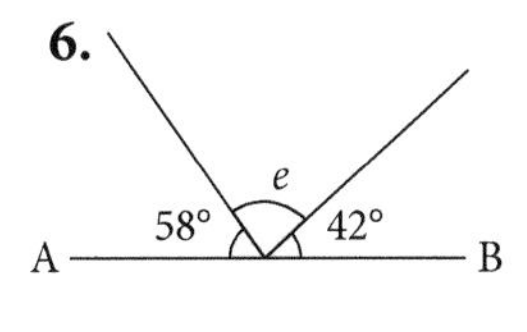

7. A, B, 100°, x, x

8.

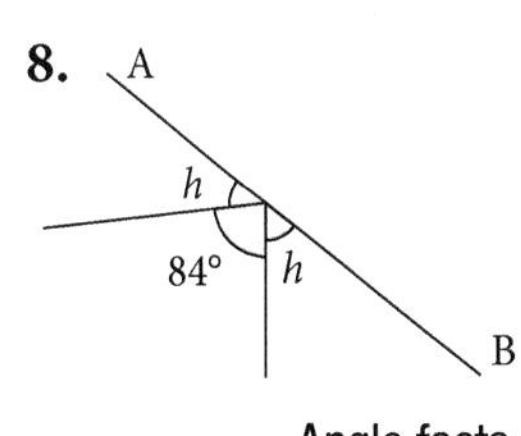

9.

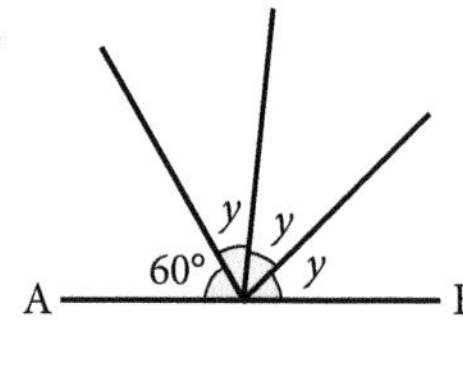

10.

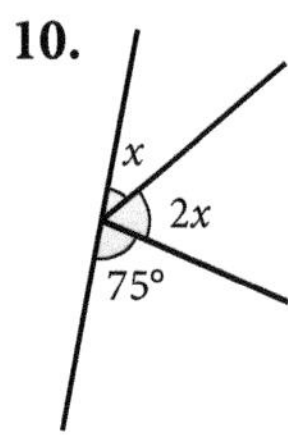

11.

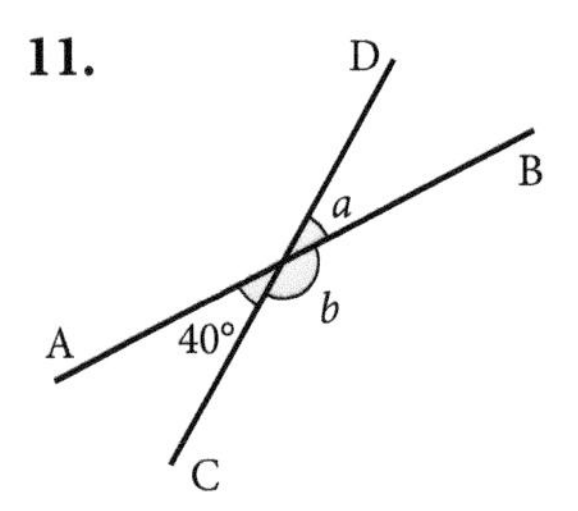

12.

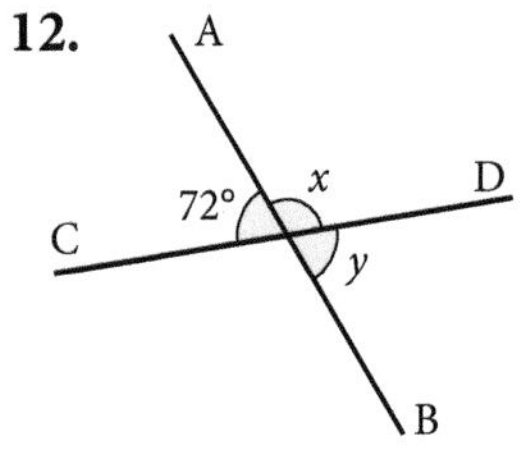

Triangles

The angles in a triangle add up to 180°.

> **Example**
>
> Find the missing angles:
>
> $a = 180° - 150° = 30°$
>
> 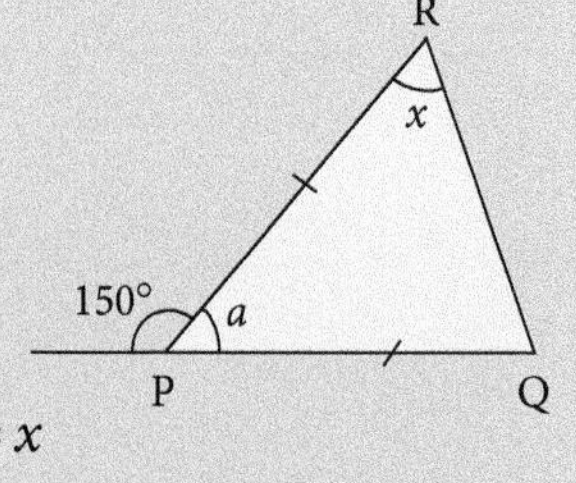
>
>
> The triangle is isosceles so angle RQP $= x$
>
> $\therefore 2x + 30° = 180°$
>
> $2x = 150°$
>
> $x = 75°$

Exercise 5

Find the angles marked with letters. For the more difficult questions it is helpful to draw a diagram.

1.

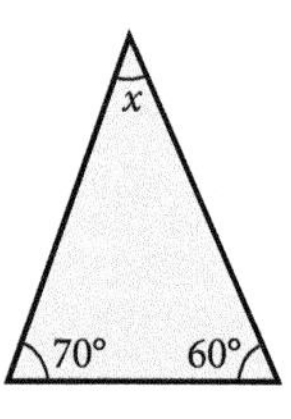

2.

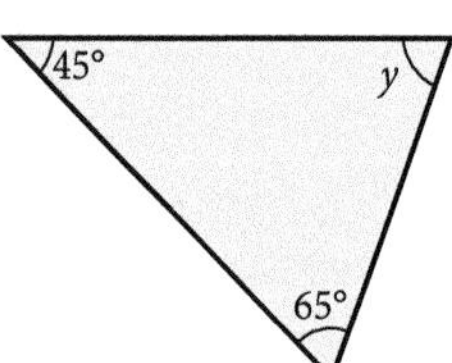

3.

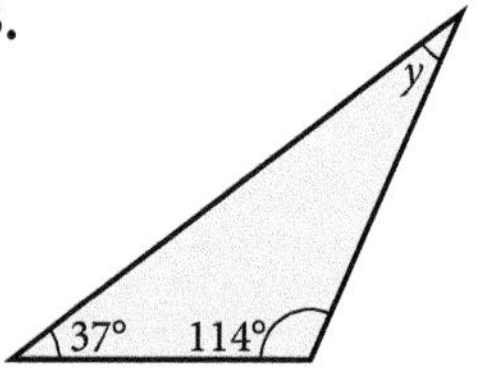

4.

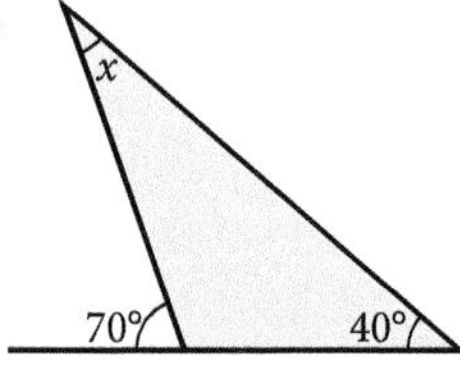

5.

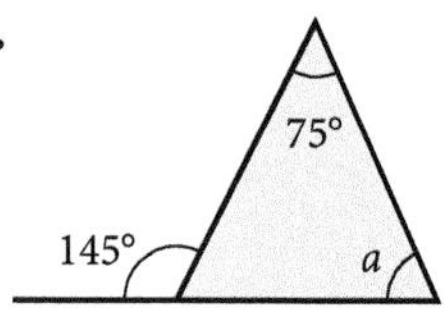

6.

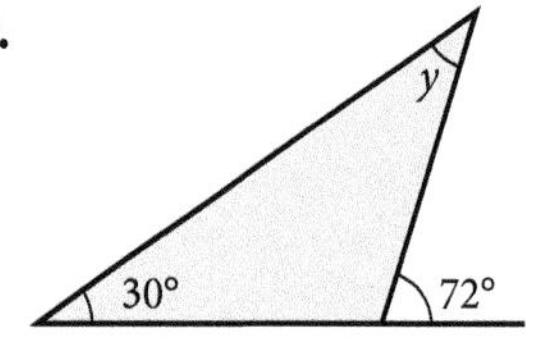

7.

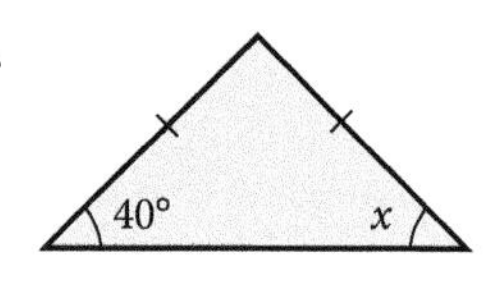

8.

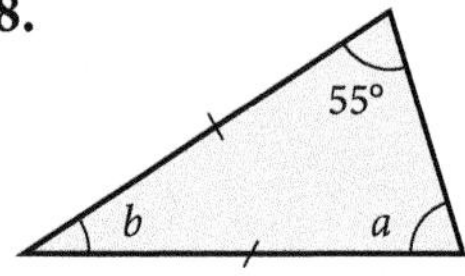

9.

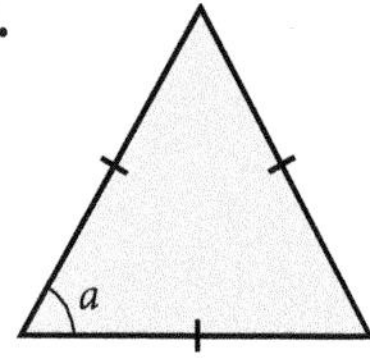

10.

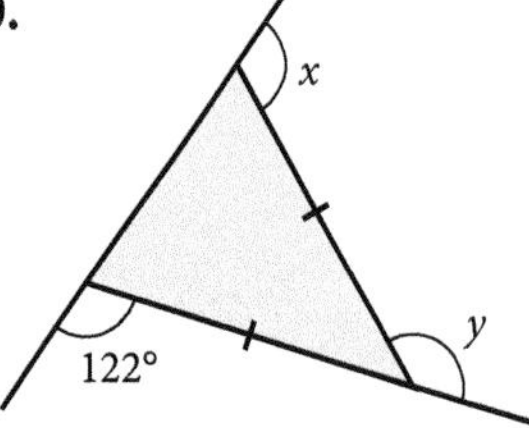

11.

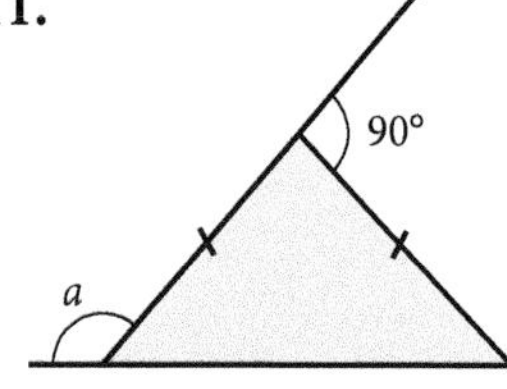

12.

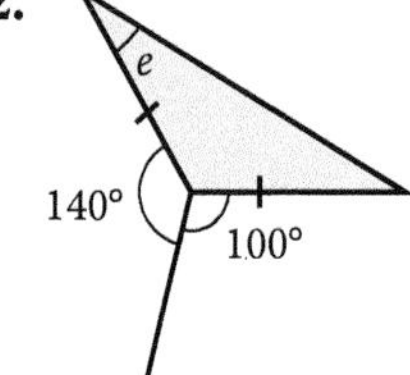

13.

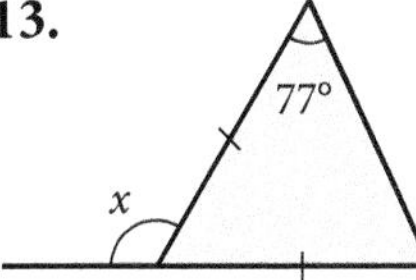

14.

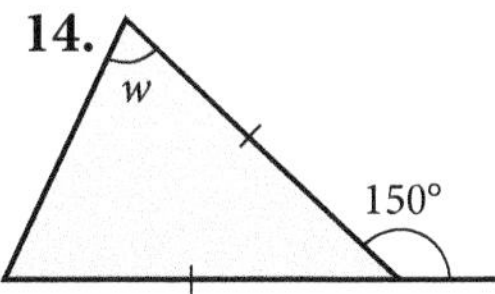

15.

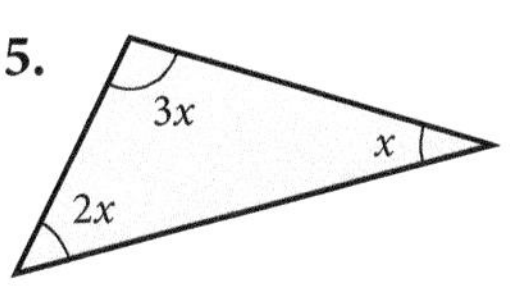

16.

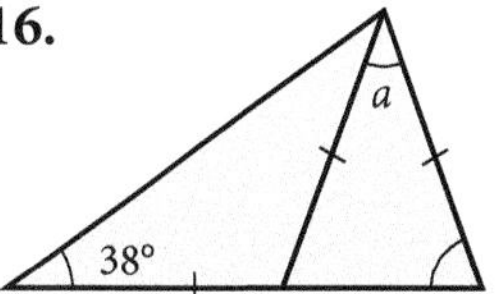

Parallel lines

When a line cuts a pair of parallel lines all the acute angles are equal and all the obtuse angles are equal.

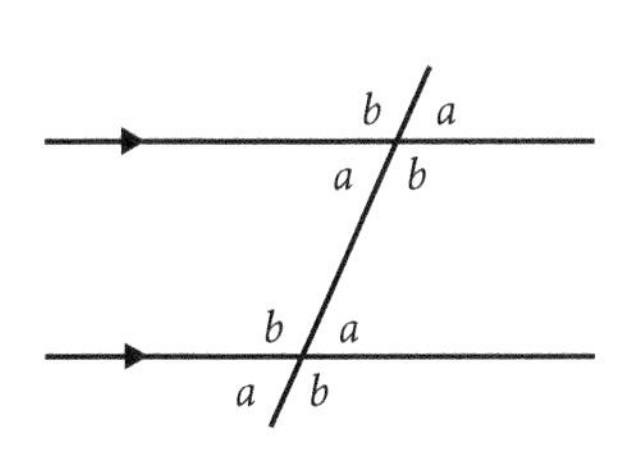

Some people remember:
'F angles'

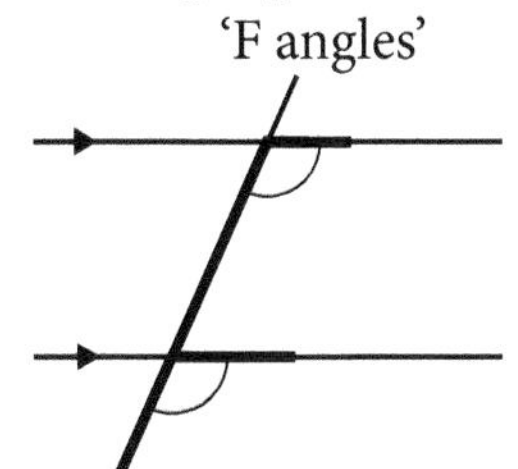

and 'Z angles'

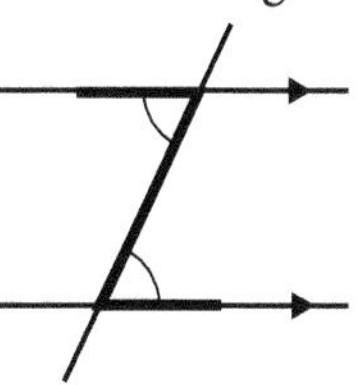

Exercise 6

Find the angles marked with letters.

1.

a

72°

2.

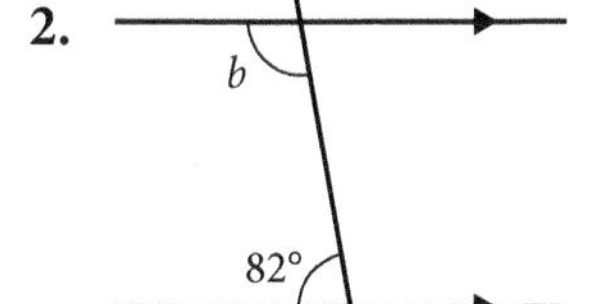

3.

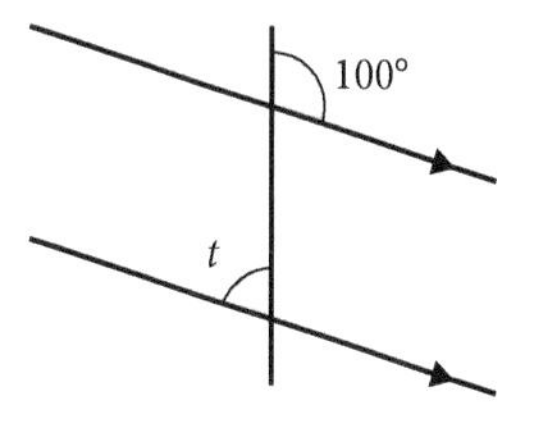

4.

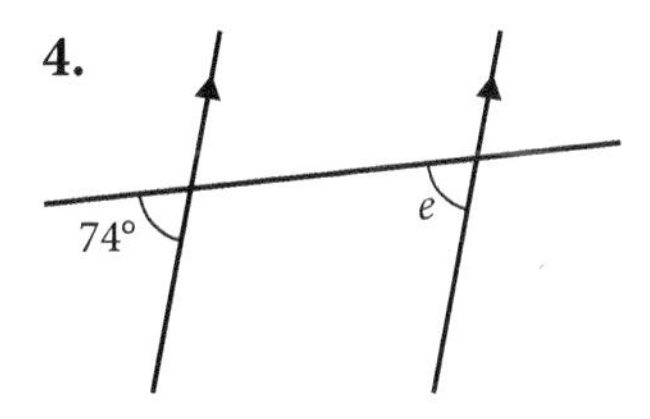

5.

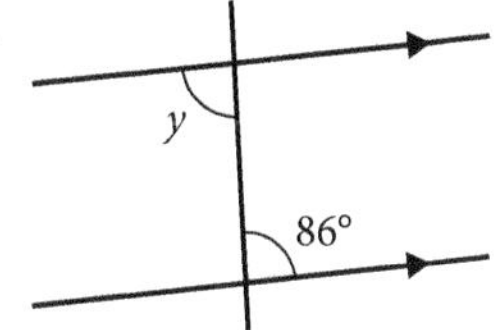

6.

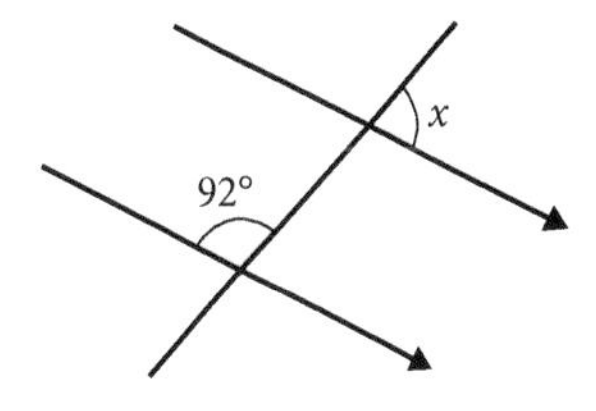

7.

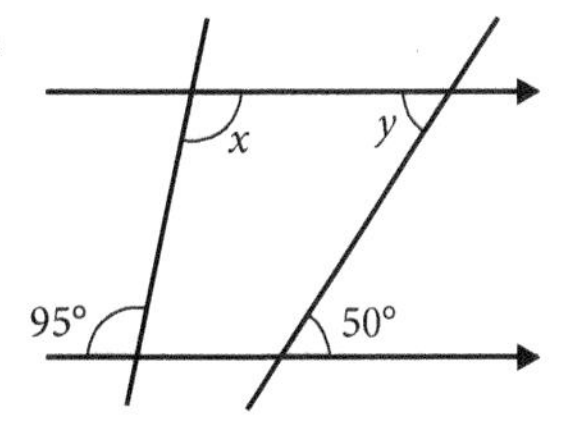

8.

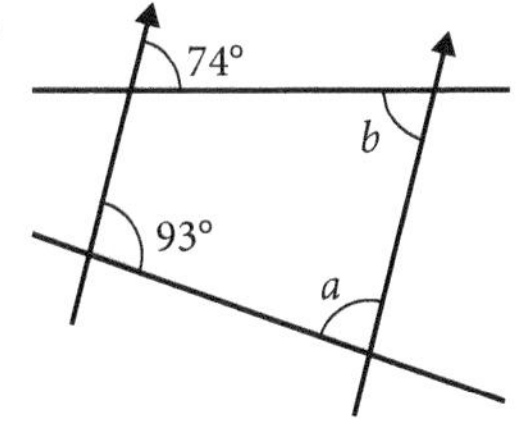

9.

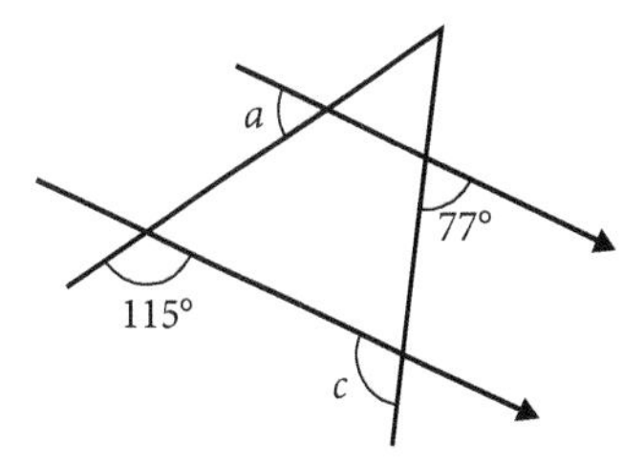

10.

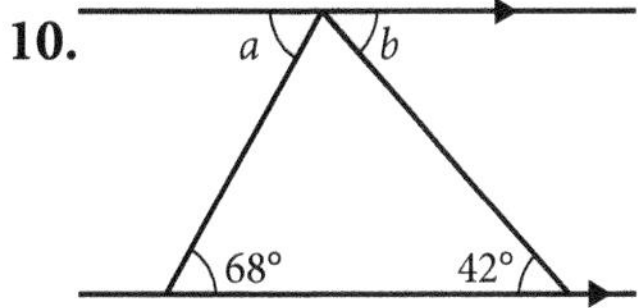

11.

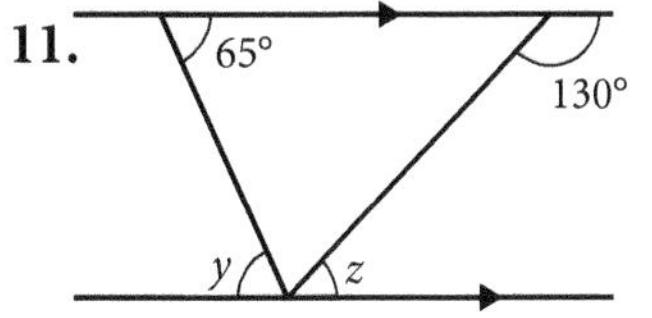

12.

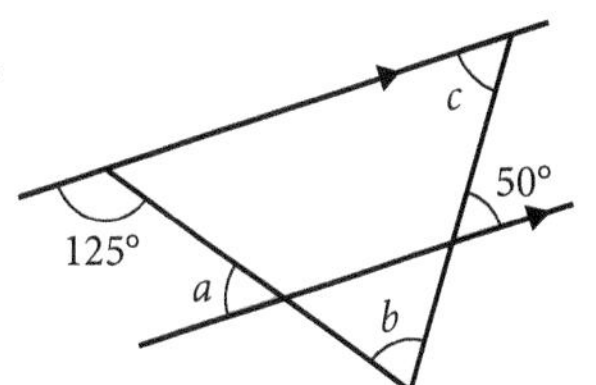

Quadrilaterals and regular polygons

The sum of the angles in a quadrilateral is 360°.

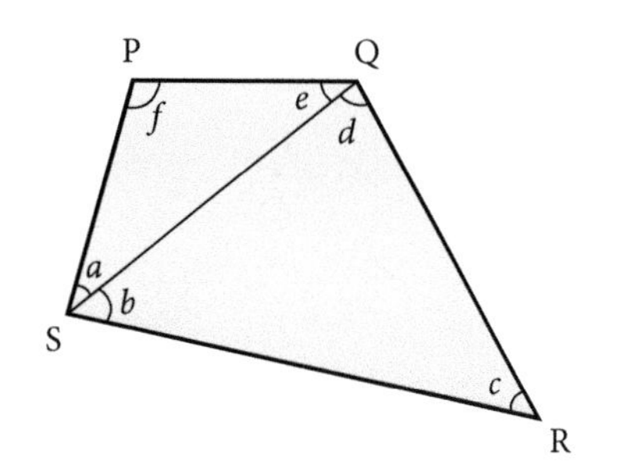

Proof: The quadrilateral PQRS has been split into two triangles.

We know that $a + e + f = 180°$

and that $b + c + d = 180°$

$\therefore a + b + c + d + e + f = 360°$

But the angles of the quadrilateral are $(a + b)$, c, $(d + e)$ and f.

$\therefore$ The sum of the angles in a quadrilateral is 360°.

Two straight lines meet at a **vertex**.

A shape with straight sides is called a **polygon**.

A **regular polygon** has equal sides and angles.

For example a square is a regular quadrilateral.

Example

Regular pentagon:

$x + x + x + x + x = 360°$

$\therefore x = 72°$

Polygons	
Name	**Number of sides**
Quadrilateral	4
Pentagon	5
Hexagon	6
Heptagon	7
Octagon	8
Nonagon	9
Decagon	10

Exercise 7

Find the angles marked with letters.

1.

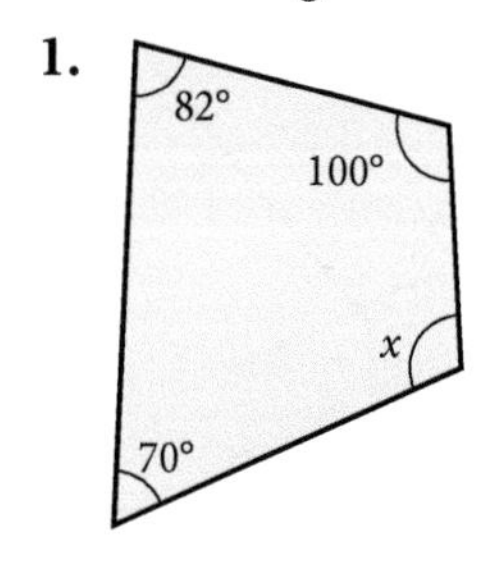

2.

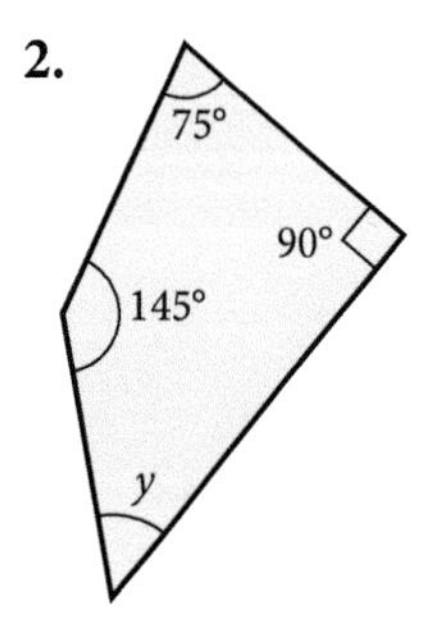

3.

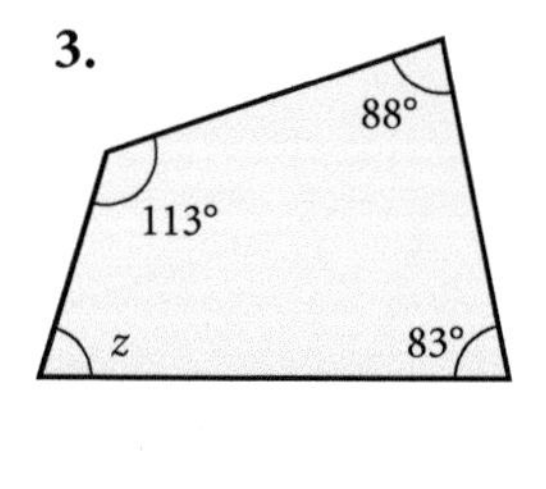

4.

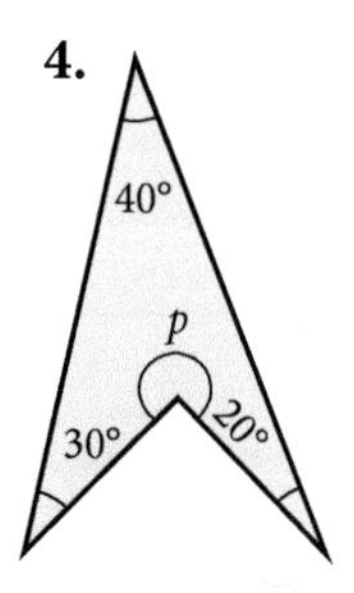

5.

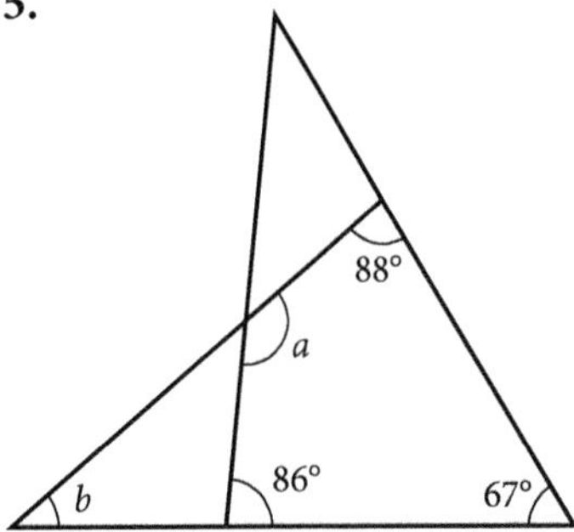

6.

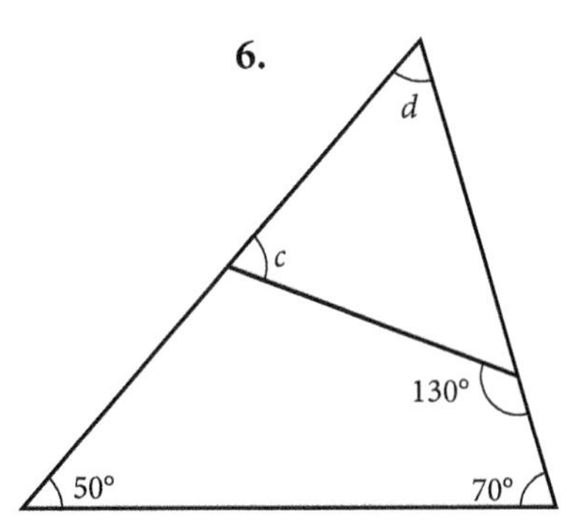

7.

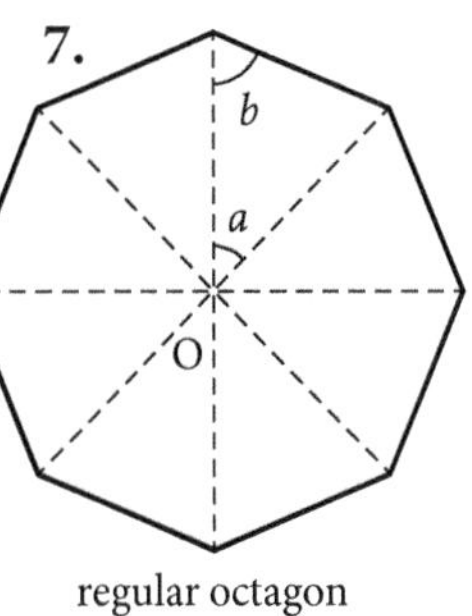

regular octagon
O is the centre

Mixed questions

The next exercise contains questions which summarise the work of the last five exercises.

Exercise 8

Find the angles marked with letters.

1.

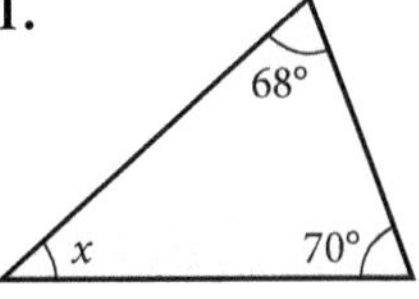

2.

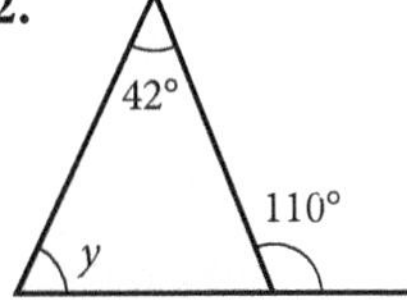

3.

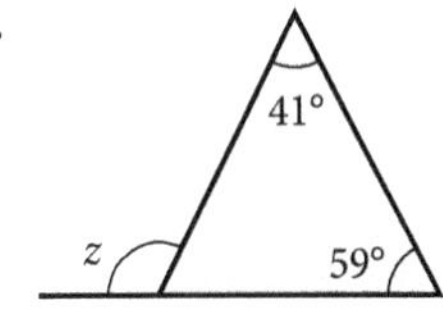

4.

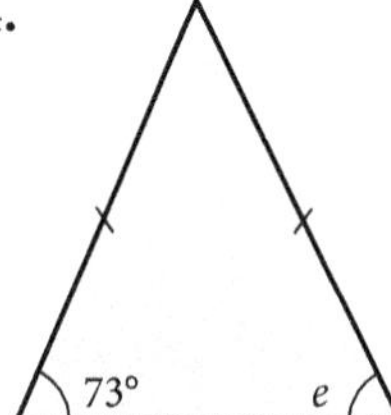

5.

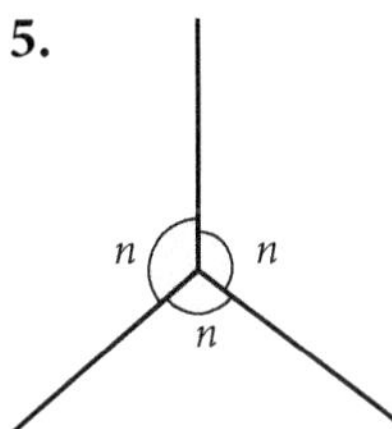

6.

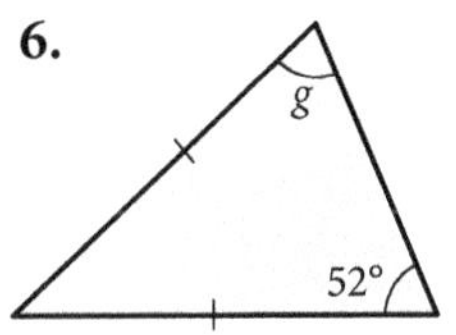

7.

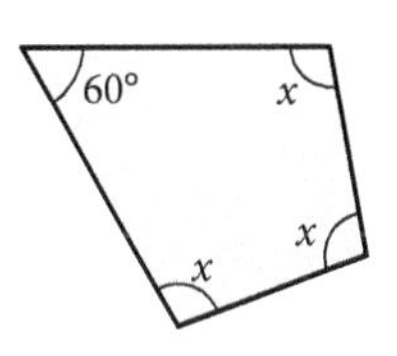

8.

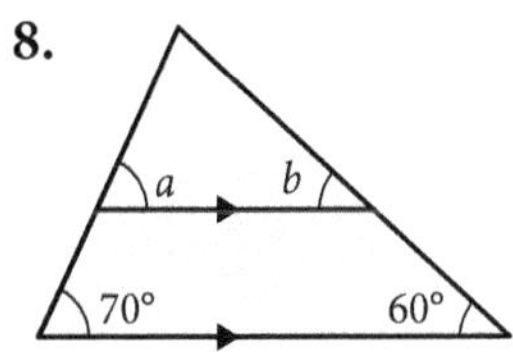

9.

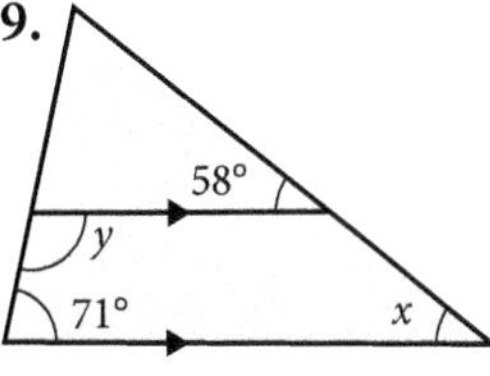

10.

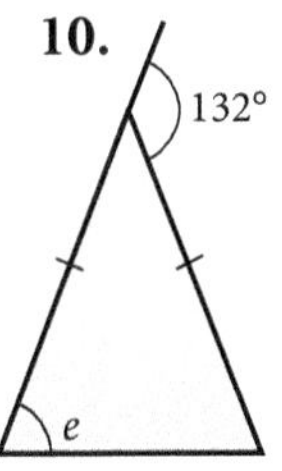

11.

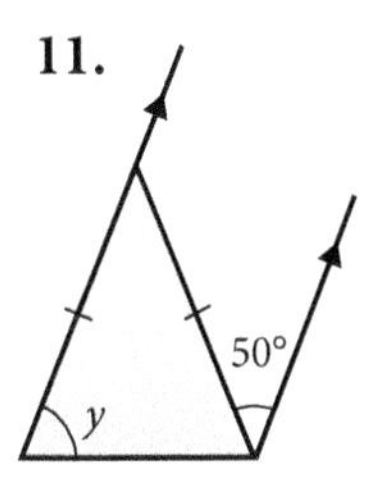

12.

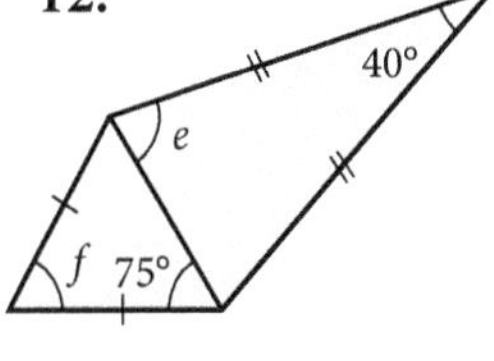

13.

14.

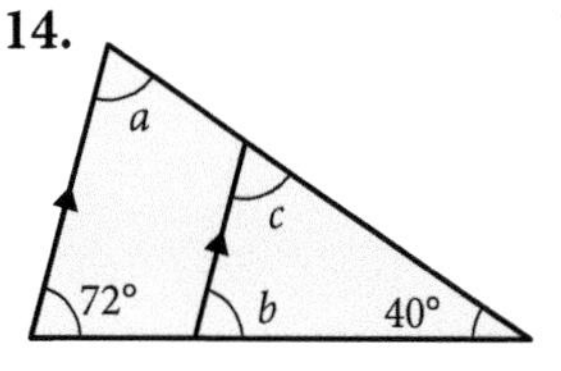

15.

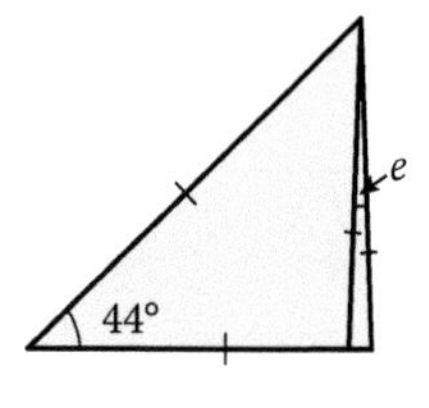

16.

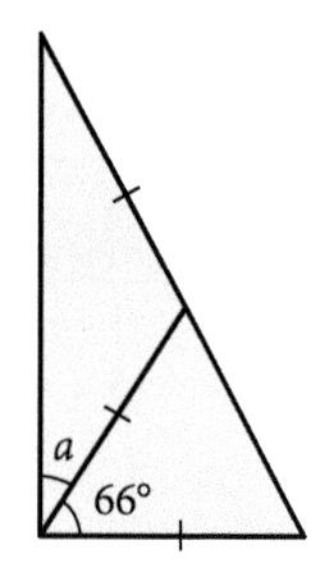

17.

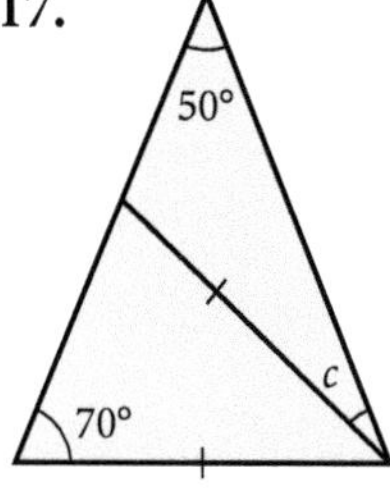

18.

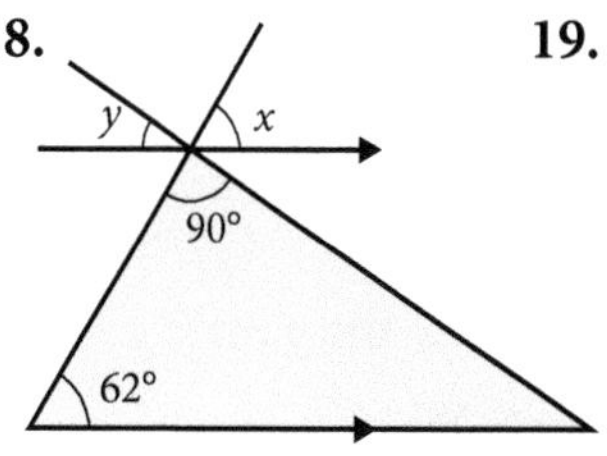

19.

20.

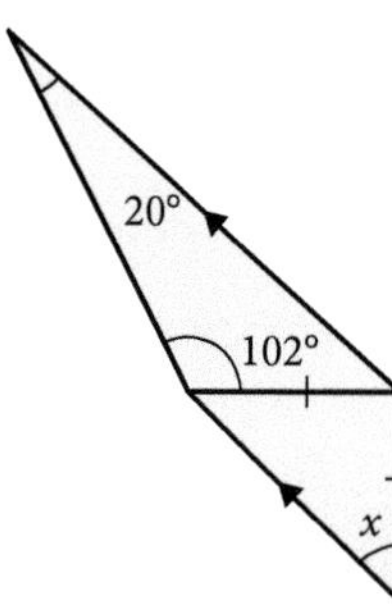

21.

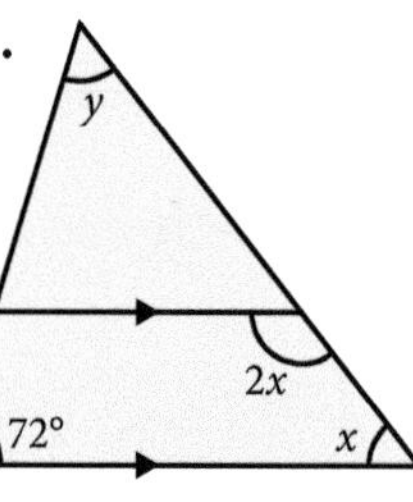

22.

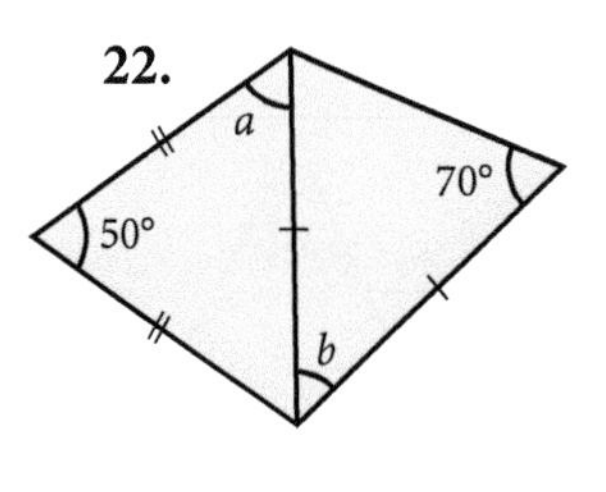

23.

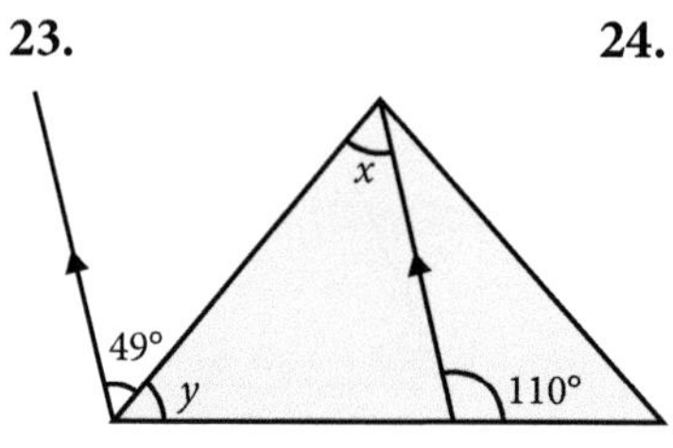

24.

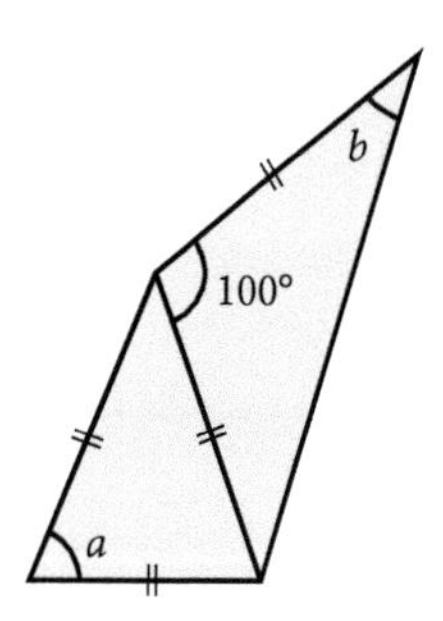

Questions **25** to **28** are more difficult.

25. The diagram shows two equal squares joined to a triangle.
Find the angle x.

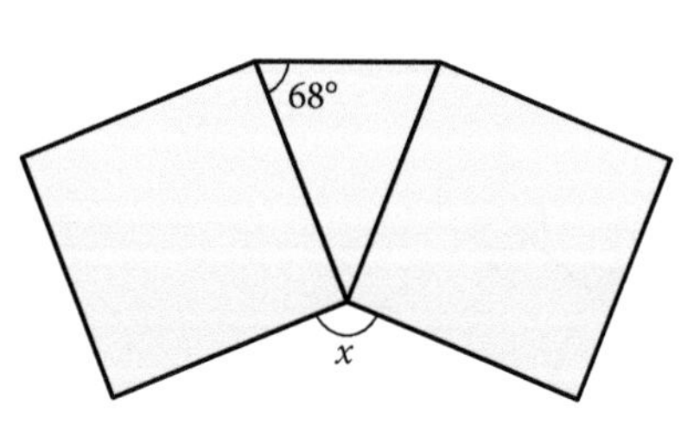

26. Find the angle a between the diagonals of the parallelogram.

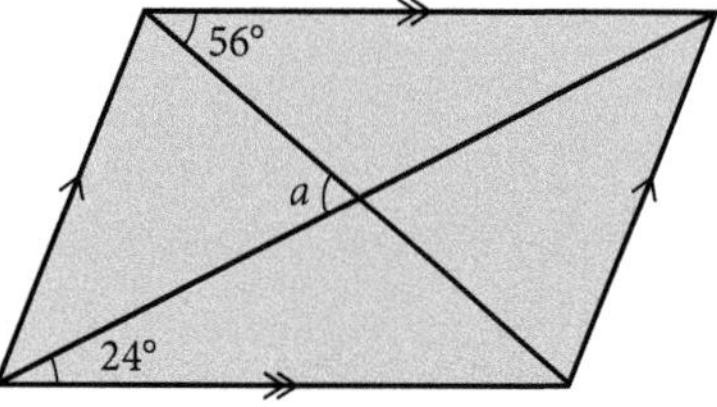
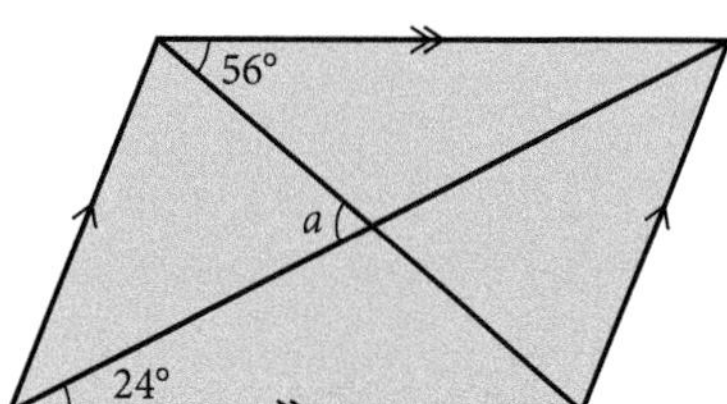

27. The diagram shows the cross-section of a roof.
PQ and RS are horizontal and ST is vertical.
Work out angles x, y and z.

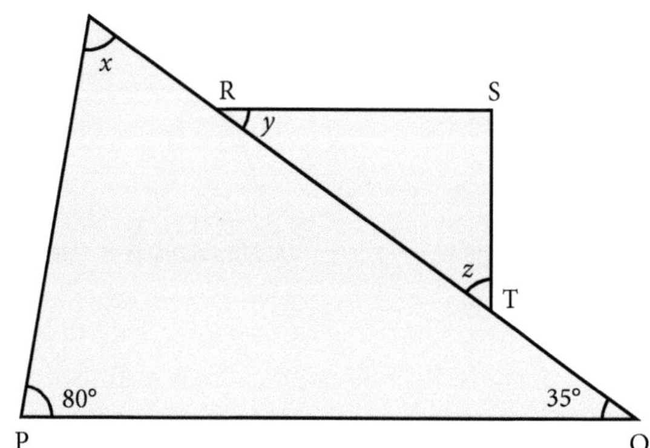

28. Given AB = AC and DA is parallel to EC, find x.

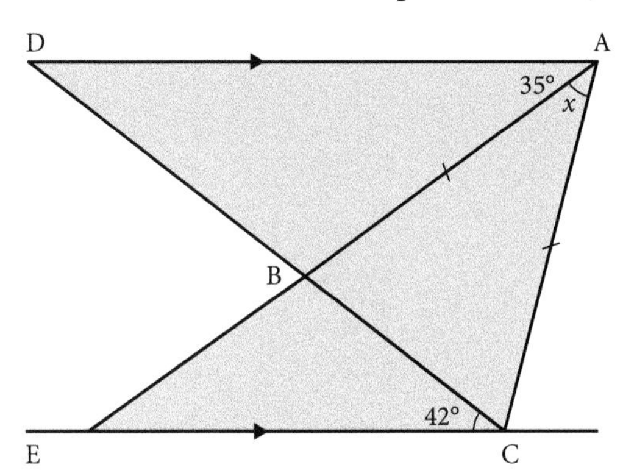

1.3 Angles in polygons and circles

Exterior angles of a polygon

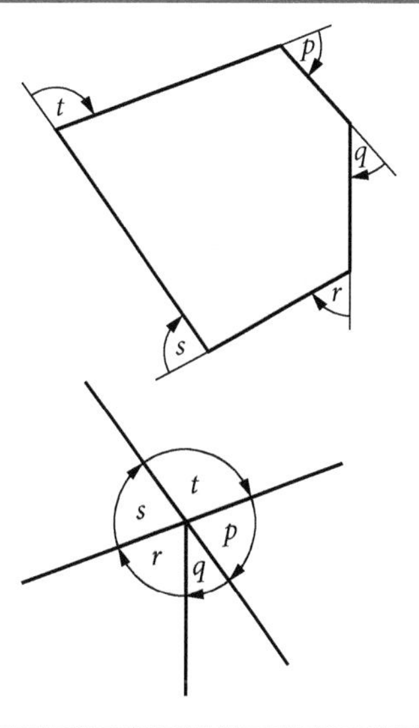

The exterior angle of a polygon is the angle between a produced side and the adjacent side of the polygon. The word 'produced' in this context means 'extended'.

If we put all the exterior angles together we can see that the sum of the angles is 360°. This is true for any polygon.

The sum of the exterior angles of a polygon = 360°.

Note:

a) In a regular polygon all exterior angles are equal.

b) For a regular polygon with n sides, each exterior angle $= \dfrac{360°}{n}$

Example

The diagram shows a regular octagon (8 sides).

a) Calculate the size of each exterior angle (marked e).

b) Calculate the size of each interior angle (marked i).

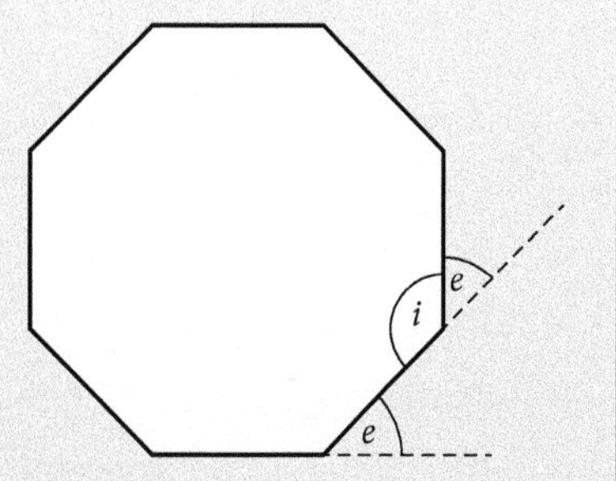

a) There are 8 exterior angles and the sum of these angles is 360°.

$\therefore$ angle $e = \dfrac{360°}{8} = 45°$

b) $e + i = 180°$ (angles on a straight line)

$\therefore\ i = 135°$

Exercise 9

1. Look at the polygon shown.
   a) Calculate each exterior angle.
   b) Check that the total of the exterior angles is 360°.

2. The diagram shows a regular decagon.
   a) Calculate the angle a.
   b) Calculate the interior angle of a regular decagon.

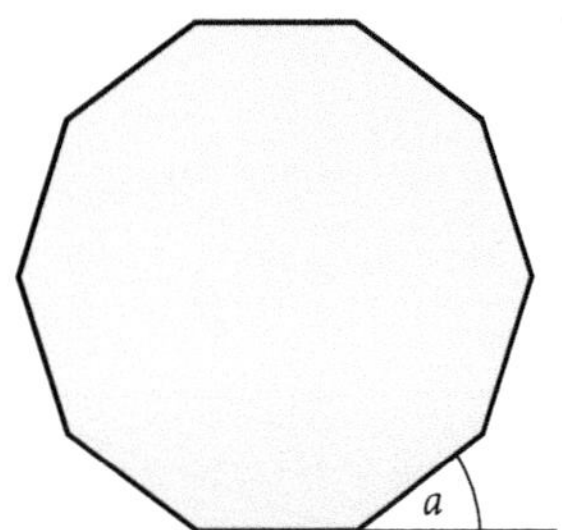

3. Find:
   a) the exterior angle
   b) the interior angle of a regular polygon with
      i) 9 sides ii) 18 sides iii) 45 sides iv) 60 sides.

4. Find the angles marked with letters.

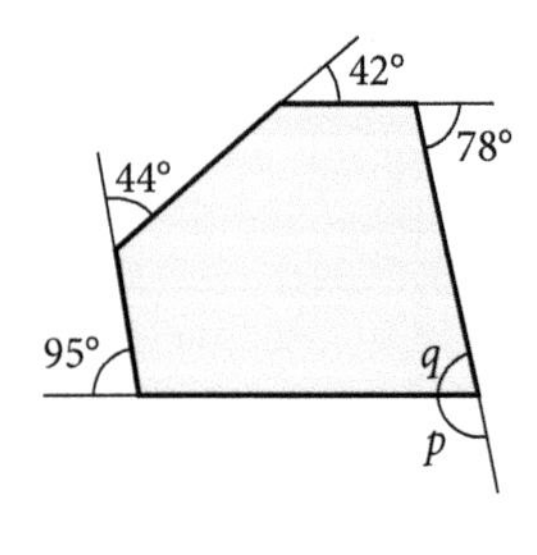

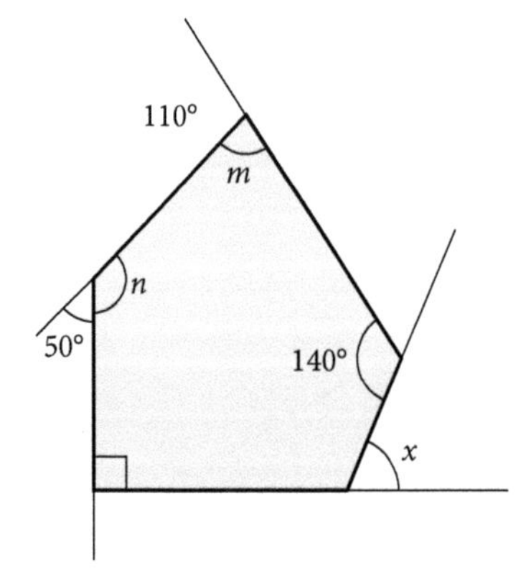

5. Each exterior angle of a regular polygon is 15°.
   How many sides has the polygon?

6. Each interior angle of a regular polygon is 140°.
   How many sides has the polygon?

7. Each exterior angle of a regular polygon is 18°.
   How many sides has the polygon?

8. The sides of a regular polygon subtend angles of 18° at the centre of the polygon.

How many sides has the polygon?

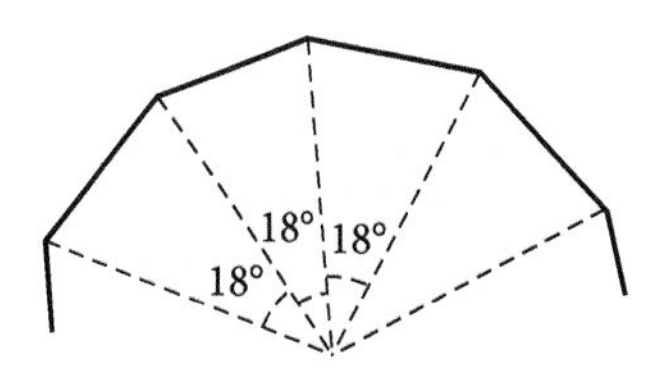

Angles in circles

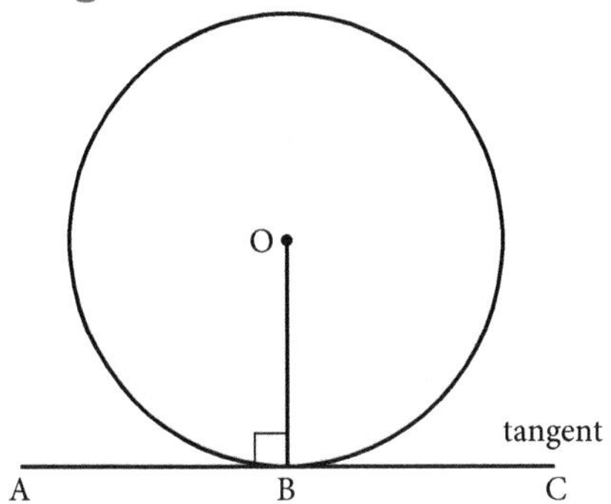

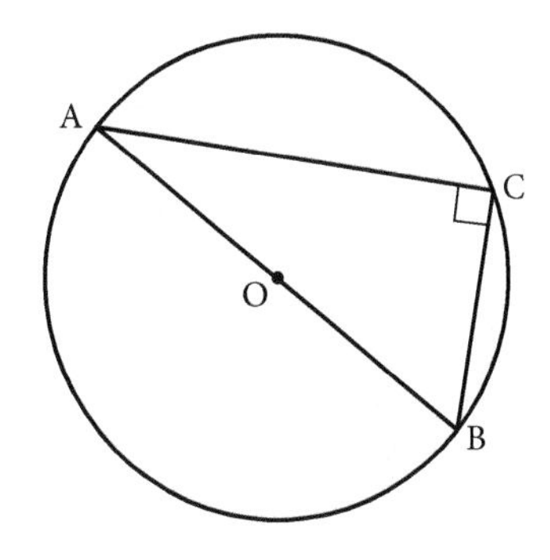

The *tangent* ABC touches the circle at B.

OB is a radius of the circle.

Angle OBA = 90°.

AB is a diameter.

The angle at the circumference, angle ACB, is 90°.

We can write $A\hat{C}B = 90°$.

Exercise 10

1. a) Draw a circle with radius 5 cm and draw any diameter AB.

b) Draw triangles ABC, ABD, ABE and measure the angles at the circumference.

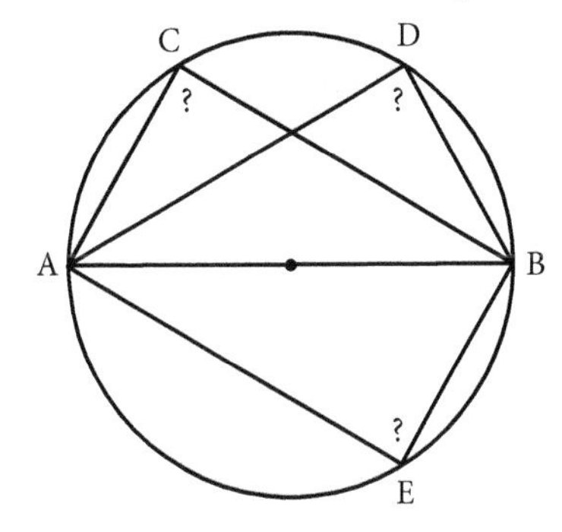

In Questions **2** to **13** find the angles marked with letters. Point O is the centre of the circle.

2.

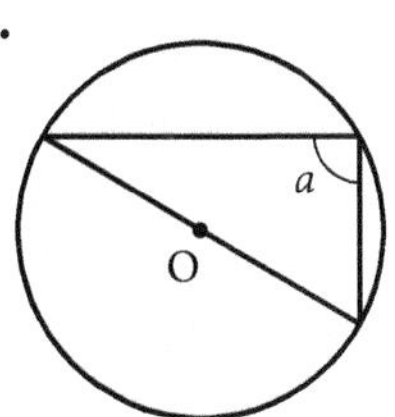

3.

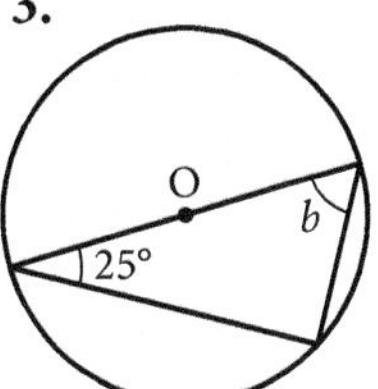

4.

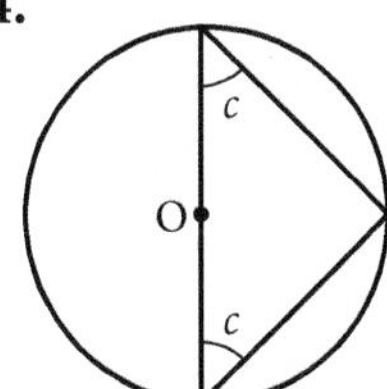

5.

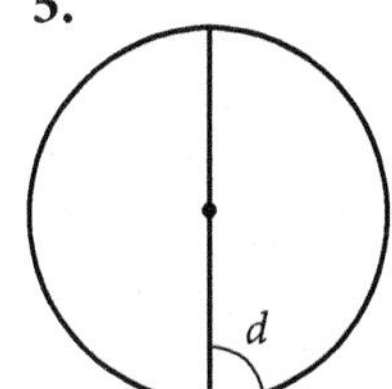

6.

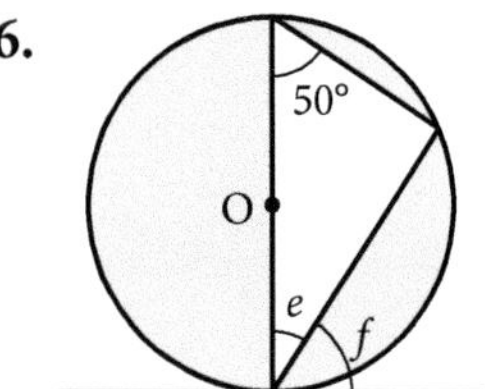

7.

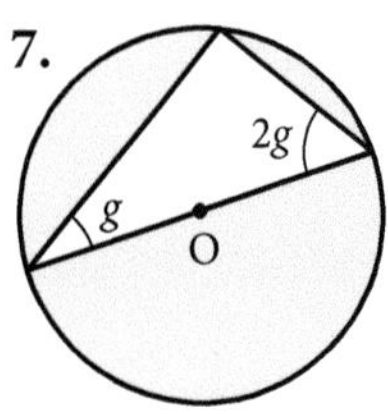

8.

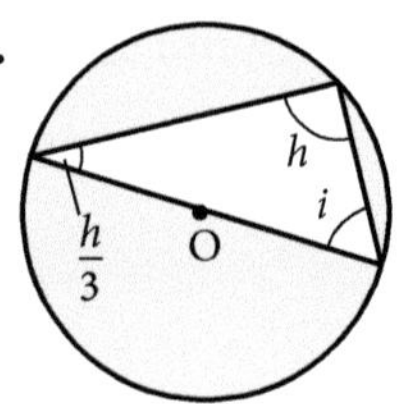

9.

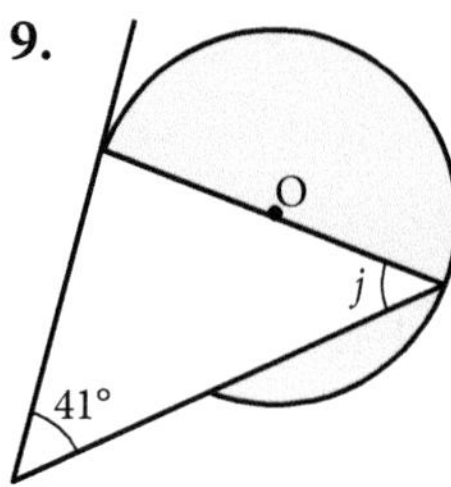

10.

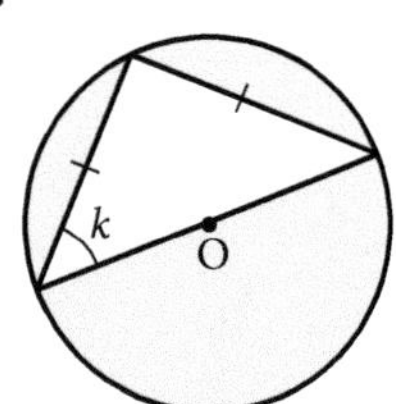

11.

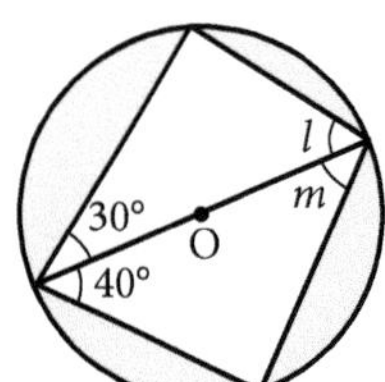

12.

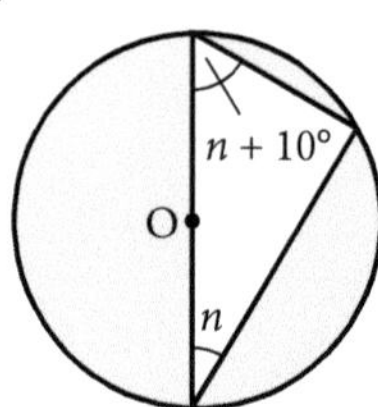

13.

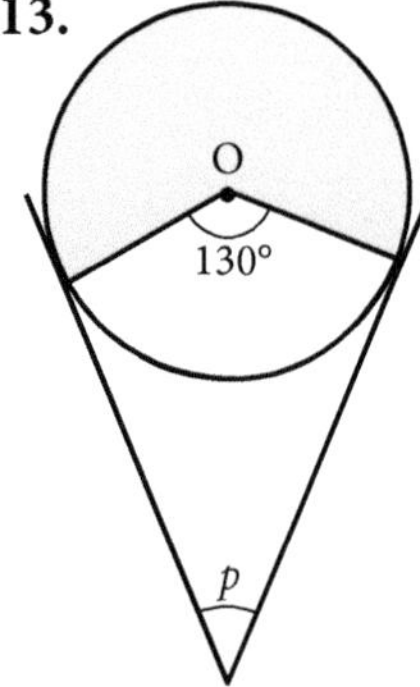

1.4 Symmetry

a) Line symmetry

The letter M has one line of symmetry, shown dotted.

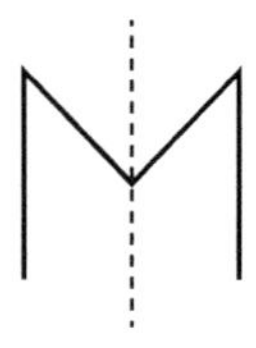

b) Rotational symmetry

The shape may be turned about O into three identical positions. It has rotational symmetry of order 3.

Note:

- Isosceles triangles have one line of symmetry but no rotational symmetry.
- Equilateral triangles have three lines of symmetry and rotational symmetry of order 3.
- Circles have an infinite number of lines of symmetry and an infinite order of rotational symmetry.

Exercise 11

For each shape state:

a) the number of lines of symmetry

b) the order of rotational symmetry.

1. 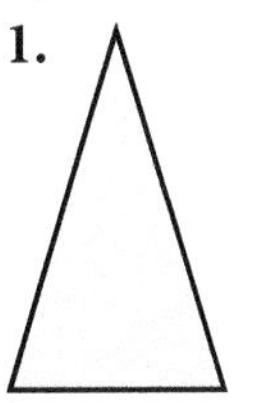

2. 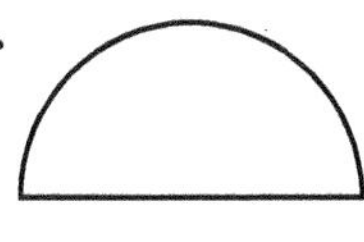

3. 

4. 

5. 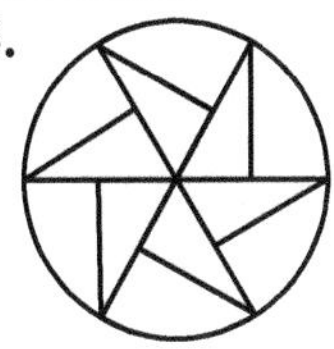

6. 

7. 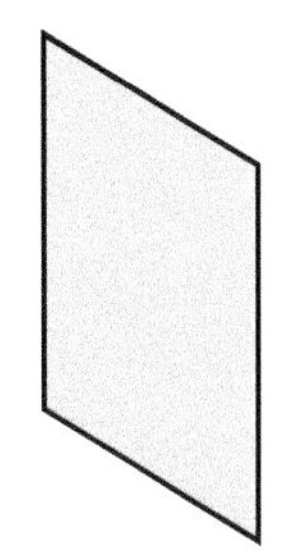

8. 

9. 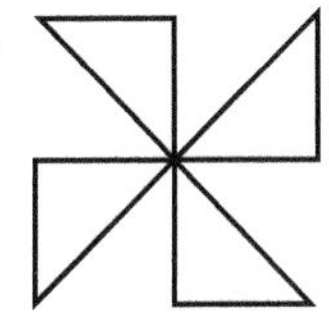

10. 

11. 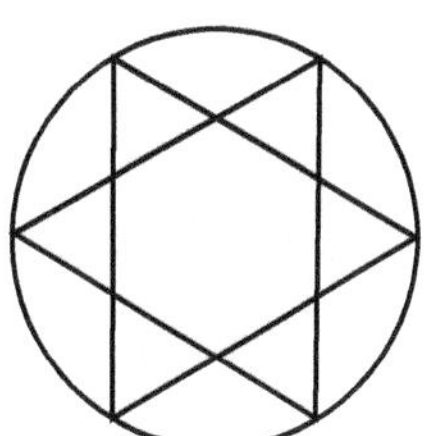

12. 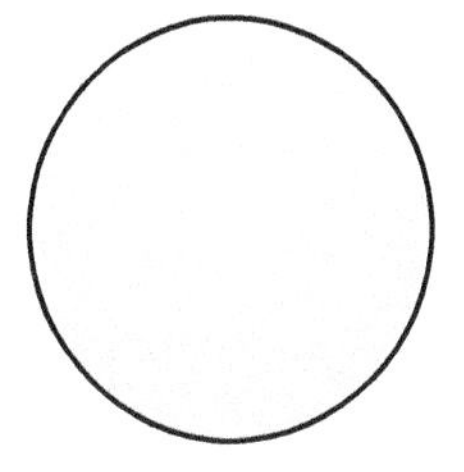

Exercise 12

In Questions **1** to **8**, the broken lines are axes of symmetry. In each question only *part of the shape* is given. Copy what is given onto squared paper and then carefully complete the shape.

1. 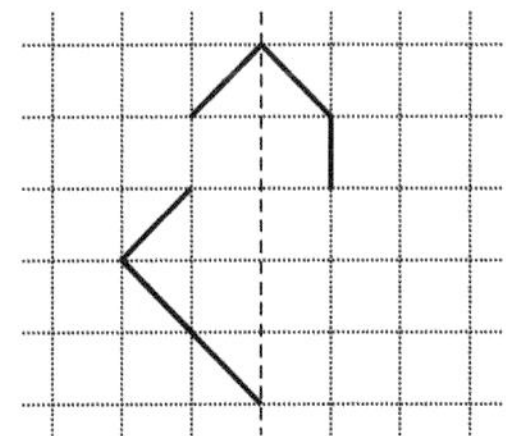

2. 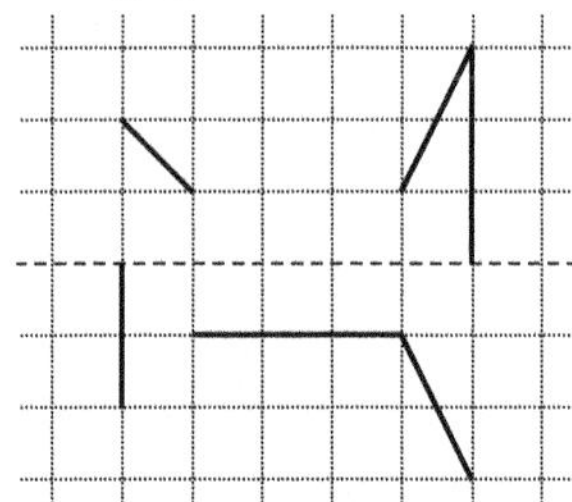

3. 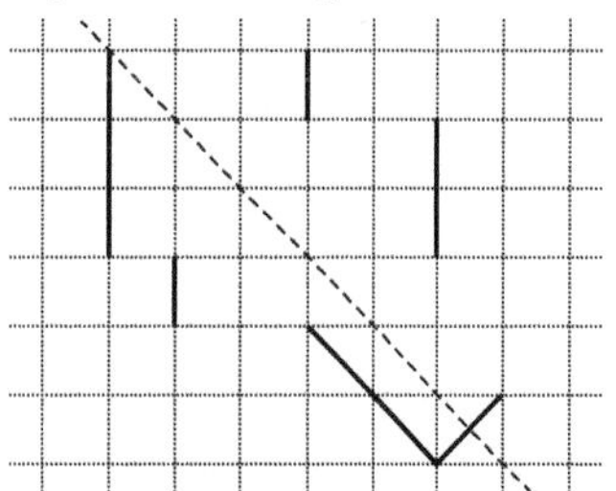

4. 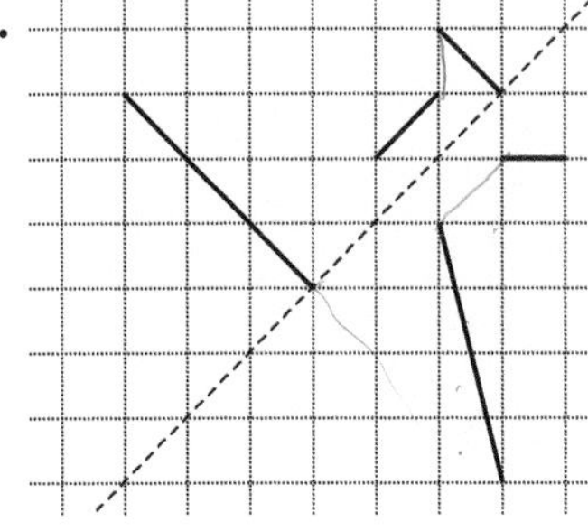

5. 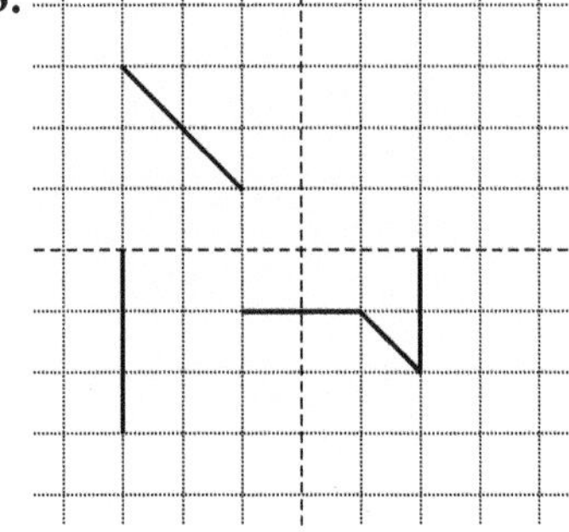

6. 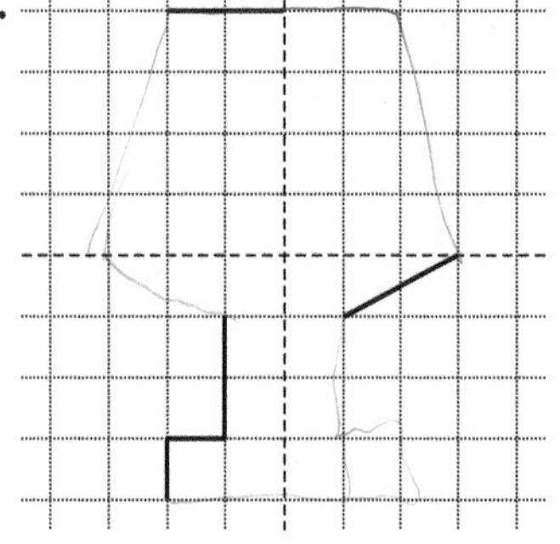

7.

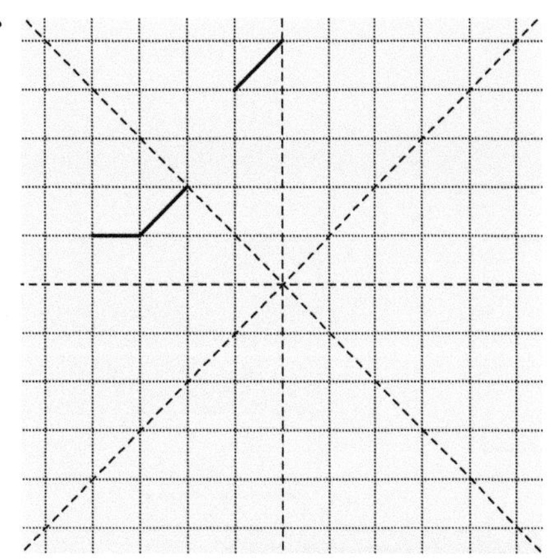

8.

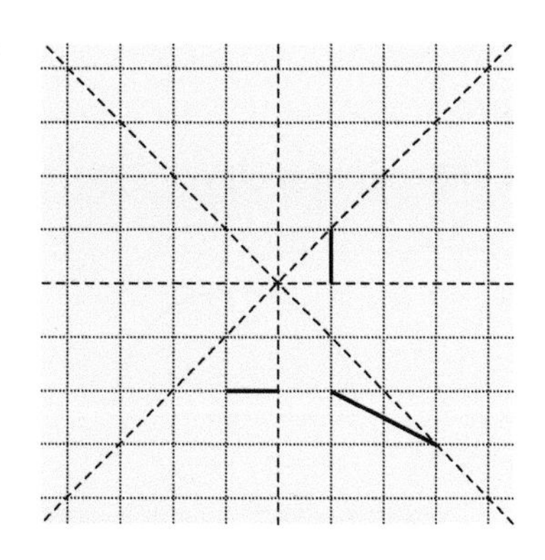

9. Fold a piece of paper twice and cut out any shape from the corner. What are the number of lines of symmetry and the order of rotational symmetry of your shape?

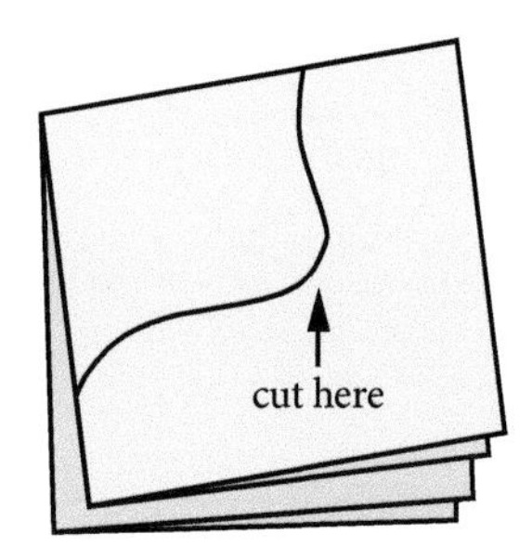

1.5 Circle calculations

Circumference of a circle

The circumference of a circle is given by $C = \pi d$.

Example

Find the circumference of this circle.

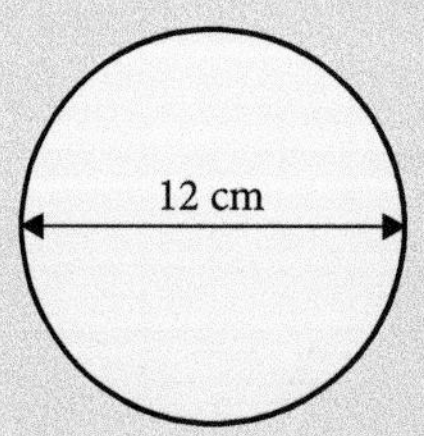

$C = \pi \times 12$ cm

$C = 37.7$ cm (to 3 s.f.)

We have used the π button on a calculator. The value of π (pi) is 3.142 approximately.

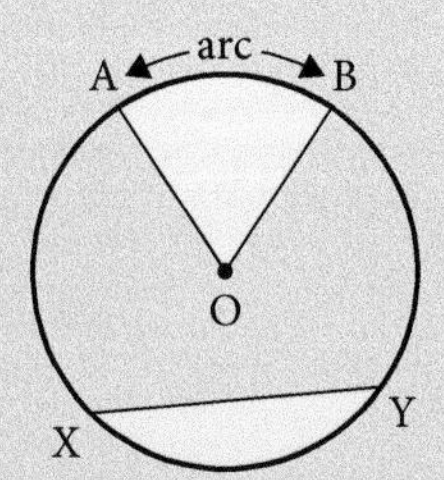

AB is an **arc** of the circle.

AOB is a **sector** of the circle.

The shaded area cut off by the **chord** XY is a **segment** of the circle.

A **semicircle** is half a circle.

The plural of radius is **radii**.

Exercise 13

In Questions **1** to **8**, find the circumference. Use the π button on a calculator or take $\pi = 3.142$. Give the answers correct to 3 significant figures.

1.

11 cm

2.

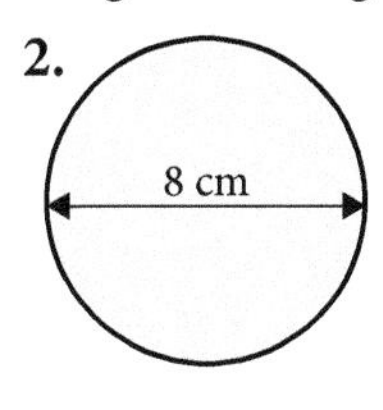

3.

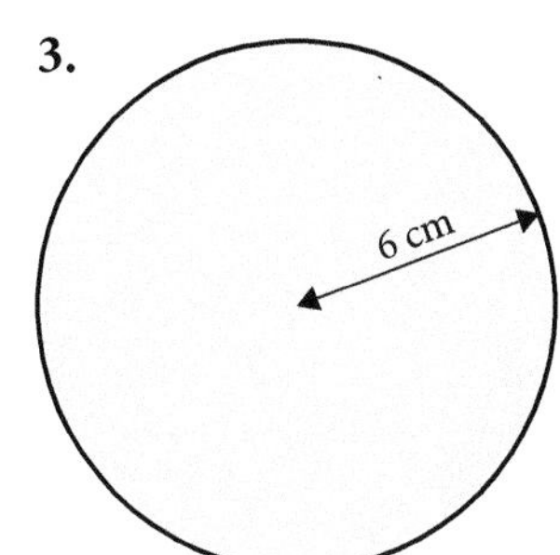

4.

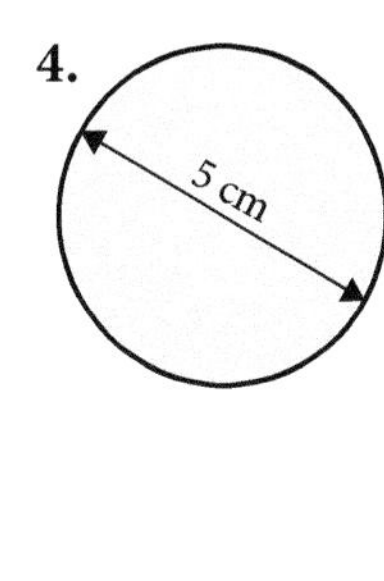

5.

4.5 cm

6.

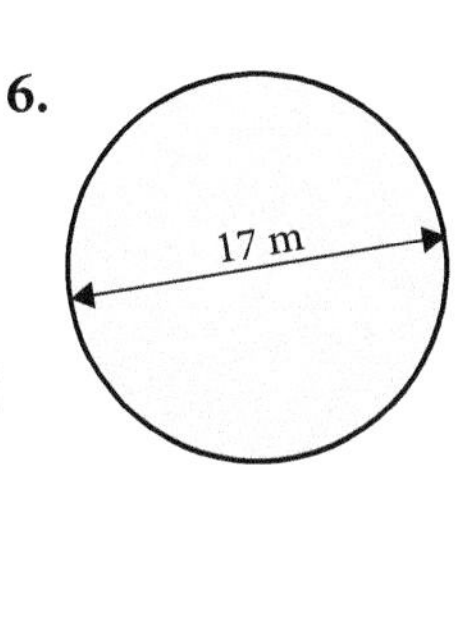

7.

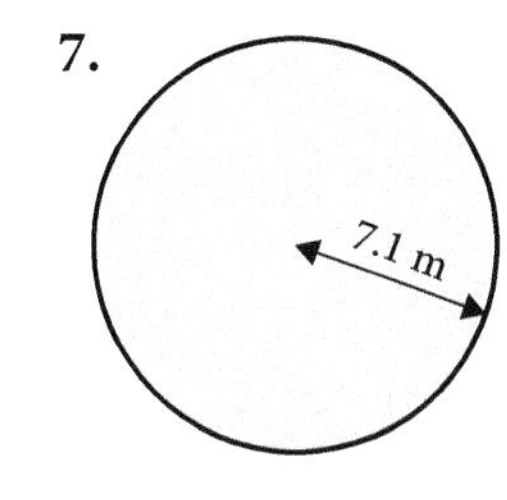

8.

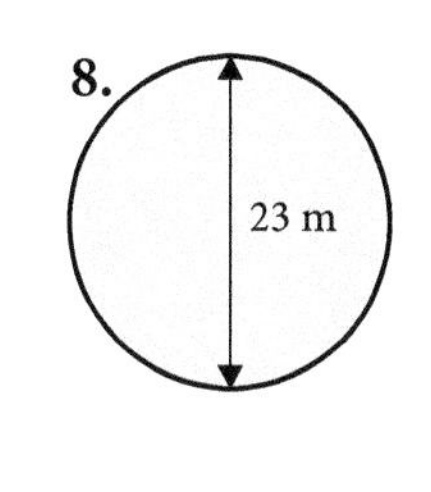

9. A circular pond has a diameter of 2.7 m.
Calculate the length of the perimeter of the pond.

10. How many complete revolutions does a cycle wheel of diameter 60 cm make in travelling 400 m?

11. A running track has two semicircular ends of radius 34 m and two straights of 93.2 m as shown.
Calculate the total distance around the track to the nearest metre.

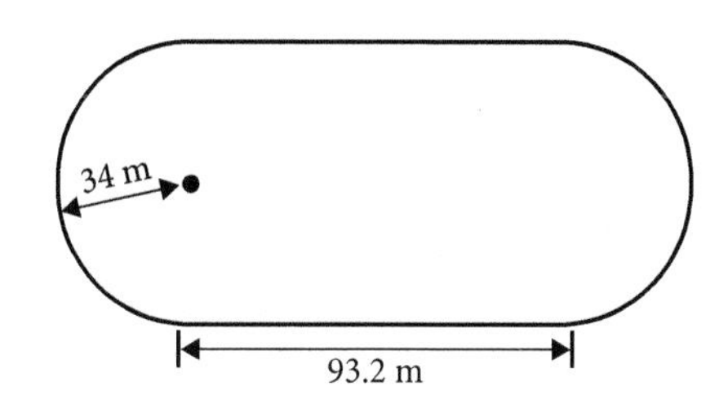

12. The minute hand of a clock is 14.4 cm long.
How far does the tip of the minute hand move between 12:00 and 12:15?

13. An old-fashioned type of bicycle is shown.
In a journey the front wheel rotates completely 156 times.
How far does the bicycle travel?

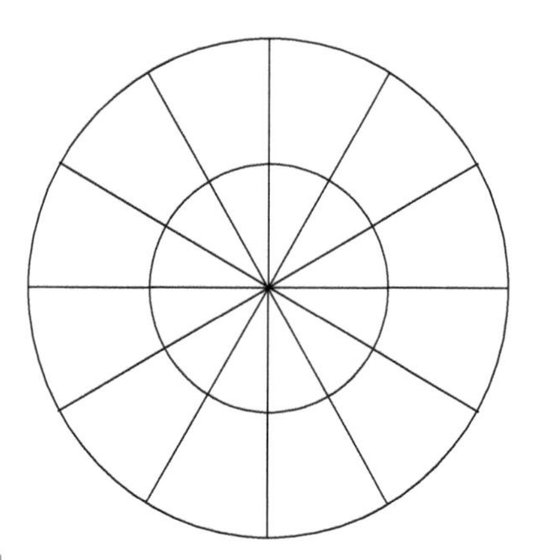

14. The diagram shows a framework for a target. The radius of the outer circle is 30 cm and the radius of the inner circle is 15 cm. Calculate the total length of wire needed for the whole framework.

Area of a circle

The area of a circle of radius r is given by $A = \pi r^2$.

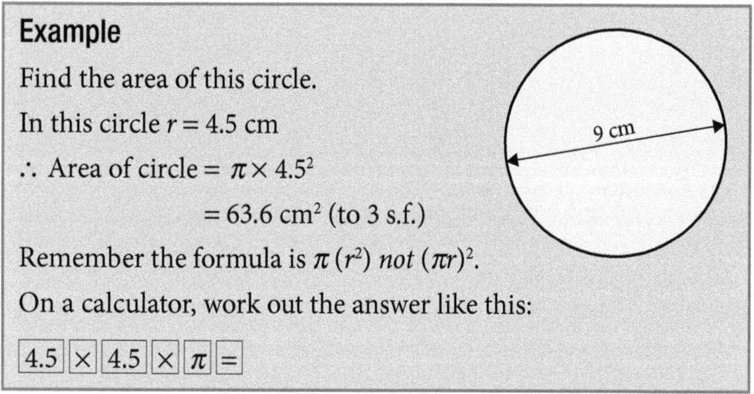

Example

Find the area of this circle.

In this circle $r = 4.5$ cm

$\therefore$ Area of circle $= \pi \times 4.5^2$

$= 63.6\ \text{cm}^2$ (to 3 s.f.)

Remember the formula is $\pi(r^2)$ *not* $(\pi r)^2$.

On a calculator, work out the answer like this:

4.5 × 4.5 × π =

Exercise 14

In Questions **1** to **8** find the area of the circle. Use the π button on a calculator or use $\pi = 3.142$. Give the answers correct to three significant figures.

1.

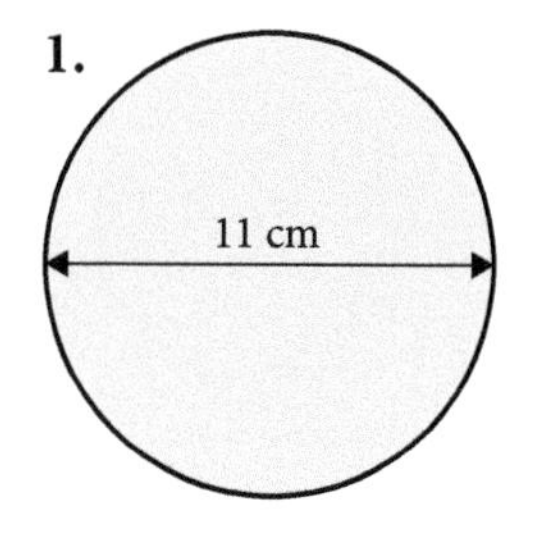

2.

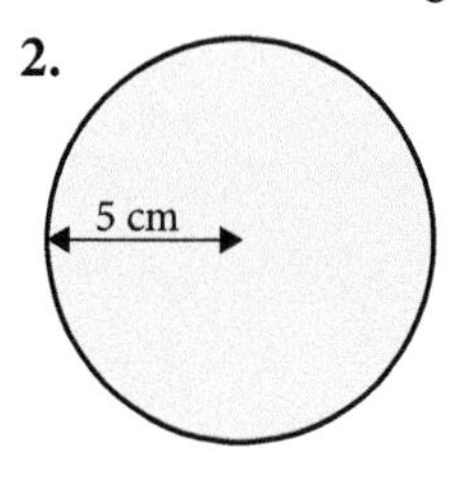

3.

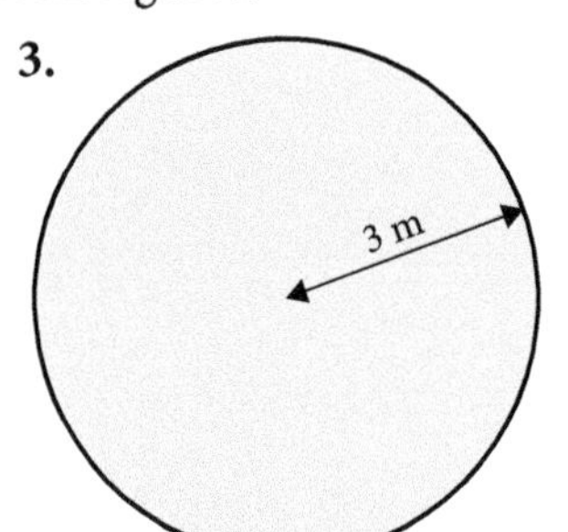

4.

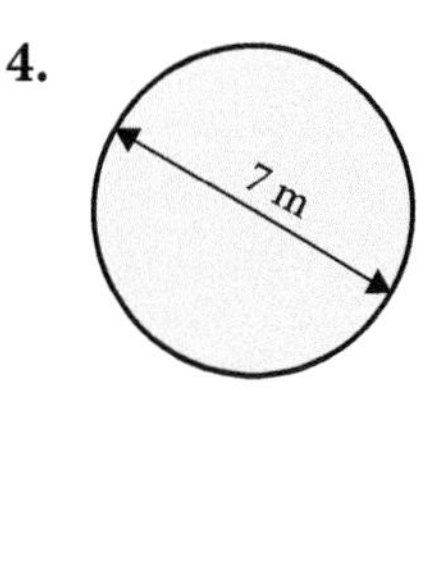

5.

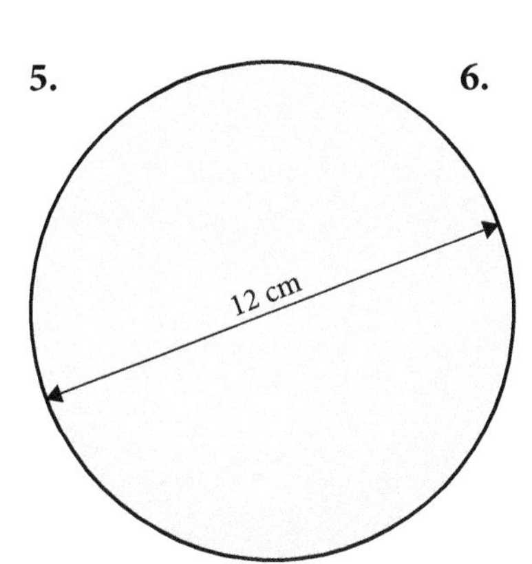

6.

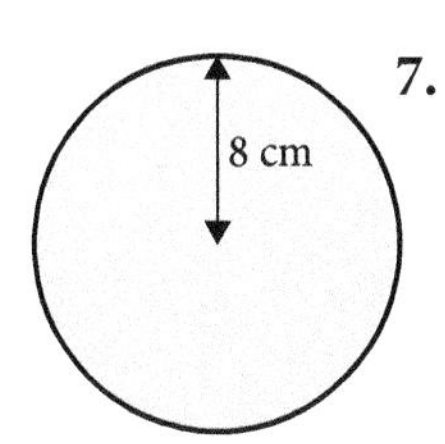

7.

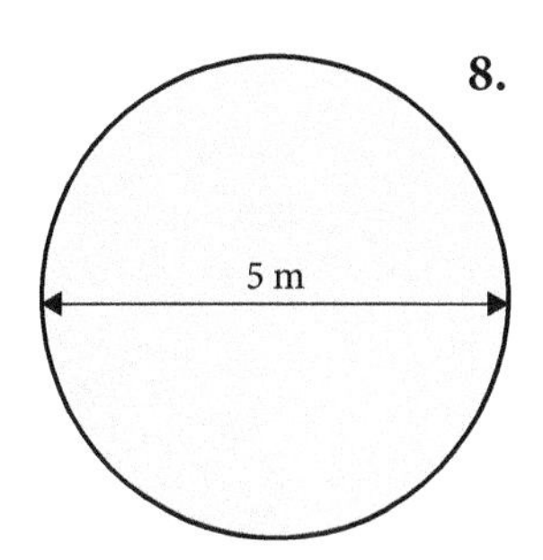

8.

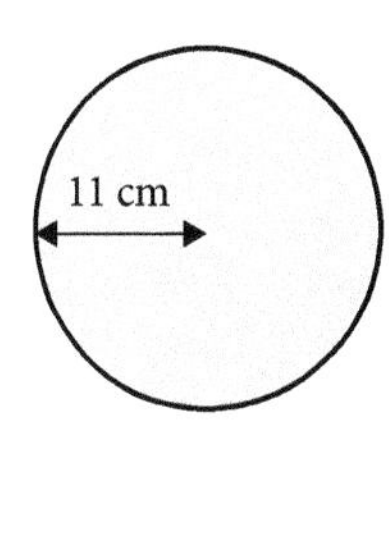

9. A spinner of radius 7.5 cm is divided into six equal sectors. Calculate the area of each sector.

10. A circular swimming pool of diameter 12.6 m is to be covered by a plastic sheet.

Work out the surface area it must cover.

11. A circle of radius 5 cm is inscribed inside a square as shown.

Find the area shaded.

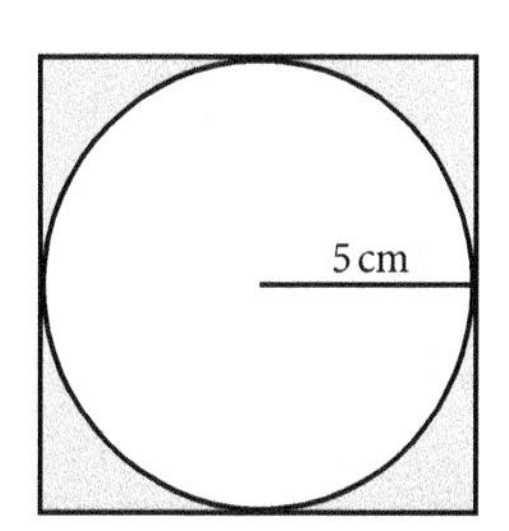

12. Each square metre of a lawn requires 2 g of weedkiller. How much weedkiller is needed for a circular lawn of radius 27 m?

13. Discs of radius 4 cm are cut from a rectangular plastic sheet of length 84 cm and width 24 cm.

a) How many complete discs can be cut out?

Find

b) the total area of the discs cut

c) the area of the sheet wasted.

14. A circular pond of radius 6 m is surrounded by a path of width 1 m.

Find the area of the path.

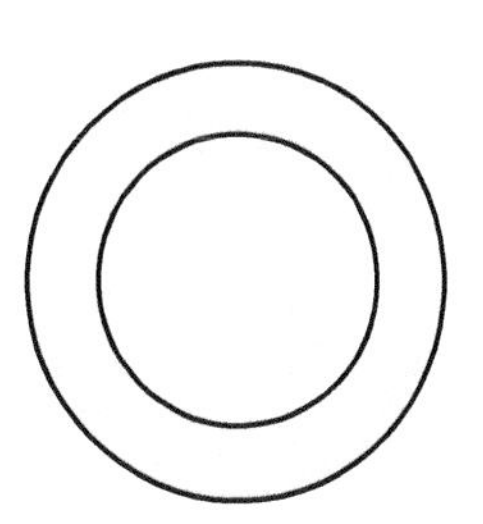

15. The diagram below shows a lawn (unshaded) surrounded by a path of uniform width (shaded). The curved end of the lawn is a semicircle of diameter 10 m.

Calculate the total area of the path.

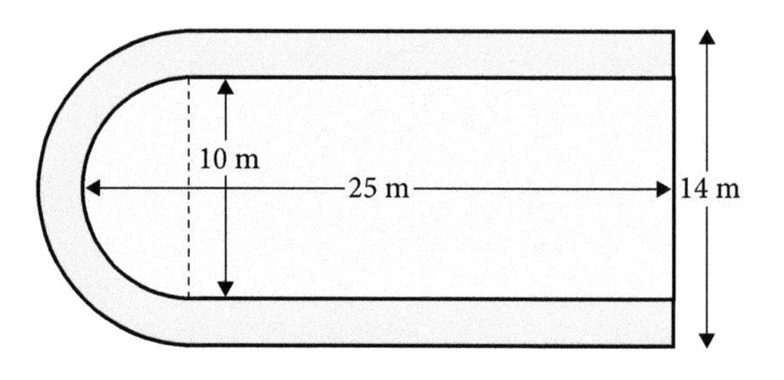

More complicated shapes

Example

For the shape below find:

a) the perimeter **b)** the area.

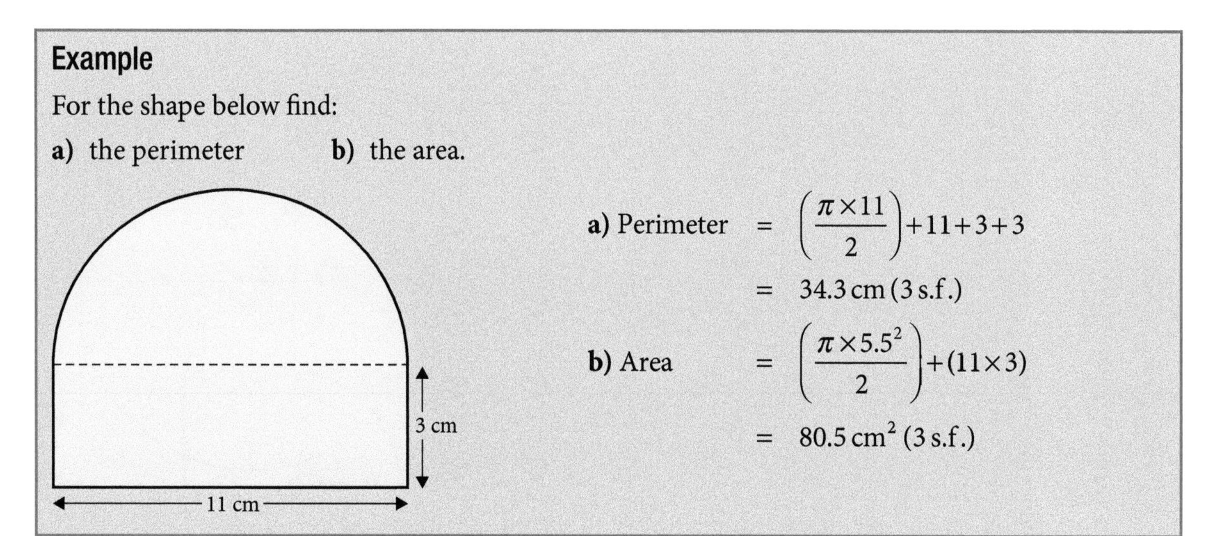

a) Perimeter $= \left(\dfrac{\pi \times 11}{2}\right) + 11 + 3 + 3$

$= 34.3\text{ cm (3 s.f.)}$

b) Area $= \left(\dfrac{\pi \times 5.5^2}{2}\right) + (11 \times 3)$

$= 80.5\text{ cm}^2\text{ (3 s.f.)}$

Exercise 15

Use the π button on a calculator or take $\pi = 3.142$. Give the answers correct to 3 s.f. For each shape find the perimeter.

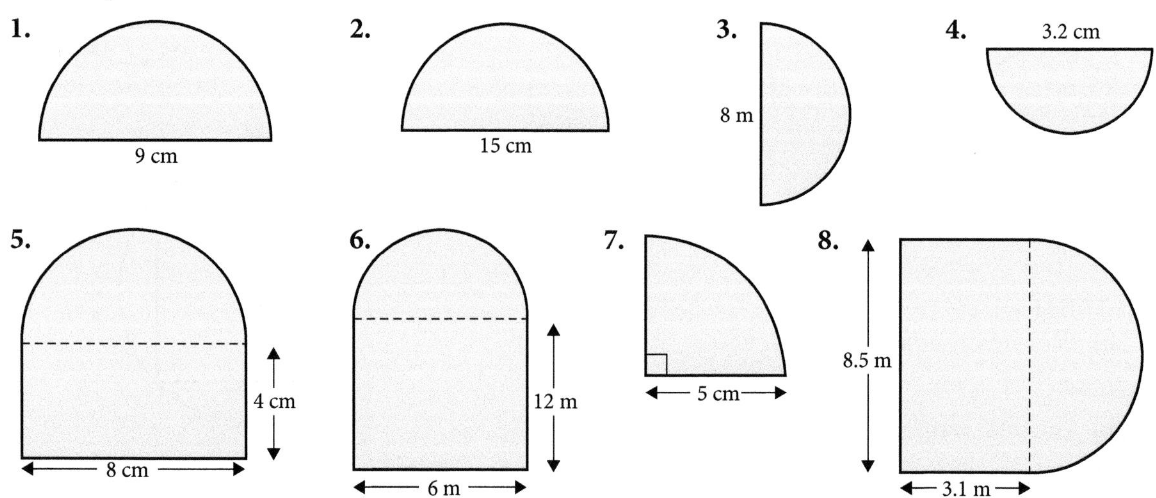

9.

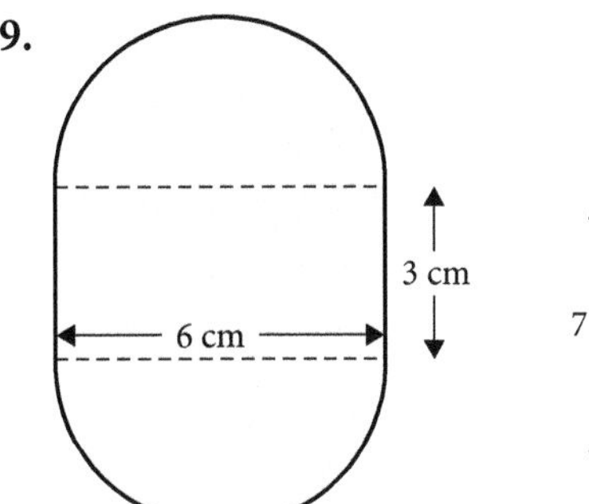

10.

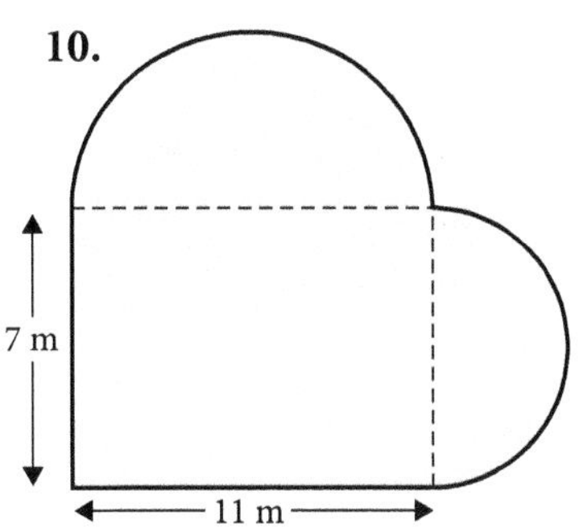

11.

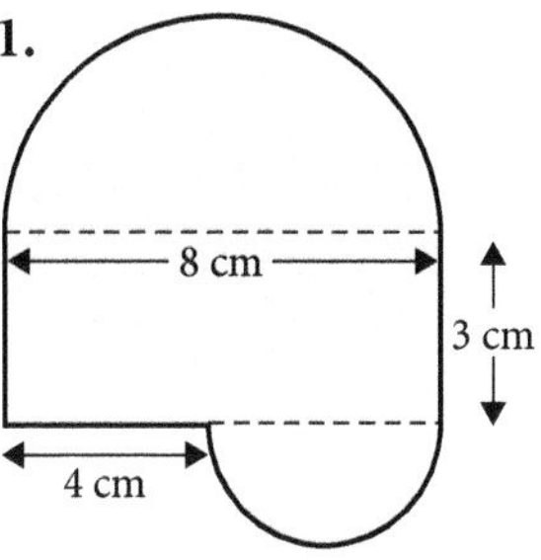

Exercise 16

Find the shaded area for each shape. All lengths are in cm.

1.

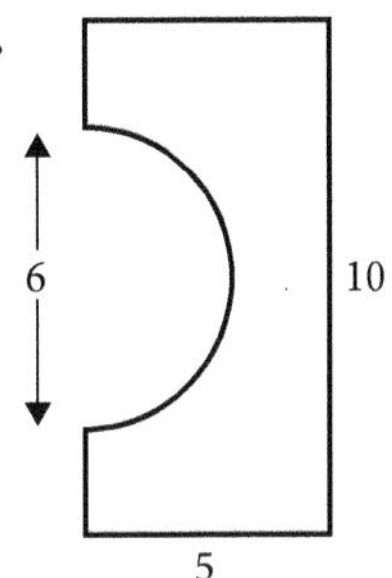

2.

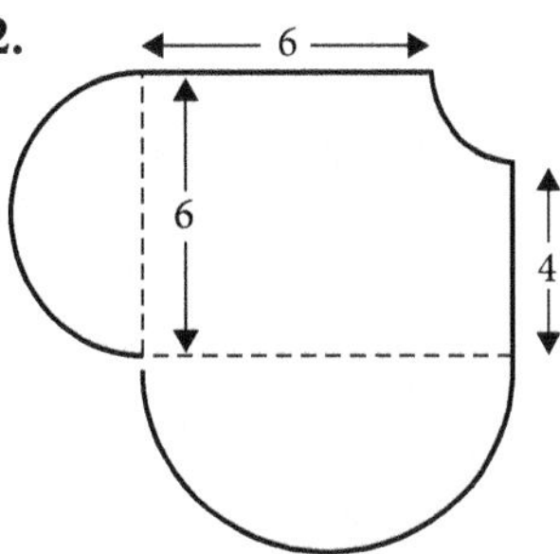

3.

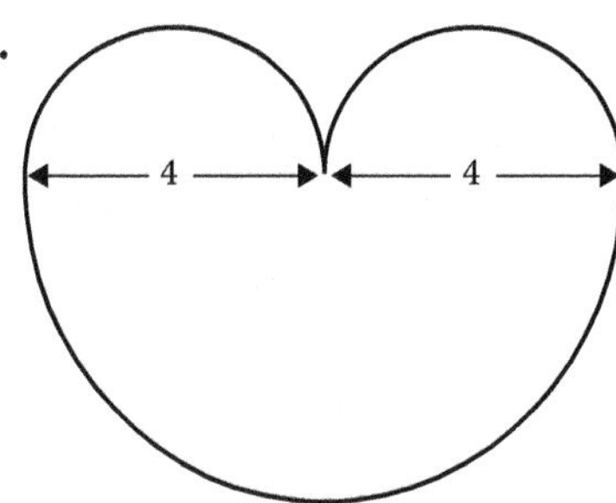

4.

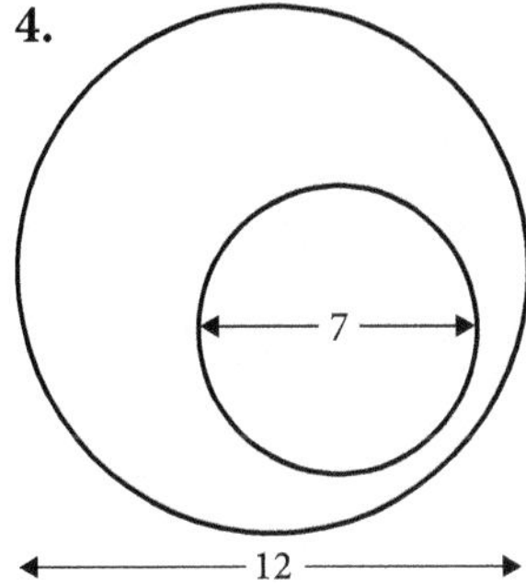

5.

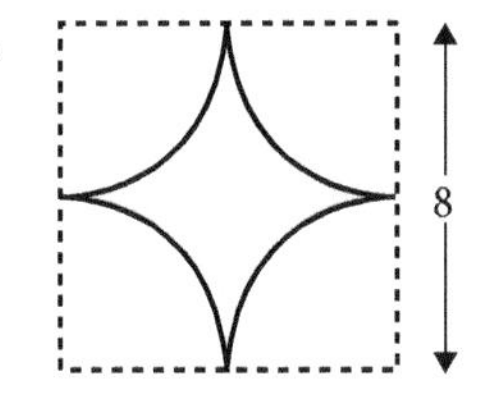

6.

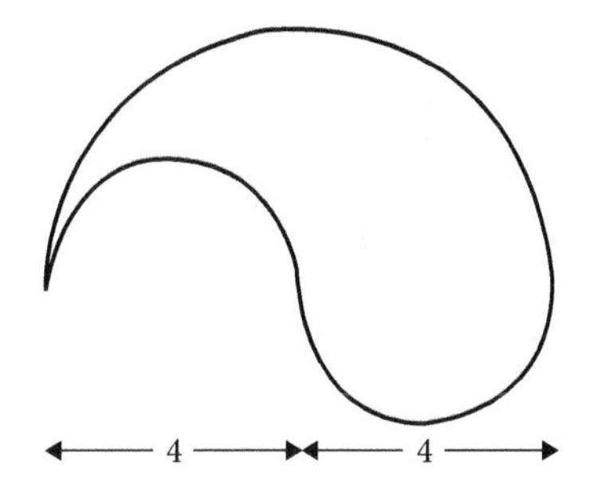

7. **a)** Find the area of triangle OAD.
   b) Hence find the area of the square ABCD.
   c) Find the area of the circle.
   d) Hence find the shaded area.

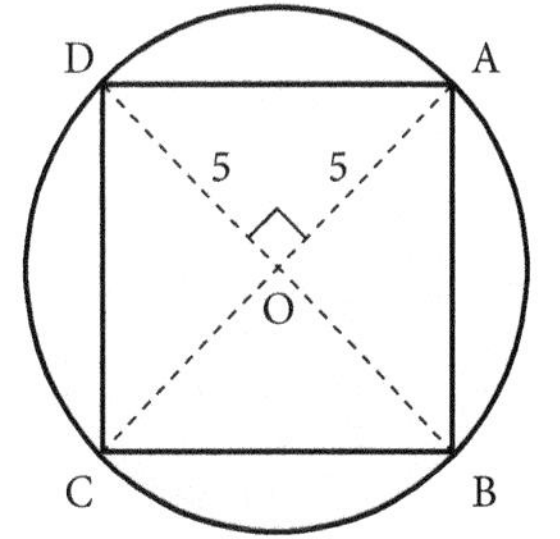

Finding the radius of a circle

Sometimes it is difficult to measure the diameter of a circle but it is fairly easy to measure the circumference.

Example

a) The circumference of a circle is 60 cm. Find the radius of the circle.

$$C = \pi d$$
$$\therefore \quad 60 = \pi d$$
$$\therefore \quad \frac{60}{\pi} = d$$
$$\therefore \quad r = \frac{(60/\pi)}{2} = 9.55 \text{ cm (to 3 s.f.)}$$

b) The area of a circle is 18 m². Find the radius of the circle.

$$\pi r^2 = 18$$
$$r^2 = \frac{18}{\pi}$$
$$r = \sqrt{\left(\frac{18}{\pi}\right)} = 2.39 \text{ m (to 3 s.f.)}$$

Exercise 17

In Questions **1** to **10** use the information given to calculate the radius of the circle. Use the π button on a calculator or take $\pi = 3.142$.

1. The circumference is 15 cm.

2. The circumference is 28 m.

3. The circumference is 7 m.

4. The area is 54 cm².

5. The area is 38 cm².

6. The area is 49 m².

7. The circumference is 16 m.

8. The area is 60 cm².

9. The circumference is 29 cm.

10. The area is 104 cm².

11. An odometer is a wheel used for measuring long distances. The circumference of the wheel is exactly one metre. Find the radius of the wheel.

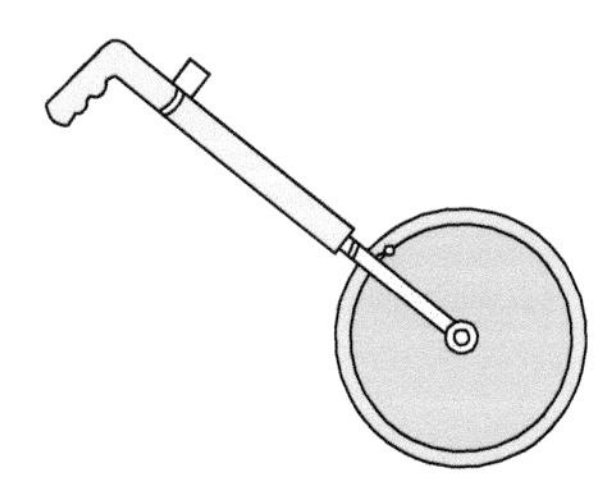

12. A sheet of paper is 32 cm by 20 cm. It is made into a hollow cylinder of height 20 cm with no overlap.

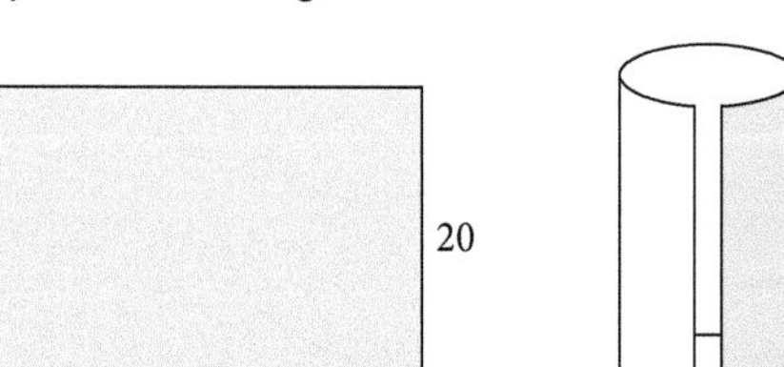

Find the radius of the cylinder.

13. The area of the centre circle on a football pitch is 265 m². Calculate the radius of the circle to the nearest 0.1 m.

14. Eight sections of curved railway track can be joined to make a circular track. Each section is 23 cm long. Calculate the diameter of the circle.

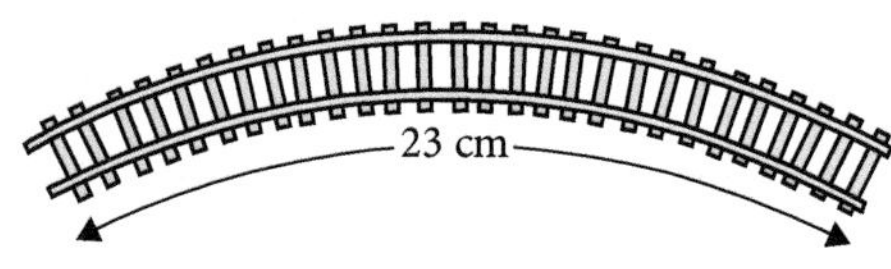

15. Calculate the radius of a circle whose area is equal to the sum of the areas of three circles of radii 2 cm, 3 cm and 4 cm.

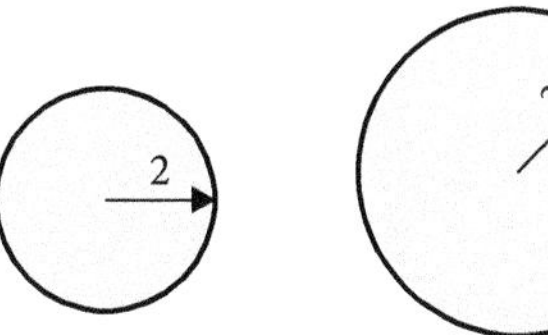

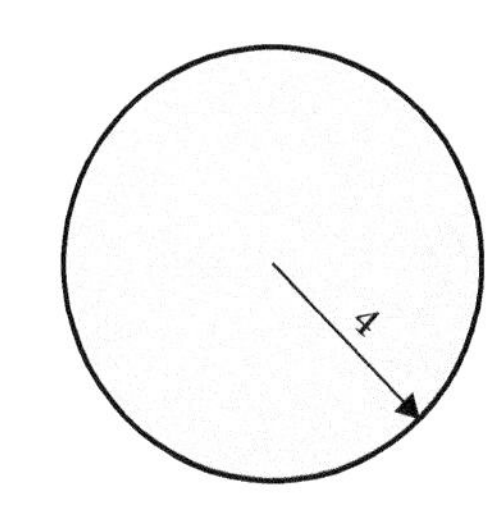

16. The handle of a paint tin is a semicircle of wire which is 28 cm long. Calculate the diameter of the tin.

17. A television transmitter is designed so that people living inside a circle of area 120 000 km^2 can receive pictures. What is the radius of this circle? Give your answer to the nearest km.

18. The circle and the square have the same area. Find the radius of the circle.

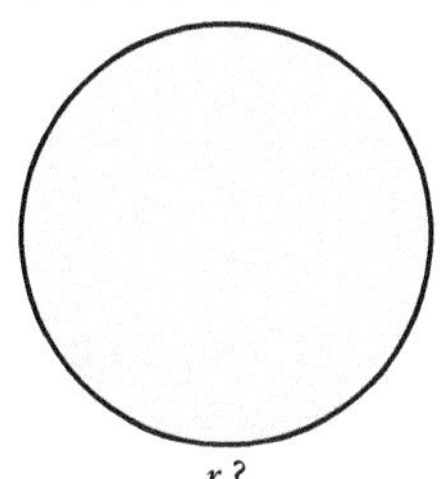

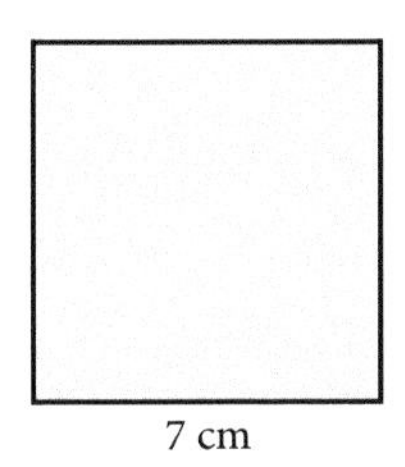

19. The circumference of this circle is 52 m. Find its area.

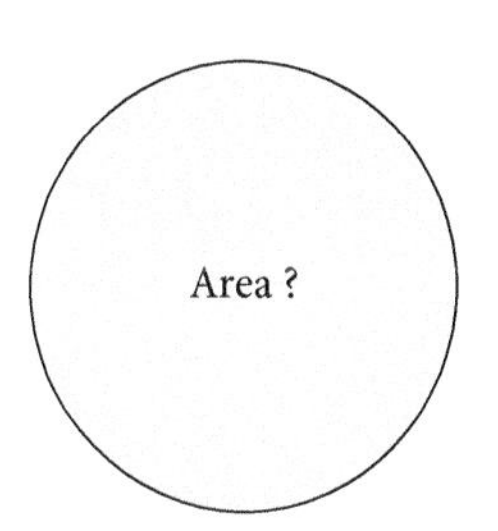

20. The area of a circular target is 1.2 m^2. Find the circumference of the target.

21. The perimeter of a circular pond is 85 m long. Work out the area of the pond.

22. The sector shown is one quarter of a circle and has an area of 23 cm^2. Find the radius of the circle.

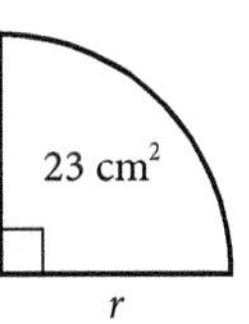

23. Grass seed is sown at a rate of 40 grams per square metre and one box contains 2.5 kg. The seed is just enough to sow a circular lawn. Calculate the radius of this lawn to the nearest 0.1 metre.

1.6 Arc length and sector area

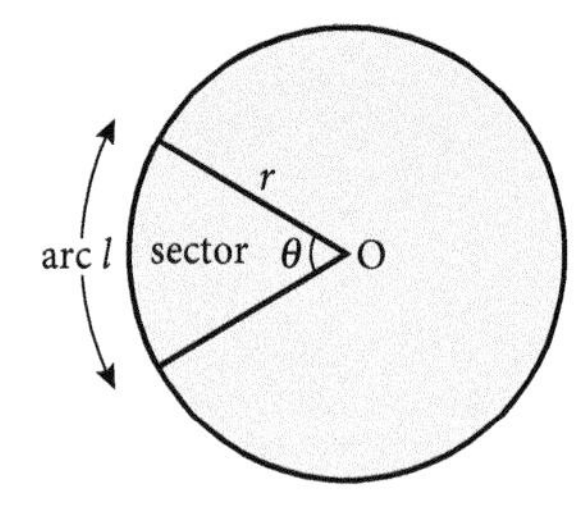

Arc length, $l = \frac{\theta}{360} \times 2\pi r$

We take a fraction of the whole circumference depending on the angle at the centre of the circle.

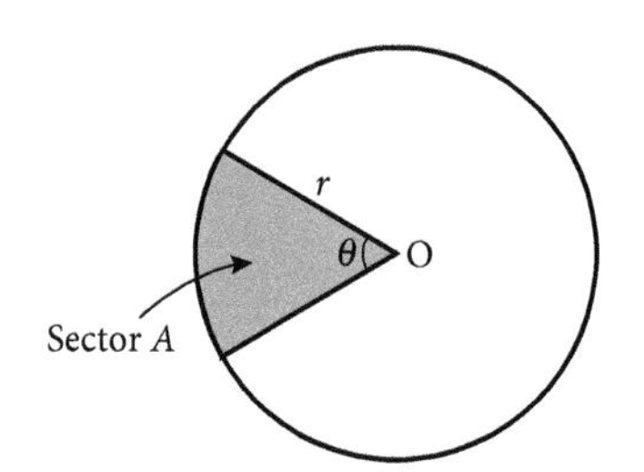

Sector area, $A = \frac{\theta}{360} \times \pi r^2$

We take a fraction of the whole area depending on the angle at the centre of the circle.

Example

a) Find the length of an arc which subtends an angle of 140° at the centre of a circle of radius 12 cm.

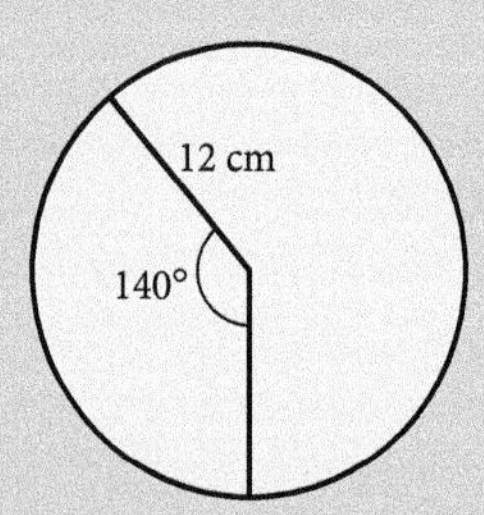

$$\text{Arc length} = \frac{140}{360} \times 2 \times \pi \times 12$$
$$= \frac{28}{3}\pi$$
$$= 29.3 \text{ cm (1 d.p.)}$$

b) A sector of a circle of radius 10 cm has an area of 25 cm². Find the angle at the centre of the circle.

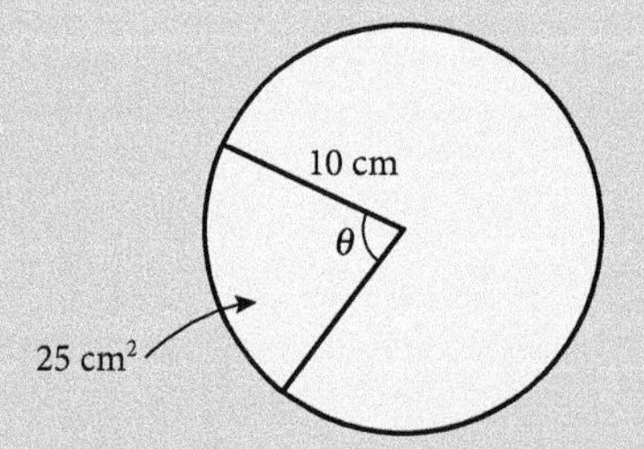

Let the angle at the centre of the circle be θ.

$$\frac{\theta}{360} \times \pi \times 10^2 = 25$$
$$\therefore \quad \theta = \frac{25 \times 360}{\pi \times 100}$$
$$\theta = 28.6° \text{ (3 s.f.)}$$

The angle at the centre of the circle is 28.6°.

Exercise 18

In Questions **1** to **6** find:

a) the sector's arc length

b) the area of the sector

c) the perimeter of the sector.

Give the answers correct to 3 significant figures.

1.

30°
5 cm

2.

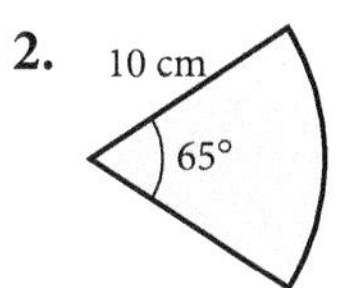

3.

8 cm

4.

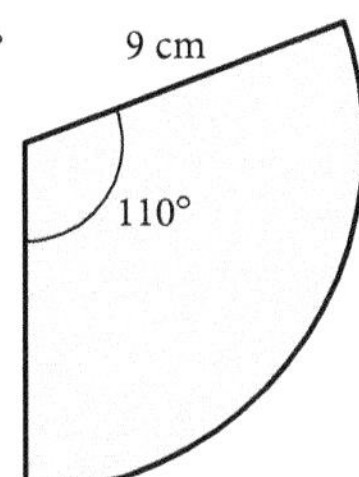

5.

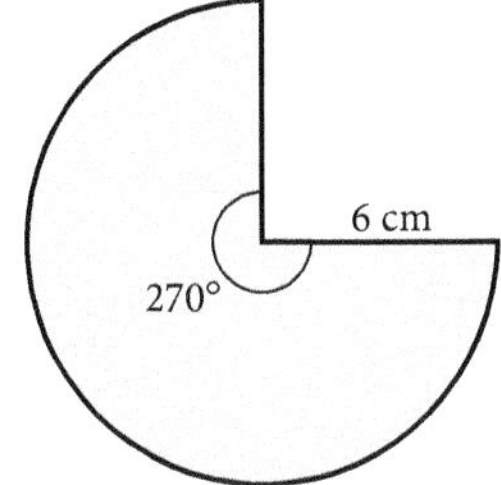

6.

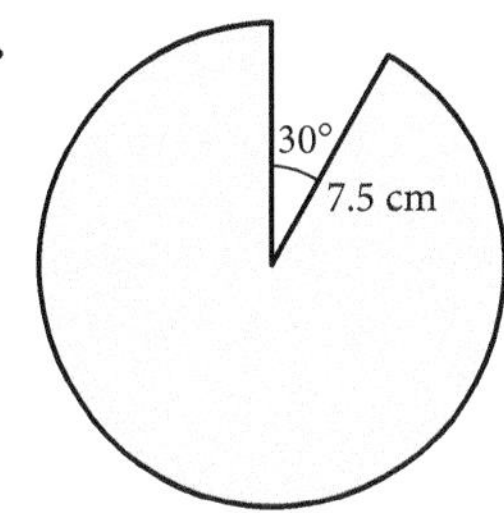

In questions **7** and **8** find the total area of the shape.

7.

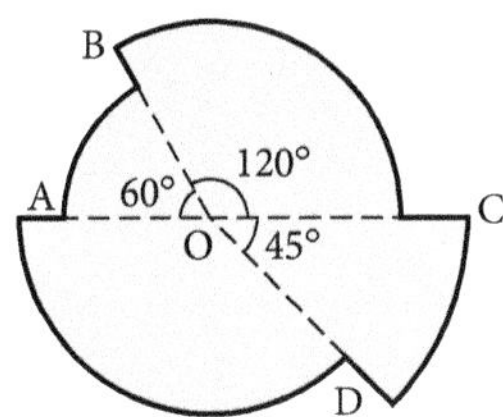

OA = 2 cm, OB = 3 cm, OC = 5 cm, OD = 3 cm.

8.

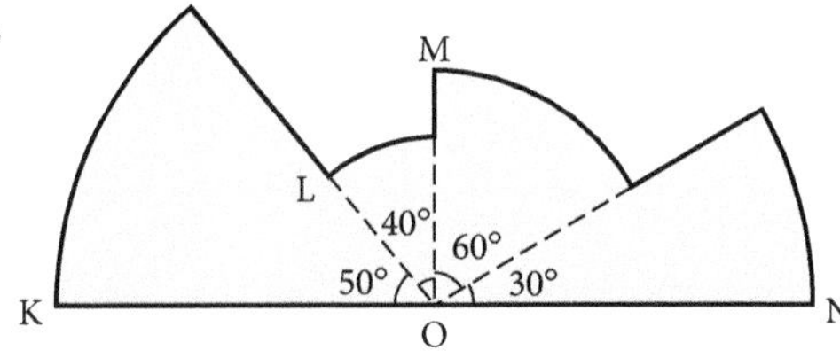

ON = 6 cm, OM = 3 cm, OL = 2 cm, OK = 6 cm.

9. Find the shaded areas.

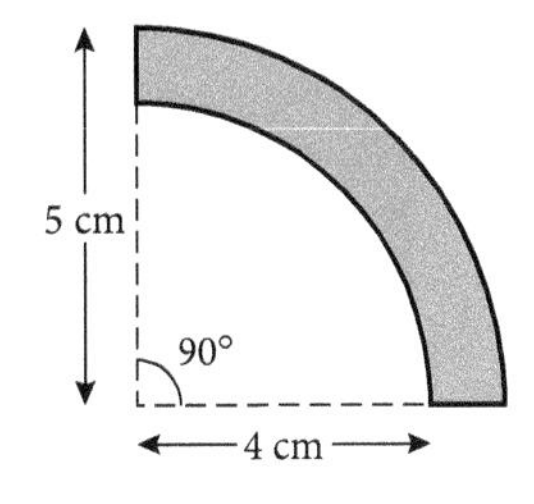

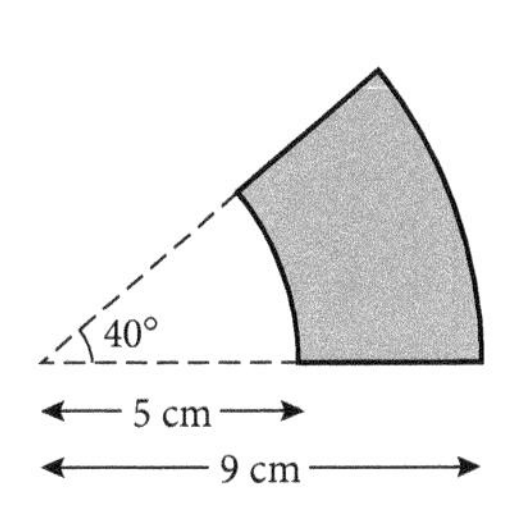

10. The area of this sector is 37.83 cm^2.

Find, correct to 3 significant figures:

a) the radius r

b) the arc length l.

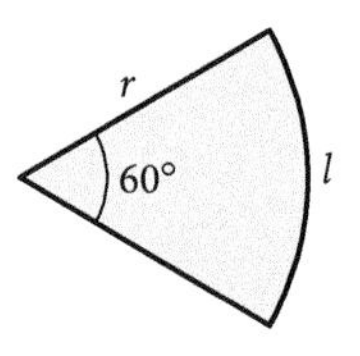

11. In the diagram the arc length is l and the sector area is A.

a) Find θ, when $r = 5$ cm and $l = 7.5$ cm.

b) Find θ, when $r = 2$ m and $A = 2$ m^2.

c) Find r, when $\theta = 55°$ and $l = 6$ cm.

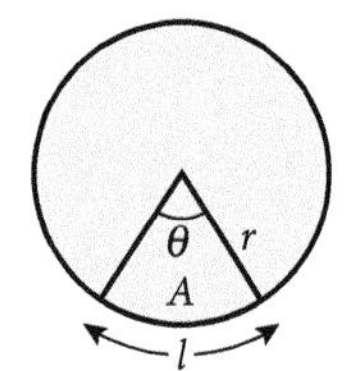

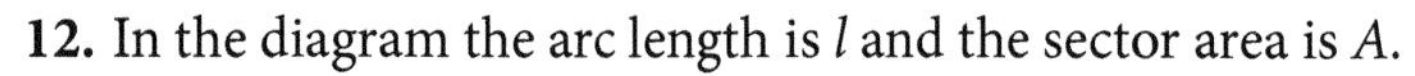

12. In the diagram the arc length is l and the sector area is A.

a) Find l, when $\theta = 72°$ and $A = 15$ cm^2.

b) Find l, when $\theta = 135°$ and $A = 162$ cm^2.

c) Find A, when $l = 11$ cm and $r = 5.2$ cm.

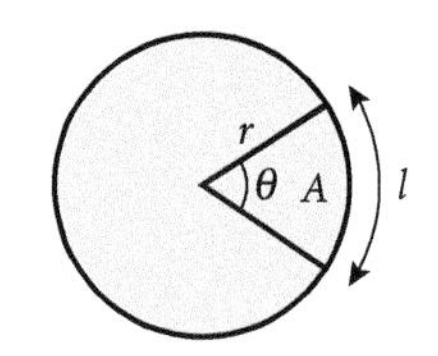

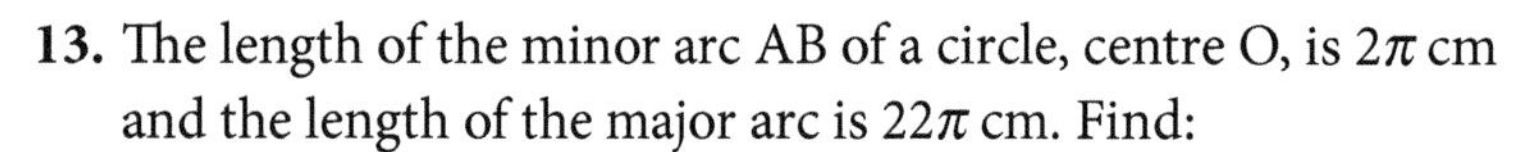

13. The length of the minor arc AB of a circle, centre O, is 2π cm and the length of the major arc is 22π cm. Find:

a) the radius of the circle

b) the acute angle AOB.

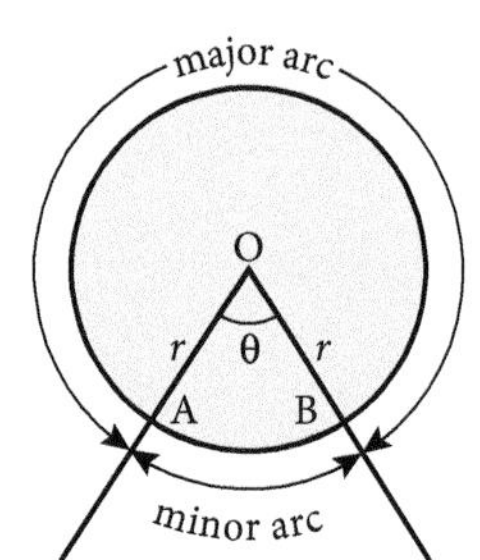

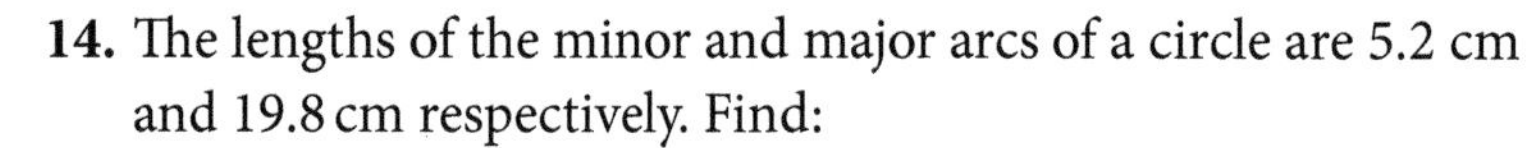

14. The lengths of the minor and major arcs of a circle are 5.2 cm and 19.8 cm respectively. Find:

a) the radius of the circle

b) the angle subtended at the centre by the minor arc.

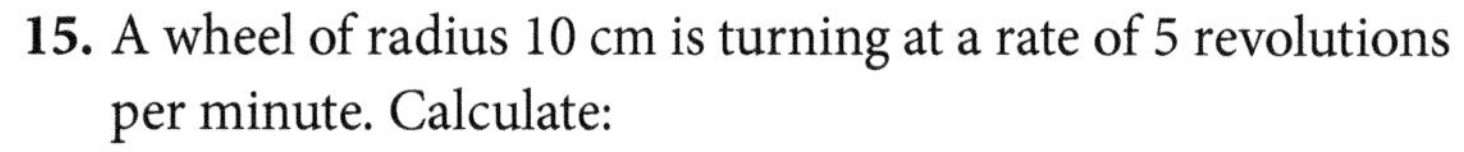

15. A wheel of radius 10 cm is turning at a rate of 5 revolutions per minute. Calculate:

a) the angle through which the wheel turns in 1 second

b) the distance moved by a point on the rim in 2 seconds.

1.7 Area

Rectangle and triangle

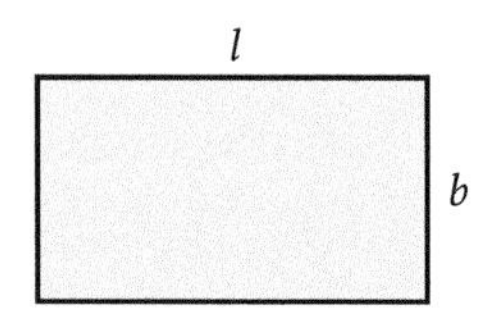

Rectangle:

area = $l \times b$

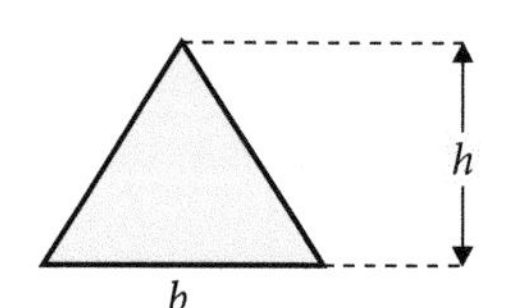

Triangle:

area = $\dfrac{b \times h}{2}$

Exercise 19

Work out the area. All lengths are in cm.

1.
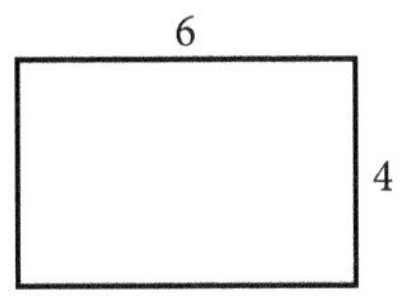

2.
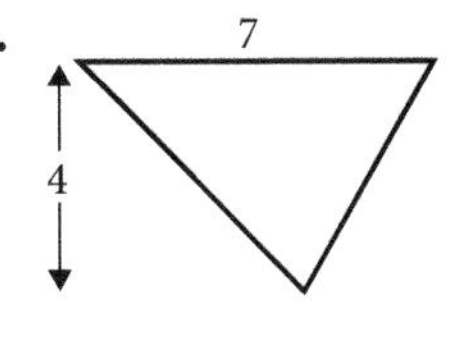

3.
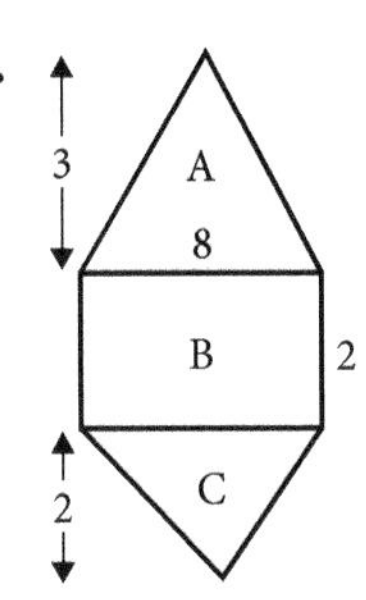

4.
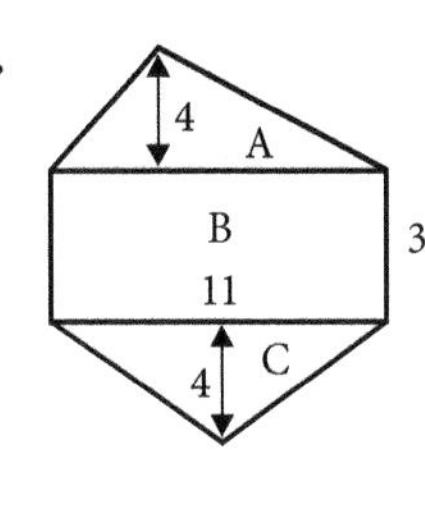

5.
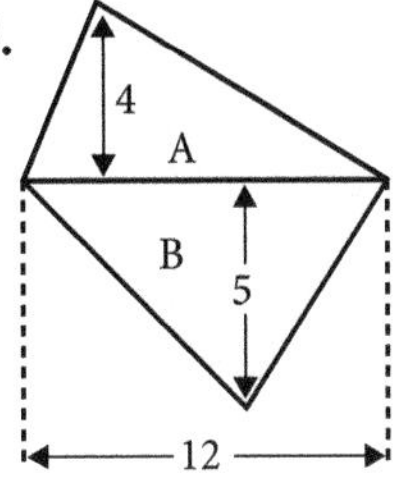

6.
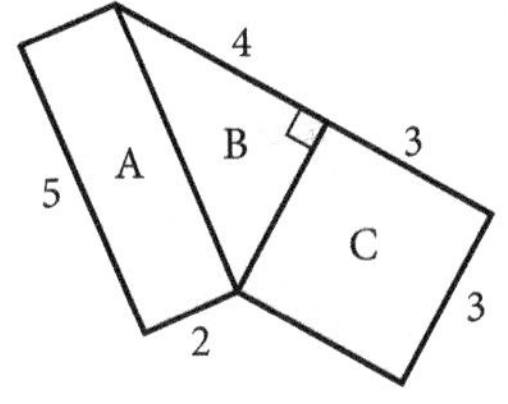

7.
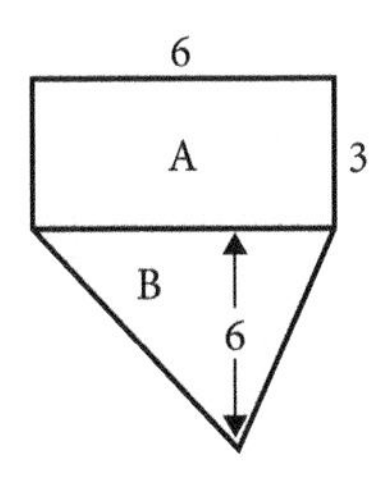

8.
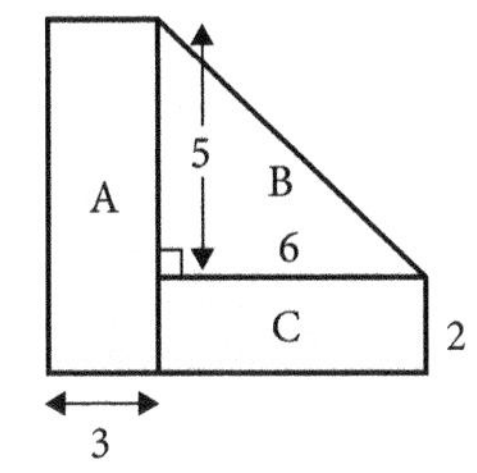

9.
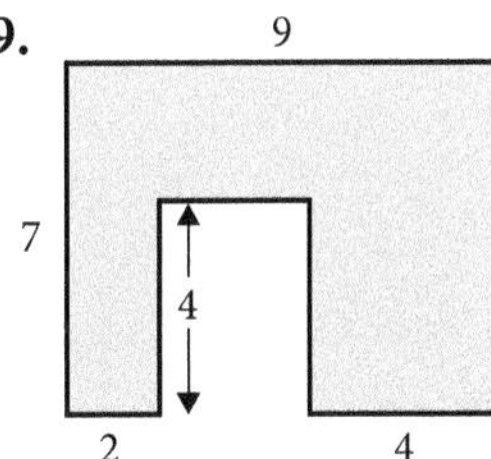

10.
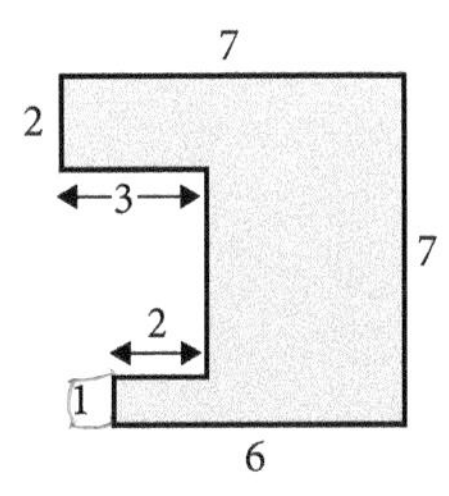

11.
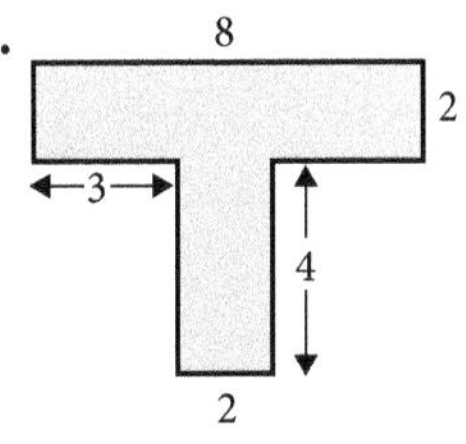

12.
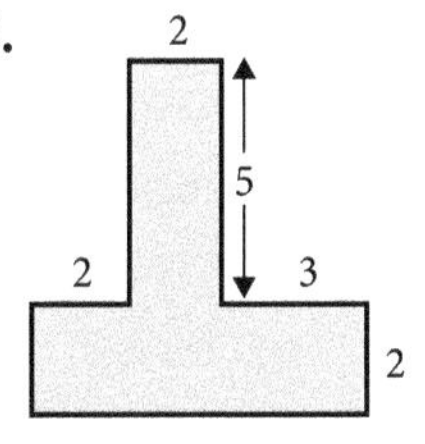

13.
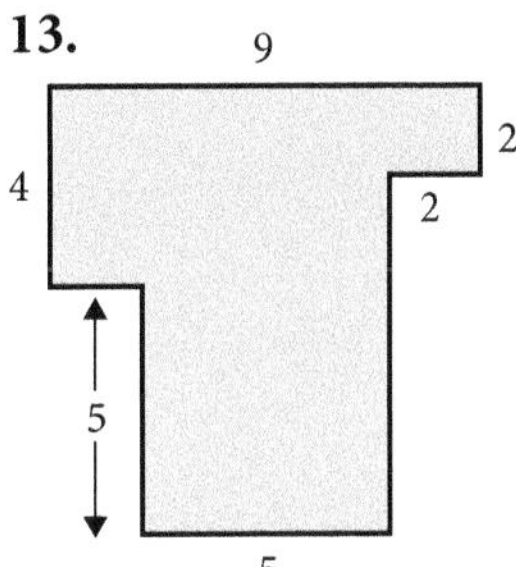

14.
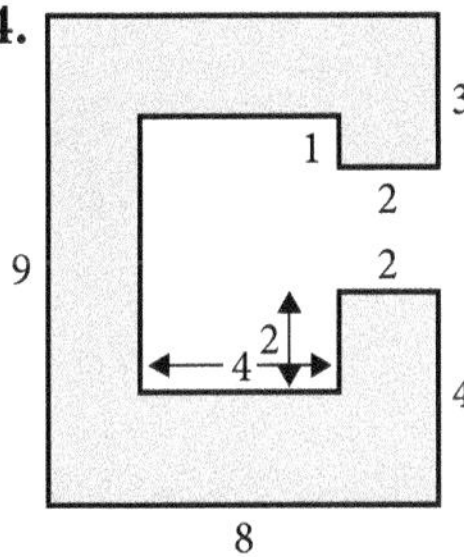

15.
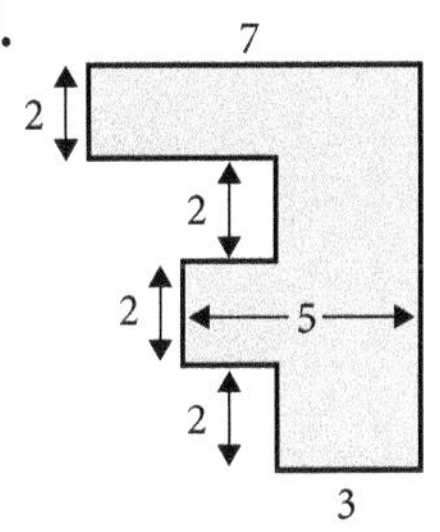

16.
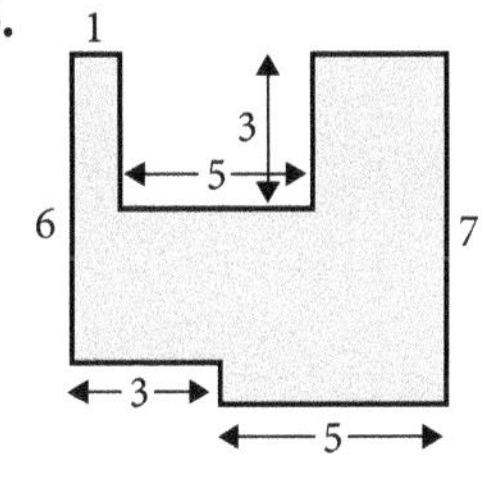

Exercise 20

1. **a)** Copy the diagram.

   b) Work out the areas of triangles A, B and C.

   c) Work out the area of the square enclosed by the broken lines.

   d) Hence work out the area of the shaded triangle. Give the answer in square units.

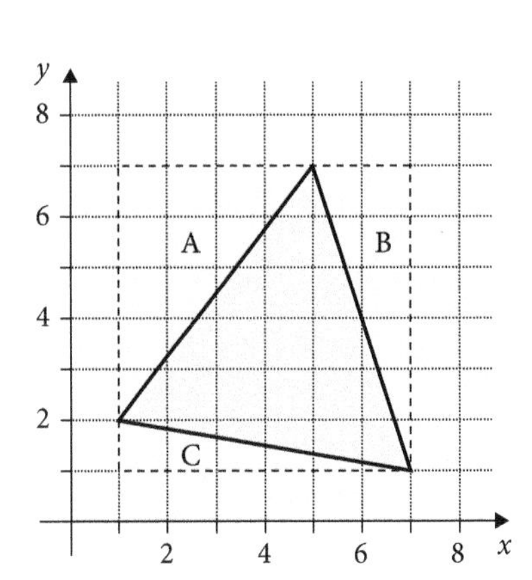

2. **a)** Copy the diagram.

   b) Work out the areas of triangles A, B and C.

   c) Work out the area of the rectangle enclosed by the broken lines.

   d) Hence work out the area of the shaded triangle. Give the answer in square units.

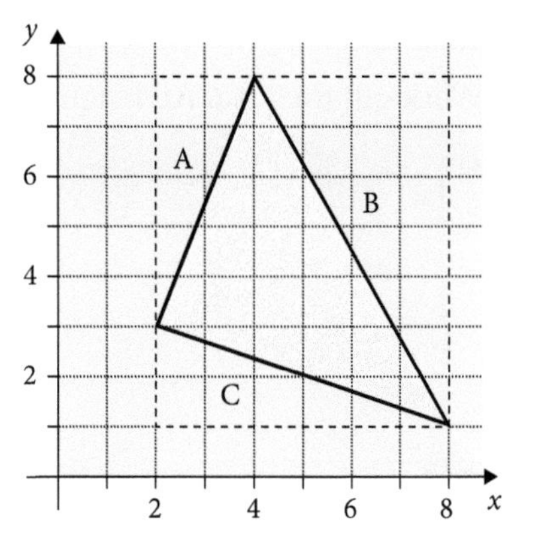

For Questions **3** to **7**, draw a pair of axes similar to those in Questions **1** and **2**. Plot the points in the order given and find the area of the shape enclosed.

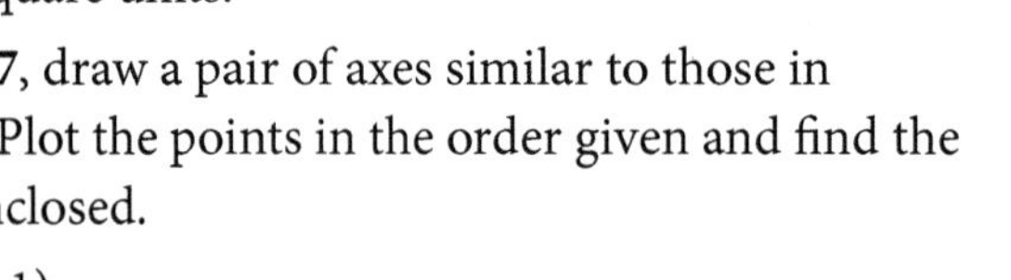

3. (1, 4), (6, 8), (4, 1)

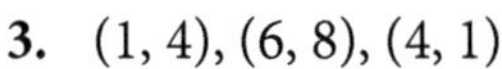

4. (1, 7), (8, 5), (4, 2)
5. (2, 4), (6, 1), (8, 7), (4, 8), (2, 4)
6. (1, 4), (5, 1), (7, 6), (4, 8), (1, 4)
7. (1, 6), (2, 2), (8, 6), (6, 8), (1, 6)
8. A wooden cuboid has the dimensions shown.

   a) Calculate the total surface area.

   b) One tin of paint can cover 3 m^2. How many cuboids can be painted using the paint in one tin?

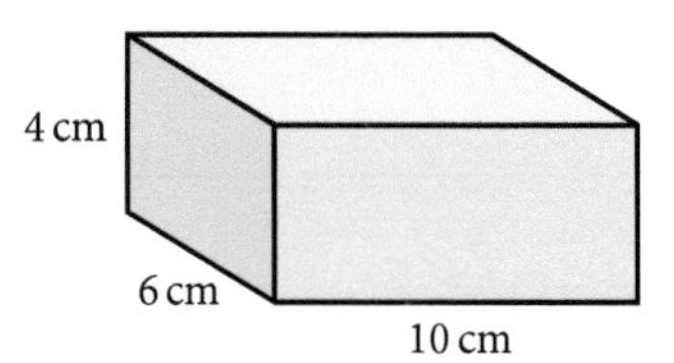

Trapezium and parallelogram

Trapezium (two parallel sides)

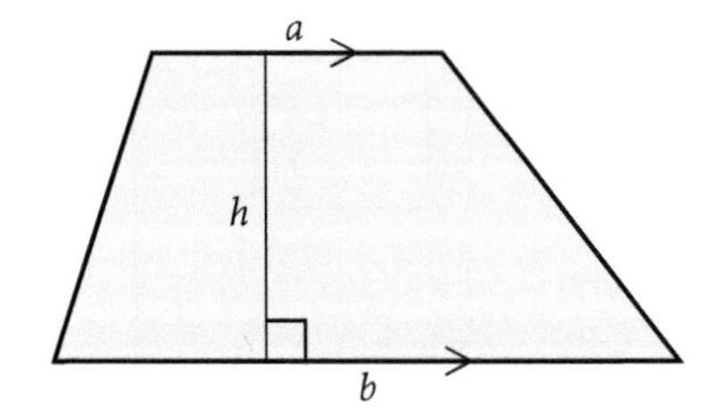

area $= \frac{1}{2}(a + b) \times h$

Parallelogram

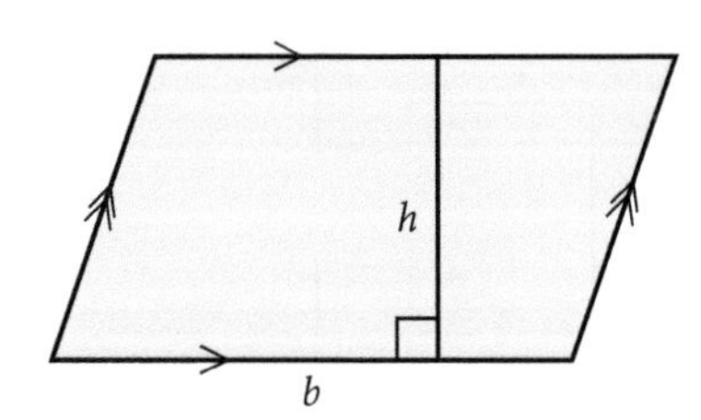

area $= b \times h$

Example

Find the area of the trapezium.

$$\text{Area of trapezium} = \frac{1}{2}(8+14)\times 7$$

$$= \frac{1}{2}\times 22\times 7$$

$$= 77 \text{ cm}^2$$

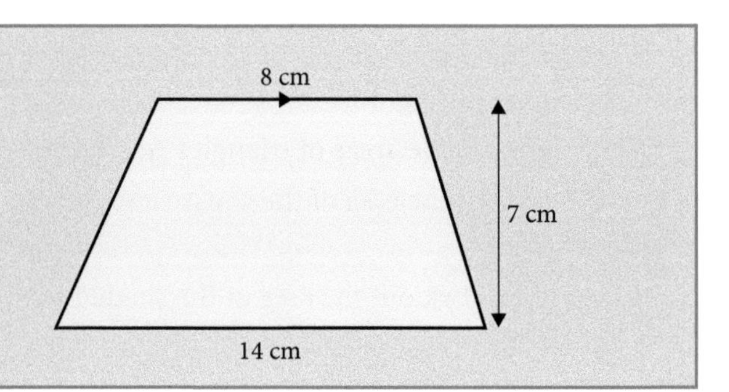

Exercise 21

In Questions **1** to **5** find the area of each shape. All lengths are in cm.

1.

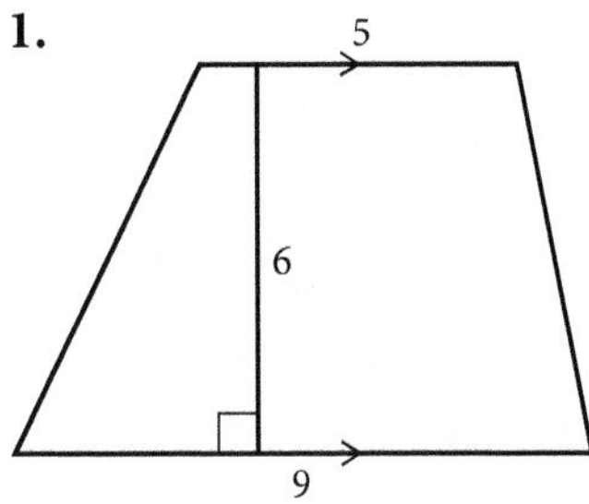

2.

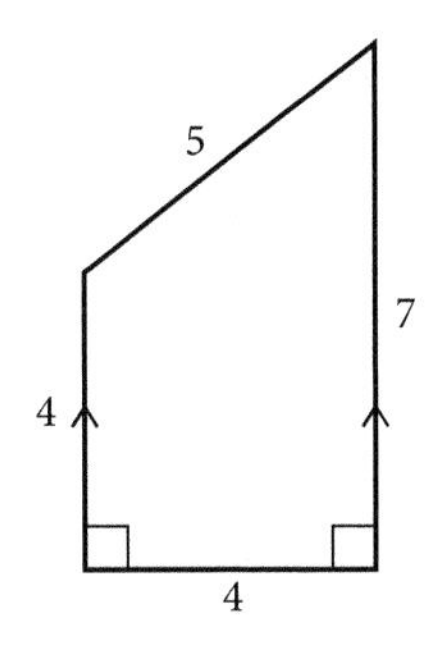

3.

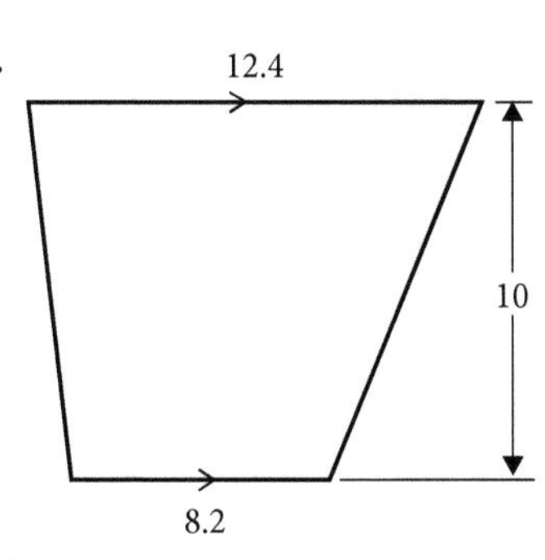

4.

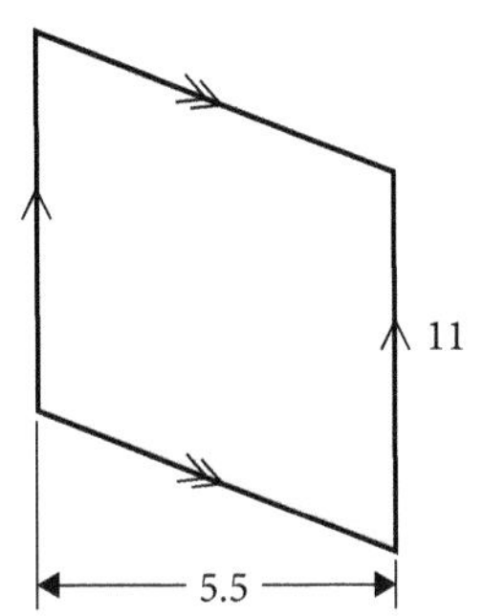

5.

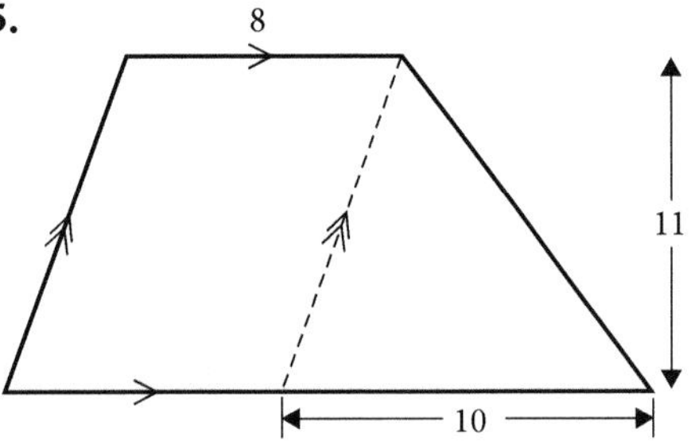

6. Large areas of land are measured in hectares. 1 hectare = 10 000 m^2.
Copy and complete the statements below:

a)

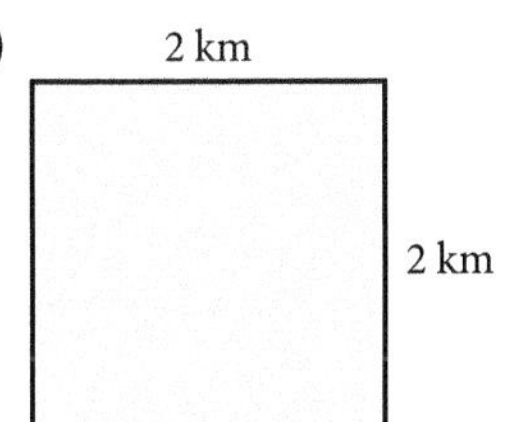

area of square = ________ m^2

area of square = ________ hectares

b)

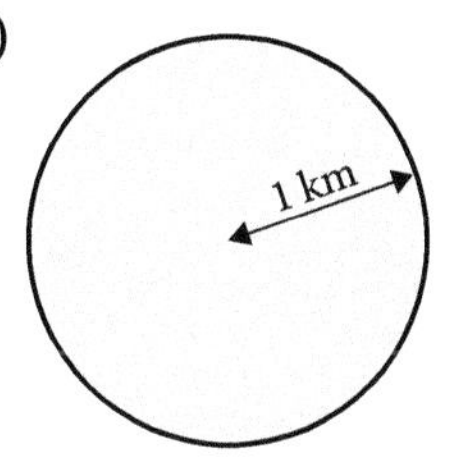

area of circle = ________ m^2

area of circle = ________ hectares

7. The field shown is sprayed at the rate of 2 litres per hectare. The cost of the spray is \$25 for 100 litres.

How much will it cost to spray this field, to the nearest dollar?

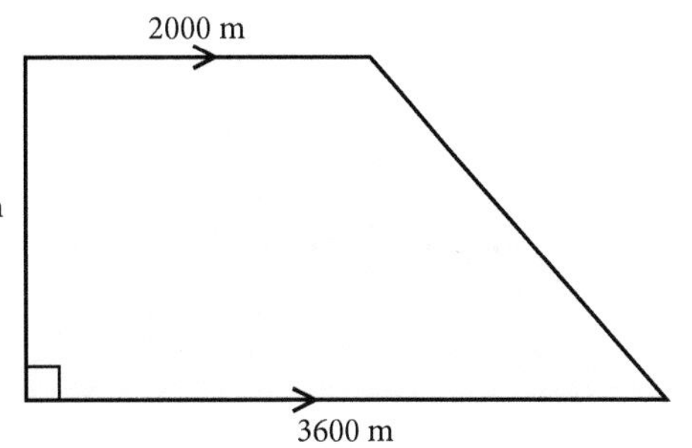

Designing square patterns

The object is to design square patterns of different sizes. The patterns are all to be made from smaller tiles all of which are themselves square. Designs for a 4×4 square:

a) 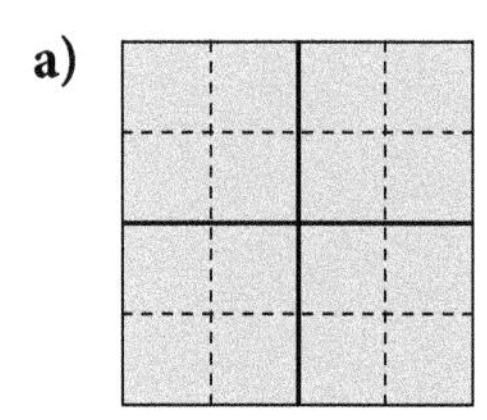

This design consists of four tiles each 2×2. The pattern is rather dull.

b) Suppose we say that the design must contain at least one 1×1 square.

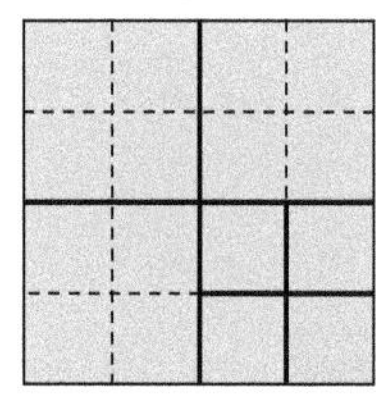

This design is more interesting and consists of seven tiles.

Exercise 22

1. Try a 5×5 square. Design a pattern which divides the 5×5 square into eight smaller squares.
2. Try a 6×6 square. Here you must include at least one 1×1 square. Design a pattern which divides the 6×6 square into nine smaller squares. Colour in the final design to make it look interesting.
3. A 7×7 square is more difficult. With no restrictions, design a pattern which divides the 7×7 square into nine smaller squares.
4. Design a pattern which divides an 8×8 square into ten smaller squares. You must not use a 4×4 square.
5. Design a pattern which divides a 9×9 square into ten smaller squares. You can use only one 3×3 square.
6. Design a pattern which divides a 10×10 square into eleven smaller squares. You must include a 3×3 square.
7. Design a pattern which divides an 11×11 square into eleven smaller squares. You must include a 6×6 square.

1.8 Volume and surface area

Prisms and cuboids

A prism is an object with a uniform cross-section.

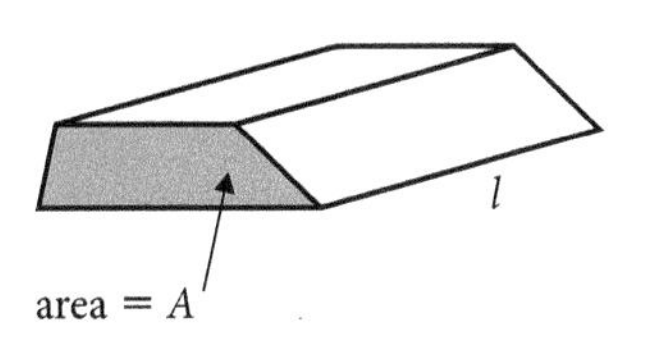

Volume $= A \times l$

A cuboid is a prism whose cross-section is a rectangle.

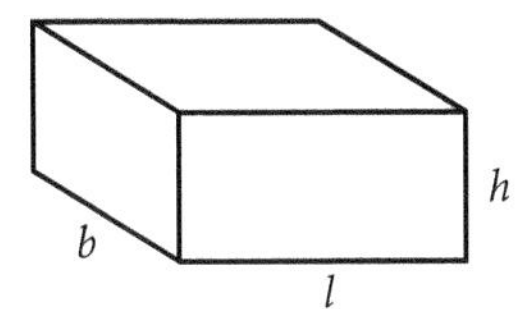

Volume $= l \times b \times h$
Surface area $= 2 \times (bl + hl + bh)$

To find the surface area of a solid, find the area of every side and add them all together.

It will not always be possible to find the surface area of a general prism.

Exercise 23

Find the volume of each prism in Questions **1** to **3**.

1.

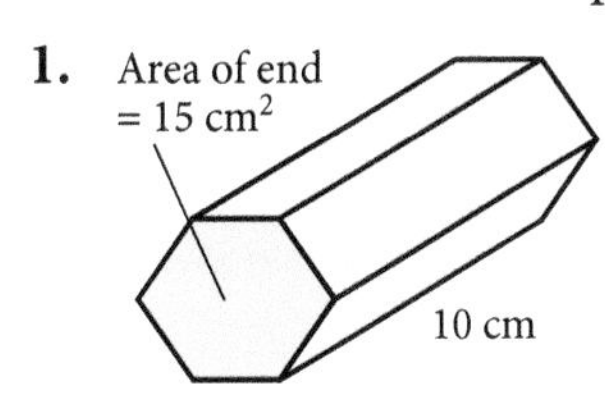

2.

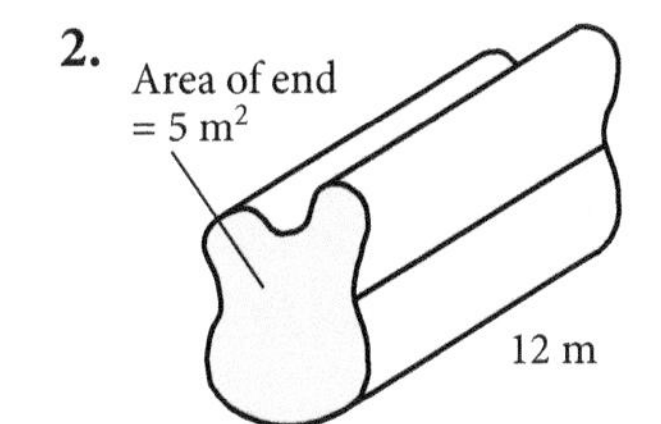

3.

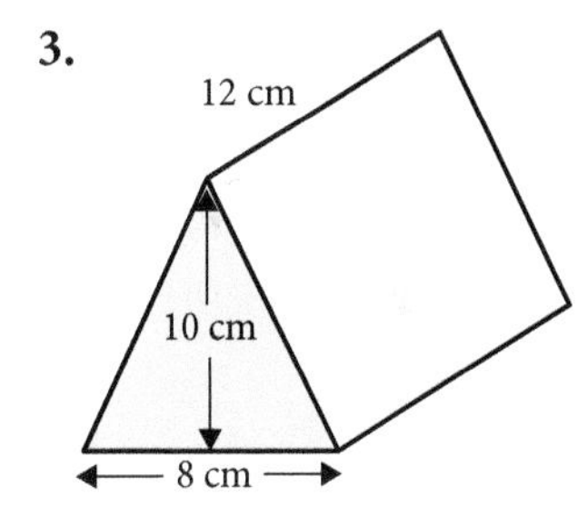

Find the volume and surface area of each prism in Questions **4** to **6**.

4.

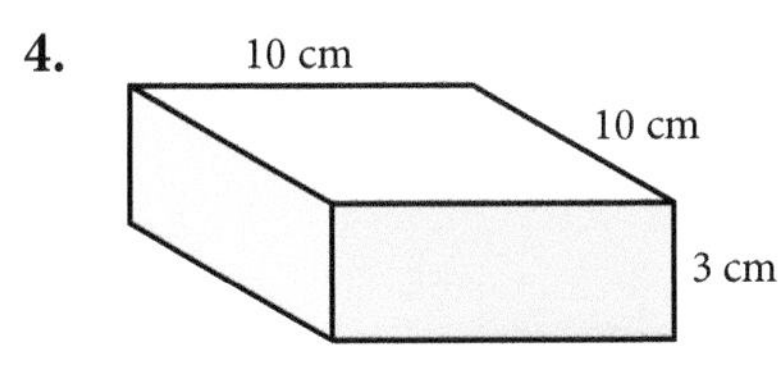

5.

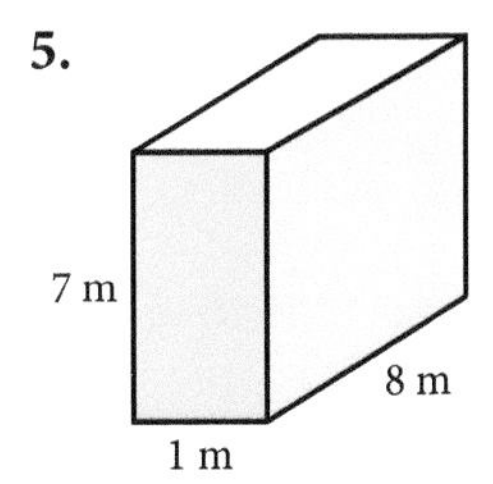

6.

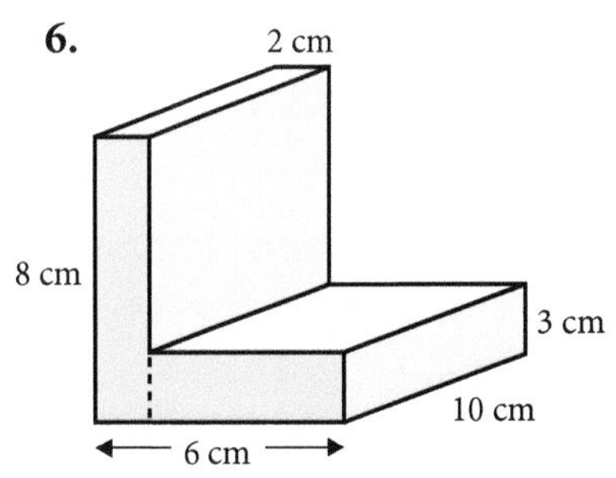

Find the volume of each prism in Questions **7** to **9**.

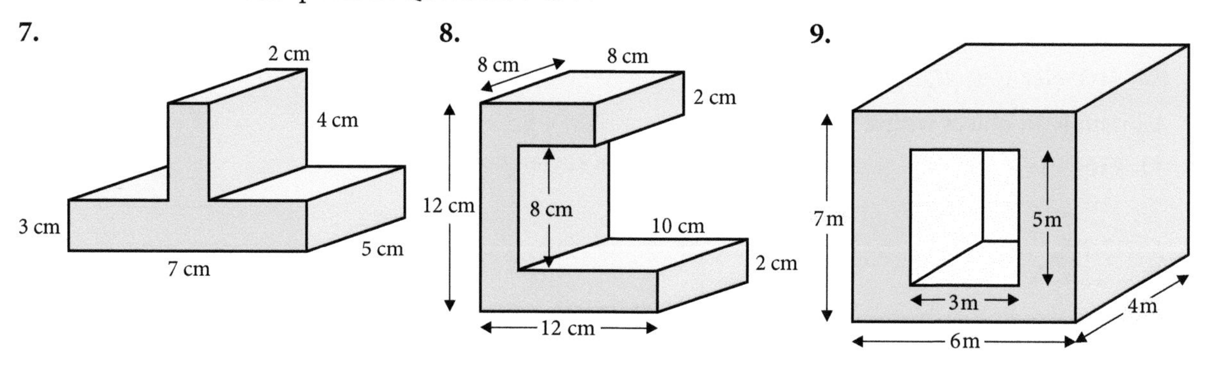

Cylinders

A cylinder is a prism with a circular cross-section.

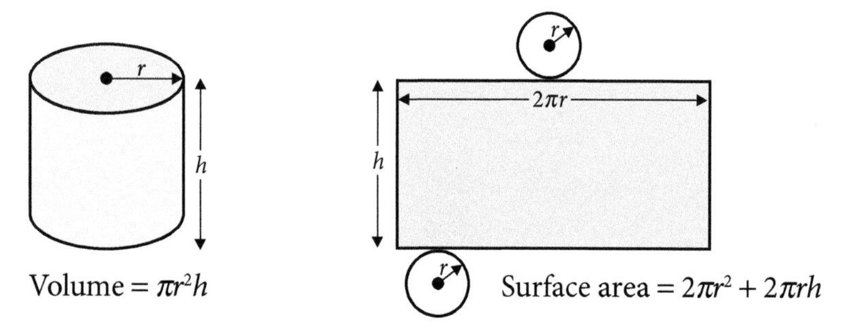

Volume = $\pi r^2 h$

Surface area = $2\pi r^2 + 2\pi rh$

Exercise 24

Find the volume and surface area of each cylinder in Questions **1** to **10**. Use the π button on a calculator or use $\pi = 3.142$. Give the answers correct to 3 s.f.

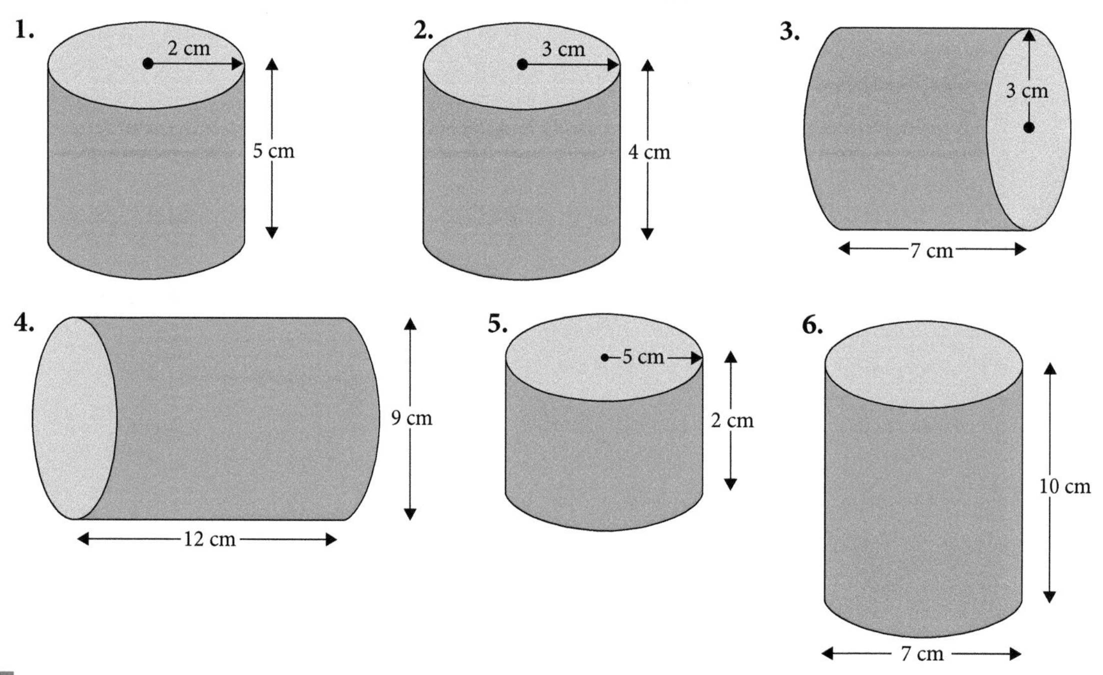

7. radius = 7 cm, height = 5 cm

8. diameter = 8 m, height = 3.5 m

9. diameter = 11 m, height = 2.4 m

10. radius = 3.2 cm, height = 15.1 cm

11. Find the capacity in litres of the oil drum shown here. (1000 cm^3 = 1 litre)

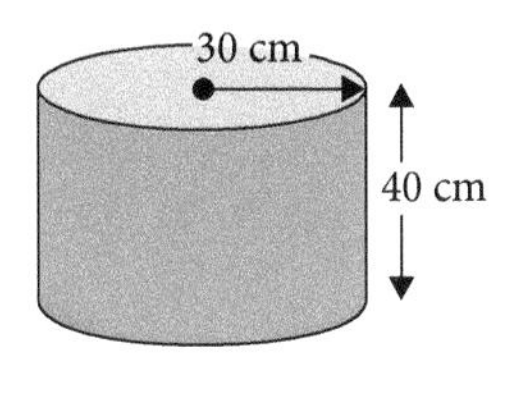

12. Cylinders are cut along the axis of symmetry to form the objects below. Find the volume of each object.

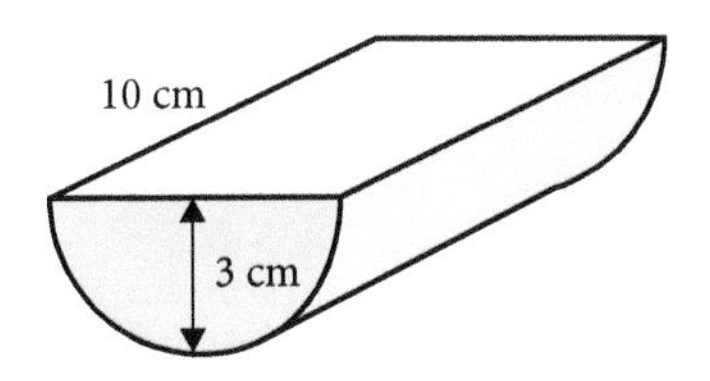

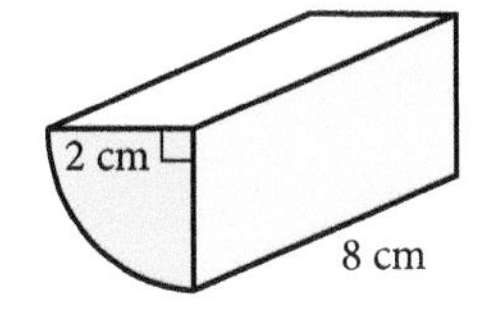

Spheres

Volume $= \frac{4}{3}\pi r^3$

Surface area $= 4\pi r^2$

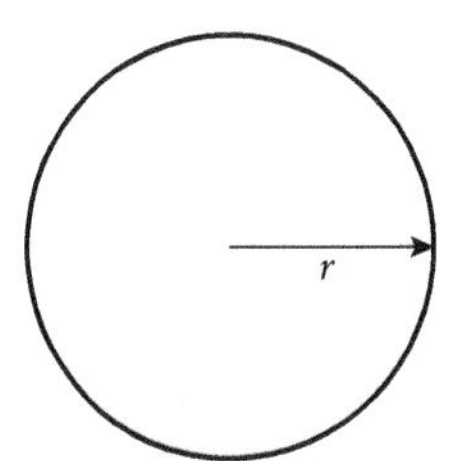

Cones

Volume $= \frac{1}{3}\pi r^2 h$

Surface area = area of circular base + area of curved surface

$= \pi r^2 + \pi rl$

where l is the slant height of the cone.

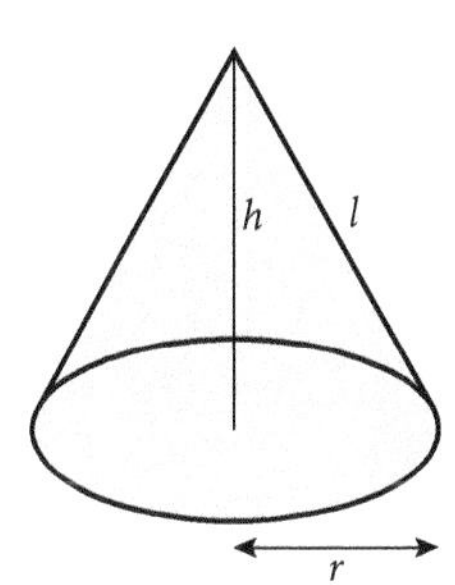

Pyramids

Volume $= \frac{1}{3}(\text{base area}) \times \text{height}$

(note the similarity with the cone formula)

There is no general formula given for the surface area of a pyramid.

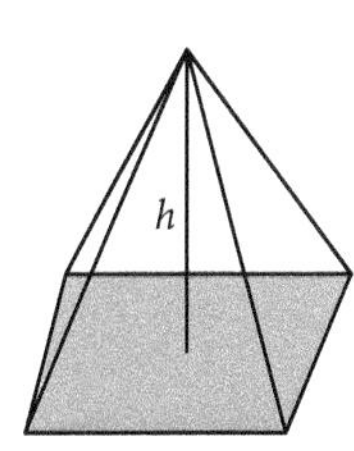

Also, note that the base of a pyramid can be any shape. It does not have to be square.

Example

a) A pyramid has a square base of side 5 m and vertical height 4 m. Find its volume.

$$\text{Volume of pyramid} = \frac{1}{3}(5 \times 5) \times 4$$
$$= 33\frac{1}{3}\text{ m}^3$$

b) Calculate the radius of a sphere of volume 500 cm³.

Let the radius of the sphere be r cm.

$$\frac{4}{3}\pi r^3 = 500$$
$$r^3 = \frac{3 \times 500}{4\pi}$$
$$r = \sqrt[3]{\left(\frac{3 \times 500}{4\pi}\right)} = 4.92 \text{ (3 s.f.)}$$

The radius of the sphere is 4.92 cm.

Exercise 25

Find the volume and surface area of the shapes in Questions **1** to **8**.

1. cone: height = 5 cm, radius = 2 cm

2. sphere: radius = 5 cm

3. sphere: radius = 10 cm

4. cone: height = 6 cm, radius = 4 cm

5. sphere: diameter = 8 cm

6. cone: height = x cm, radius = $2x$ cm

7. sphere: radius = 0.1 m

8. cone: height $= \frac{1}{\pi}$ cm, radius = 3 cm

Find the volume of the shapes in Questions **9** to **11**.

9. pyramid: rectangular base 7 cm by 8 cm; height = 5 cm

10. pyramid: square base of side 4 m, height = 9 m

11. pyramid: equilateral triangular base of side = 8 cm, height = 10 cm

12. Find the height of a pyramid of volume 20 m³ and base area 12 m².

13. Find the radius of a sphere of volume 60 cm³.

14. Find the height of a cone of volume 2.5 litre and radius 10 cm.

15. A spherical ball is immersed in water contained in a vertical cylinder.

Assuming the water covers the ball, calculate the rise in the water level if:

a) sphere radius = 3 cm, cylinder radius = 10 cm

b) sphere radius = 2 cm, cylinder radius = 5 cm.

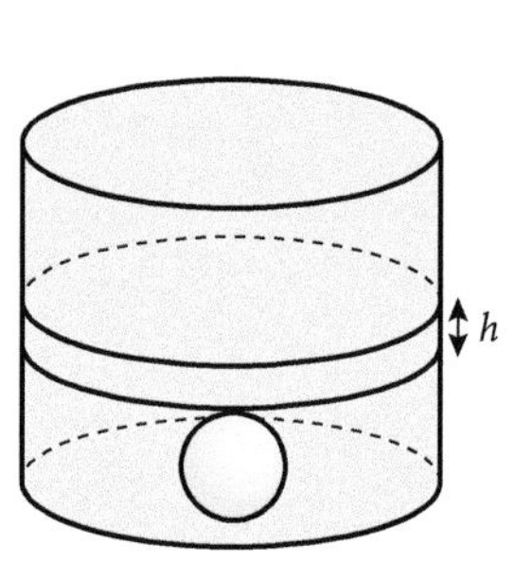

Exercise 26

This exercise contains a mixture of questions involving the volumes of a wide variety of different objects.

Where necessary give answers correct to 3 s.f.

1. A cylinder has a cross-sectional area of 12 cm^2 and a length of two metres. Calculate its volume in cm^3.

2. The diagram represents a building.

a) Calculate the area of the shaded end.

b) Calculate the volume of the building.

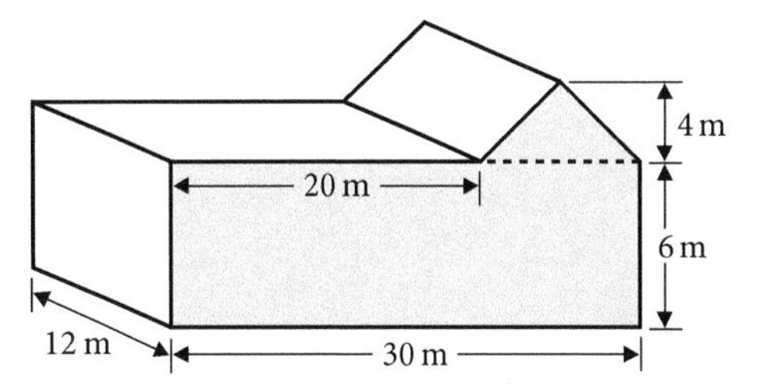

3. A rectangular block has dimensions 20 cm × 7 cm × 7 cm. Find the volume of the largest solid cylinder which can be cut from this block.

4. Metal discs are made with a circular cross-section, shown opposite.

a) Find the surface area of the disc.

b) The discs are 0.2 cm thick. Calculate the volume of the disc.

c) Find, in cm^3, the volume of brass needed to make 10 000 of these discs.

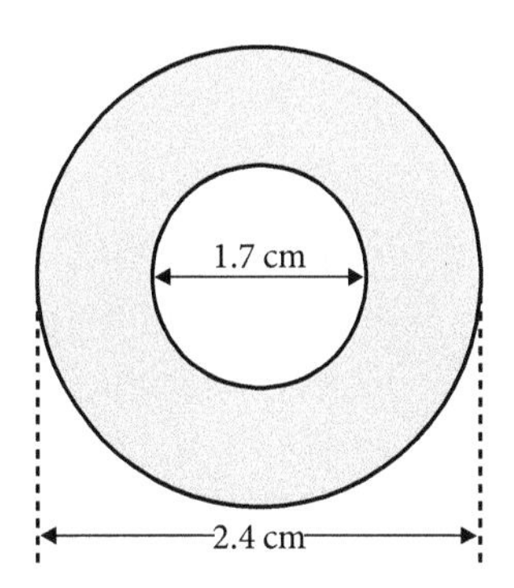

5. a) A cylindrical water tank has internal diameter 40 cm and height 50 cm. Calculate the volume of the tank.

b) A cylindrical mug has internal diameter 8 cm and height 10 cm. Calculate the volume of the mug.

c) If the tank is full, how many mugs can be filled from the tank?

6. In the diagram all the angles are right angles and the lengths are in cm.

Find the volume of the shape.

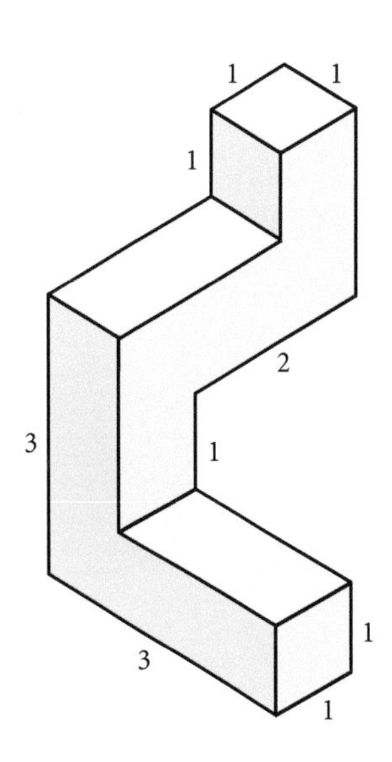

7. The diagram shows the cross-section of a steel bar which is 4 m long.

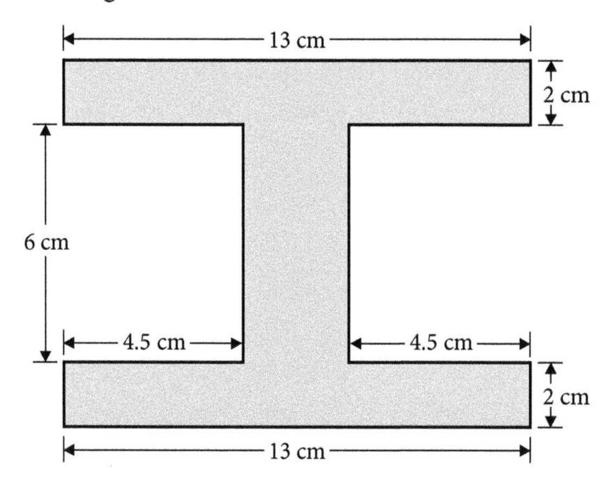

a) Calculate the cross-sectional area in cm^2.

b) Calculate the volume of the bar in cm^3.

c) If 1 cm^3 of steel weighs 7.8 g, find the weight of the bar in kg.

d) How many bars can be carried on a lorry if it can't carry more than 8 tonnes? (1 tonne = 1000 kg)

8. Rahim decided to build a garage. The garage was to be 6 m by 4 m and 2.5 m in height. Each brick measures 22 cm by 10 cm by 7 cm. Rahim estimated that he would need about 40 000 bricks.

Is this a reasonable estimate?

9. A cylindrical tin of height 15 cm and radius 4 cm is filled with sand from a rectangular box that is 50 cm by 40 cm by 20 cm. How many times bigger is the box than the cylinder?

10. Water pours into the trough shown at a rate of 2 litres/min. How long, to the nearest minute, will it take to fill the trough? (1 litre = 1000 cm^3)

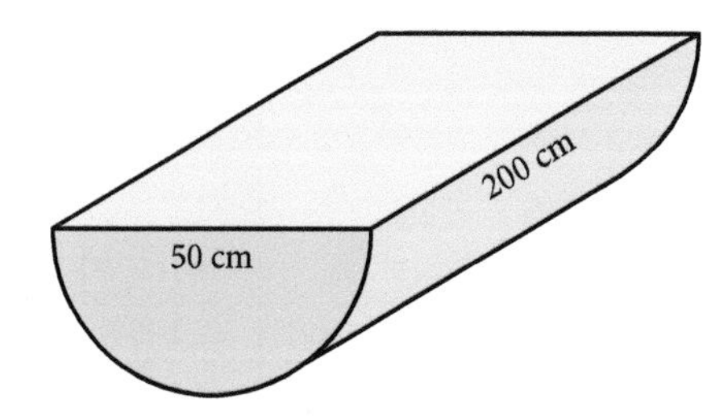

1.9 Scale drawing

Exercise 27

Draw an accurate scale drawing of each shape below using the scale shown.

1. Scale: 1 cm for 1 m.

   Measure and write down the length of AB (in cm).

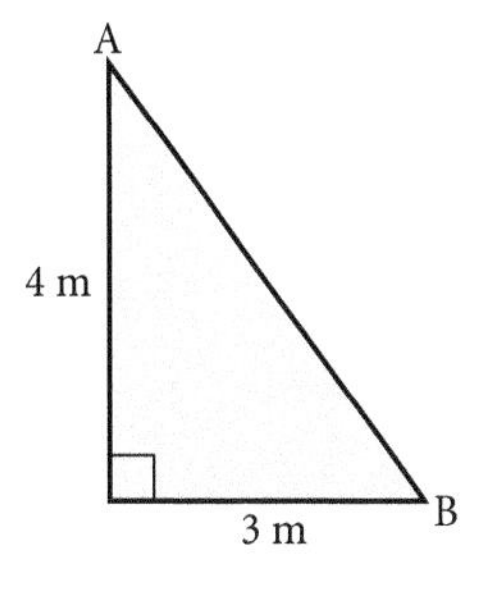

2. Scale: 1 cm for every 3 m.

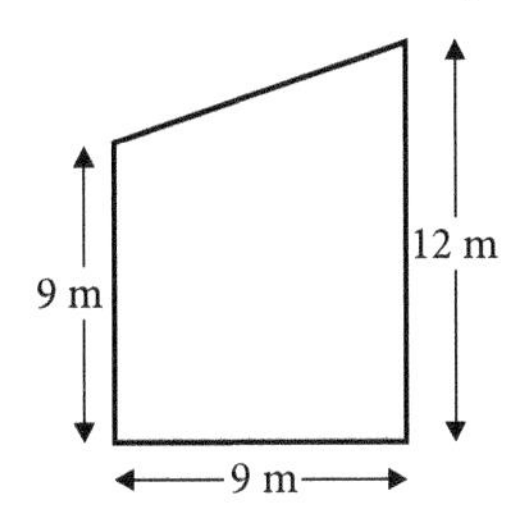

3. Scale: 2 cm for every 1 m.

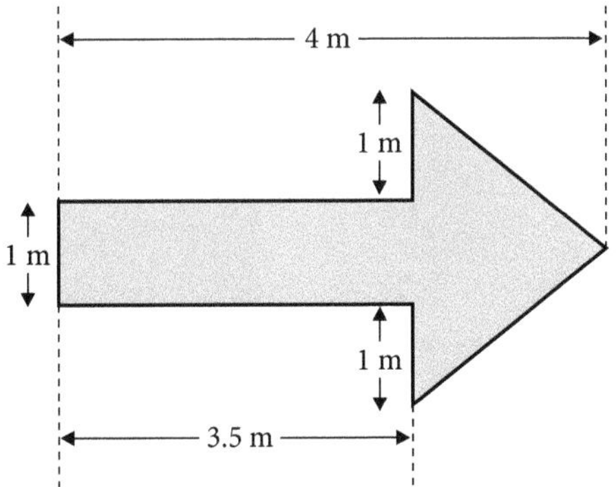

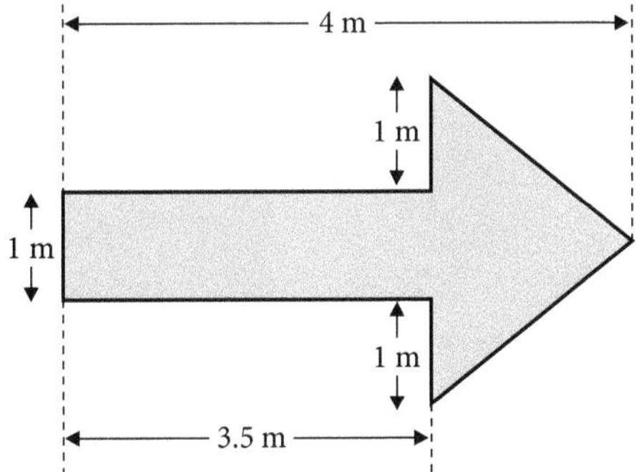

4. A hut is 3 m high and $1\frac{1}{2}$ m wide. It has a door $\frac{1}{2}$ m wide and 2 m high.

   Make an accurate scale drawing using a scale of 2 cm for every 1 m.

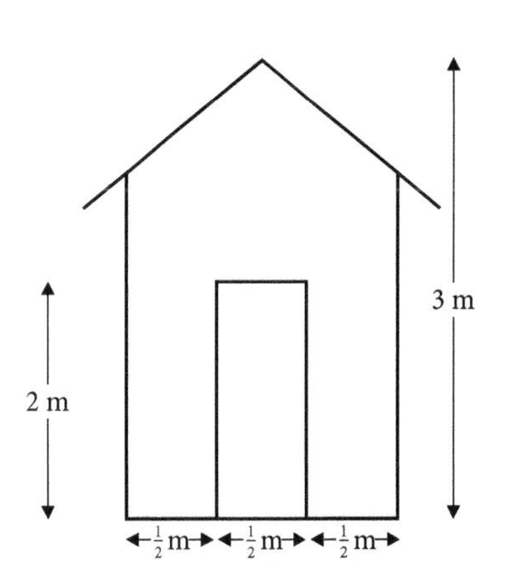

5. A bird leaves its nest and makes three flights.

   a) Make a scale drawing to show the journey.

   b) How far does the bird have to fly to return to its nest?

	Direction	Distance
1st stage	west	5 km
2nd stage	south-east	6 km
3rd stage	east	12 km

6. Sea

P ← 10 km → Q

Land

The diagram above shows ports P and Q where P is 10 km west of Q. A boat A is 9 km north-east of P. A lighthouse S is 4 km north-west of Q. The light can be seen up to 4 km from the lighthouse. Will the boat see the light?

7. A pirate has buried treasure in the field shown.

Make a scale drawing of the field and shade the region where you think the treasure lies. Use a scale of 1 cm to 100 m.

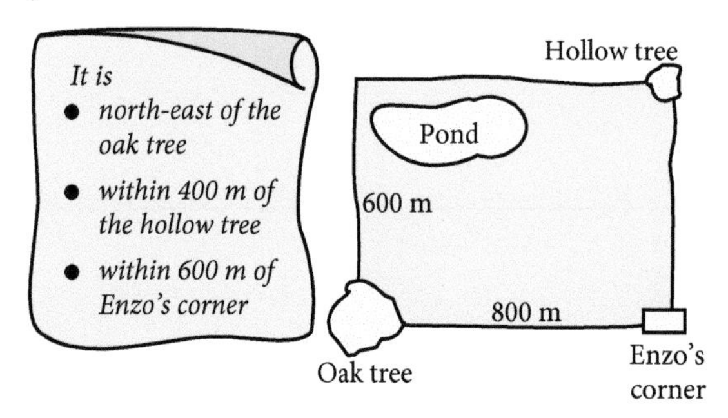

8. Here is a sketch of a logo which is to be painted onto a ship.

Make a scale drawing of the logo with a scale of 1 cm to 1 m and find the height of the logo.

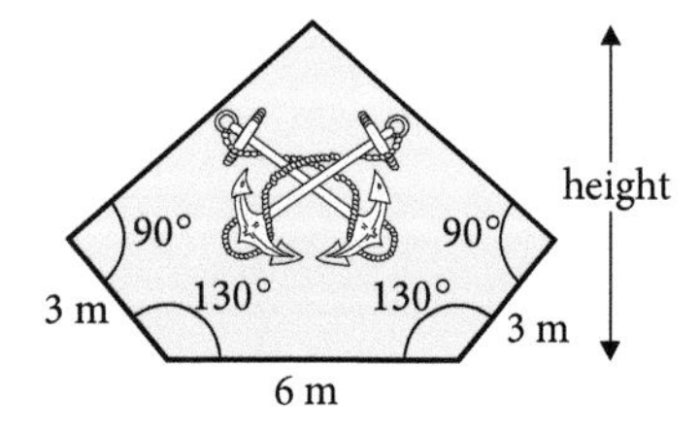

9. Make a scale drawing of a room in your house. Design a layout for the furniture you would like to have in the room.

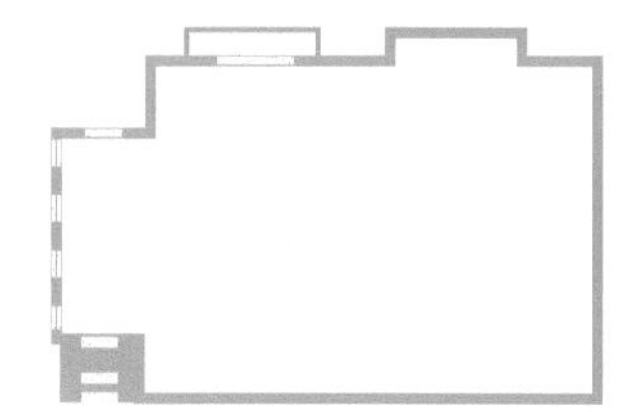

10. This is a plan of a house and gardens. It has been drawn to a scale of 1 cm for every 2 m.

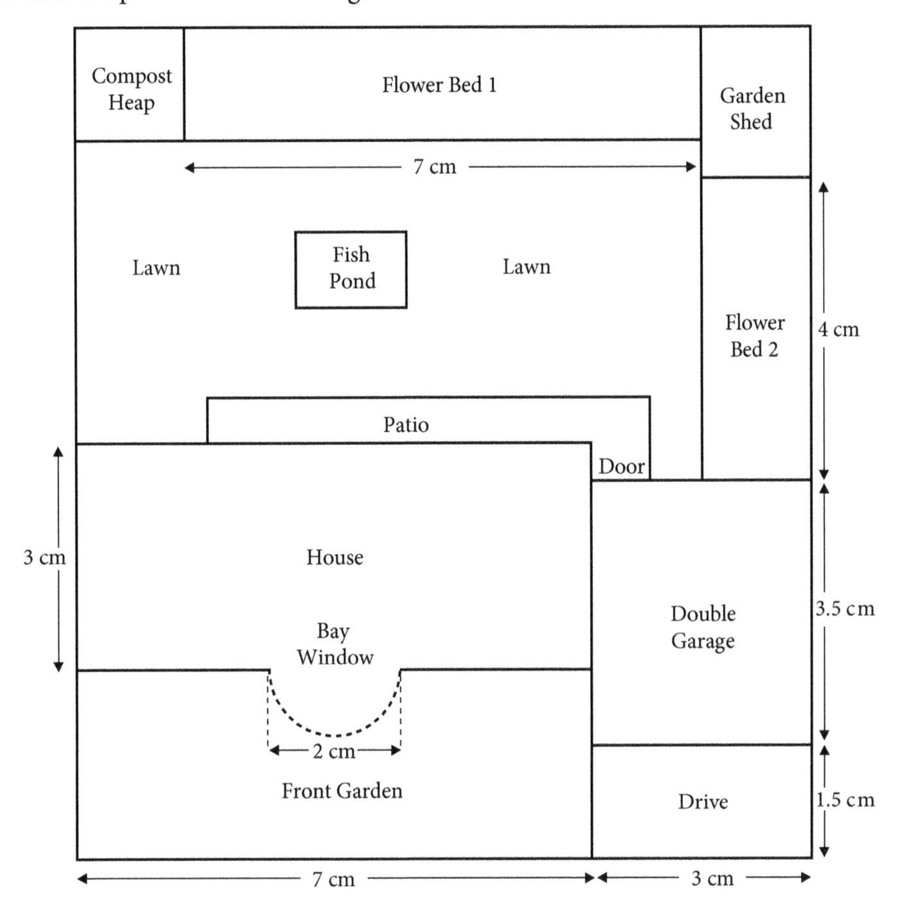

a) How wide is:

i) the front garden **ii)** the drive **iii)** the bay window?

b) How long is flower bed 2?

c) How wide is flower bed 1?

d) If the fish pond is 4 m wide, what size should it be on the plan?

e) Measure carefully the width of the patio on the plan. How many *metres* wide is the real patio?

f) What is the real *area* of the double garage?

Revision exercise 1A

1. Which of the nets below can be used to make a cube?

a)

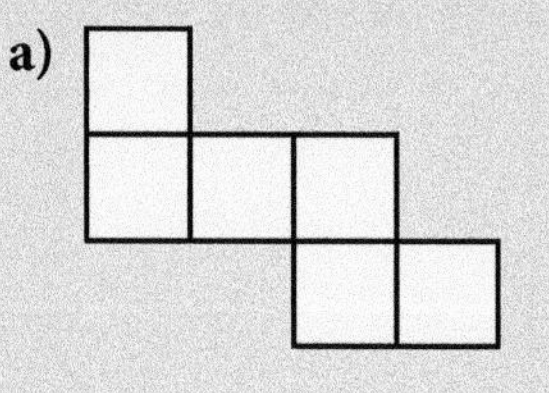

b)

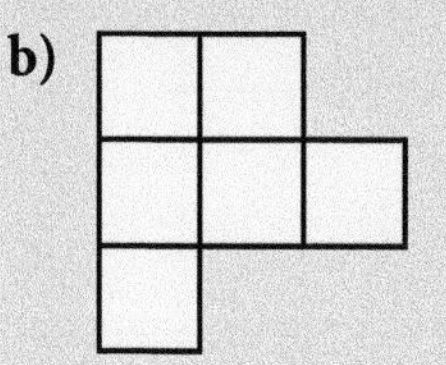

c)

2. Find the area, correct to 3 s.f.

a) **b)**

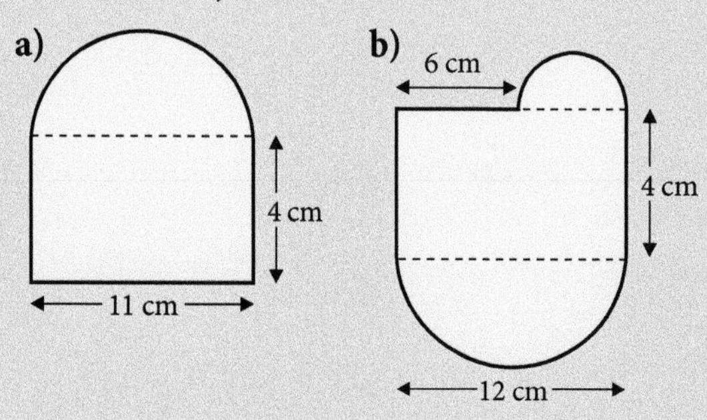

3. The faces of a round and square clock are exactly the same area. If the round clock has a radius of 10 cm, how wide is the square clock?

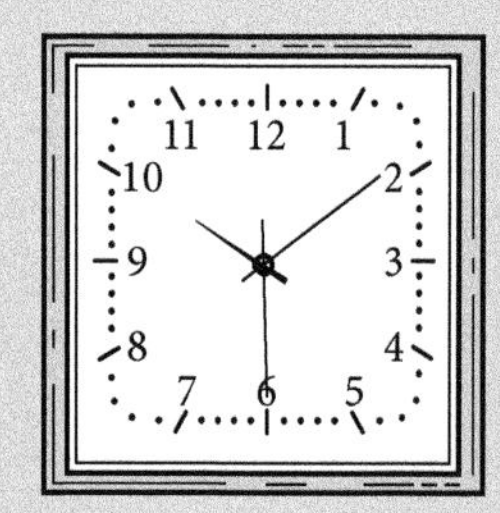

4. A large metal cylinder has a length 7 cm and radius 3 cm.

a) Calculate the volume, in cm^3, of the cylinder.

The cylinder is to be melted down and used to make cylindrical coins of thickness 3 mm and radius 12 mm.

b) Calculate the volume, in mm^3, of each coin.

c) Calculate the number of coins which can be made from the large cylinder.

5. Two girls walk at the same speed from A to B. Aruni takes the large semicircle and Deepa takes the three small semicircles. Who arrives at B first?

6. In Figure 1 a circle of radius 4 cm is drawn in a square. In Figure 2 a square is drawn in a circle of radius 4 cm.

Calculate the shaded area in each diagram.

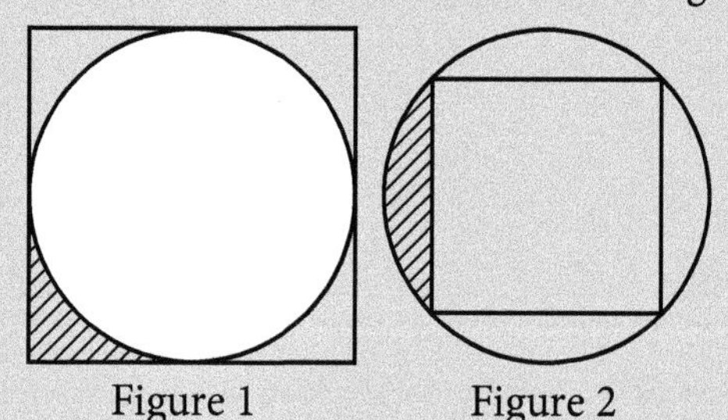

Figure 1 Figure 2

7. A cylinder of radius 8 cm has a volume of 2 litres. Calculate the height of the cylinder.

8. Twenty-seven small cubes fit exactly inside a cubical box without a lid. How many of the small cubes are touching the sides or the bottom of the box?

9. The square below has sides of length 3 cm and the arcs have centres at the corners. Find the shaded area.

10. A circle with radius 10 cm has the same area as a sector of another circle with radius r cm and an angle of 40°. Find the value of r.

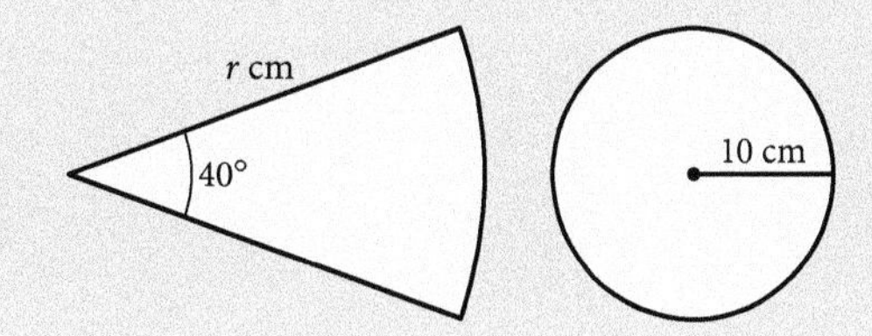

Examination-style exercise 1B

1. In the diagram AB is parallel to CD. Calculate the value of a. [2]

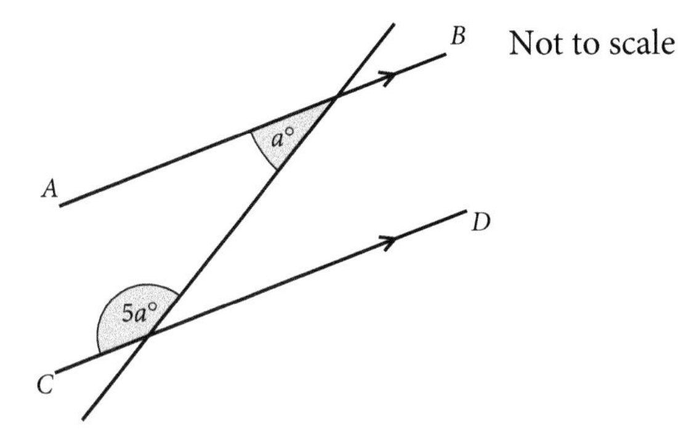

Cambridge IGCSE Mathematics 0580
Paper 11 Q4 June 2009

2.

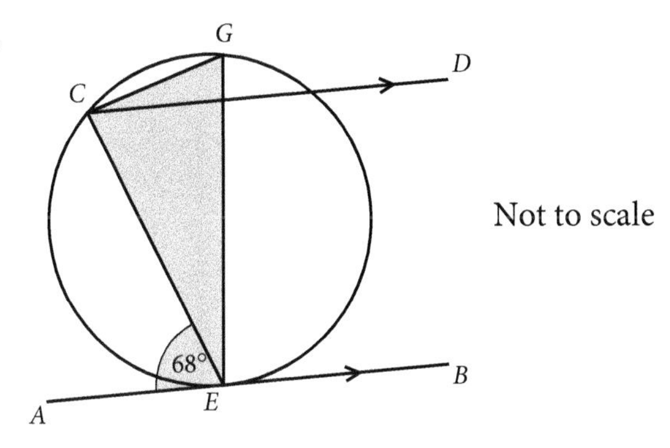

EG is a diameter of the circle through E, C and G. The tangent AEB is parallel to CD and angle $AEC = 68°$. Calculate the size of the following angles and give a reason for each answer.

(a) Angle CEG [2]

(b) Angle ECG [2]

(c) Angle CGE [2]

(d) Angle ECD [2]

Cambridge IGCSE Mathematics 0580
Paper 3 Q4 November 2008

3. The diagram shows a regular pentagon and an equilateral triangle.

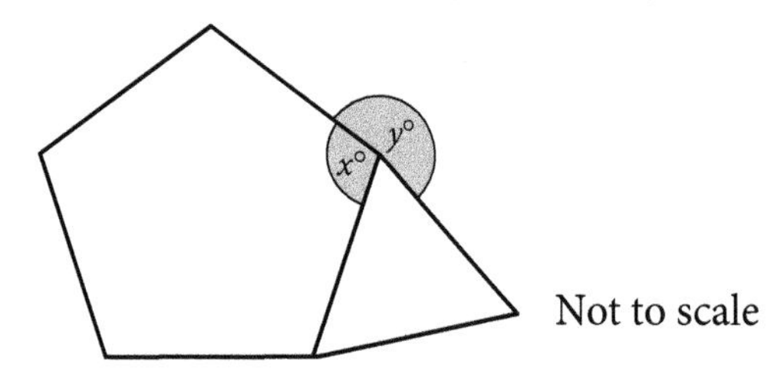

Calculate the values of x and y. [3]

4.

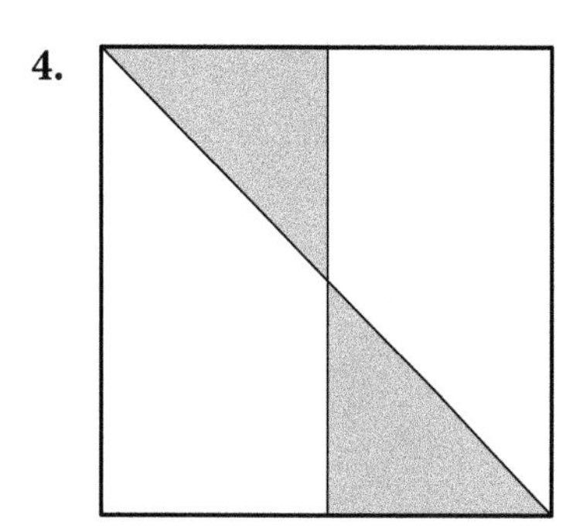

Write down the order of rotational symmetry of the diagram above. [1]

Cambridge IGCSE Mathematics 0580
Paper 11 Q2 November 2008

5. Find the area of a circle of radius 6.4 cm. Write down your answer

(a) exactly as it appears on your calculator, [1]

(b) correct to the nearest square centimetre. [1]

6. The diagram shows a square tile of side 10 centimetres with 4 identical quarter circles shaded.

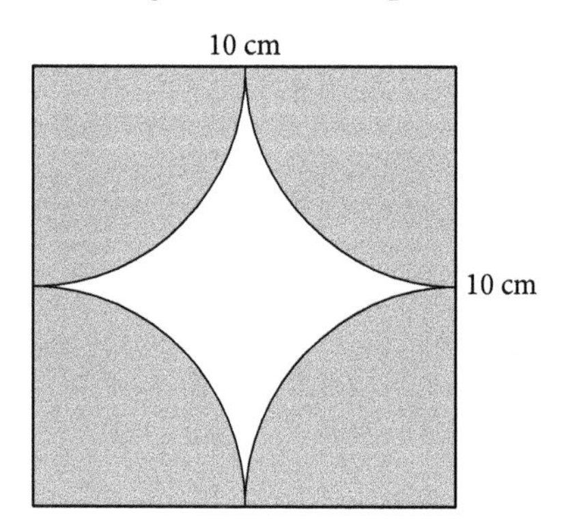

Calculate the area of the **unshaded** region. [4]

Cambridge IGCSE Mathematics 0580
Paper 11 Q16 June 2009

7. The area of a square is 17.64 cm^2.

Work out the perimeter of the square. [1]

8. A 400 metre running track has two straight sections, each of length 120 metres, and two semicircular ends.

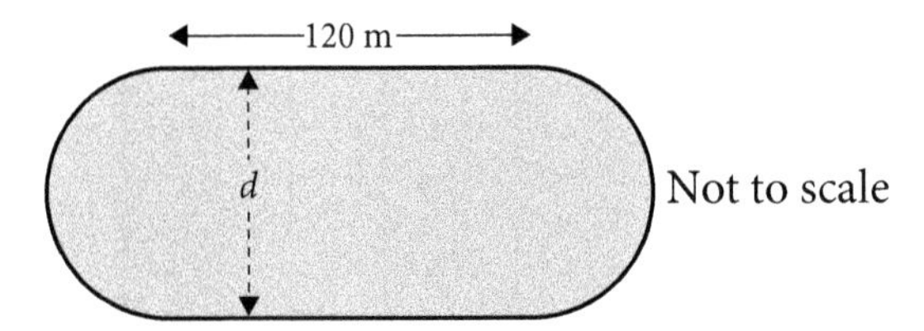

(a) Calculate the **total** length of the **curved** sections of the track. [1]

(b) Calculate d, the distance between the parallel straight sections of the track. [2]

Cambridge IGCSE Mathematics 0580
Paper 1 Q18 November 2005

9.

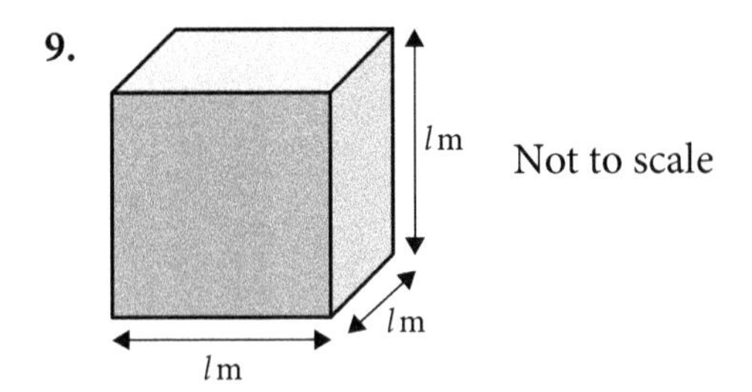

A cube of side l metres has a volume of 20 cubic metres. Calculate the length of l. [2]

Cambridge IGCSE Mathematics 0580
Paper 1 Q5 June 2006

10. (a) Calculate the volume of a cylinder of radius 50 cm and height 138 cm. [2]

(b) Write your answer to part (a) in cubic metres. [1]

Cambridge IGCSE Mathematics 0580
Paper 11 Q18 November 2008

11.

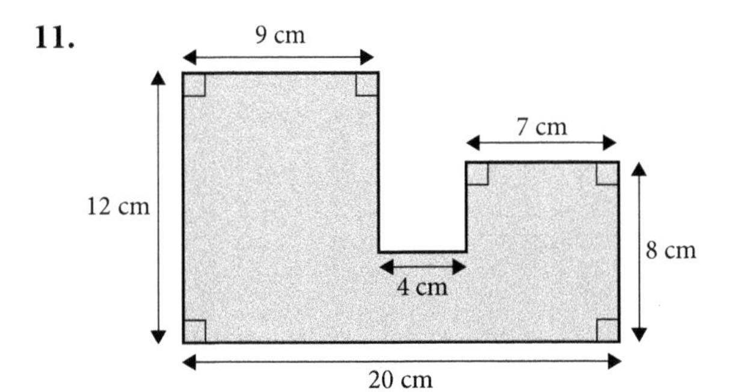

For the shape above, work out

(a) the perimeter, [1]

(b) the area. [2]

12.

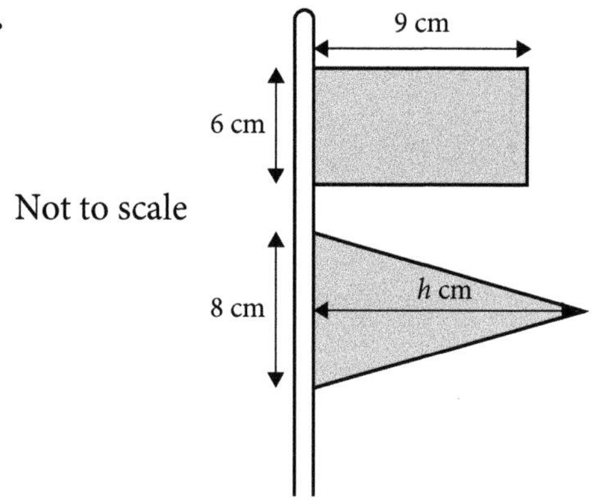

A model ship is flying two flags.
The first is a rectangle 6 centimetres by 9 centimetres.
The second is an isosceles triangle with base 8 centimetres and height h.
The flags are equal in area.
Find the value of h. [2]

Cambridge IGCSE Mathematics 0580
Paper 12 Q13 June 2008

13. (a) Calculate the size of one exterior angle of a regular heptagon (seven-sided polygon).
Give your answer correct to 1 decimal place. [3]

(b)

Not to scale

In the diagram above, DAE and $FBCG$ are parallel lines. $AC = BC$ and angle $FBA = 130°$.

i) What is the special name given to triangle ABC? [1]

ii) Work out the values of p, q, r, s and t. [5]

(c) J, K and L lie on a circle centre O.
KOL is a straight line and angle $JKL = 65°$.
Find the value of y. [2]

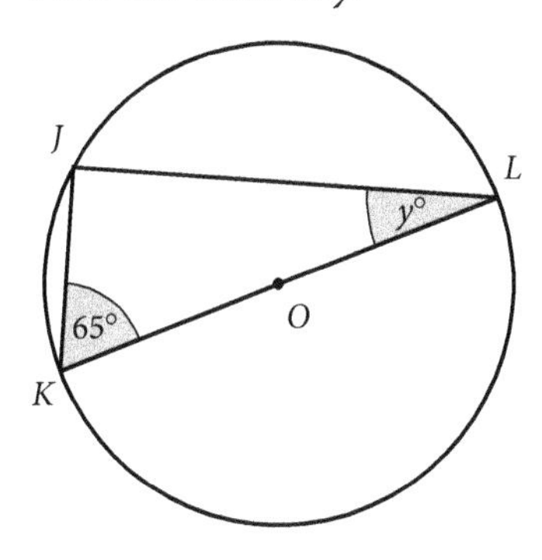

Cambridge IGCSE Mathematics 0580
Paper 3 Q9 November 2005

14. A candle, made from wax, is in the shape of a cylinder.

The radius is 1.5 centimetres and the height is 20 centimetres.

(a) Calculate, correct to the nearest cubic centimetre, the volume of wax in the candle.

[The volume of a cylinder, radius r, height h, is $\pi r^2 h$.] [2]

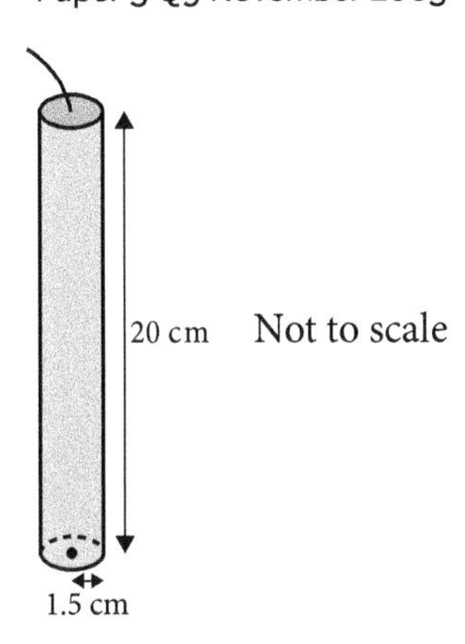

(b) The candle burns 0.8 cm^3 of wax every minute. How long, in hours and minutes, will it last? Write your answer correct to the nearest minute.

(c) The candles are stored in boxes which measure x cm by 24 cm by 20 cm. Each box contains 96 candles. Calculate the minimum value of x.

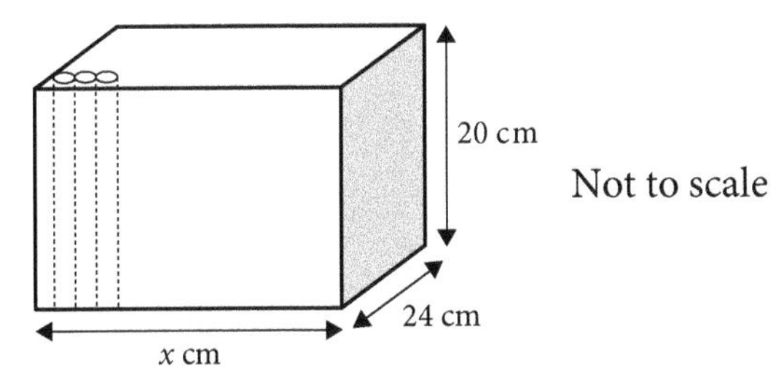

(d) A shopkeeper pays $25 for one box of 96 candles. He sells all the candles for 35 cents each.

i) How much profit does he make? [2]

ii) Calculate his profit as a percentage of his cost price. [3]

Cambridge IGCSE Mathematics 0580
Paper 3 Q2 June 2006

15. A circular pizza with a diameter of 30 cm is shared equally between 5 friends.

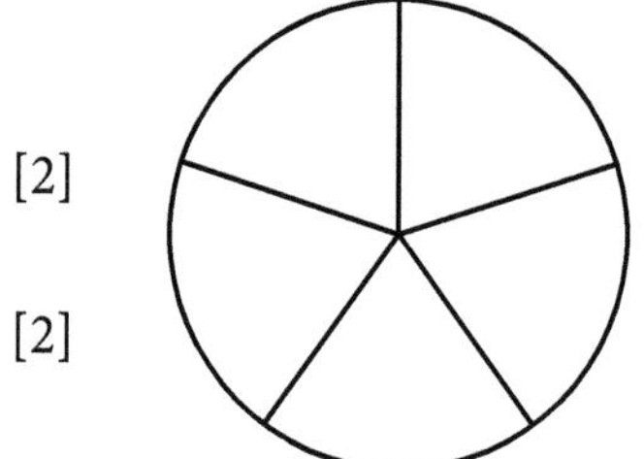

(a) What is the area of each person's slice of pizza? [2]

(b) If I had a circular pizza with the same area as each person's slice, what would its diameter be? [2]

16. Three spherical tennis balls, each with radius r cm, are packed tightly into a cylindrical box, also with radius r, so that the top and bottom balls are in contact with the top and bottom of the box.

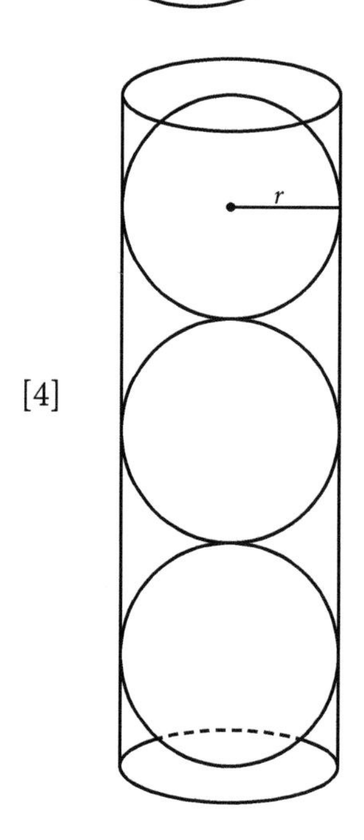

What fraction of the space inside the box is taken up by the balls?

You may use the formula

volume of a sphere $= \frac{4}{3}\pi r^3$ [4]

2 Algebra 1

C2.1 Use letters to express generalised numbers and express basic arithmetic processes algebraically. Substitute numbers for words and letters in formulae. Rearrange simple formulae. Construct simple expressions and set up simple equations.

C2.5 Derive and solve simple linear equations in one unknown.

C2.7 Continue a given number sequence. Recognise patterns in sequences including the term-to-term rule and relationships between different sequences.

C2.10 Draw graphs from given data.

C2.11 Construct tables of values for functions of the form $ax + b$, $\pm x^2 + ax + b$, $\frac{a}{x}$ $(x \neq 0)$, where a and b are integer constants. Draw and interpret these graphs. Solve linear and quadratic equations approximately, including finding and interpreting roots by graphical methods. Recognise, sketch and interpret graphs of functions.

C3.1 Demonstrate familiarity with Cartesian coordinates in two dimensions.

C3.2 Find the gradient of a straight line.

C3.4 Interpret and obtain the equation of a straight line graph in the form $y = mx + c$.

C3.5 Determine the equation of a straight line parallel to a given line.

2.1 Sequences

Exercise 1

1. Find the next number in each sequence.

a) 1, 5, 9, 13, . . . **b)** 39, 36, 33, 30, . . .

c) 3, 6, 12, 24, . . . **d)** 4, 9, 15, 22, . . .

e) 200, 100, 50, 25, . . . **f)** 88, 99, 110, . . .

2. Write down each sequence and find the missing number.

a) 1, 6, ☐, 16 **b)** 1, 2, 4, 8, ☐

c) ☐, 2, 5, 8, 11 **d)** 2400, 240, 24, ☐

e) 1, 2, 4, 7, ☐, 16 **f)** 12, 8, 4, ☐, −4

3. Here is the start of a sequence: 1, 3, 4, . . .

Each new term is found by adding the last two terms.

For example, $4 = 1 + 3$

The next term will be 7.

a) Write down the next six terms.

b) Use the same rule to write down the next four terms of the sequence which starts 2, 5, 7, . . .

4. a) Write down the next two lines of the sequence:

$3 \times 4 = 3 + 3^2$

$4 \times 5 = 4 + 4^2$

$5 \times 6 = 5 + 5^2$

b) Complete the lines below:

$10 \times 11 =$

$30 \times 31 =$

5. Copy the pattern and write down the next three lines.

$1 + 9 \times 0 \quad = \quad 1$

$2 + 9 \times 1 \quad = \quad 11$

$3 + 9 \times 12 \quad = \quad 111$

$4 + 9 \times 123 \quad = \quad 1111$

$5 + 9 \times 1234 \quad =$

6. For the sequence 2, 3, 8, . . . each new term is found by squaring the last term and then subtracting one.
Write down the next two terms.

7. The sequence 3, 3, 5, 4, 4 is obtained by counting the letters in 'one, two, three, four, five, . . .'.
Write down the next three terms.

8. The odd numbers 1, 3, 5, 7, 9, . . . can be added to give an interesting sequence.

$$
\begin{aligned}
1 &= 1 = 1 \times 1 \times 1 \\
3 + 5 &= 8 = 2 \times 2 \times 2 \\
7 + 9 + 11 &= 27 = 3 \times 3 \times 3 \\
13 + 15 + 17 + 19 &= 64 = 4 \times 4 \times 4
\end{aligned}
$$

1, 8, 27, 64 are *cube* numbers.

We write $2^3 = 8$ ['two cubed equals eight']

$4^3 = 64$

Continue adding the odd numbers in the same way as before.
Do we *always* get a cube number?

9. a) Write down the next three lines of this pattern.

$$
\begin{aligned}
1^3 &= 1^2 = 1 \\
1^3 + 2^3 &= (1 + 2)^2 = 9 \\
1^3 + 2^3 + 3^3 &= (1 + 2 + 3)^2 = 36
\end{aligned}
$$

b) Work out as simply as possible:

$1^3 + 2^3 + 3^3 + 4^3 + 5^3 + 6^3 + 7^3 + 8^3 + 9^3 + 10^3$

10. Here is the sequence of the first six odd and even numbers.

	1st	2nd	3rd	4th	5th	6th
odd	1	3	5	7	9	11
even	2	4	6	8	10	12

Find **a)** the 8th even number **b)** the 8th odd number

c) the 13th even number **d)** the 13th odd number.

You can use a rule to work out the answers.

e) If the 57th even number is 114, what is the 57th odd number?

f) Write down:

i) the 45th even number **ii)** the 53rd odd number

iii) the 100th odd number **iv)** the 219th odd number.

11. Here we have written the numbers in three columns.

a) What number will you get on the right of:

i) line 8 **ii)** line 12 **iii)** line 25?

b) Write down the number in the middle of:

i) line 8 **ii)** line 12 **iii)** line 20.

c) What number will you get in:

i) line 10 on the left

ii) line 13 on the right

iii) line 17 in the middle

iv) line 30 on the left?

d) Find the missing number:

i) 120 is on the right of line _____.

ii) 61 is on the left of line _____.

iii) 92 is in the middle of line _____.

iv) 148 is on the left of line _____.

			Line
1	2	3	**1**
4	5	6	**2**
7	8	9	**3**
10	11	12	**4**
13	14	15	**5**
16	17	18	**6**
19	20	21	**7**

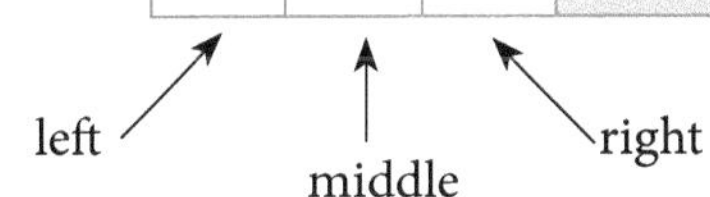

2.2 Solving equations

We can think of equations as weighing scales which are balanced. The scales stay balanced so long as you add or take away the same weight from both sides.

The same is true of equations.

Exercise 2

The scales are balanced. Work out the weight of the object x in each case. Each small weight □ is 1 kg.

1.

2.

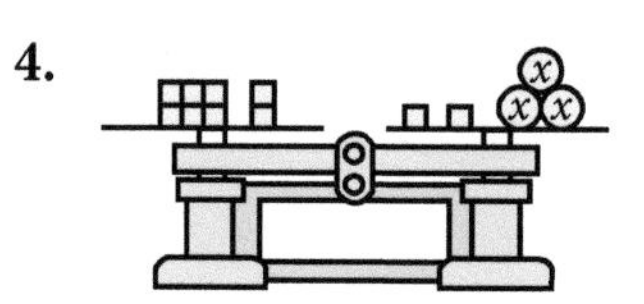

3.

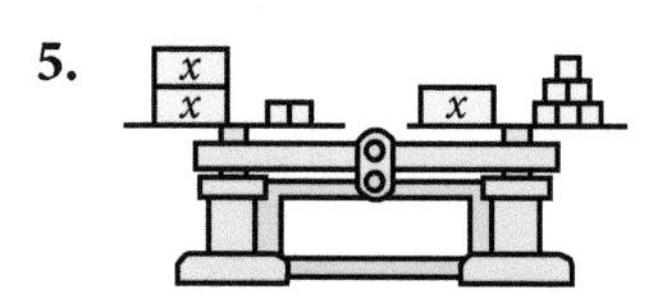

4.

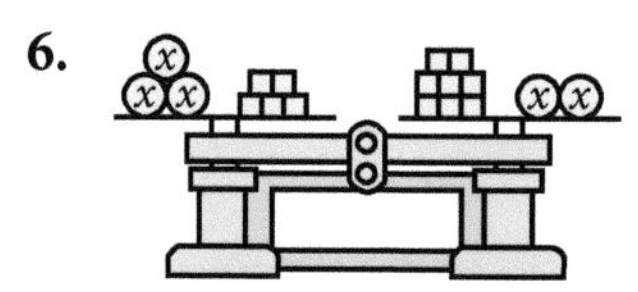

5.

6.

We solve equations by doing the same thing to both sides.

> **Example**
>
> Solve the equations.
>
> **a)** $x + 6 = 11$
>
> $x = 11 - 6$ [take away 6]
>
> $x = 5$
>
> **b)** $3x + 14 = 16$
>
> $3x = 16 - 14$ [take away 14]
>
> $3x = 2$
>
> $x = \frac{2}{3}$ [divide by 3]
>
> **c)** $4x - 5 = -2$
>
> $4x = -2 + 5$ [add 5]
>
> $4x = 3$
>
> $x = \frac{3}{4}$ [divide by 4]
>
> **d)** $7 = 2x + 15$
>
> $-15 + 7 = 2x$ [take away 15]
>
> $-8 = 2x$
>
> $-4 = x$ [divide by 2]

Exercise 3

Solve the equations.

1. $x - 7 = 5$ **2.** $x + 11 = 20$ **3.** $x + 12 = 30$ **4.** $x - 6 = -2$

5. $x - 8 = 9$ **6.** $x + 5 = 0$ **7.** $x - 13 = -7$ **8.** $x + 10 = 3$

9. $5 + x = 9$ **10.** $9 + x = 17$ **11.** $y - 6 = 11$ **12.** $y + 8 = 3$

13. $3x + 1 = 16$ **14.** $4x + 3 = 27$ **15.** $2x - 3 = 1$ **16.** $5x - 3 = 1$

17. $3x - 7 = 0$ **18.** $2x + 5 = 20$ **19.** $6x - 9 = 2$ **20.** $7x + 6 = 6$

21. $9x - 4 = 1$ **22.** $11x - 10 = 1$ **23.** $15y + 2 = 5$ **24.** $7y + 8 = 10$

25. $4y - 11 = -8$ **26.** $3z - 8 = -6$ **27.** $4p + 25 = 30$ **28.** $5t - 6 = 0$

29. $9m - 13 = 1$ **30.** $4 + 3x = 5$ **31.** $7 + 2x = 8$ **32.** $5 + 20x = 7$

33. $3 + 8x = 0$ **34.** $50y - 7 = 2$ **35.** $200y - 51 = 49$ **36.** $5u - 13 = -10$

37. $9x - 7 = -11$ **38.** $11t + 1 = 1$ **39.** $3 + 8y = 40$ **40.** $12 + 7x = 2$

41. $6 = 3x - 1$ **42.** $8 = 4x + 5$ **43.** $9 = 2x + 7$ **44.** $11 = 5x - 7$

45. $0 = 3x - 1$ **46.** $40 = 11 + 14x$ **47.** $-4 = 5x + 1$ **48.** $-8 = 6x - 3$

49. $13 = 4x - 20$ **50.** $-103 = 2x + 7$

Equations with x on both sides

…mple

…ns.

$$9 = 18 - 7x$$
$$7x = 18 - 9$$
$$10x = 9$$
$$x = \frac{9}{10}$$

$5x + 4 = 2x + 9$ **3.** $6x - 2 = x + 8$

$7x - 10 = 3x - 8$ **6.** $5x - 12 = 2x - 6$

7. **8.** $8x - 8 = 3x - 2$ **9.** $11x + 7 = 6x + 7$

10. $9x + 8 = 10$ **11.** $5 + 3x = x + 8$ **12.** $4 + 7x = x + 5$

13. $6x - 8 = 4 - 3x$ **14.** $5x + 1 = 7 - 2x$ **15.** $6x - 3 = 1 - x$

16. $3x - 10 = 2x - 3$ **17.** $5x + 1 = 6 - 3x$ **18.** $11x - 20 = 10x - 15$

19. $6 + 2x = 8 - 3x$ **20.** $7 + x = 9 - 5x$ **21.** $3y - 7 = y + 1$

22. $8y + 9 = 7y + 8$ **23.** $7y - 5 = 2y$ **24.** $3z - 1 = 5 - 4z$

25. $8 = 13 - 4x$ **26.** $10 = 12 - 2x$ **27.** $13 = 20 - 9x$

28. $8 = 5 - 2x$ **29.** $5 + x = 7 - 8x$ **30.** $3x + 11 = 2 - 3x$

Example

Solve the equations.

a) $3(x-1) = 2(x+7)$

$3x - 3 = 2x + 14$

$3x - 2x = 14 + 3$

$x = 17$

b) $5(2x+1) = 3(x-2) + 20$

$10x + 5 = 3x - 6 + 20$

$10x - 3x = -6 + 20 - 5$

$7x = 9$

$x = \frac{9}{7}$ or $1\frac{2}{7}$

Exercise 5

Solve the equations.

1. $2(x+1) = x + 5$

2. $4(x-2) = 2(x+1)$

3. $5(x-3) = 3(x+2)$

4. $3(x+2) = 2(x-1)$

5. $5(x-3) = 2(x-7)$

6. $6(x+2) = 2(x-3)$

7. $10(x-3) = x$

8. $3(2x-1) = 4(x+1)$

9. $4(2x+1) = 5(x+3)$

10. $3(x-1) + 7 = 2(x+1)$

11. $5(x+1) + 3 = 3(x-1)$

12. $7(x-2) - 3 = 2(x+2)$

13. $5(2x+1) - 5 = 3(x+1)$

14. $3(4x-1) - 3 = x + 1$

15. $2(x-10) = 4 - 3x$

16. $3x + 2(x+1) = 3x + 12$

17. $4x - 2(x+4) = x + 1$

18. $2x - 3(x+2) = 2x + 1$

19. $5x - 2(x-2) = 6 - 2x$

20. $3(x+1) + 2(x+2) = 10$

Equations with fractions

Example

Solve the equations.

a) $\frac{7}{x} = 8$

$7 = 8x$

$\frac{7}{8} = x$

b) $3 = \frac{8}{x}$

$3x = 8$

$x = \frac{8}{3}$

$x = 2\frac{2}{3}$

Exercise 6

Solve the equations.

1. $\frac{3}{x}=5$
2. $\frac{4}{x}=7$
3. $\frac{11}{x}=12$
4. $\frac{6}{x}=11$
5. $\frac{2}{x}=3$
6. $\frac{5}{y}=9$
7. $\frac{7}{y}=9$
8. $\frac{4}{t}=3$
9. $\frac{3}{a}=6$
10. $\frac{8}{x}=12$
11. $\frac{3}{p}=1$
12. $\frac{15}{q}=10$
13. $\frac{x}{4}=6$
14. $\frac{x}{5}=3$
15. $\frac{y}{5}=-2$
16. $\frac{a}{7}=3$
17. $\frac{t}{3}=7$
18. $\frac{m}{4}=\frac{2}{3}$
19. $\frac{x}{7}=\frac{5}{8}$
20. $\frac{2x}{3}=1$
21. $\frac{4x}{5}=3$
22. $\frac{3y}{2}=2$
23. $\frac{5t}{6}=3$
24. $\frac{m}{8}=\frac{1}{4}$
25. $8=\frac{5}{x}$
26. $19=\frac{7}{y}$
27. $-5=\frac{3}{a}$
28. $-6=\frac{k}{4}$
29. $\frac{n}{7}=-10$
30. $4=\frac{33}{q}$
31. $\frac{x}{2}=100$
32. $\frac{500}{y}=-1$
33. $-99=\frac{98}{f}$
34. $\frac{x}{3}+5=7$
35. $\frac{x}{5}-2=4$

Exercise 7

In this exercise □, △, ○, and represent weights which are always balanced.

1. a)

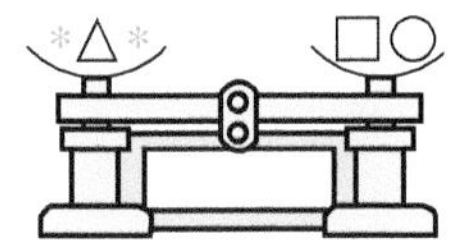

b)

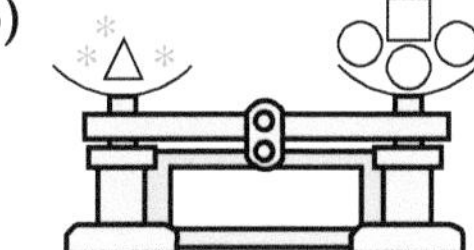

c)

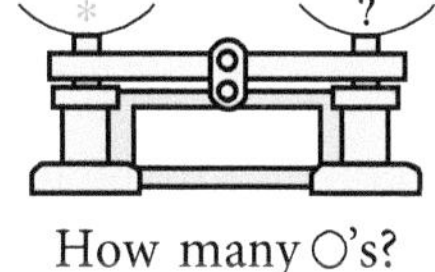

How many ○'s?

2. a)

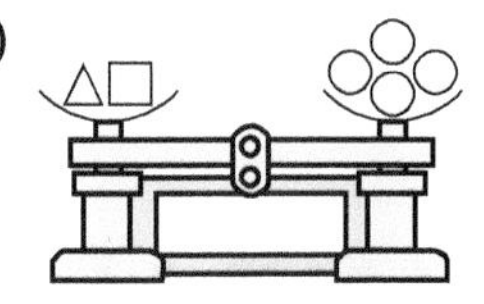

b)

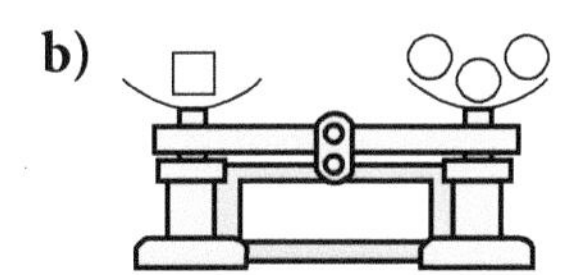

c)

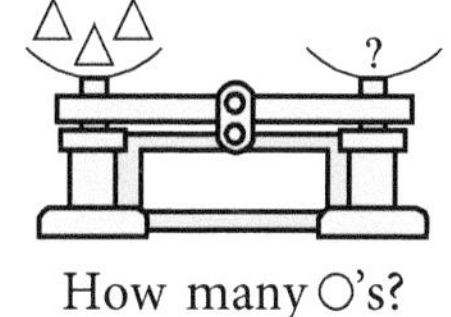

How many ○'s?

3. **a)** ○○□ =
b) □□○ =   ○
c) □ = How many ○'s?

4. **a)** □○○ = △□□□
b) □□□○ = △△□
c) □○ = △□
d) ○ = How many □'s?

5. a) □□ = ○△
   b) ○○○□ = □△
   c) ○□□□ = △△○
   d) □ = How many ○'s?

6. a) ○○□ = ✻○
   b) ✻✻ = ○○○
   c) □✻ = ○○
   d) ✻ = How many □'s?

7. a) ○□□ = △✻
   b) ✻✻✻ = △△
   c) ○□ = △
   d) △△△△ = How many □'s?

8. a) ○□ = △
   b) ○ = □✻
   c) ○○□ = △✻✻
   d) □ = How many ✻'s?

Solving problems with equations

Example

If I multiply a 'mystery' number by 2 and then add 3 the answer is 14.

Find the 'mystery' number.

Let the mystery number be x.

Then $2x + 3 = 14$

$$2x = 11$$

$$x = 5\frac{1}{2}$$

The 'mystery' number is $5\frac{1}{2}$

Exercise 8

Find the 'mystery' number in each question by forming an equation and then solving it.

1. If I multiply the number by 3 and then add 4, the answer is 13.
2. If I multiply the number by 4 and then add 5, the answer is 8.
3. If I multiply the number by 2 and then subtract 5, the answer is 4.
4. If I multiply the number by 10 and then add 19, the answer is 16.
5. If I add 3 to the number and then multiply the result by 4, the answer is 10.
6. If we subtract 11 from the number and then treble the result, the answer is 20.
7. If we double the number, add 4 and then multiply the result by 3, the answer is 13.
8. If we treble the number, take away 6 and then multiply the result by 2, the answer is 18.
9. If we double the number and subtract 7, we get the same answer as when we add 5 to the number.

10. If we multiply the number by 5 and subtract 4, we get the same answer as when we add 3 to the number and then double the result.

11. If we multiply the number by 6 and add 1, we get the same answer as when we add 5 to the number and then treble the result.

12. If I add 5 to the number and then multiply the result by 4, I get the same answer as when I add 1 to the number and then multiply the result by 2.

Example

The length of a rectangle is twice the width.

If the perimeter is 36 cm, find the width.

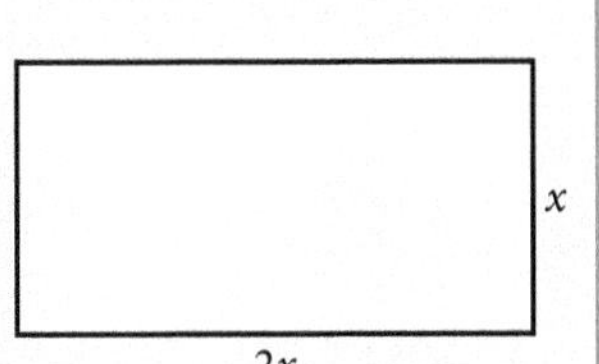

a) Let the width of the rectangle be x cm. Then the length of the rectangle is $2x$ cm.

b) Form an equation.

$x + 2x + x + 2x = 36$

c) Solve. $6x = 36$

$x = 6$

The width of the rectangle is 6 cm.

Exercise 9

Answer these questions by forming an equation and then solving it.

1. Find x if the perimeter is 7 cm.

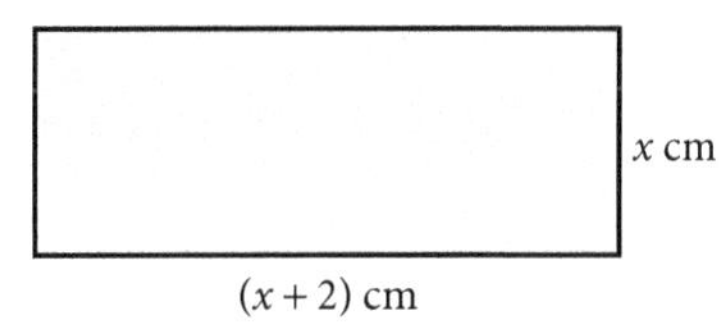

2. Find x if the perimeter is 5 cm.

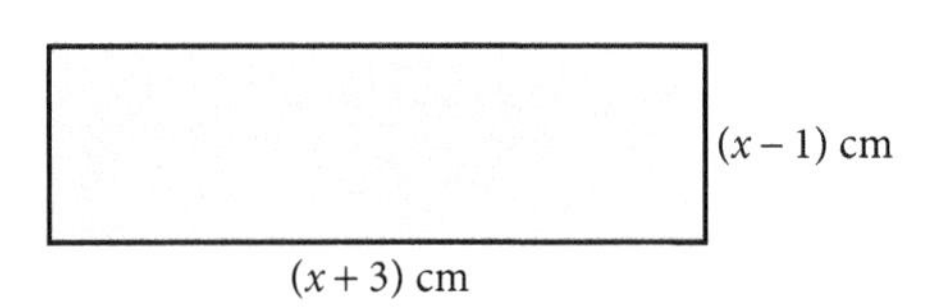

3. The length of a rectangle is 3 times its width. If the perimeter of the rectangle is 11 cm, find its width.

Let the width be x cm.

4. The length of a rectangle is 4 cm more than its width. If its perimeter is 13 cm, find its width.

5. The width of a rectangle is 5 cm less than its length. If the perimeter of the rectangle is 18 cm, find its length.

6. Find x in the following rectangles:

a) Area = 18 cm^2, x cm, 5 cm

b) Area = 15 cm^2, $(x+3)$ cm, 4 cm

7. Find x in the following triangles:

a) $2x°$, $(x+16)°$, $x°$

b)

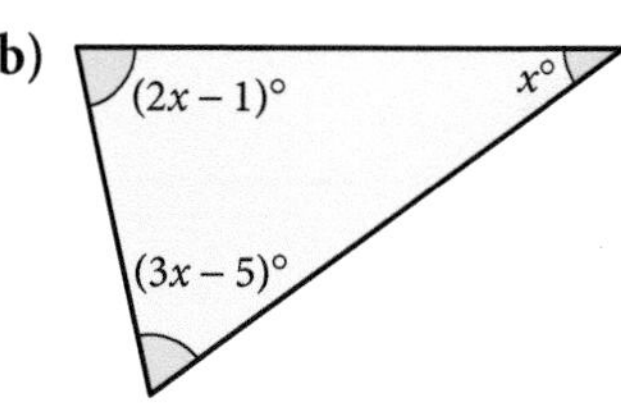

8. The angles of a triangle are 32°, x° and $(4x + 3)$°.
Find the value of x.

9. Find a in the diagrams below

a)

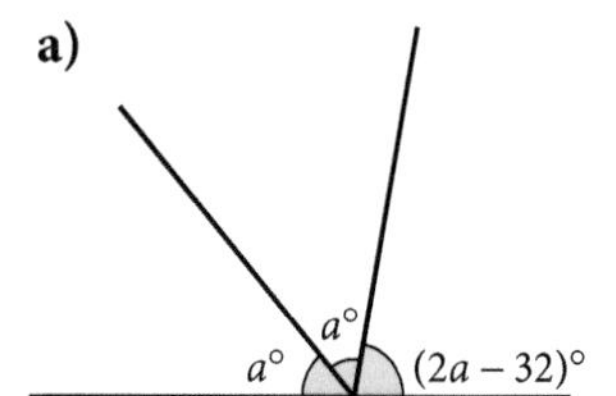

b)

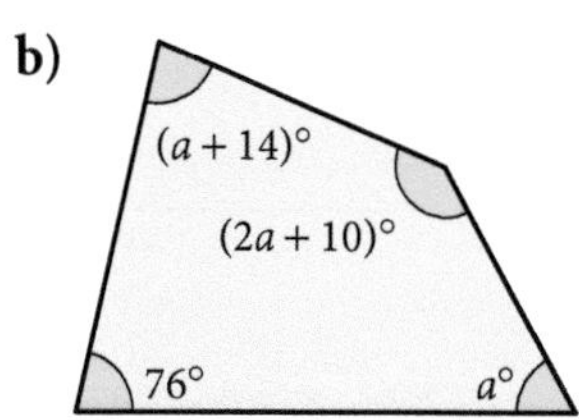

10. The sum of three consecutive whole numbers is 168. Let the first number be x. Form an equation and hence find the three numbers.

11. The sum of four consecutive whole numbers is 170.
Find the numbers.

12. In this triangle AB = x cm.

BC is 3 cm shorter than AB.

AC is twice as long as BC.

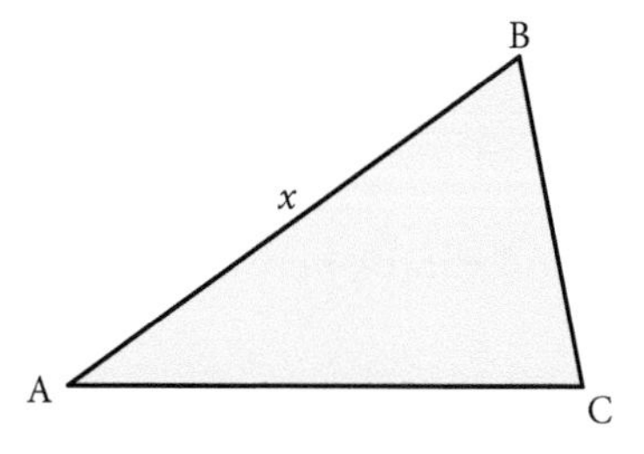

a) Write down, in terms of x, the lengths of:

i) BC

ii) AC

The perimeter of the triangle is 41 cm.

b) Write down an equation in x and solve it to find x.

13. This is a rectangle. Work out x and hence find the perimeter of the rectangle.

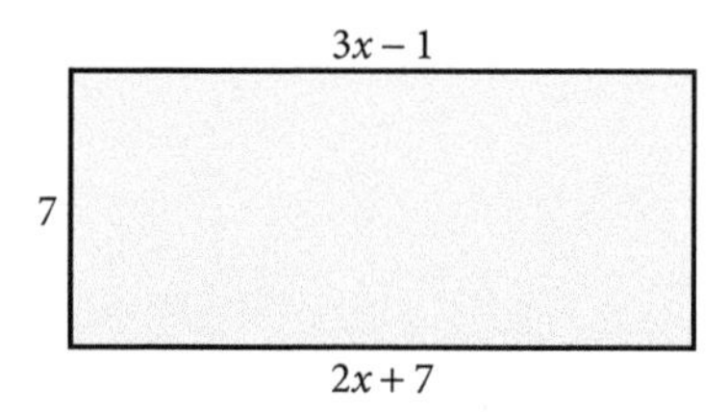

14. Find the length of the sides of this equilateral triangle.

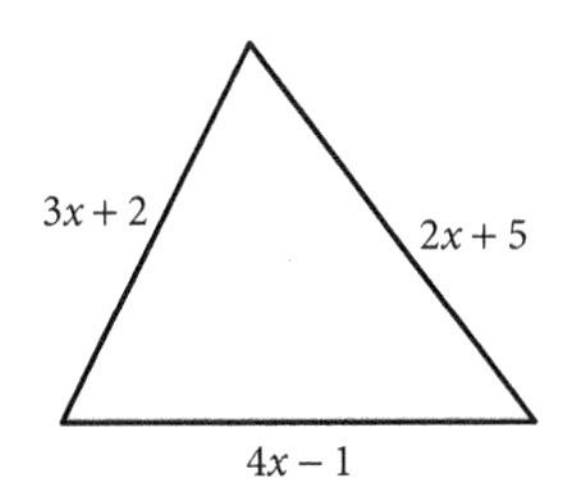

15. Petra has \$12 and Suki has nothing. They both receive the same money for doing a delivery job.
Now Petra has three times as much as Suki.
How much did they get for the job?

16. The area of rectangle A is twice the area of rectangle B. Find x.

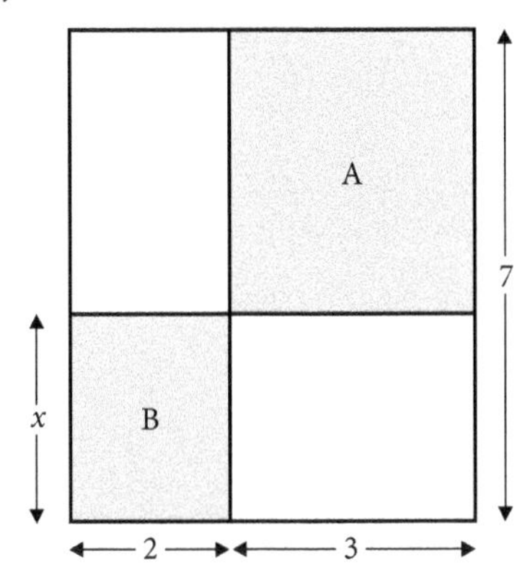

2.3 Drawing graphs

Example

Draw the graph of $y = 4 - 2x$ for values of x from -2 to $+3$.

a)

x	-2	-1	0	1	2	3
4	4	4	4	4	4	4
$-2x$	4	2	0	-2	-4	-6
y	8	6	4	2	0	-2

b) Plot the values of x and y from the table.

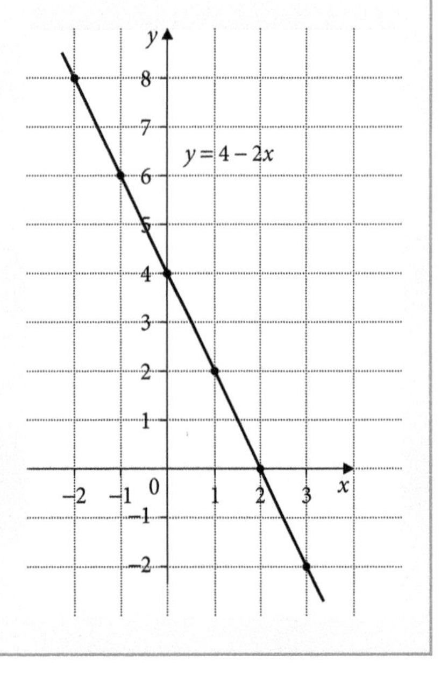

Exercise 10

For each question make a table of values and then draw the graph.
Suggested scales: 1 cm to 1 unit on both axes, unless otherwise stated.

1. $y = 2x + 1$; x from -3 to $+3$.

x	-3	-2	-1	0	1	2	3
$2x$	-6	-4					
$+1$	1	1	1				
y	-5	-3					

2. $y = 3x - 5$; x from -2 to $+3$.

3. $y = x + 2$; x from -4 to $+4$.

4. $y = 2x - 7$; x from -2 to $+5$.

5. $y = 4x + 1$; x from -3 to $+3$.
(Use scales of 1 cm to 1 unit on the x-axis and 1 cm to 2 units on the y-axis.)

6. $y = x - 3$; x from -2 to $+5$.

7. $y = 2x + 4$; x from -4 to $+2$.

8. $y = 3x + 2$; x from -3 to $+3$.

9. $y = x + 7$; x from -5 to $+3$.

10. $y = 4x - 3$; x from -3 to $+3$.
(Use scales of 1 cm to 1 unit on the x-axis and 1 cm to 2 units on the y-axis.)

11. $y = 8 - 2x$; x from -2 to $+4$.

Curved graphs

Example 1

Draw the graph of $y = x^2 + x - 2$ for values of x from -3 to $+3$.

a)

x	-3	-2	-1	0	1	2	3
x^2	9	4	1	0	1	4	9
$+x$	-3	-2	-1	0	1	2	3
-2	-2	-2	-2	-2	-2	-2	-2
y	4	0	-2	-2	0	4	10

b) Plot the x and y values from the table.

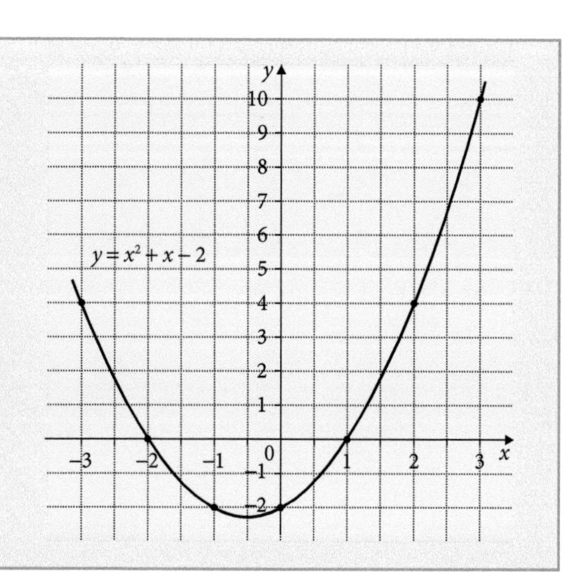

Example 2

Draw the graph of $y = 2x - x^2$ for values of x from −2 to +3.

Be careful! The '$-x^2$' term means $-(x^2)$.

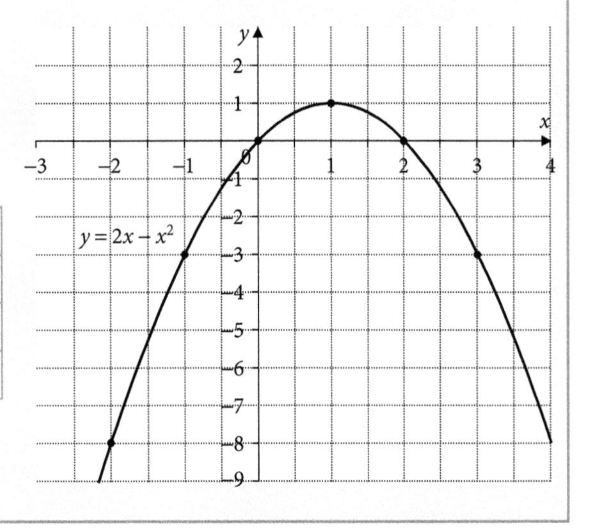

a)

x	−2	−1	0	1	2	3
$2x$	−4	−2	0	2	4	6
$-x^2$	−4	−1	0	−1	−4	−9
y	−8	−3	0	1	0	−3

b) Plot the x and y values from the table.

Exercise 11

For Questions **1** to **16** make a table of values and then draw the graph.

Suggested scales: 2 cm to 1 unit on the x-axis and 1 cm to 1 unit on the y-axis.

1. $y = x^2 + 2$; x from −3 to +3.

x	−3	−2	−1	0	1	2	3
x^2	9	4	1	0	1		
+2	2	2	2				
y	11	6	3				

2. $y = x^2 + 5$; x from −3 to +3.

3. $y = x^2 - 4$; x from −3 to +3.

4. $y = x^2 - 8$; x from −3 to +3.

5. $y = x^2 + 2x$; x from −4 to +2.

x	−4	−3	−2	−1	0	1	2
x^2	16	9					4
$+2x$	−8	−6					4
y	8	3					8

6. $y = x^2 + 4x$; x from −5 to +1.

7. $y = x^2 + 4x - 1$; x from −2 to +4.

8. $y = x^2 + 2x - 5$; x from -4 to $+2$.

9. $y = x^2 + 3x + 1$; x from -4 to $+2$.

10. $y = 6 - x^2$; x from -3 to $+3$.

11. $y = 3x - x^2$; x from -1 to $+4$.

12. $y = 2 + x - x^2$; x from -3 to $+3$.

These graphs are more difficult.

13. $y = x^3 + 1$; x from -3 to $+3$.

Scales: 2 cm to 1 unit for x;

1 cm to 5 units for y.

14. $y = \frac{12}{x}$; x from 1 to 12.

15. $y = 2x^2 + 3x - 1$; x from -4 to $+2$.

Scales: 2 cm to 1 unit for x;

1 cm to 1 unit for y.

(Remember $2x^2 = 2(x^2)$. Work out x^2 and then multiply by 2.)

16. $y = \frac{16}{x}$; x from 1 to 10.

Scales: 1 cm to 1 unit for x;

1 cm to 1 unit for y.

17. A rectangle has a perimeter of 14 cm and length x cm.

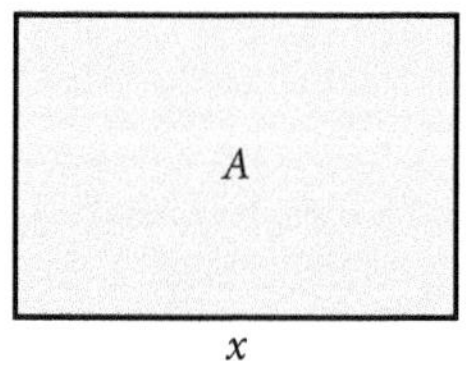

a) Show that the width of the rectangle is $(7 - x)$ cm and hence that the area A of the rectangle is given by the formula $A = x(7 - x)$.

b) Draw the graph, plotting x on the horizontal axis with a scale of 2 cm to 1 unit, and A on the vertical axis with a scale of 1 cm to 1 unit. Take x from 0 to 7.

From the graph find,

c) the area of the rectangle when $x = 2.25$ cm

d) the dimensions of the rectangle when its area is 9 cm^2

e) the maximum area of the rectangle

f) the length and width of the rectangle corresponding to the maximum area.

2.4 Gradient, $y = mx + c$

- If we know the coordinates of two points on a line, we can use the formula

  $$\text{Gradient} = \frac{\text{Difference between } y\text{-coordinates}}{\text{Difference between } x\text{-coordinates}}$$

  The gradient of a line tells us how steep it is.

- Consider the line which passes through (1, 2) and (3, 6).

  $$\text{Gradient} = \frac{6-2}{3-1} = \frac{4}{2} = 2$$

Notice that:

- a line sloping upwards to the right has a positive gradient;
- a line sloping downwards to the right has a negative gradient.

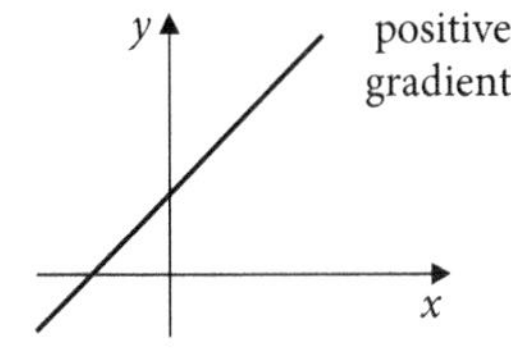

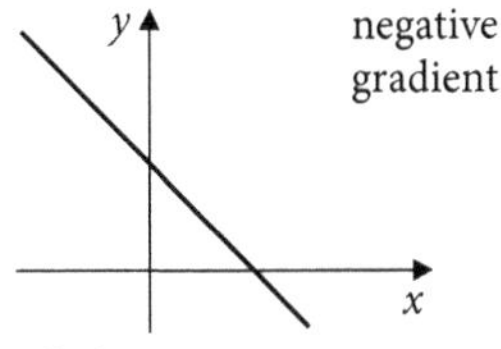

[Some people think of a capital 'N' for negative.]

Exercise 12

1. Find the gradient of the line joining

a) (1, 3) and (2, 6) **b)** (1, 3) and (3, 7)

c) (2, 5) and (6, 7) **d)** (3, 9) and (9, 11)

e) (1, 4) and (3, 2) **f)** (2, 5) and (5, −1)

g) (6, 2) and (2, 10) **h)** (3, −2) and (−3, 2)

i) (−2, −4) and (−1, 2) **j)** (2, −3) and (−2, 6)

2. Find the gradient of the line joining

a) A and B

b) B and C

c) C and D

d) D and A.

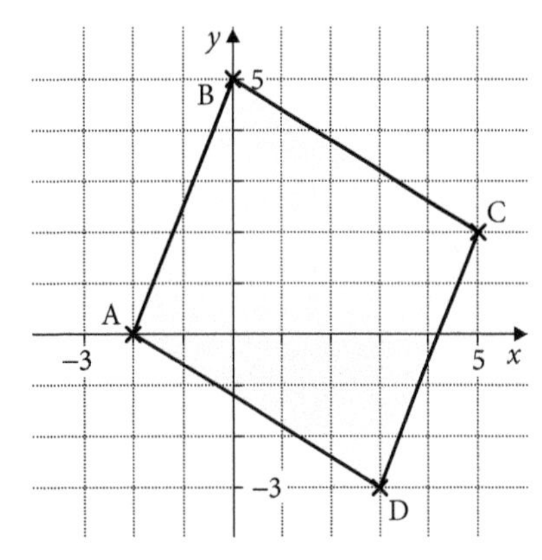

Gradient and intercept

A straight line can be described in terms of

a) its gradient

b) where it crosses the y-axis (the y-intercept).

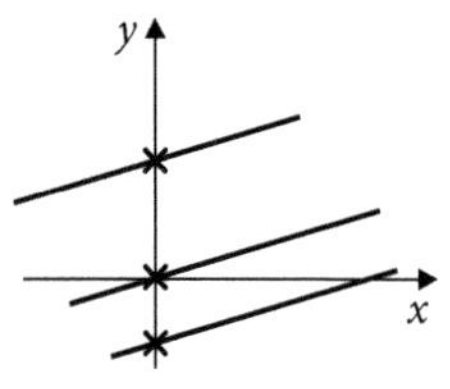

same gradient,
different y-intercepts

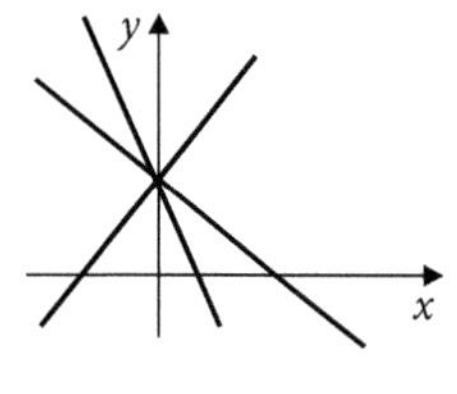

same y-intercept,
different gradients

Notice that parallel lines have the same gradient.

Exercise 13

Sketch the following straight lines. Use a new pair of axes for each question. Draw about six sketches on one page of your book.

1. Gradient 2, y-intercept 3.
2. Gradient 1, y-intercept -3.
3. Gradient 2, y-intercept 0.
4. Gradient -1, y-intercept 4.
5. Gradient -3, y-intercept 0.
6. Gradient -2, y-intercept -2.
7. Give the gradient and y-intercept of each line in the graph on the right.

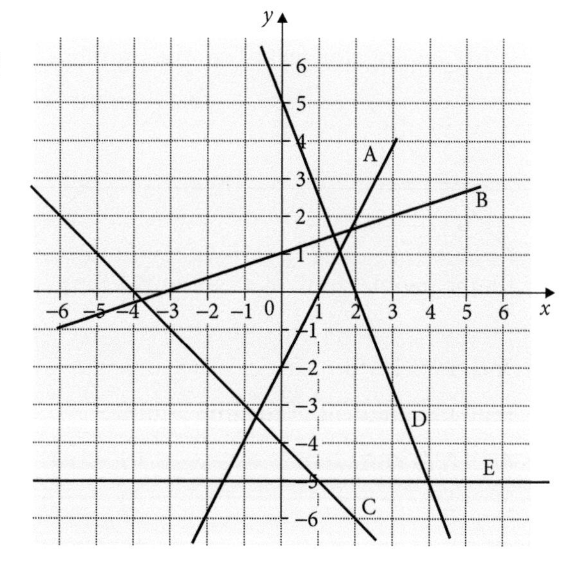

The line $y = mx + c$

$y = mx + c$ is the equation of a straight line with

- gradient m, and
- intercept c. [Hereafter the word 'intercept' is taken to be the y-intercept.]

Example 1

Sketch the line with equation $y = 3x - 1$.

Gradient = 3.

Intercept = -1

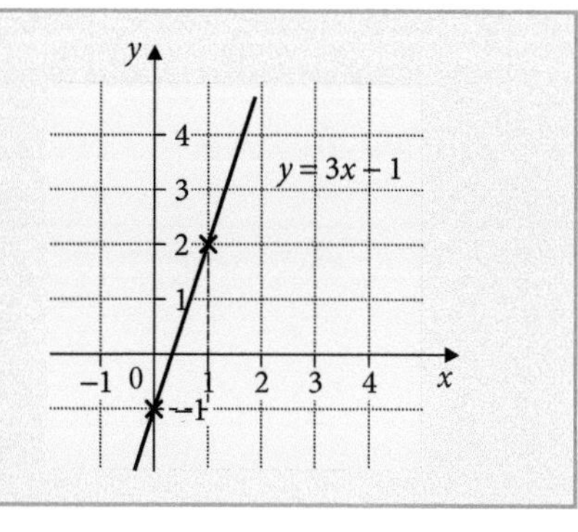

Example 2

Draw the line $x + 2y - 6 = 0$ on a sketch graph.

a) Rearrange the equation to make y the subject.

$$x + 2y - 6 = 0$$
$$2y = -x + 6$$
$$y = -\frac{1}{2}x + 3$$

b) The line has a gradient of $-\frac{1}{2}$ and cuts the y-axis at (0, 3).

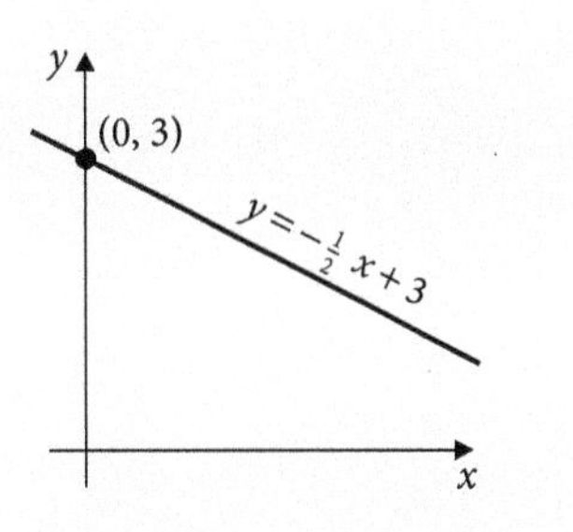

Exercise 14

Write down the gradient and intercept of each of the following lines.

1. $y = 2x - 3$

2. $y = 3x + 2$

3. $y = -x - 4$

4. $y = \frac{1}{2}x + 3$

5. $y = -\frac{2}{3}x - 4$

6. $y = 2 - 3x$ ← Be careful!

7. $y = 4 - 7x$

8. $y = 2x - 1$

9. $y = 3 - \frac{1}{2}x$

10. $y = 7 - 2x$

In Questions **11** to **16** make y the subject and write down the gradient and intercept of the corresponding line.

11. $2x + y - 6 = 0$

12. $y - 3x + 7 = 0$

13. $y - 2x = 8$

14. $3x + 6y - 10 = 0$

15. $2x - 5y + 12 = 0$

16. $3y - 9x + 2 = 0$

Sketch each of the following lines.

17. $y = x + 2$

18. $y = 2x - 4$

19. $y = 3 - 2x$

20. $y = \frac{3}{4}x - 1$

21. $y = 2 - \frac{1}{3}x$

22. $y - 2x + 2 = 0$

23. $2x + 4y + 1 = 0$

24. $3y - 9x - 1 = 0$

Exercise 15

In Questions **1** to **6** match each diagram with the correct equation from the list below.

1.

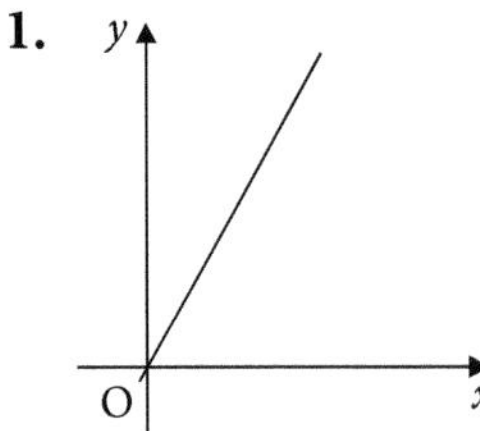

2.

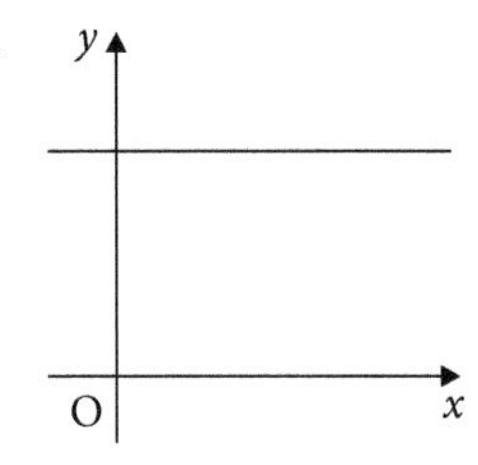

3.

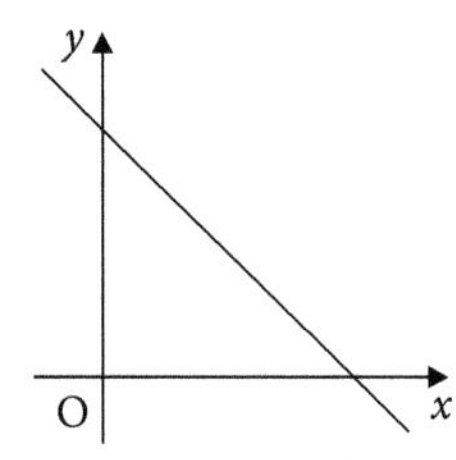

4.

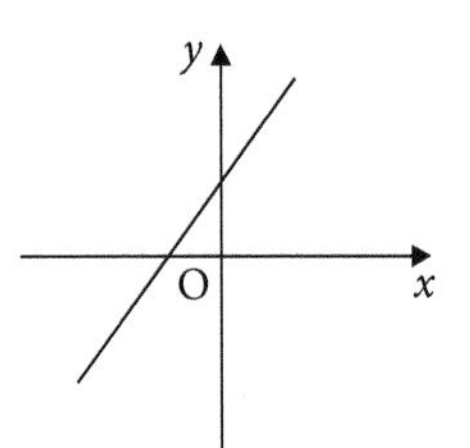

5.

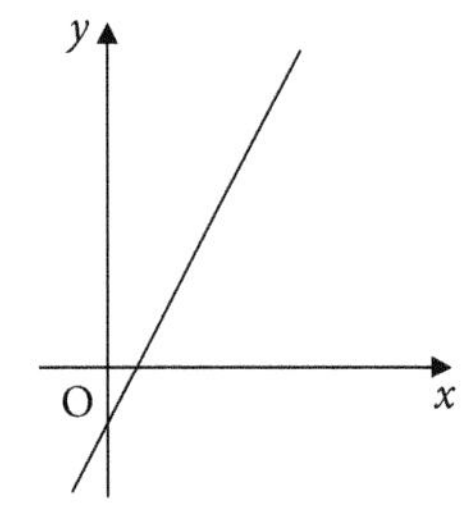

6.

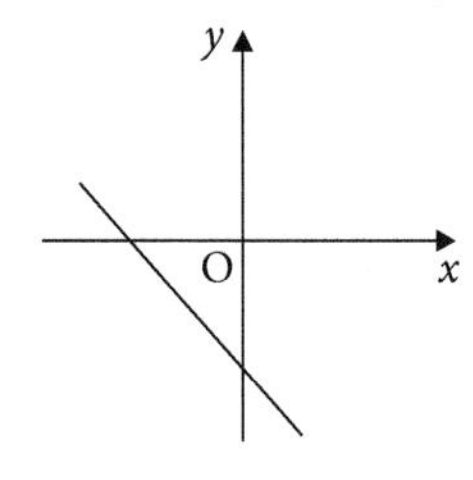

a) $y = -x - 4$ **b)** $y = 2x - 1$ **c)** $y = 2x + 3$

d) $y = 3x$ **e)** $y = 3 - x$ **f)** $y = 5$

7. Find the equations of the lines A and B.

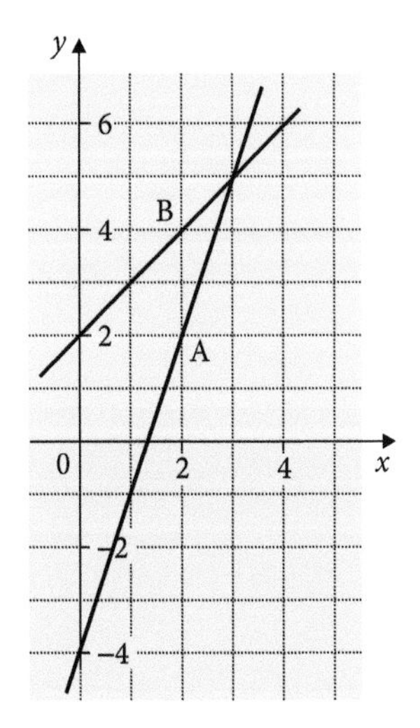

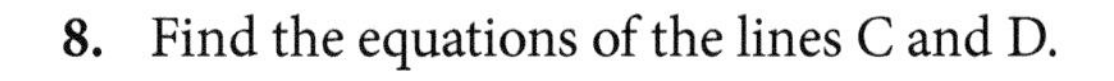

8. Find the equations of the lines C and D.

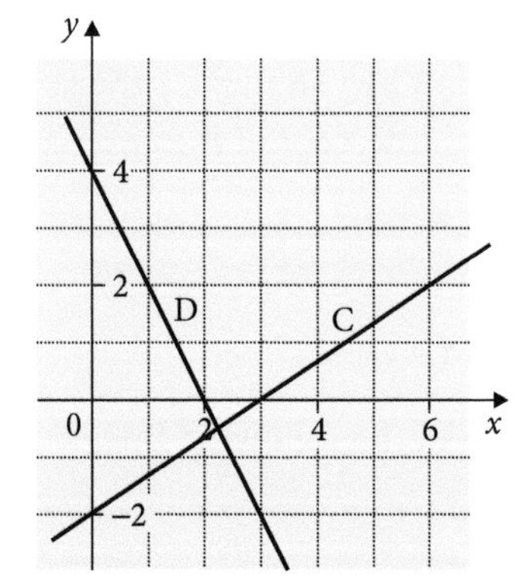

9. Look at the graph.

   a) Find the equation of the line which is parallel to line A and which passes through the point (0, 5).

   b) Find the equation of the line which is parallel to line B and which passes through the point (0, 3).

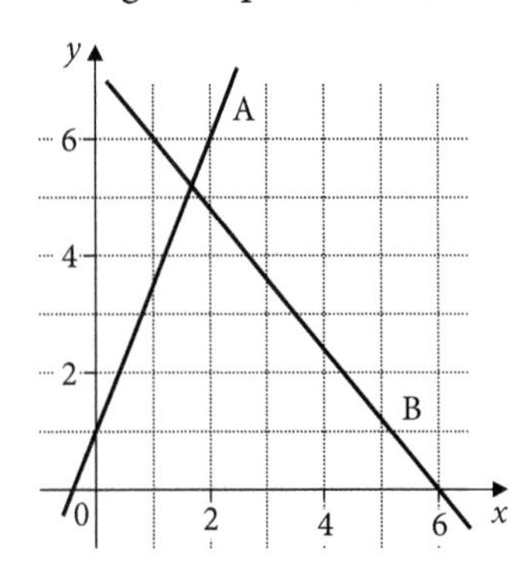

10. Look at the graphs in Question **7**.

   a) Find the equation of the line which is parallel to line A and which passes through the point (0, 1).

   b) Find the equation of the line which is parallel to line B and which passes through the point (0, –2).

Graphical solution of equations

Accurately drawn graphs enable approximate solutions to be found for a wide range of equations, many of which are impossible to solve exactly by other methods.

Example

Draw the graph of the function $y = 2x^2 - x - 3$ for $-2 \leqslant x \leqslant 3$ and use it to solve the equations:

$2x^2 - x - 3 = 6$ and $2x^2 - x - 3 = 0$

a) To solve the equation

$2x^2 - x - 3 = 6$,

the line $y = 6$ is drawn.

At the points of intersection (A and B), y simultaneously equals both 6 and $(2x^2 - x - 3)$.

So we may write

$2x^2 - x - 3 = 6$

The solutions are the x-values of the points A and B,

i.e. $x = -1{\cdot}9$ and $x = 2{\cdot}4$ approximately.

b) To solve the equation $2x^2 - x - 3 = 0$,

the line $y = 0$ is drawn.

[The line $y = 0$ is the x-axis.]

The solutions of the equation are given by the x-values of C and D where the curve cuts the x-axis,

i.e. $x = -1$ and $x = 1.5$ approximately.

Exercise 16

1. In the diagram shown, the graphs of $y = x^2 - 2x - 3$, $y = 3$ and $y = -2$ have been drawn.

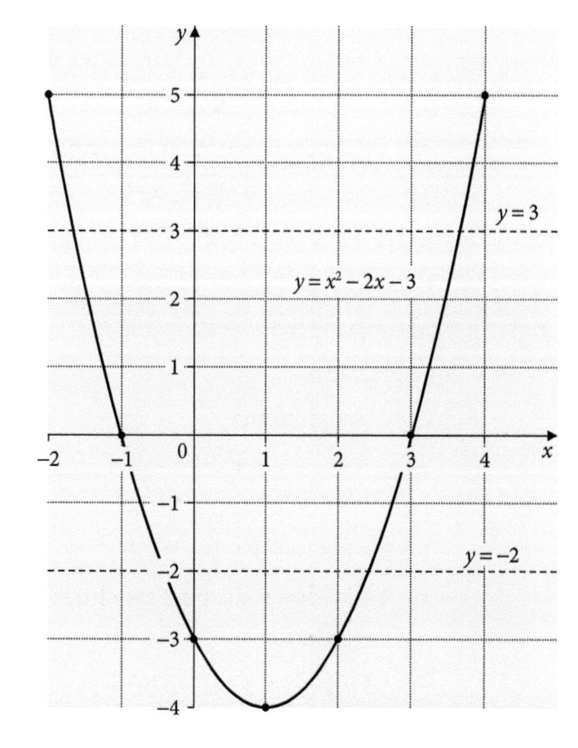

Use the graphs to find approximate solutions to the following equations:

a) $x^2 - 2x - 3 = 3$ **b)** $x^2 - 2x - 3 = -2$ **c)** $x^2 - 2x - 3 = 0$

In Questions **2** to **5** use a scale of 2 cm to 1 unit for x and 1 cm to 1 unit for y.

2. Draw the graph of the function $y = x^2 - 2x$ for $-1 \leqslant x \leqslant 4$. Hence find approximate solutions of the equations

a) $x^2 - 2x = 1$ **b)** $x^2 - 2x = 0$

3. Draw the graph of the function $y = x^2 - 3x + 5$ for $-1 \leqslant x \leqslant 5$. Hence find approximate solutions of the equations

a) $x^2 - 3x + 5 = 5$ **b)** $x^2 - 3x + 5 = 8$

4. Draw the graph of $y = x^2 - 2x + 2$ for $-2 \leqslant x \leqslant 4$. By drawing other graphs, solve the equations

a) $x^2 - 2x + 2 = 8$ **b)** $x^2 - 2x + 2 = 3$

5. Draw the graph of $y = x^2 - 7x$ for $0 \leqslant x \leqslant 7$.

a) Use the graph to find approximate solutions of the equation $x^2 - 7x = -3$

b) Explain why the equation $x^2 - 7x = -14$ does not have a solution.

Revision exercise 2A

1. Write down each sequence and find the next two numbers.

a) 2, 9, 16, 23, . . . **b)** 20, 18, 16, 14, . . .

c) −5, −2, 1, 4, . . . **d)** 128, 64, 32, 16, . . .

e) 8, 11, 15, 20, . . .

2. Solve the equations

a) $x - 6 = 3$ **b)** $x + 9 = 20$

c) $x - 5 = -2$ **d)** $3x + 1 = 22$

3. Solve the equations

a) $3x - 1 = 20$ **b)** $4x + 3 = 4$

c) $5x - 7 = -3$

4. Look at the number pattern below.

$(2 \times 1) - 1 = 2 - 1$

$(3 \times 3) - 2 = 8 - 1$

$(4 \times 5) - 3 = 18 - 1$

$(5 \times 7) - 4 = 32 - 1$

$(6 \times a) - 5 = b - 1$

a) What number does the letter a stand for?

b) What number does the letter b stand for?

c) Write down the next line in the pattern.

5. $1 + 3 = 2^2$ $1 + 3 + 5 = 3^2$

a) $1 + 3 + 5 + 7 = x^2$

Calculate x.

b) $1 + 3 + 5 + \cdots + n = 100$

Calculate n.

6. Here is a sequence:

$$1 + 2 + 1 = 2^2$$

$$1 + 2 + 3 + 2 + 1 = 3^2$$

$$1 + 2 + 3 + 4 + 3 + 2 + 1 = 4^2$$

a) Write down the next two lines of the sequence.

b) Complete the line below:

$1 + 2 + 3 + \cdots + 1 = 9^2$

7. In the diagram, the equations of the lines are $y = 3x$, $y = 6$, $y = 10 - x$ and $y = \frac{1}{2}x - 3$.

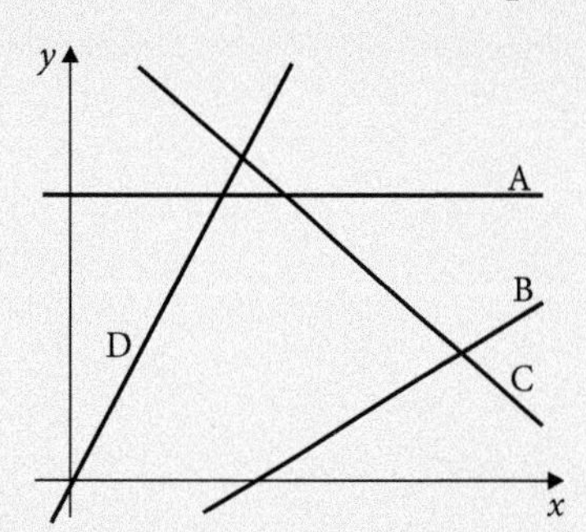

Find the equation corresponding to each line.

8. The shaded region A is formed by the lines $y = 2$, $y = 3x$ and $x + y = 6$.

Draw the three lines on a graph and then work out the area of the region A.

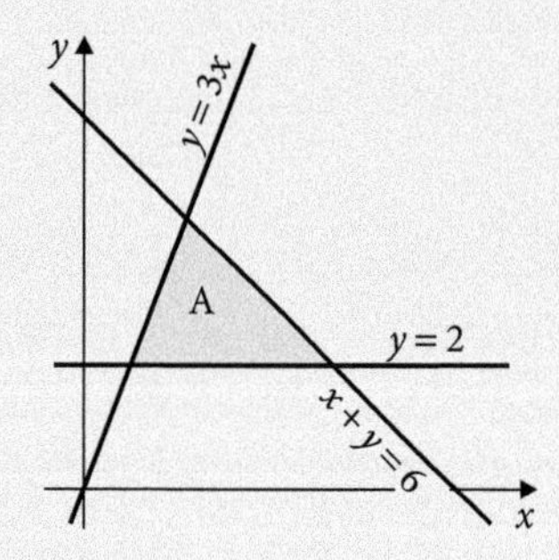

9. The shaded triangle B is formed by the lines $x = 0$, $y = x - 2$ and $x + y = 7$.

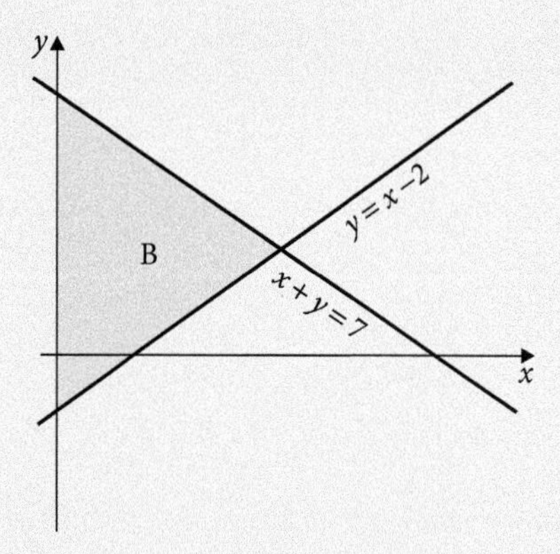

Draw a graph and use it to find the coordinates of the vertices of triangle B.

10. Nadia said: 'I thought of a number, multiplied it by 6, then added 15. My answer was less than 200'.

 a) Write down Nadia's statement in symbols, using x as the starting number.

 b) Nadia actually thought of a prime number. What was the largest prime number she could have thought of?

Examination-style exercise 2B

1. Solve the equation $5x - 7 = 8$. [2]

 Cambridge IGCSE Mathematics 0580
 Paper 1 Q5 November 2005

2. Solve the equation $2 - 3x = x + 10$. [2]

 Cambridge IGCSE Mathematics 0580
 Paper 12 Q3 November 2007

3. (a) The equation of a straight line is $y = mx + c$.

 Which letter in this equation represents the gradient? [1]

(b) Write down the equation of the line shown on the grid below. [2]

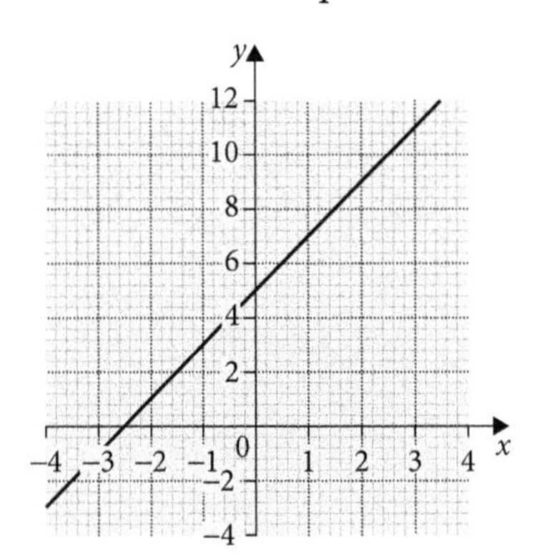

(c) Complete the table of values for $y = 12 - x^2$.

x	−4	−3	−2	−1	0	1	2	3	4
y	−4	3		11		11	8		−4

[3]

(d) On a copy of the grid above, draw the graph of $y = 12 - x^2$. [3]

(e) Write down the coordinates of the points of intersection of the straight line with your curve. [2]

Cambridge IGCSE Mathematics 0580
Paper 3 Q7 June 2006

4. **(a)** **i)** Copy and complete the table of values for $y = x^2 - 2x - 3$.

x	−3	−2	−1	0	1	2	3	4	5
y	12		0		−4	−3	0	5	

[3]

ii) Draw the graph of $y = x^2 - 2x - 3$. [4]

iii) Use your graph to find the solutions to $x^2 - 2x - 3 = -1$.
Give your answers to 1 decimal place. [2]

(b) **i)** Copy and complete the table of values for the equation $y = \frac{2}{x}$.

x	0.25	0.5	1	2	3	4	5
y		4		1	0.7	0.5	0.4

[1]

ii) On the same grid draw the graph of $y = \frac{2}{x}$ for $0.25 \leqslant x \leqslant 5$. [3]

iii) Write down the x-coordinate of the point of intersection of your two graphs. [1]

Cambridge IGCSE Mathematics 0580
Paper 3 Q3 November 2005

5. Write down the equation of the straight line through (0, –3) which is parallel to $y = 2x + 3$. [2]

Cambridge IGCSE Mathematics 0580
Paper 12 Q12 June 2007

6. A straight line, l, crosses the x-axis at (6, 0) and the y-axis at (0, 3).

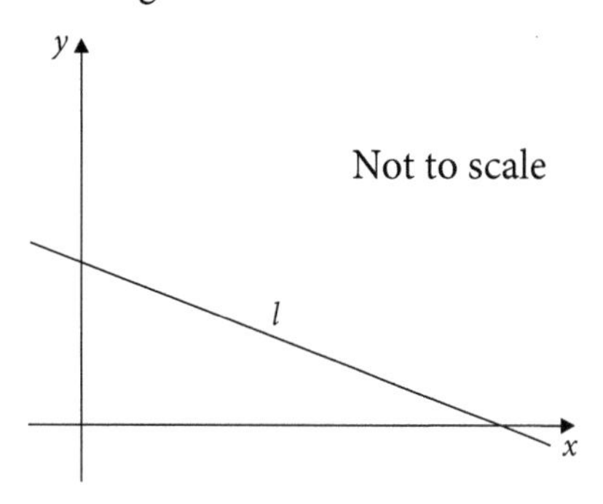

(a) Work out the gradient of the line l. [1]

(b) Write down the equation of the line l, in the form $y = mx + c$. [2]

7. (a) The width of a rectangle is x centimetres.
The length of the rectangle is 3 centimetres more than the width.
Write down an expression, in terms of x, for

i) the length of the rectangle, [1]

ii) the area of the rectangle. [1]

iii) The area of the rectangle is 7 square centimetres.
Show that $x^2 + 3x - 7 = 0$. [1]

(b) i) Copy and complete the tables of values for the equation $y = x^2 + 3x - 7$. [3]

x	–5	–4	–3	–2	–1	0	1	2
y	3		–7	–9		–7		3

ii) Draw axes using a scale of 1 cm to 1 unit for x and 2 cm to 1 unit for y.
Draw the graph of $y = x^2 + 3x - 7$ for $-5 \leqslant x \leqslant 2$. [4]

(c) i) Use your graph to find the solutions to the equation $x^2 + 3x - 7 = 0$. [2]

ii) Find the length of the rectangle in part (a). [1]

(d) Mark the point A(1, –1) on the grid.

i) Draw a straight line through A with a gradient of 2. [1]

ii) Write down the equation of this line in the form $y = mx + c$. [2]

Cambridge IGCSE Mathematics 0580
Paper 3 Q8 June 2008

8. **(a)** Simplify the expression $5p - 2q - (p + q)$. [2]

(b) Solve the equation $3(2x - 5) = 27$. [3]

(c) A kite has sides of length j cm and k cm.

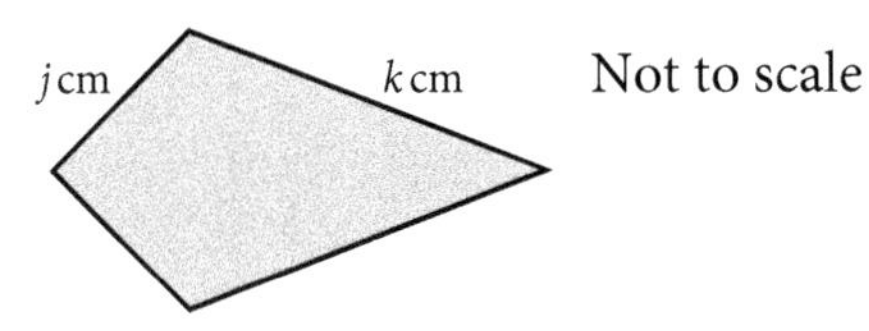

Not to scale

i) Write down an expression in terms of j and k cm for the perimeter of the kite. [1]

ii) The perimeter of the kite is 72 centimetres. Write down an equation in j and k. [1]

iii) If $k = 2j$, find the value of k. [2]

(d) i) Use the formula $w = \frac{s - t}{r}$ to find the value of w when $s = \frac{5}{6}$, $t = \frac{2}{3}$ and $r = \frac{1}{2}$.

Show all your working clearly. [3]

ii) Rearrange the formula in part **(d)(i)** to find s in terms of w, r and t. [2]

Cambridge IGCSE Mathematics 0580
Paper 3 Q3 June 2006

3 Number 1

C1.1 Identify and use natural numbers, integers (positive, negative and zero), prime numbers, square and cube numbers, common factors and common multiples, rational and irrational numbers (e.g. π, $\sqrt{2}$), real numbers, reciprocals.

C1.6 Order quantities by magnitude and demonstrate familiarity with the symbols $=, \neq, >, <, \geqslant, \leqslant$

C1.8 Use the four rules for calculations with whole numbers, decimals and fractions (including mixed numbers and improper fractions), including correct ordering of operations and use of brackets.

C1.9 Make estimates of numbers, quantities and lengths, give approximations to specified numbers of significant figures and decimal places and round off answers to reasonable accuracy in the context of a given problem.

C1.11 Demonstrate an understanding of ratio and proportion. Calculate average speed. Use common measures of rate.

C1.12 Calculate a given percentage of a quantity. Express one quantity as a percentage of another. Calculate percentage increase or decrease.

C1.14 Calculate times in terms of the 24-hour and 12-hour clock. Read clocks, dials and timetables.

C1.15 Calculate using money and convert from one currency to another.

C1.16 Use given data to solve problems on personal and small business finance involving earnings, simple interest and compound interest. Extract data from tables and charts.

C5.1 Use current units of mass, length, area, volume and capacity in practical situations and express quantities in terms of larger or smaller units.

3.1 Place value

Whole numbers are made up from units, tens, hundreds, thousands and so on.

thousands	hundreds	tens	units
3	2	6	4

In the number 3264:

the digit 3 means 3 thousands
the digit 2 means 2 hundreds
the digit 6 means 6 tens
the digit 4 means 4 units (ones)

In words we write ‘three thousand, two hundred and sixty-four’.

Exercise 1

In Questions **1** to **8** state the value of the figure underlined.

1. $\underline{2}7$ **2.** $\underline{4}16$ **3.** $23\underline{8}2$ **4.** $51\underline{6}$

5. $\underline{6}008$ **6.** $\underline{2}6\ 104$ **7.** $\underline{5}\ 250\ 000$ **8.** $\underline{8}26\ 111$

In Questions **9** to **16** write down the number which goes in each box.

9. $293 = \square + 90 + 3$

10. $574 = 500 + \square + 4$

11. $816 = 800 + \square + 6$

12. $899 = \square + 90 + 9$

13. $6217 = \square + 200 + 10 + 7$

14. $5065 = 5000 + \square + 5$

15. $63\ 410 = 60\,000 + 3000 + \square + 10$

16. $75\ 678 = \square + 5000 + 600 + \square + 8$

17. Write these numbers in figures:

a) Seven hundred and twenty

b) Five thousand, two hundred and six

c) Sixteen thousand, four hundred and thirty

d) Half a million

e) Three hundred thousand and ninety

f) Eight and a half thousand.

18. Here are four number cards:

a) Use all the cards once only to make the largest possible number.

b) Use all the cards once only to make the smallest possible number.

19. Write these numbers in words:

a) 4620 **b)** 607 **c)** 25 400

d) 6 800 000 **e)** 21 425

20. Here are five numbers cards:

a) Use all the cards to make the largest possible *odd* number.

b) Use all the cards to make the smallest possible *even* number.

21. Write down the number that is ten more than:

a) 247 **b)** 3211 **c)** 694

22. Write down the number that is one thousand more than:

a) 392 **b)** 25 611 **c)** 256 900

23. a) Prini puts a 2-digit whole number into her calculator. She multiplies the number by 10.

Fill in *one* other digit which you know must now be on the calculator.

[5][ ][ ].

b) Prini starts again with the same 2-digit number and this time she multiplies it by 1000.

Fill in all five digits on the calculator this time.

[ ][2][ ][ ][ ].

24. Write these numbers in order, from the smallest to the largest:

a) 2142, 2290, 2058, 2136

b) 5329, 5029, 5299, 5330

c) 25 117, 25 200, 25 171, 25 000, 25 500

25. Find a number n so that $5n + 7 = 507$.

26. Find a number x so that $6x + 8 = 68$.

27. Find a pair of numbers a and b for which $8a + b = 807$.

28. Find a pair of numbers p and q for which $7p + 5q = 7050$.

3.2 Arithmetic without a calculator

Here are examples to remind you of non-calculator methods.

a) $\begin{array}{r} 427 \\ +\,5186 \\ \hline 5613 \\ \hline {\scriptstyle 11} \end{array}$

b) $\begin{array}{r} 27^{7}\!\!\not{8}\,{}^{1}4 \\ -\,635 \\ \hline 2149 \\ \hline \end{array}$

c) $57 \times 100 = 5700$ [add two zeros]

d) $\begin{array}{r} 374 \\ \times\,6 \\ \hline 2244 \\ \hline {\scriptstyle 42} \end{array}$

e) $7\overline{)37^{2}9^{1}4}$ = 542

f) $5\overline{)6^{1}9^{4}4}$ = 138 r 4 or $138\frac{4}{5}$

Exercise 2

Work out, without a calculator:

1. 653 + 2844	**2.** 2106 + 329	**3.** 64 + 214 + 507	**4.** 65 941 + 2580
5. 387 − 175	**6.** 527 − 486	**7.** 927 − 68	**8.** 1024 − 816
9. 27 × 10	**10.** 5 × 1000	**11.** 73 × 5	**12.** 214 × 4
13. 316 × 8	**14.** 9224 × 7	**15.** 340 ÷ 4	**16.** 1944 ÷ 6
17. 3195 ÷ 5	**18.** 2600 ÷ 8	**19.** 364 ÷ 7	**20.** 520 ÷ 10
21. 289 + 15 + 1714	**22.** 9704 − 5135	**23.** 6001 − 5994	**24.** 54 × 20
25. 2906 − 1414	**26.** 4716 ÷ 9	**27.** 725 × 8	**28.** 1504 ÷ 8
29. 7 + 1609 + 25	**30.** 289 + 154 − 78	**31.** 7 + 295 − 48	**32.** 53 × 400

Speed tests

These questions can be done either:

- with books open, or
- read out by the teacher with books closed.

In either case write down the *answer only*. Be as quick as possible.

	Test 1	Test 2	Test 3	Test 4
1.	$30-8$	$6+16$	8×5	5×7
2.	9×5	$32-5$	$17+23$	$36-18$
3.	$40\div5$	9×6	$60\div6$	$103-20$
4.	$24+34$	$90\div2$	$101-20$	$56\div7$
5.	11×7	$98+45$	49×2	8×4
6.	$60-12$	$16-7$	$52+38$	$53+36$
7.	9×4	$45\div9$	$66\div11$	$51-22$
8.	$27\div3$	13×100	$105-70$	$36\div3$
9.	$55+55$	$99+99$	13×4	20×5
10.	$60-18$	$67-17$	$220-30$	$99+55$
11.	8×6	$570\div10$	$100\div20$	$200-145$
12.	$49\div7$	7×3	$2\times2\times2$	$88\div8$
13.	$99+17$	$55-6$	$91+19$	50×100
14.	$80-59$	$19+18$	$200-5$	$199+26$
15.	9×100	$60\div5$	16×2	$80-17$

3.3 Inverse operations

The word inverse means 'opposite'.

- The inverse of adding is subtracting: $5+19=24$, $5=24-19$
- The inverse of subtracting is adding: $31-6=25$, $31=25+6$
- The inverse of multiplying is dividing: $7\times6=42$, $7=42\div6$
- The inverse of dividing is multiplying: $30\div3=10$, $30=10\times3$

Example

Find the missing digits.

a) $\square 4 \div 6 = 14$

Work out 14×6 because multiplying is the inverse of dividing.
Since $14 \times 6 = 84$, the missing digit is 8.

b) $2\square 8 \times 5 = 1340$

Work out $1340 \div 5$ because dividing is the inverse of multiplying.
Since $1340 \div 5 = 268$, the missing digit is 6.

c)
$$\begin{array}{r} 3\ \square\ 7 \\ +\ 2\ 5\ \square \\ \hline \square\ 3\ 9 \\ \hline \end{array}$$

Start from the right: $7 + 2 = 9$
Middle column: $8 + 5 = 13$

Check
$$\begin{array}{r} 387 \\ +\ 252 \\ \hline 639 \\ \hline {}_{1}\ \ \ \end{array}\ ✓$$

Exercise 3

Find the missing digits.

1. a)
$$\begin{array}{r} 2\ 8\ 5 \\ +\ \square\ 1\ 4 \\ \hline 7\ \square\ \square \end{array}$$

b)
$$\begin{array}{r} 6\ 3\ \square \\ +\ \square\ 5\ 2 \\ \hline 8\ \square\ 9 \end{array}$$

c)
$$\begin{array}{r} \square\ 3\ 5 \\ +\ 3\ 4\ \square \\ \hline 9\ \square\ 9 \end{array}$$

2. a)
$$\begin{array}{r} 3\ 5\ 6 \\ +\ 5\ \square\ 6 \\ \hline \square\ 8\ \square \end{array}$$

b)
$$\begin{array}{r} 2\ \square\ 4 \\ +\ 5\ 3\ 7 \\ \hline \square\ 6\ 1 \end{array}$$

c)
$$\begin{array}{r} 3\ 8\ 8 \\ +\ \square\ 2\ \square \\ \hline 8\ \square\ 3 \end{array}$$

3. a)
$$\begin{array}{r} 4\ \square \\ \times\ \ \ \ 3 \\ \hline 1\ 4\ 4 \end{array}$$

b)
$$\begin{array}{r} 3\ \square \\ \times\ \ \ \ 7 \\ \hline 2\ 3\ 1 \end{array}$$

c)
$$\begin{array}{r} \square\ \square\ 1 \\ \times\ \ \ \ \ \ \ 5 \\ \hline 1\ 6\ 0\ 5 \end{array}$$

4. a) $\square\square\square \div 3 = 50$ **b)** $\square\square \times 4 = 60$

c) $9 \times \square = 81$ **d)** $\square\square\square \div 6 = 92$

5. a)
$$\begin{array}{r} 4\ \square\ 5 \\ +\ 2\ 8\ \square \\ \hline \square\ 3\ 0 \end{array}$$

b)
$$\begin{array}{r} 4\ \square\ 7 \\ +\ \square\ 7\ \square \\ \hline 6\ 0\ 4 \end{array}$$

c)
$$\begin{array}{r} \square\ 3\ \square \\ +\ 2\ \square\ 4 \\ \hline 7\ 9\ 9 \end{array}$$

6. a) $\square\boxed{5} \times 7 = 245$ **b)** $\square\square \times 10 = 580$ **c)** $32 \div \square = 8$ **d)** $\square\square\square \div 5 = 190$

7. a) $\square\square + 29 = 101$ **b)** $\square\square\square - 17 = 91$

c)
$$\begin{array}{r} \square\ 8\ 9 \\ -\ 3\ \square\ 6 \\ \hline 5\ 4\ \square \end{array}$$

d)
$$\begin{array}{r} 3\ 3\ 5 \\ -\ 2\ 1\ \square \\ \hline \square\ \square\ 7 \end{array}$$

8. There is more than one correct answer for each of these questions. Ask a friend to check your solutions.

a) [2][3] + [ ][ ] − [ ][ ] = 23

b) [8][5] − [ ][ ] + [ ][ ] = 86

c) [2][5] × [ ] ÷ [ ] = 25

d) [4][0] × [ ][ ] ÷ [ ] = 80

9. In each calculation the same number is missing from all three boxes. Find the missing number in each case.

a) $\square \times \square - \square = 12$

b) $\square \div \square + \square = 9$

c) $\square \times \square + \square = 72$

10. In the circle write +, −, × or ÷ to make the calculation correct.

a) $7 \times 4 \bigcirc 3 = 25$

b) $8 \times 5 \bigcirc 2 = 20$

c) $7 \bigcirc 3 - 9 = 12$

d) $12 \bigcirc 2 + 4 = 10$

e) $75 \div 5 \bigcirc 5 = 20$

11. Write the following with the correct signs.

a) $5 \times 4 \times 3 \bigcirc 3 = 63$

b) $5 + 4 \bigcirc 3 \bigcirc 2 = 4$

c) $5 \times 2 \times 3 \bigcirc 1 = 31$

3.4 Decimals

Look at these numbers.

tens	units	•	$\frac{1}{10}$	$\frac{1}{100}$	$\frac{1}{1000}$
5	3	•	6	2	
	0	•	8	7	3

Notice that $53.62 = 50 + 3 + \frac{6}{10} + \frac{2}{100}$

$$0.873 = \frac{8}{10} + \frac{7}{100} + \frac{3}{1000}$$

When writing decimals in order of size it is helpful to write them with the same number of figures after the decimal point.

Example

Write these three numbers in order: 0.08, 0.107, 0.1

$$0.08 \rightarrow 0.080$$

$$0.107 \rightarrow 0.107$$

$$0.1 \rightarrow 0.100$$

Now we can see that the correct order from lowest to highest is 0.08, 0.1, 0.107.

Exercise 4

In Questions **1** to **8** write down each statement and decide whether it is true (T) or false (F).

1. 0.3 is less than 0.31.

2. 0.82 is more than 0.825.

3. 0.7 is equal to 0.70.

4. 0.17 is less than 0.71.

5. 0.02 is more than 0.002.

6. 0.6 is less than 0.06.

7. 0.1 is equal to $\frac{1}{10}$.

8. 5 is equal to 5.00.

9. The number 43.6 can be written $40 + 3 + \frac{6}{10}$.
Write the number 57.2 in this way.

10. Write the decimal numbers for these additions

a) $200 + 30 + 5 + \frac{1}{10}$

b) $60 + 7 + \frac{2}{10} + \frac{3}{100}$

c) $90 + 8 + \frac{3}{10} + \frac{2}{100}$

d) $3 + \frac{1}{10} + \frac{6}{100} + \frac{7}{1000}$

In Questions **11** to **18** arrange the numbers in order of size, smallest first.

11. 0.41, 0.31, 0.2

12. 0.75, 0.58, 0.702

13. 0.43, 0.432, 0.41

14. 0.609, 0.61, 0.6

15. 0.04, 0.15, 0.2, 0.35

16. 1.8, 0.18, 0.81, 1.18

17. 0.7, 0.061, 0.07, 0.1

18. 0.2, 0.025, 0.03, 0.009

19. Here are numbers with letters.
Put the numbers in order and then write down the letters to make a word.

R 0.1

C 0.01

20. Increase these numbers by $\frac{1}{10}$:

a) 32.41 **b)** 0.753 **c)** 1.06

21. Increase these numbers by $\frac{1}{100}$:

a) 5.68 **b)** 0.542 **c)** 1.29

22. Write the following amounts in dollars:

a) 350 cents **b)** 15 cents **c)** 3 cents

d) 10 cents **e)** 1260 cents **f)** 8 cents

23. Copy each statement and say whether it is true or false.

a) $5.4 = $5 + 40c **b)** $0.6 = 6c

c) 5c = $0.05 **d)** 50c is more than $0.42

Scale readings

Exercise 5

Work out the value indicated by the arrow.

1. 4 5

2. 0 1

3. 9 10

4. 0 2

5. 0 20

6. 10 11

7. 17 19

8. 120 140

9. 0 1000

10. 0.2 0.3

11. 1.9 2

12.

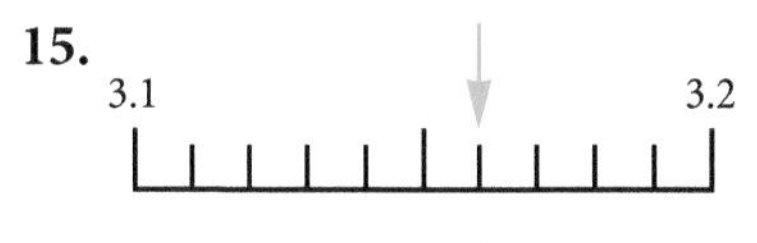

13. 0 0.1

14. 1.7 1.9

15. 3.1 3.2

16. 80 120

17. 0 400

18. 0 200

Multiplying and dividing decimals by 10, 100, 1000

To *multiply*, move the decimal point to the *right*.

$3.24 \times 10 = 32.4$

$10.61 \times 10 = 106.1$

$4.134 \times 100 = 413.4$

$8.2 \times 100 = 820$

To *divide*, move the decimal point to the *left*.

$15.2 \div 10 = 1.52$

$624.9 \div 100 = 6.249$

$509 \div 1000 = 0.509$

Exercise 6

Work out:

1. 0.634×10	**2.** 0.838×10	**3.** 0.815×100
4. 0.074×100	**5.** 7.245×1000	**6.** 0.032×1000
7. 0.63×10	**8.** 1.42×100	**9.** 0.041×100
10. 0.3×100	**11.** 0.71×1000	**12.** 3.95×10
13. $6.24 \div 10$	**14.** $8.97 \div 10$	**15.** $17.5 \div 100$
16. $23.6 \div 100$	**17.** $127 \div 1000$	**18.** $705 \div 1000$
19. $13 \div 10$	**20.** $0.8 \div 10$	**21.** $0.7 \div 100$
22. $218 \div 10$	**23.** $35 \div 1000$	**24.** $8.6 \div 1000$
25. 0.95×100	**26.** 11.11×10	**27.** $3.2 \div 10$
28. 0.07×1000	**29.** $57.6 \div 10$	**30.** $999 \div 100$
31. 66×10	**32.** $100 \div 100$	**33.** $42 \div 1000$
34. $0.62 \times 10\,000$	**35.** $0.9 \div 100$	**36.** $555 \div 10\,000$

37. Here are some number cards 

a) Jason picks the cards 1 3 and 4 to make the number 314.

What extra card could he take to make a number ten times as big as 314?

b) Mel chooses three cards to make 5.2.

i) What cards could she take to make a number ten times as big as 5.2?

ii) What cards could she take to make a number 100 times as big as 5.2?

iii) What cards could she take to make a number which is $\frac{1}{100}$ of 5.2?

Adding and subtracting decimals

Remember: Line up the decimal points.

a) $4.2 + 1.76$

$$\begin{array}{r} 4.20 \\ +1.76 \\ \hline 5.96 \\ \hline \end{array}$$

←Put a zero

b) $26 - 1.7$

$$\begin{array}{r} 2\overset{5}{\not{6}}.\overset{1}{0} \\ -\ 1.7 \\ \hline 24.3 \\ \hline \end{array}$$

c) $0.24 + 5 + 12.7$

$$\begin{array}{r} 0.24 \\ 5.00 \\ +\ 12.70 \\ \hline 17.94 \\ \hline \end{array}$$

extra zeros

Exercise 7

Work out, without a calculator:

1. $2.84 + 7.3$ **2.** $18.6 + 2.34$ **3.** $25.96 + 0.75$

4. $212.7 + 4.25$ **5.** $3.6 + 6$ **6.** $7 + 16.1$

7. $8 + 0.34 + 0.8$ **8.** $12 + 5.32$ **9.** $0.004 + 0.058$

10. $4.81 - 3.7$ **11.** $6.92 - 2.56$ **12.** $8.27 - 5.86$

13. $3.6 - 2.24$ **14.** $8.4 - 2.17$ **15.** $8.24 - 5.78$

16. $15.4 - 7$ **17.** $8 - 5.2$ **18.** $13 - 2.7$

19. $0.5 - 0.32$ **20.** $5 - 0.99$ **21.** $6 + 0.06 + 0.6$

22. $12.4 + 28.71$ **23.** $11 - 7.4$ **24.** $8.2 + 9.54 - 11.3$

Multiplying decimals

Count up the number of figures to the right of the decimal points in the question. Put the same number of figures to the right of the decimal point in the answer.

Example

a) $0.\underline{2} \times 0.\underline{8}$

2 figures after the decimal points

$[2 \times 8 = 16]$

So $0.2 \times 0.8 = 0.\underline{16}$

b) $0.\underline{4} \times 0.\underline{07}$

3 figures after the decimal points

$[4 \times 7 = 28]$

So $0.4 \times 0.07 = 0.\underline{028}$

Exercise 8

Work out, without a calculator:

1. 0.2×0.3 **2.** 0.5×0.3 **3.** 0.4×0.3

4. 0.2×0.03 **5.** 0.6×3 **6.** 0.7×5

7. 0.9×2 **8.** 8×0.1 **9.** 0.4×0.9

10. 0.02×0.7 **11.** 2.1×0.6 **12.** 4.7×0.5

13. 21.3×0.4 **14.** 5.2×0.6 **15.** 4.2×0.03

16. 212×0.6 17. 0.85×0.2 18. 3.27×0.1

19. 12.6×0.01 20. 0.02×17 21. 0.05×1.1

22. 52×0.01 23. 65×0.02 24. 0.5×0.002

Dividing by a decimal

Example

a) $9.36 \div 0.4$ Multiply both numbers by 10 so that you can divide by a *whole number*. [Move the decimal points to the right.]

So work out $93.6 \div 4$

$$4\overline{)9^{1}3.^{1}6} = 23.4$$

b) $0.0378 \div 0.07$ Multiply both numbers by 100 so that you can divide by a whole number. [Move the decimal points to the right.]

So work out $3.78 \div 7$

$$7\overline{)3.7^{2}8} = 0.54$$

Exercise 9

Work out, without a calculator:

1. $0.84 \div 0.4$ 2. $0.93 \div 0.3$ 3. $0.872 \div 0.2$

4. $0.8 \div 0.2$ 5. $2.8 \div 0.7$ 6. $1.25 \div 0.5$

7. $8 \div 0.5$ 8. $40 \div 0.2$ 9. $7 \div 0.1$

10. $0.368 \div 0.4$ 11. $0.915 \div 0.03$ 12. $0.248 \div 0.04$

13. $0.625 \div 0.05$ 14. $8.54 \div 0.07$ 15. $1.272 \div 0.006$

16. $4.48 \div 0.08$ 17. $0.12 \div 0.002$ 18. $7.5 \div 0.005$

19. $0.09 \div 0.3$ 20. $0.77 \div 1.1$ 21. $0.055 \div 0.11$

22. $21.28 \div 7$ 23. $22.48 \div 4$ 24. $3.12 \div 4$

25. $0.7 \div 5$ 26. $3 \div 0.8$ 27. $0.3 \div 4$

28. $1.2 \div 8$ 29. $0.732 \div 0.6$ 30. $0.1638 \div 0.001$

31. $1.05 \div 0.6$ 32. $7.52 \div 0.4$

33. A cake weighing 7.2 kg is cut into several pieces each weighing 0.6 kg. How many pieces are there?

34. A phone call costs \$0.04. How many calls can I make if I have \$3.52?

35. A sheet of paper is 0.01 cm thick. How many sheets are there in a pile of paper 5.8 cm thick?

Crossnumbers

Make three copies of the crossnumber and then fill in the numbers using the clues given.

1			2		3	
		4				
	5			6		7
8			9		10	
					11	
12		13		14		
		15			16	

A

Across

1. 13×7
2. $0.214 \times 10\,000$
4. $265 - 248$
5. $2 \times 2 \times 2 \times 2 \times 2 \times 2$
7. $90 - (9 \times 9)$
8. 14×5
9. $2226 \div 7$
11. $216 \div (18 \div 3)$
12. $800 - 363$
14. $93 - (6 \times 2)$
15. 0.23×100
16. $8 \times 8 - 1$

Down

1. $101 - 7$
2. $2 - 7 \div 0.1$
3. $44.1 + 0.9$
4. $(2 \times 9) - (8 \div 2)$
6. 9^2
8. $6523 + 917$
9. $418 \div 11$
10. $216 + (81 \times 100)$
13. $2 \times 2 \times 2 \times 3 \times 3$

B

Across

1. 2.4×40
2. $1600 - 27$
4. $913 - 857$
5. $2 + (9 \times 9)$
7. $0.4 \div 0.05$
8. $27 \times 5 - 69$
9. $4158 \div 7$
11. $2^6 + 6$
12. $5.22 \div 0.03$
14. $201 - 112$
15. 7 million $\div$ 100 000
16. $\frac{1}{4}$ of 372

Down

1. $558 \div 6$
2. $6.4 \div 0.4$
3. 0.071×1000
4. $11.61 + 4.2 + 37.19$
6. $(7 - 3.1) \times 10$
8. $8 \times 8 \times 100 - 82$
9. 0.08×700
10. $40 \times 30 \times 4 - 1$
13. $\frac{1}{5}$ of 235

C

Across

1. 2.6×10
2. 6.314×1000
4. $600 - 563$
5. 0.25×100
7. $3 \div 0.5$
8. 0.08×1000
9. $3.15 \div 0.01$
11. 1.1×70
12. $499 + 103$
14. $1 \div 0.1$
15. 0.01×5700
16. $1000 - 936$

Down

1. 0.2×100
2. $6.7 \div 0.1$
3. $1800 \div 100$
4. $21 \div 0.6$
6. 420×0.05
8. $0.8463 \times 10\,000$
9. 0.032×1000
10. $5.706 \div 0.001$
13. 5^2

Pricing your holiday

The table below shows the prices in dollars per person for two adults to share a twin/double room in different hotels in Hong Kong. The price includes travelling by air from Canada and includes breakfast in the hotel.

Hotels	**Hotel Rio**		**Tulip Hotel**		**Carling Hotel**		**Hotel Eden**	
Holiday starting date	**1 night**	**extra night**	**1 night**	**extra night**	**1 night**	**extra night**	**1 night**	**extra night**
01 Apr – 27 Oct	174	77	185	84	210	99	216	105
28 Oct – 10 Nov	161	62	185	84	198	86	191	85
11 Nov – 5 Dec	161	62	171	73	210	99	190	84
6 Dec – 21 Dee	161	62	171	73	210	99	216	105
22 Dec – 5 Jan	174	77	187	88	219	103	216	105
6 Jan – 10 Jan	174	77	185	84	214	101	212	101
11 Jan – 20 Jan	159	60	171	73	187	81	186	75
21 Jan – 2 Mar	159	62	171	73	187	81	188	77
3 Mar – 10 Mar	161	63	175	74	192	83	218	107
11 Mar – 18 Mar	161	62	175	74	198	86	220	109
19 Mar – 31 Mar	179	81	191	86	215	103	228	117

Weekend supplement: \$12 per person for holidays starting Friday or Saturday.

Seasonal supplement of \$12 per person applies for holidays starting between: 28 April–3 May, 28–31 May, 26–30 August, 24–27 December, 30 December–2 January.

'Weekend supplement' means each person pays \$12 extra if the holiday starts on a Friday or Saturday.

'Seasonal supplement' means each person pays \$12 extra if the holiday starts on the dates shown.

Example

Two people want to spend 4 nights at the Carling Hotel, starting on 15 November.
How much will this cost?

Look along the '11 Nov–5 Dec' row and stop at the Carling Hotel column.
The cost per person is \$210 plus \$99 for each extra night.
Total cost per person for 4 nights = $210 + 297 = \$507$.
Total cost for 2 people = $507 \times 2 = \$1014$.

Exercise 10

1. Two people want to spend 3 nights at the Hotel Eden starting on 23 January. How much will this cost?
2. Mr. and Mrs. Chen want to spend 2 nights at the Carling Hotel, starting on 10 May which is a Friday. How much will the holiday cost?
3. Four people want to spend 5 nights at the Hotel Rio, starting on 3 March. What is the total cost of this holiday?
4. Two people want to spend 4 nights at the Hotel Rio, starting on 20 September, which is a Saturday. How much will the holiday cost for these two people?
5. A party of 10 people want to spend 2 nights at the Tulip Hotel starting on 27 August (a seasonal supplement will be payable). What is the total cost of the holiday?
6. Chandresh and Mahima are celebrating their wedding anniversary by spending 3 nights at the Carling Hotel. They plan to begin their holiday on 9 December, which is a Friday. How much will this holiday cost?
7. Six people want to spend 7 nights at the Hotel Eden, starting on 20 March. What is the total cost of this holiday?
8. Four people want to spend 6 nights at the Hotel Rio, starting on 28 May (a seasonal supplement will be payable). How much will this holiday cost?

3.5 Flow diagrams

Find the operation

Exercise 11

In the flow charts, the boxes A, B, C and D each contain a single mathematical operation (like +5, ×4, −15, ÷2).

Look at flow charts **(i)** and **(ii)** together and work out what is the same operation which will replace A. Complete the flow chart by replacing B, C and D.

Now copy and complete each flow chart overleaf, using the same operations.

1. **i)** 1 → A → 8 → B → 16 → C → 5 → D → 15 →

ii) 3 → A → 10 → B → 20 → C → 9 → D → 27 →

a) 4 → A → ? → B → ? → C → ? → D → ? →

b) 5 → A → ? → B → ? → C → ? → D → ? →

c) ? → A → ? → B → 28 → C → ? → D → ? →

d) ? → A → 16 → B → ? → C → ? → D → ? →

e) ? → A → ? → B → ? → C → 25 → D → ? →

f) ? → A → ? → B → ? → C → ? → D → 87 →

2. **i)** 2 → A → 4 → B → 19 → C → 12 → D → 3 →

ii) 4 → A → 8 → B → 23 → C → 16 → D → 4 →

a) 6 → A → ? → B → ? → C → ? → D → ? →

b) 3 → A → ? → B → ? → C → ? → D → ? →

c) ? → A → 16 → B → ? → C → ? → D → ? →

d) ? → A → ? → B → 35 → C → ? → D → ? →

e) ? → A → ? → B → ? → C → ? → D → $2\frac{1}{2}$ →

f) ? → A → ? → B → ? → C → ? → D → 8 →

3. **i)** 2 → A → 17 → B → 34 → C → 12 → D → 3 →

ii) 4 → A → 19 → B → 38 → C → 16 → D → 4 →

a) 7 → A → ? → B → ? → C → ? → D → ? →

b) 10 → A → ? → B → ? → C → ? → D → ? →

c) ? → A → ? → B → 62 → C → ? → D → ? →

d) ? → A → $15\frac{1}{2}$ → B → ? → C → ? → D → ? →

e) ? → A → ? → B → ? → C → 208 → D → ? →

f) ? → A → ? → B → ? → C → ? → D → 14 →

4. **i)** 2 → [A] → 4 → [B] → 12 → [C] → 2 → [D] → 1

ii) 3 → [A] → 9 → [B] → 27 → [C] → 17 → [D] → $8\frac{1}{2}$

a) 4 → [A] → 16 → [B] → ? → [C] → ? → [D] → ?

b) 5 → [A] → ? → [B] → ? → [C] → ? → [D] → ?

c) ? → [A] → ? → [B] → 108 → [C] → ? → [D] → ?

d) ? → [A] → ? → [B] → ? → [C] → 182 → [D] → ?

e) ? → [A] → ? → [B] → 3 → [C] → ? → [D] → ?

f) ? → [A] → ? → [B] → ? → [C] → ? → [D] → 145

In Questions **5**, **6** and **7** find the operations A, B, C and D.

5. **i)** 4 → [A] → 16 → [B] → 4 → [C] → −6 → [D] → 12

ii) 9 → [A] → 36 → [B] → 6 → [C] → −4 → [D] → 8

6. **i)** 5 → [A] → $\frac{1}{5}$ → [B] → 1.2 → [C] → 1.44 → [D] → 0.48

ii) $\frac{1}{2}$ → [A] → 2 → [B] → 3 → [C] → 9 → [D] → 3

7. **i)** −1 → [A] → 2 → [B] → 8 → [C] → −4 → [D] → 96

ii) 7 → [A] → 10 → [B] → 1000 → [C] → −500 → [D] → −400

3.6 Properties of numbers

- **Natural numbers** (0, 1, 2, ...) are used for counting and ordering, e.g. she is 4th tallest in the class.
- **Integers** are the natural numbers together with the negatives of the non-zero natural numbers.

Order of operations

Some people use the word 'BIDMAS' to help them remember the correct order of operations.

Brackets
Indices
Divide
Multiply
Add
Subtract

Here are four examples:

- $8 + 6 \div 6 = 8 + 1 = 9$
- $20 - 8 \times 2 = 20 - 16 = 4$
- $(13 - 7) \div (6 - 4) = 6 \div 2 = 3$
- $20 - 8 \div (5 + 3) = 20 - 8 \div 8 = 19$

Exercise 12

Work out, without a calculator

1. $5 + 7 \times 2$

2. $9 - 12 \div 2$

3. $24 + 6 \times 2$

4. $(8 + 9) \times 2$

5. $17 - (2 + 5)$

6. $5 \times 8 + 6 \times 3$

7. $5 \times 6 - 8 \div 2$

8. $102 \div (17 - 15)$

9. $15 \div 15 + 15$

10. $11 - 3 \times 3$

11. $7 + 9 \div 3$

12. $20 - (11 + 3)$

13. $9 \times 4 - 20$

14. $100 - 10 \div 10$

15. $36 \div (5 + 7)$

16. $2 \times (8 + 4 \times 3) - 7$

17. $(8 + 5) \times (20 - 16)$

18. $18 \div (9 - 12 \div 4)$

Indices

3^2 means '3 to the power 2' or 3×3

5^4 means '5 to the power 4' or $5 \times 5 \times 5 \times 5$

In these examples the '2' and the '4' are indices.

In the order of operations, BIDMAS, we perform operations involving indices after operations in brackets.

For example $3^2 \times 5 = 9 \times 5 = 45$

$$(5 + 4) - 2^3 = 9 - 2^3$$
$$= 9 - 8 = 1$$

Exercise 13

Work out the following using 'BIDMAS'.

1. $33 + 4^2$

2. $(8 - 5)^2$

3. $(4^2 + 1) \times 2$

4. $5 \times 4 - 2^3$

5. $3^2 - 5 + 1$

6. $(4^2 - 12)$

7. $(11 - 3^2) \times 5$

8. $4^2 \div (12 - 8 \div 2)$

9. $(10^2 - 9^2) + 11$

- **Factors** Any number which divides exactly into 8 is a **factor** of 8. The factors of 8 are 1, 2, 4, 8.
- **Multiples** Any number in the 8-times table is a **multiple** of 8. The first five multiples of 8 are 8, 16, 24, 32, 40.
- **Prime** A **prime** number has just two different factors: 1 and itself. The number 1 is **not** prime. [It does not have two different factors.] The first five prime numbers are 2, 3, 5, 7, 11.
- **Prime factor** The factors of 8 are 1, 2, 4, 8. The only **prime factor** of 8 is 2. It is the only prime number which is a factor of 8.

L.C.M. and H.C.F.

a) The first few multiples of 4 are 4, 8, 12, 16, (20), 24, 28, …

The first few multiples of 5 are 5, 10, 15, (20), 25, 30, 35, …

The *Least Common Multiple* (L.C.M.) of 4 and 5 is 20.

It is the lowest number which is in both lists.

b) The factors of 12 are 1, 2, 3, (4), 6, 12

The factors of 20 are 1, 2, (4), 5, 10, 20

The *Highest Common Factor* (H.C.F.) of 12 and 20 is 4.

It is the highest number which is in both lists.

Exercise 14

1. Write down all the factors of the following numbers:

a) 6 **b)** 15 **c)** 18 **d)** 21 **e)** 40

2. Write down all the prime numbers less than 20.

3. Write down two prime numbers which add up to another prime number. Do this in two different ways.

4. Use a calculator to find which of the following are prime numbers:

a) 91 **b)** 101 **c)** 143 **d)** 151 **e)** 293

Divide by the prime numbers 2, 3, 5, 7, 11 and so on.

5. Prime factors can be found using a 'factor tree'.

- Here is a factor tree for 140.

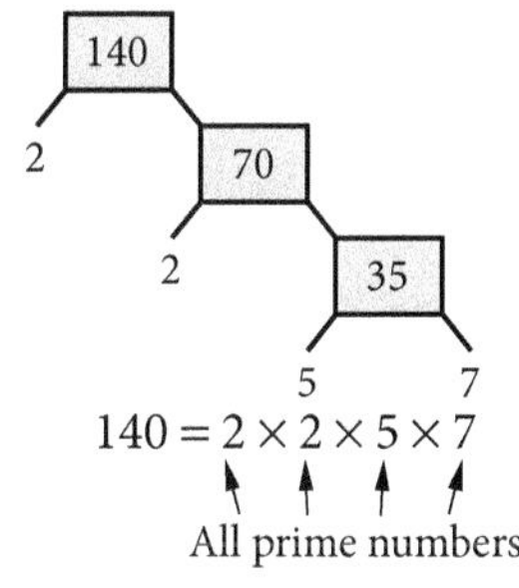

- Here is a factor tree for 40.

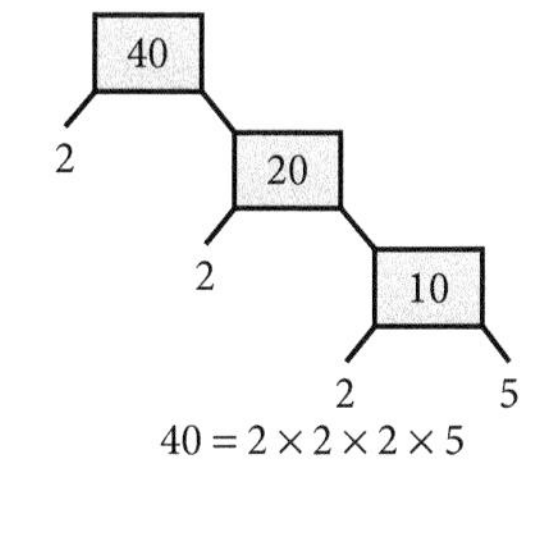

Draw a factor tree for each of these numbers. Remember to start with the smallest prime number in each case.

a) 36 **b)** 60 **c)** 216 **d)** 200 **e)** 1500

6. Here is the number 600 written as the product of its prime factors.

$600 = 2 \times 2 \times 2 \times 3 \times 5 \times 5$

Use this information to write 1200 as a product of its prime factors.

7. Write down the first four multiples of:

a) 3 **b)** 4 **c)** 10 **d)** 11 **e)** 20

8. Find the 'odd one out'.

a) multiples of 6: 12, 18, 24, 32, 48

b) multiples of 9: 18, 27, 45, 56, 72

9. Write down two numbers that are multiples of both 3 and 4.

10. Copy and complete each sentence:

a) An [odd/even] number is exactly divisible by 2.

b) An [__________] number leaves a remainder of 1 when divided by 2.

c) All [__________] numbers are multiples of 2.

11. Copy the table and then write the numbers 1 to 9, *one in each box*, so that all the numbers satisfy the conditions for both the row and the column.

	Prime number	**Multiple of 3**	**Factor of 16**
Number greater than 5			
Odd number			
Even number			

12. Find each of the mystery numbers below.

a) I am an odd number and a prime number. I am a factor of 14.

b) I am a two-digit multiple of 50.

c) I am one less than a prime number which is even.

d) I am odd, greater than one and a factor of both 20 and 30.

13. a) Write down the first six multiples of 2.

b) Write down the first six multiples of 5.

c) Write down the L.C.M. of 2 and 5.

14. a) Write down the first four multiples of 4.

b) Write down the first four multiples of 12.

c) Write down the L.C.M. of 4 and 12.

15. Find the L.C.M. of

a) 6 and 9 **b)** 8 and 12 **c)** 14 and 35

d) 2, 4 and 6 **e)** 3, 5 and 10 **f)** 4, 7 and 9

16. The table shows the factors and common factors of 24 and 36.

number	**factors**	**common factors**
24	1, 2, 3, 4, 6, 8, 12, 24	} 1, 2, 3, 4, 6, 12
36	1, 2, 3, 4, 6, 9, 12, 18, 36	

Write down the H.C.F. of 24 and 36.

17. The table shows the factors and common factors of 18 and 24.

number	**factors**	**common factors**
18	1, 2, 3, 6, 9 18	} 1, 2, 3, 6
24	1, 2, 3, 4, 6, 8, 12, 24	

Write down the H.C.F. of 18 and 24.

18. Find the H.C.F. of

a) 12 and 18 **b)** 22 and 55 **c)** 45 and 72

d) 12, 18 and 30 **e)** 36, 60 and 72 **f)** 20, 40 and 50

19. Don't confuse your L.C.M.s with your H.C.F.s!

a) Find the H.C.F. of 12 and 30.

b) Find the L.C.M. of 8 and 20.

c) Write down two numbers whose H.C.F. is 11.

d) Write down two numbers whose L.C.M. is 10.

20. Given that $30 = 2 \times 3 \times 5$ and $165 = 3 \times 5 \times 11$, find the highest common factor of 30 and 165 [i.e. the highest number that goes into 30 and 165].

21. If $315 = 3 \times 3 \times 5 \times 7$ and $273 = 3 \times 7 \times 13$, find the highest common factor of 315 and 273.

Rational and irrational numbers

- A rational number can always be written exactly in the form $\frac{a}{b}$ where a and b are whole numbers.

$\frac{3}{7}$	$1\frac{1}{2} = \frac{3}{2}$	$5.14 = \frac{257}{50}$	$0.\dot{6} = \frac{2}{3}$
All these are rational numbers.			

- An irrational number cannot be written in the form $\frac{a}{b}$. $\sqrt{2}, \sqrt{5}, \pi, \sqrt[3]{2}$ are all irrational numbers.
- In general $\sqrt{n}$ is irrational unless n is a square number.

In this triangle the length of the hypotenuse is exactly $\sqrt{5}$.

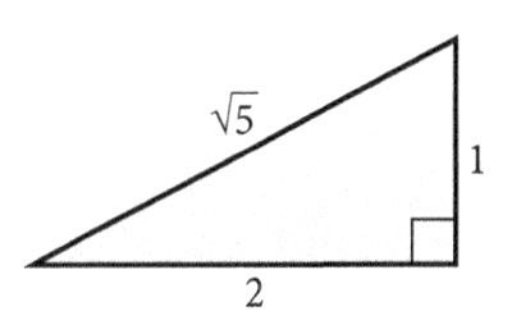

On a calculator, $\sqrt{5} = 2.236068$. This value of $\sqrt{5}$ is *not* exact and is correct only to 6 decimal places.

Exact means leaving your answer as a fraction or with the square root sign.

Exercise 15

1. Which of the following numbers are rational?

$\frac{\pi}{2}$	$\sqrt{5}$	$\left(\sqrt{17}\right)^2$	$\sqrt{3}$
3.14	$\frac{\sqrt{12}}{\sqrt{3}}$	π^2	$\frac{1}{3} + \frac{1}{9}$
$\frac{1}{\sqrt{7}}$	$\frac{22}{7}$	$\sqrt{2} + 1$	$\sqrt{2.25}$

2. a) Write down any rational number between 4 and 6.

b) Write down any irrational number between 4 and 6.

c) Find a rational number between $\sqrt{2}$ and $\sqrt{3}$.

d) Write down any rational number between π and $\sqrt{10}$.

3. a) For each shape state whether the *perimeter* is rational or irrational.

   b) For each shape state whether the *area* is rational or irrational.

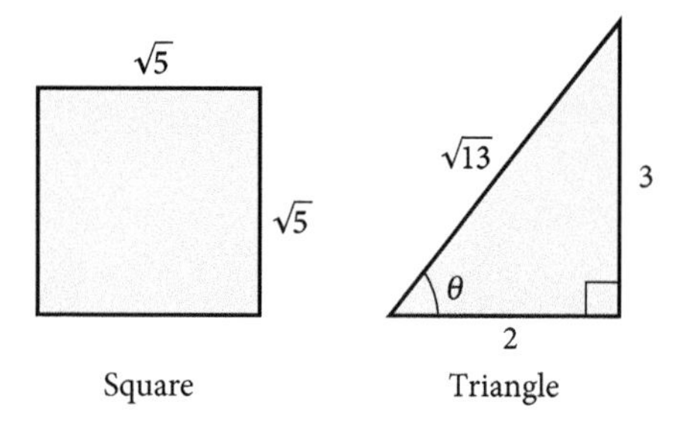

Square   Triangle

4. The diagram shows a circle of radius 3 cm drawn inside a square. Write down the exact value of the following and state whether the answer is rational or not:

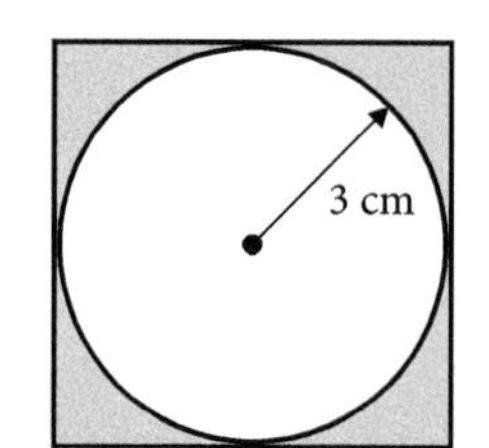

   a) the circumference of the circle
   b) the diameter of the circle
   c) the area of the square
   d) the area of the circle
   e) the shaded area.

5. Think of two *irrational numbers* x and y such that $\frac{x}{y}$ is a *rational* number.

6. Explain the difference between a rational number and an irrational number.

7. a) Is it possible to multiply a rational number and an irrational number to give an answer which is rational?

   b) Is it possible to multiply two irrational numbers together to give a rational answer?

   c) If either or both are possible, give an example.

3.7 Inequalities

Symbols

- There are four inequality symbols.

  $x < 4$ means 'x is **less than** 4'

  $y > 7$ means 'y is **greater than** 7'

  $z \leqslant 10$ means 'z is **less than or equal to** 10'

  $t \geqslant -3$ means 't is **greater than or equal to** -3'

  Also $h \neq 4$ means 'h is not equal to 4'

- If there are two symbols in one statement, look at each part separately.

For example, if n is an **integer** and $3 < n \leqslant 7$, n has to be greater than 3 but at the same time it has to be less than or equal to 7.

An integer is a whole number.

So n could be 4, 5, 6 or 7 only.

Example

Show on a number line the range of values of x stated.

a) $x > 1$ **b)** $x \leqslant -2$ **c)** $1 \leqslant x < 4$

a) $x > 1$ 

Use an open circle to show that 1 is not included.

b) $x \leqslant -2$ 

Use a filled in circle to show that −2 is included.

c) $1 \leqslant x < 4$ 

Exercise 16

1. Write each statement with either < or > in the box.

a) 3 ☐ 7 **b)** 0 ☐ −2 **c)** 3.1 ☐ 3.01

d) −3 ☐ −5 **e)** 100 m ☐ 1 m **f)** 1 kg ☐ 1 lb

2. Write the inequality shown. Use x for the variable.

a) 

b) 

c) 

d) 

e) 

f) 

3. Draw number lines to show these inequalities.

a) $x \geqslant 7$ **b)** $x < 2.5$ **c)** $1 < x < 7$ **d)** $0 \leqslant x \leqslant 4$ **e)** $-1 < x \leqslant 5$

4. Write an inequality for each statement.

a) You must be at least 16 to get married.
[Use A for age.]

b) Vitamin J1 is not recommended for people over 70 or for children 3 years or under.

c) To braise a rabbit the oven temperature should be between 150 °C and 175 °C.
[Use T for temperature.]

d) To ride a rollercoaster you must be at least 1.5 m tall.
[Use h for height.]

5. Answer 'true' or 'false'.

   a) n is an integer and $1 < n \leqslant 4$, so n can be 2, 3 or 4 only.

   b) x is an integer and $2 \leqslant x < 5$, so x can be 2, 3 or 4 only.

   c) p is an integer and $p \geqslant 10$, so p can be 10, 11, 12, 13, ...

6. Write each statement with either = or ≠ in the box.

   a) 15 cm ☐ 150 mm   b) 200 g ☐ 2 kg   c) 11 mm ☐ 1.1 cm

   d) 350 ml ☐ 3.5 litres   e) $\frac{2}{100}$ ☐ 0.02   f) 0.1×0.1 ☐ 0.1

For Questions **7** to **9** list the solutions which satisfy the given condition.

7. $3a + 1 < 20$; a is a positive integer.

8. $b - 1 \geqslant 6$; b is a prime number less than 20.

9. $1 < z < 50$; z is a square number.

10. Given that $-4 \leqslant a \leqslant 3$ and $-5 \leqslant b \leqslant 4$, find

    a) the largest possible value of a^2

    b) the smallest possible value of ab

    c) the largest possible value of ab

    d) the value of b if $b^2 = 25$.

3.8 Time

Analogue – 12-hour watch

Digital – 24-hour watch

The 24-hour clock

The times which most people use in their everyday lives are times measured from midnight or from mid-day (noon). In the morning 9 o'clock is 9 hours after midnight and is written 9.00 a.m. In the afternoon 4 o'clock is 4 hours after mid-day (noon) and is written 4.00 p.m.

Using the 24-hour clock all times are measured from midnight. This means 9.00 a.m. is written 09:00 and 4.00 p.m. is written 16:00.

Here are three times converted from the 12-hour clock to the 24-hour clock:

a) 8.00 a.m. = 08:00

b) 9.30 p.m. = 21:30

c) 3.15 p.m. = 15:15

a.m. is an abbreviation of ante meridiem and means before mid-day
p.m. is an abbreviation of post meridiem and means after mid-day.

Exercise 17

Write down the following in the 24-hour system.

1. 8.00 a.m.
2. 9.30 p.m.
3. 6.00 p.m.
4. 5.30 a.m.
5. 7.40 p.m.
6. 10.00 p.m.
7. 7.15 p.m.
8. 10.45 p.m.
9. 8.30 a.m.
10. 4.15 a.m.
11. 2.25 a.m.
12. 1.30 p.m.
13. 7.20 p.m.
14. 6.50 a.m.
15. 7.10 a.m.
16. Two minutes before midnight.
17. Two and a half hours before midnight.
18. Five minutes before noon.
19. Three and a half hours after noon.
20. One hour after midnight.
21. One and a half hours before noon.
22. Twenty minutes after midnight
23. Five hours before midnight.
24. Six minutes after noon.
25. Fifty minutes after midnight.

Write the following in the 12-hour system.

26. 07:00
27. 19:30
28. 11:20
29. 04:45
30. 20:30
31. 21:15
32. 09:10
33. 11:45
34. 23:10
35. 20:00
36. 12:00
37. 01:40
38. 04:00
39. 07:07
40. 13:13
41. 12:15
42. 12:30
43. 15:45
44. 16:20
45. 05:16

Time intervals

- Find the time interval between 15:40 and 18:05.
  From 15:40 to 16:00 : 20 minutes (count on to the next hour)
  From 16:00 to 18:05 : 2 hours 5 minutes (count on from 16:00)
  Altogether there is 2 hours 25 minutes.

Exercise 18

Find the number of hours and minutes between the following.

1. 20:10 and 21:20
2. 21:40 and 23:50
3. 22:15 and 23:10
4. 19:30 and 20:05
5. 20:16 and 23:36
6. 11:25 and 13:10

7. 09:40 and 12:00
8. 21:17 and 23:10
9. 23:04 and 23:57
10. 17:45 and 23:10
11. 05:15 and 07:05
12. 11:26 and 14:40
13. 9.50 a.m. and 11.05 a.m.
14. 9.30 a.m. and 2.05 p.m.
15. 11.10 a.m. and 1.30 p.m.
16. 7.30 a.m. and 7.30 p.m.
17. 10.40 a.m. and 12.40 p.m
18. 5.40 a.m. and 1.00 p.m.
19. 11.55 a.m. and 3.10 p.m.
20. 1.35 a.m. and 8.40 a.m.

21. 22:30 on Monday to 03:30 on Tuesday
22. 21:00 on Thursday to 01:40 on Friday
23. 17:30 on Monday to 02:00 on Tuesday
24. 23:45 on Saturday to 02:10 on Sunday
25. 22:50 on Thursday to 07:00 on Friday
26. 07:00 on Friday to 02:00 on Saturday
27. 09:30 on Monday to 04:30 on Tuesday
28. 09:15 on Wednesday to 02:45 on Thursday
29. 22:10 on Friday to 07:35 on Saturday
30. 06:30 on Friday to 16:30 on Saturday

Exercise 19

Here is a timetable for trains from Florence to Rome.

Florence	07:10	08:35	11:35	13:50
Pontassieve	07:35	–	12:00	14:15
Figline Valdarno	07:55	09:21	12:21	–
Bucine	08:16	–	12:42	–
Arezzo	08:36	09:54	13:17	15:08
Orvieto	09:24	10:42	14:07	15:48
Orte	10:01	–	14:53	16:34
Rome	10:27	11:42	15:18	16:59

1. How long does it take the 07:10 from Florence to travel to:
   a) Pontassieve b) Figline Valdarno c) Bucine?
2. At how many stations does the 11:35 from Florence stop?
3. At what time does the 08:35 from Florence reach Arezzo?
4. If you had to be in Rome by 15:30 which train would you catch from Florence?
5. You arrive at Florence at 08:20. How long do you have to wait for the next train to Rome?

6. The 11:35 from Florence runs 10 minutes late. At what time will it reach Bucine?

7. How long does it take the 11:35 from Florence to travel to:

   a) Arezzo b) Orvieto c) Rome?

8. At how many stations does the 08:16 from Bucine stop before it reaches Orte?

9. At what time does the 12:21 from Figline Valdarno reach Orvieto?

10. If you had to be in Rome by 12:00 which train would you catch from Figline Valdarno?

11. You arrive at Florence at 11:08. How long do you have to wait for the next train to Rome?

12. The 08:35 from Florence runs 19 minutes late. At what time will it reach Rome?

3.9 Long multiplication and division

To work out 327×53 we will use the fact that $327 \times 53 = (327 \times 50) + (327 \times 3)$

Set out the working like this.

```
   3 2 7
     5 3 ×
---------
 1 6 3 5 0  →  This is 327 × 50
     9 8 1  →  This is 327 × 3
---------
 1 7 3 3 1  →  This is 327 × 53
---------
   1 1
```

Here is another example.

```
   5 4 1
     8 4 ×
---------
 4 3 2 8 0  →  This is 541 × 80
   2 1 6 4  →  This is 541 × 4
---------
 4 5 4 4 4  →  This is 541 × 84
---------
   1
```

Exercise 20

Work out, without a calculator.

1. 35×23 2. 27×17 3. 26×25
4. 31×43 5. 45×61 6. 52×24
7. 323×14 8. 416×73 9. 504×56

10. 306×28 11. 624×75 12. 839×79

13. 694×83 14. 973×92 15. 415×235

With ordinary 'short' division, we divide and find remainders. The method for 'long' division is really the same but we set it out so that the remainders are easier to find.

Example

Work out $736 \div 32$

$$\begin{array}{r} 23 \\ 32\overline{)736} \\ 64\downarrow \\ \hline 96 \\ 96 \\ \hline 0 \end{array}$$

a) 32 into 73 goes 2 times

b) $2 \times 32 = 64$

c) $73 - 64 = 9$

d) 'bring down' 6

e) 32 into 96 goes 3 times

Exercise 21

Work out, without a calculator:

1. $672 \div 21$ 2. $425 \div 17$ 3. $576 \div 32$

4. $247 \div 19$ 5. $875 \div 25$ 6. $574 \div 26$

7. $806 \div 34$ 8. $748 \div 41$ 9. $666 \div 24$

10. $707 \div 52$ 11. $951 \div 27$ 12. $806 \div 34$

13. $2917 \div 45$ 14. $2735 \div 18$ 15. $56\,274 \div 19$

Exercise 22

Solve each problem without a calculator.

1. Eetu sells 56 bars of chocolate at 84c each. How much does he make altogether?

2. Eggs are packed eighteen to a box.

How many boxes are needed for 828 eggs?

3. Simi makes 146 telephone calls a week. How many does he make in a year?

4. Soraga wants to buy as many 23c stamps as possible. She has $5 to buy them. How many can she buy and how much change is left?
5. How many 49-seater coaches will be needed for a school trip for 366 students?
6. An office building has 24 windows on each of 8 floors. A window cleaner charges 42c for each window. How much is he paid for the whole building?

7. A prize of $238 million was shared equally between 17 people. How much did each person receive?
8. It costs $7905 to hire a plane for a day. A trip is organised for 93 people. How much does each person pay?
9. A farmer finds an oil well on his grounds. The oil comes out of the well at a rate of $15 for every minute of the day and night. How much does he receive in a 24-hour day?

Exercise 23

Each empty square contains either a number or a mathematical symbol (+, −, ×, ÷). Copy each square and fill in the details.

1.

5			→	60
×		÷		
		24	→	44
↓		↓		
	×	$\frac{1}{2}$	→	50

2.

	×	6	→	42
÷		÷		
14	−		→	
↓		↓		
		2	→	1

3.

	×	2	→	38
−		÷		
			→	48
↓		↓		
7	−		→	$6\frac{1}{2}$

4.

17	×		→	170
−		÷		
	÷		→	
↓		↓		
8	−	0.1	→	

5.

0.3	×	20	→	
		−		
11	÷		→	
↓		↓		
11.3	−		→	2.3

6.

	×	50	→	25
−		÷		
		$\frac{1}{2}$	→	0.6
↓		↓		
0.4	×		→	

7.

7	×		→	0.7
÷		×		
	÷		→	
↓		↓		
1.75	+	0.02	→	

8.

	+	8	→	9.4
−				
	×	0.1	→	
↓		↓		
1.3		0.8	→	2.1

9.

	×		→	30
−				
	÷	10	→	0.25
↓		↓		
97.5	+	3	→	

10.

3	÷	2	→	
÷		÷		
8	÷		→	
↓		↓		
	+	$\frac{1}{8}$	→	

11.

	−	$\frac{1}{16}$	→	$\frac{3}{16}$
×				
	÷	4	→	
↓		↓		
$\frac{1}{8}$		$\frac{1}{4}$	→	$\frac{3}{8}$

12.

0.5	−	0.01	→	
		×		
	×		→	35
↓		↓		
4	÷	0.1	→	

13.

	−	1.8	→	3.4
−		÷		
	×		→	
↓		↓		
	+	0.36	→	1

14.

	×	30	→	21
×		−		
	−		→	35
↓		↓		
	−	49	→	

15.

	×	−6	→	72
÷		+		
4	+		→	
↓		↓		
	+	1	→	−2

3.10 Percentages

Example

a) Work out 22% of $40.

$$\frac{22}{100} \times \frac{40}{1} = \frac{880}{100}$$

Answer: $8.80

b) Work out 16% of $85.
[Alternative method]
Since $16\% = \frac{16}{100}$ we can replace 16% by 0.16

So 16% of $\$85 = 0.16 \times 85$
$= \$13.60$

Exercise 24

Work out:

1. 20% of $60 **2.** 10% of $80 **3.** 5% of $200
4. 6% of $50 **5.** 4% of $60 **6.** 30% of $80
7. 9% of $500 **8.** 18% of $400 **9.** 61% of $400
10. 12% of $80 **11.** 6% of $700 **12.** 11% of $800
13. 5% of 160 kg **14.** 20% of 60 kg **15.** 68% of 400 g
16. 15% of 300 m **17.** 2% of 2000 km **18.** 71% of $1000
19. 26% of 19 kg **20.** 1% of 6000 g **21.** 8.5% of $2400

Example

Work out 6.5% of $17.50 correct to the nearest cent.

$$\frac{6.5}{100} \times \frac{17.5}{1} = \frac{113.75}{100}$$

$= \$1.1375$

Answer: $1.14 to the nearest cent.

Exercise 25

Give the answers to the nearest cent where necessary.

1. 4.5% of $6.22 **2.** 17% of $6.84 **3.** 15% of $8.11
4. 17% of $17.07 **5.** 37% of $9.64 **6.** 3.5% of $12.90
7. 8% of $11.64 **8.** 68% of $54.45 **9.** 73% of $23.24
10. 2.5% of $15.20 **11.** 6.3% of $12.50 **12.** 8.2% of $19.50
13. 87% of $15.40 **14.** 80% of $62.50 **15.** 12% of $24.50
16. $12\frac{1}{2}\%$ of $88.50 **17.** $7\frac{1}{2}\%$ of $16.40 **18.** $5\frac{1}{2}\%$ of $80
19. $12\frac{1}{2}\%$ of $90 **20.** 19% of $119.50 **21.** 8.35% of $110

Example 1

A coat originally cost \$24. Calculate the new price after a 5% reduction.

Price reduction = 5% of \$24

$= \frac{5}{100} \times \frac{24}{1} = \$1.20$

New price of coat = \$24 – \$1.20

= \$22.80

Example 2

A CD originally cost \$11.60. Calculate the new price after a 7% increase.

We could work out 7% of \$11.60 as in the example above.

There is, however, a *quicker* way which many people prefer.

If we increase the price by 7% the final price is 107% of the old price.

∴ new price = 107% of \$11.60

$= 1.07 \times 11.6$

= \$12.41 to the nearest cent.

For a 5% *reduction* as in Example 1 we would multiply by 0.95.

Exercise 26

1. Increase a price of \$60 by 5%

2. Reduce a price of \$800 by 8%

3. Reduce a price of \$82.50 by 6%

4. Increase a price of \$65 by 60%

5. Reduce a price of \$2000 by 2%

6. Increase a price of \$440 by 80%

7. Increase a price of \$66 by 100%

8. Reduce a price of \$91.50 by 50%

9. Increase a price of \$88.24 by 25%

10. Reduce a price of \$63 by $33\frac{1}{3}\%$

In the remaining questions give the answers to the nearest cent.

11. Increase a price of \$8.24 by 46%

12. Increase a price of \$7.65 by 24%

13. Increase a price of \$5.61 by 31%

14. Reduce a price of \$8.99 by 22%

15. Increase a price of \$11.12 by 11%

16. Reduce a price of \$17.62 by 4%

17. Increase a price of \$28.20 by 13%

18. Increase a price of \$8.55 by $5\frac{1}{2}\%$

19. Reduce a price of \$9.60 by $7\frac{1}{2}\%$

20. Increase a price of \$12.80 by $10\frac{1}{2}\%$

Exercise 27

1. In a sale a shop reduces all its prices by 20%.
Find the sale price of a sari which previously cost \$44.

2. The price of a car was \$5400 but it is increased by 6%.
What is the new price?

3. The price of a small Persian rug was $245 but it has been reduced by 30%. What is the new price?
4. A music shop offers a 7% discount for cash. How much does a cash-paying customer pay for a CD advertised at $9.50?
5. A rabbit weighs 2.8 kg. After eating, its weight is increased by 1%. How much does it weigh now?
6. The insurance premium for a car is normally $90. With a 'no-claim bonus' the premium is reduced by 35%. What is the reduced premium?
7. The population of a town increased by 32% between 1975 and 2015. If there were 45 000 people in 1975, what was the 2015 population?
8. A restaurant adds a 12% 'service charge' onto the basic price of meals. How much do I pay for a meal with a basic price of $8.50?
9. A new-born baby weighs 3.1 kg. Her weight increases by 8% over the next two weeks. What does she weigh then?
10. At the beginning of the year a car is valued at $3250. During the year its value falls by 15%. How much is it worth at the end of the year?

Exercise 28

In Questions **1** to **4** find the total bill.

1. 2 hammers at $5.30 each
   50 screws at 25c for 10
   5 bulbs at 38c each
   1 tape measure at $1.15
   Tax at 17.5% is added to the total cost.

2. 5 litres of oil at 85c per litre
   3 spanners at $1.25 each
   2 manuals at $4.30 each
   200 bolts at 90c for 10
   Tax at 17.5% is added to the total cost.

3. 12 exercise books at $3.70 each
   3 erasers at $0.55 each
   2 rulers at $2.40 each
   1 calculator at $15.50
   Tax at 17.5% is added to the total cost.

4. 5 golf clubs at $12.45 each
   48 golf balls at $15 per dozen
   100 tees at 1c each
   1 bag at $21.50
   1 umbrella at $12.99
   Tax at 17.5% is added to the total cost.

5. In a sale a soft toy priced at $35 is reduced by 20%. At the end of the week the *sale price* is reduced by a further 25%. Calculate:
   a) the price in the original sale
   b) the final price.
6. a) In 2015 a club has 40 members who each pay $120 per year. What is the total income from the members?
   b) In 2016 the fee is increased by 35% and the membership increases to 65.
      i) What is the 2016 fee?
      ii) What is the total income from the members in 2016?

Simple interest

When a sum of money $\$P$ is invested for T years at $R\%$ interest per annum (each year), then the interest gained, I, is given by:

$$I = \frac{P \times R \times T}{100}$$

This is known as simple interest.

Example

Joel invests $400 for 6 months at 5%.
Work out the simple interest gained.

$P = \$400 \qquad R = 5 \qquad T = 0.5 \qquad$ (6 months is half a year)

$$\text{so } I = \frac{400 \times 5 \times 0.5}{100}$$

$$I = \$10$$

Exercise 29

1. Calculate:
   a) the simple interest on $1200 for 3 years at 6% per annum
   b) the simple interest on $700 at 8.25% per annum for 2 years
   c) the length of time for $5000 to earn $1000 if invested at 10% per annum
   d) the length of time for $400 to earn $160 if invested at 8% per annum.
2. Khalid invests $6750 at 8.5% per annum. How much interest has he earned and what is the total amount in his account after 4 years?
3. Petra invests $10 800. After 4 years she has earned $3240 in interest. At what annual rate of interest did she invest her money?

Compound interest

Suppose a bank pays fixed interest of 10% on money in deposit accounts. A man puts \$500 in the bank.

After one year he has

\$500 + 10% of \$500 = \$550

After two years he has

\$550 + 10% of \$550 = \$605

[Check that this is $1.10^2 \times 500$]

After three years he has

\$605 + 10% of \$605 = \$665.50

[Check that this is $1.10^3 \times 500$]

Exercise 30

1. A bank pays interest of 9%.

Sabira puts \$2000 in the bank. How much has she after

a) one year **b)** two years **c)** three years?

2. A bank pays interest of 11%. Jorge puts \$5000 in the bank. How much has he after

a) one year **b)** three years **c)** five years?

3. A student gets a grant of \$10 000 a year. Assuming her grant is increased by 7% each year, what will her grant be in four years' time?

4. Isoke's salary in 2012 is \$30 000 per year. Every year her salary is increased by 5%.

In 2013 her salary was $30\,000 \times 1.05$ = \$31 500

In 2014 her salary was $30\,000 \times 1.05 \times 1.05$ = \$33 075

In 2015 her salary was $30\,000 \times 1.05 \times 1.05 \times 1.05$ = \$34 728.75

And so on.

a) What will her salary be in 2016?

b) What will her salary be in 2018?

5. The rental price of a dacha was \$9000 in 2015. At the end of each month the price is increased by 6%.

a) Find the price of the house after 1 month.

b) Find the price of the house after 3 months.

c) Find the price of the house after 10 months.

6. Assuming an average inflation rate of 8%, work out the probable cost of the following items in 10 years:

   a) motor bike \$6500 **b)** iPod \$340 **c)** car \$50 000

7. A new scooter is valued at \$15 000. At the end of each year its value is reduced by 15% of its value at the start of the year. What will it be worth after 3 years?

Example

Workers generally pay tax on their earnings. Sometimes they are entitled to a *tax free* allowance before paying a percentage tax on the rest of their earnings.

Vivien earns \$42 000 per year and she gets a tax free allowance of \$6000. If she pays 20% tax on the next \$30 000 and 40% on the rest, how much tax does she pay in total?

$\$42\,000 - \$6000 = \$36\,000$

20% of $\$30\,000 = \$30\,000 \div 5 = \$6000$

$\$36\,000 - \$30\,000 = \$6000$

40% of $\$6000 = \$6000 \times 0.4 = \$2400$

Total tax $= \$6000 + \$2400 = \$8400$

Exercise 31

1. Tomas earns \$37 000 per year. He gets a tax free allowance of \$8000 and pays 25% tax on the rest. How much tax will he pay in a year?
2. Juliette earns \$4500 per month. She gets a tax free allowance of \$10 000 per year and pays tax at 20% on the rest. How much tax will she pay in a year?
3. Elise gets a tax free allowance of \$6000 and pays tax at 25% on the next \$20 000. She pays tax at a rate of 30% on the rest. If she earns \$72 000 per year, how much tax must she pay?
4. Johan earns \$650 per week and works 48 weeks a year. If he gets a tax free allowance of \$8000, pays tax at a rate of 10% on the next \$10 000 and 20% on the rest, how much tax will he pay in a year?

3.11 Map scales and ratio

The map below is drawn to a scale of 1 : 50 000. In other words, 1 cm on the map represents 50 000 cm on the land.

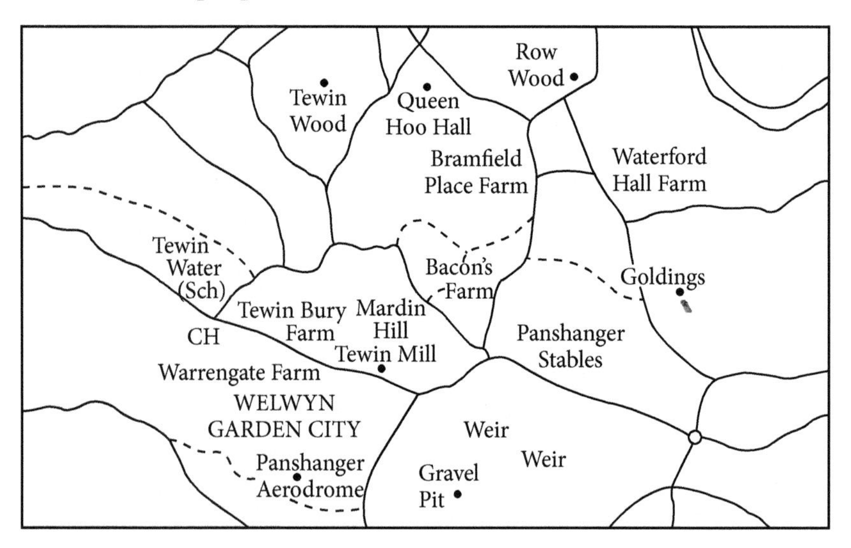

Example

On a map of scale 1:25 000 two towns appear 10 cm apart. What is the actual distance between the towns in km?

1 cm on map = 25 000 cm on land

10 cm on map = 250 000 cm on land

250 000 cm = 2500 m

= 2.5 km

The towns are 2.5 km apart.

Exercise 32

1. The scale of a map is 1 : 1000. Find the actual length in metres represented on the map by 20 cm.
2. The scale of a map is 1 : 10 000. Find the actual length in metres represented on the map by 5 cm.
3. Copy and complete the table.

Map scale	Length on map	Actual length on land
a) 1 : 10 000	10 cm	1 km
b) 1 : 2000	10 cm	m
c) 1 : 25 000	4 cm	km
d) 1 : 10 000	6 cm	km

4. Find the actual distance in metres between two points which are 6.3 cm apart on a map whose scale is 1 : 1000.
5. On a map of scale 1 : 300 000 the distance between Paris and Bonnieres is 8 cm. What is the actual distance in km?
6. A builder's plan is drawn to a scale of 1 cm to 10 m. How long is a road which is 12 cm on the plan?
7. The map on page 107 is drawn to a scale of 1 : 50 000. Make your own measurements to find the actual distance in km between:
   a) Goldings and Tewin Wood (marked •).
   b) Panshanger Aerodrome and Row Wood.
   c) Gravel Pit and Queen Hoo Hall.

Example

The distance between two towns is 18 km.

How far apart will they be on a map of scale 1:50 000?

18 km = 1 800 000 cm

$1\,800\,000 \text{ cm on land} = \frac{1}{50000} \times 1\,800\,000 \text{ cm on map}$

Distance between towns on map = 36 cm

Exercise 33

1. The distance between two towns is 15 km. How far apart will they be on a map of scale 1 : 10 000?
2. The distance between two points is 25 km. How far apart will they be on a map of scale 1 : 20 000?
3. The length of a road is 2.8 km. How long will the road be on a map of scale 1 : 10 000?
4. The length of a reservoir is 5.9 km. How long will it be on a map of scale 1 : 100 000?
5. Copy and complete the table.

Map scale	Actual length on land	Length on map
a) 1:20 000	12 km	cm
b) 1:10 000	8.4 km	cm
c) 1:50 000	28 km	cm
d) 1:40 000	56 km	cm
e) 1:5000	5 km	cm

6. The scale of a drawing is 1 cm to 10 m.
   The length of a wall is 25 m. What length will the wall be on the drawing?

Ratio

A **ratio** shows the relative size of two or more quantities or values.

> **Example**
>
> Share \$60 in the ratio 2 : 3.
>
> Total number of shares = 2 + 3 = 5
>
> ∴ One share = \$60 ÷ 5 = \$12
>
> ∴ The two amounts are \$24 and \$36.

Exercise 34

1. Share \$30 in the ratio 1 : 2.
2. Share \$60 in the ratio 3 : 1.
3. Divide 880 g of food between a cat and a dog in the ratio 3 : 5.
4. Divide \$1080 between Isobel and Carlota in the ratio 4 : 5.
5. Share 126 litres of petrol between Maya and Tashu in the ratio 2 : 5.
6. Share \$60 in the ratio 1 : 2 : 3.
7. Anwar, Belusa and Nabila divided \$560 between them in the ratio 2 : 1 : 5. How much did Belusa receive?
8. A sum of \$120 is divided in the ratio 3 : 4 : 5. What is the largest share?
9. At an election 7800 people voted Democrats, Socialists or Republicans in the ratio 4 : 3 : 5. How many people voted Republicans?

Example

In a class, the ratio of boys to girls is 3 : 4.

If there are 9 boys, how many girls are there?

boys : girls = 3 : 4

Multiply both parts by 3.

boys : girls = 9 : 12

So there are 9 boys and 12 girls.

Exercise 35

1. In a room, the ratio of boys to girls is 3 : 2.
   If there are 12 boys, how many girls are there?
2. In a room, the ratio of men to women is 4 : 1.
   If there are 20 men, how many women are there?
3. In a box, the ratio of nails to screws is 5 : 3.
   If there are 15 nails, how many screws are there?
4. An alloy consists of copper, zinc and tin in the ratio 1 : 3 : 4.
   If there is 10 g of copper in the alloy, find the mass of zinc and tin.
5. In a shop the ratio of oranges to apples is 2 : 5.
   If there are 60 apples, how many oranges are there?
6. A recipe for 5 people calls for 1.5 kg of meat. How much meat is required if the recipe is adapted to feed 8 people?
7. A cake for 6 people requires 4 eggs. How many eggs are needed to make a cake big enough for 9 people?
8. A photocopier enlarges the original in the ratio 2 : 3.
   The height of a tree is 12 cm on the original.
   How tall is the tree on the enlarged copy?

original

enlarged copy

9. A photocopier enlarges copies in the ratio 4 : 5. The length of the headline 'BRIDGE COLLAPSES' is 18 cm on the original.
   How long is the headline on the enlarged copy?

10. A photocopier *reduces* in the ratio 5 : 3. The height of a tower is 12 cm on the original. How tall is the tower on the reduced copy?

11. A cake weighing 550 g has three ingredients: flour, sugar and butter. There is twice as much flour as sugar and one and a half times as much sugar as butter. How much flour is there?

12. If $\frac{5}{8}$ of the children in a school are boys, what is the ratio of boys to girls?

13. A man and a woman share $1000 between them in the ratio 1 : 4. The woman shares her part between herself, her mother and her daughter in the ratio 2 : 1 : 1. How much does her daughter receive?

14. The number of pages in a newspaper is increased from 36 to 54. The price is increased in the same ratio. If the old price was 28c, what will the new price be?

15. Two friends bought a house for $220 000. Sam paid $140 000 and Joe paid the rest. Three years later they sold the house for $275 000. How much should Sam receive from the sale?

16. Concrete is made from 1 part cement, 2 parts sand and 5 parts aggregate. How much cement is needed to make 2 m^3 of concrete?

3.12 Proportion

Example 1

If 11 litres of petrol cost $20.46, find the cost of 27 litres.

The cost of petrol is *directly* proportional to the quantity bought.

11 litres cost $20.46
$\therefore$ 1 litre costs $20.46 ÷ 11 = $1.86
$\therefore$ 27 litres cost $1.86 × 27
= $50.22

Example 2

A farmer has enough hay to feed 5 horses for 6 days. How long would the hay last for 3 horses?

The length of time for which the horses can be fed is *inversely* proportional to the number of horses to be fed.

5 horses can be fed for 6 days
$\therefore$ 1 horse can be fed for 30 days
$\therefore$ 3 horses can be fed for 10 days.

In the first example above it was helpful to work out the cost of *one* litre of petrol.

In the second example we found the time for which *one* horse could be fed.

To do these questions you need to think logically.

- If five men can paint a tower in 10 days, how long would it take one man?
- If 33 books cost $280.50, how much will one book cost?

Exercise 36

The first seven questions involve *direct* proportion.

The last seven questions involve *inverse* proportion.

1. If 5 pizzas cost $20, find the cost of 7 pizzas.
2. Magazines cost $16 for 8. Find the cost of 3 magazines.
3. Find the cost of 2 cakes if 7 cakes cost $10.50.
4. A machine fills 1000 bottles in 5 minutes.
   How many bottles will it fill in 2 minutes?
5. A train travels 100 km in 20 minutes.
   How long will it take to travel 50 km?
6. Eleven pens cost $13.20. Find the cost of 4 pens.
7. Fishing line costs $1.40 for 50 m. Find the cost of 300 m.
8. If 12 men can build a house in 6 days, how long will it take 6 men?
9. Six women can dig a hole in 4 hours. How long would it take 2 women to dig the same hole?
10. A farmer has enough hay to feed 20 horses for 3 days. How long would the hay last for 60 horses?

11. Twelve people can clean an office building in 3 hours. How long would it take 4 people?
12. Usually it takes 12 hours for 8 men to do a job. How many men are needed to do the same job in 4 hours?
13. Five teachers can mark 60 exam papers in 4 hours. How long would it take one teacher to mark all 60 papers?
14. 10 ladybirds eat 400 greenflies in 3 hours.

    Copy and complete the following:

    a) 20 ladybirds eat * greenflies in 3 hours.

    b) 20 ladybirds eat * greenflies in 9 hours.

    c) 10 ladybirds eat 200 greenflies in * hours.

    d) * ladybirds eat 4000 greenflies in 3 hours.

Exercise 37

1. If 7 packets of coffee cost \$8.54, find the cost of 3 packets.
2. Find the cost of 8 bottles of cola, given that 5 bottles cost \$11.90.
3. If 7 cartons of milk hold 14 litres, find how much milk there is in 6 cartons.
4. 5 builders took 6 hours to dig a trench. How long would it have taken 3 builders to dig an identical trench?
5. 10 people exploring a desert took enough water to last 5 days. How long would the water have lasted if there had been only 5 people?
6. A worker takes 8 minutes to make 2 circuit boards. How long would it take to make 7 circuit boards?
7. On a rose bush there are enough greenflies to last 9 ladybirds 4 hours. How long would the greenflies last if there were only 6 ladybirds?
8. The total weight of 8 tiles is 1720 g. How much do 17 tiles weigh?
9. A machine can fill 3000 bottles in 15 minutes. How many bottles will it fill in 2 minutes?
10. A train travels 40 km in 120 minutes. How long will it take to travel 55 km at the same speed?
11. If 4 grapefruit can be bought for \$2.96, how many can be bought for \$8.14?

12. \$15 can be exchanged for £9.74. How many British pounds can be exchanged for \$37.50?
13. Usually it takes 10 hours for 4 men to build a wall. How many men are needed to build the same wall in 8 hours?
14. A car travels 280 km on 35 litres of petrol. How much petrol is needed for a journey of 440 km?
15. Ten bags of corn will feed 60 hens for 3 days. Copy and complete the following:
    - **a)** 30 bags of corn will feed $*$ hens for 3 days.
    - **b)** 10 bags of corn will feed 20 hens for $*$ days.
    - **c)** 10 bags of corn will feed $*$ hens for 18 days.
    - **d)** 30 bags of corn will feed 90 hens for $*$ days.

16. Four machines produce 5000 batteries in 10 hours. How many batteries would 6 machines produce in 10 hours?

17. Newtonian spiders can spin webs in straight lines. If 15 spiders can spin a web of length 1 metre in 30 minutes, how long will it take 6 spiders to spin a web of the same length?

18. It takes b beavers n hours to build a dam. How long will it take half the beavers to build the same size dam?

Foreign exchange

Money is changed from one currency into another using the method of proportion.

Exchange rate for US dollars ($):

Country	*Rate of exchange*
Argentina (pesos)	$1 = 3.79 ARS
Australia (dollar)	$1 = 1.13 AUD
Eurozone (euros)	$1 = €0.70 EUR
India (rupees)	$1 = 46.50 INR
Japan (yen)	$1 = 91.20 JPY
Kuwait (dinars)	$1 = 0.29 KWD
UK (pounds)	$1 = £0.63 GBP

Example

Convert: **a)** $22.50 to dinars **b)** €300 to dollars.

a) $1 = 0.29 dinars (KWD)

so $22.50 = 0.29 × 22.50 KWD

= 6.53 KWD

b) €0.70 = $1

so €1 = $\frac{1}{0.70}$

so €300 = $\$\frac{1}{0.70} \times 300$

= $428.57

Exercise 38

Give your answers correct to two decimal places. Use the exchange rates given above.

1. Change the amount of dollars into the foreign currency stated.

a) $20 [euros] **b)** $70 [pounds]

c) $200 [pesos] **d)** $1.50 [rupees]

e) $2.30 [yen] **f)** 90c [dinars]

2. Change the amount of foreign currency into dollars.

   a) €500 **b)** £2500

   c) 7.50 rupees **d)** 900 dinars

   e) 125.24 pesos **f)** 750 AUD

3. A CD costs £9.50 in London and \$9.70 in Chicago. How much cheaper, in British money, is the CD when bought in the US?

4. An MP3 player costs €20.46 in Spain and £12.60 in the UK. Which is the cheaper in dollars, and by how much?

5. The monthly rent of a flat in New Delhi is 32 860 rupees. How much is this in euros?

6. A Persian kitten is sold in several countries at the prices given below.

   Kuwait 150 dinars

   France 550 euros

   Japan 92 000 yen

   Write out in order a list of the prices converted into GBP.

7. An Australian in Germany has 700 AUD. If he changes the money, how many euros will he receive?

3.13 Speed, distance and time

Calculations involving these three quantities are simpler when the speed is *constant*. The formulae connecting the quantities are as follows:

a) distance = speed × time

b) $\text{speed} = \dfrac{\text{distance}}{\text{time}}$

c) $\text{time} = \dfrac{\text{distance}}{\text{speed}}$

A helpful way of remembering these formulae is to write the letters D, S and T in a triangle,

thus:

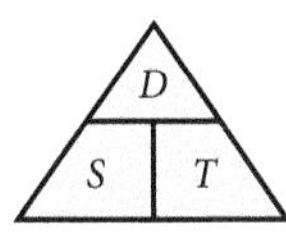

to find D, cover D and we have ST

to find S, cover S and we have $\dfrac{D}{T}$

to find T, cover T and we have $\dfrac{D}{S}$

Great care must be taken with the units in these questions.

Example 1

A man is running at a speed of 8 km/h for a distance of 5200 metres. Find the time taken in minutes.

5200 metres = 5.2 km

$$\text{time taken in hours} = \left(\frac{D}{S}\right) = \frac{5.2}{8}$$

$$= 0.65 \text{ hours}$$

$$\text{time taken in minutes} = 0.65 \times 60$$

$$= 39 \text{ minutes}$$

Example 2

Change the units of a speed of 54 km/h into metres per second.

54 km/hour = 54 000 metres/hour

$$= \frac{54000}{60} \text{ metres/minute}$$

$$= \frac{54000}{60 \times 60} \text{ metres/second}$$

$$= 15 \text{ m/s}$$

Exercise 39

1. Find the time taken for the following journeys:

a) 100 km at a speed of 40 km/h

b) 250 miles at a speed of 80 miles per hour

c) 15 metres at a speed of 20 cm/s (answer in seconds)

d) 10^4 metres at a speed of 2.5 km/h

2. Change the units of the following speeds as indicated:

a) 72 km/h into m/s

b) 108 km/h into m/s

c) 300 km/h into m/s

d) 30 m/s into km/h

e) 22 m/s into km/h

f) 0.012 m/s into cm/s

g) 9000 cm/s into m/s

h) 600 miles/day into miles per hour

3. Find the speeds of the bodies which move as follows:

a) a distance of 600 km in 8 hours

b) a distance of 31.64 km in 7 hours

c) a distance of 136.8 m in 18 seconds

d) a distance of 4×10^4 m in 100 seconds

e) a distance of 5×10^5 cm in 5 seconds

f) a distance of 10^8 mm in 30 minutes (in km/h)

g) a distance of 500 m in 10 minutes (in km/h)

4. Find the distance travelled (in metres) in the following:

a) at a speed of 55 km/h for 2 hours

b) at a speed of 40 km/h for $\frac{1}{4}$ hour

c) at a speed of 338.4 km/h for 10 minutes

d) at a speed of 15 m/s for 5 minutes

e) at a speed of 14 m/s for 1 hour

f) at a speed of 4×10^3 m/s for 400 seconds

g) at a speed of 8×10^5 cm/s for 2 minutes

5. A car travels 60 km at 30 km/h and then a further 180 km at 160 km/h. Find:

a) the total time taken

b) the average speed for the whole journey.

6. A cyclist travels 25 kilometres at 20 km/h and then a further 80 kilometres at 25 km/h. Find:

a) the total time taken

b) the average speed for the whole journey.
[Work out (total distance travelled) ÷ (time taken)]

7. A swallow flies at a speed of 50 km/h for 3 hours and then at a speed of 40 km/h for a further 2 hours. Find the average speed for the whole journey.

Example

Speed is a common measure of *rate*. A speed given in kilometres *per* hour tells us how many kilometres we travel in one hour. Other common measures of rate include litres *per* minute, when filling a bath with water, for example, and kilowatt hours *per* day when measuring energy consumption.

Exercise 40

1. Find the following rates in the units given:

a) 4 litres in 5 minutes (litres per minute)

b) 12 litres in 45 minutes (litres per hour)

c) 78 litres in 12 minutes (litres per hour)

   d) 800 kilowatt hours in 2 months (kilowatt hours per year)
   e) 12 kilowatt hours in 3 days (kilowatt hours per year)

2. Find the time taken (in minutes) to fill the following containers:
   a) a 3 litre bowl at a rate of 2 litres per minute.
   b) a 30 litre bucket at a rate of 0.2 litres per second.
   c) a 120 litre hot water tank at a rate of 80 litres per hour.
   d) a 300 ml beaker at a rate of 0.5 litres per hour.

3. A bath is filled with 80 litres of water in 6 minutes. Find the rate at which it is being filled.

4. A typical household uses 4600 kilowatt hours of energy in a year. Find the rate at which the household uses energy in kilowatt hours per day.

5. Water is dripping from a tap at a rate of 5 millilitres per second. How long will it take, in minutes, to fill a bowl with a capacity of 2.5 litres? (Give your answer in days.)

6. A rain butt with a capacity of 60 litres fills completely with water each day.
   a) Find the rate of fill in millilitres per hour.
   b) A gardener can use all of the water to hose his garden in 15 minutes. Find the rate of flow of the water from the hose in millilitres per second.

3.14 Approximations

A car travels a distance of 158 km in $3\frac{1}{2}$ hours. What is the average speed?

$$\text{speed} = \frac{\text{distance}}{\text{time}} = \frac{158}{3.5}$$

On a calculator the answer is 45.142 857 14 km/h.
It is not sensible to give all these figures in the answer. We have used a distance and a time which may not be all that accurate. It would be reasonable to give the answer as '45 km/h'.

We can approximate in two ways:

a) we can give *significant figures* (s.f.)

b) we can give *decimal places* (d.p.)

Each type of approximation is described below.

Significant figures

Example

Write the following numbers correct to three significant figures (3 s.f.).

a) 2.6582 = 2.66 (to 3 s.f.)
↑

b) 0.5142 = 0.514 (to 3 s.f.)
↑

c) 84 660 = 84 700 (to 3 s.f.)
↑

d) 0.04031 = 0.0403 (to 3 s.f.)
↑

In each case we look at the number marked with an arrow to see if it is 'five or more'.

Exercise 41

In Questions **1** to **8** write the numbers correct to three significant figures.

1. 2.3462	**2.** 0.814 38	**3.** 26.241	**4.** 35.55
5. 112.74	**6.** 210.82	**7.** 0.8254	**8.** 0.031 162

In Questions **9** to **16** write the numbers correct to two significant figures.

9. 5.894	**10.** 1.232	**11.** 0.5456	**12.** 0.7163
13. 0.1443	**14.** 1.831	**15.** 24.83	**16.** 31.37

In Questions **17** to **24** write the numbers correct to four significant figures.

17. 486.72	**18.** 500.36	**19.** 2.8888	**20.** 3.1125
21. 0.071 542	**22.** 3.0405	**23.** 2463.5	**24.** 488 852

In Questions **25** to **36** write the numbers to the degree of accuracy indicated.

25. 0.5126 (3 s.f.)	**26.** 5.821 (2 s.f.)	**27.** 65.89 (2 s.f.)	**28.** 587.55 (4 s.f.)
29. 0.581 (1 s.f.)	**30.** 0.0713 (1 s.f.)	**31.** 5.8354 (3 s.f.)	**32.** 87.84 (2 s.f.)
33. 2482 (2 s.f.)	**34.** 52 666 (3 s.f.)	**35.** 0.0058 (1 s.f.)	**36.** 6568 (1 s.f.)

Decimal places

Example

Write the following numbers correct to two decimal places (2 d.p.).

a) 8.358 = 8.36 (to 2 d.p.)

b) 0.0328 = 0.03 (to 2 d.p.)

c) 74.355 = 74.36 (to 2 d.p.)
↑

In each case we look at the number marked with an arrow to see if it is 'five or more'.
Here we count figures after the decimal point.

Exercise 42

In Questions **1** to **8** write the numbers correct to two decimal places (2 d.p.).

1. 5.381
2. 11.0482
3. 0.414
4. 0.3666
5. 8.015
6. 87.044
7. 9.0062
8. 0.0724

In Questions **9** to **16** write the numbers correct to one decimal place.

9. 8.424
10. 0.7413
11. 0.382
12. 0.095
13. 6.083
14. 19.53
15. 8.111
16. 7.071

In Questions **17** to **28** write the numbers to the degree of accuracy indicated.

17. 8.155 (2 d.p.)
18. 3.042 (1 d.p.)
19. 0.5454 (3 d.p.)
20. 0.005 55 (4 d.p.)
21. 0.7071 (2 d.p.)
22. 6.8271 (2 d.p.)
23. 0.8413 (1 d.p.)
24. 19.646 (2 d.p.)
25. 0.071 35 (4 d.p.)
26. 60.051 (1 d.p.)
27. −7.30 (1 d.p.)
28. −5.424 (2 d.p.)

29. Use a ruler to measure the dimensions of the rectangles below.

a) Write down the length and width in cm correct to 1 d.p.

b) Work out the area of each rectangle and give the answer in cm^2 correct to 1 d.p.

i)

ii)

Exercise 43

Write the answers to the degree of accuracy indicated.

1. 0.153×3.74 (2 d.p.)
2. $18.09 \div 5.24$ (3 s.f.)
3. 184×2.342 (3 s.f.)
4. $17.2 \div 0.89$ (1 d.p.)
5. $58 \div 261$ (2 s.f.)
6. 88.8×44.4 (1 d.p.)
7. $(8.4 - 1.32) \times 7.5$ (2 s.f.)
8. $(121 + 3758) \div 211$ (3 s.f.)
9. $(1.24 - 1.144) \times 0.61$ (3 d.p.)
10. $1 \div 0.935$ (1 d.p.)
11. 78.3524^2 (3 s.f.)
12. $(18.25 - 6.941)^2$ (2 d.p.)
13. $9.245^2 - 65.2$ (1 d.p.)
14. $(2 - 0.666) \div 0.028$ (3 s.f.)
15. 8.43^3 (1 d.p.)
16. $0.924^2 - 0.835^2$ (2 d.p.)

3.15 Metric units

Length	Mass	Volume
10 mm = 1 cm	1000 g = 1 kg	1000 ml = 1 litre
100 cm = 1m	1000 kg = 1 t	1000 l = 1 m^3
1000 m = 1 km	(t for tonne)	Also 1 ml = 1 cm^3

Exercise 44

Copy and complete.

1. 85 cm = m	**2.** 2.4 km = m	**3.** 0.63 m = cm	**4.** 25 cm = m
5. 7 mm = cm	**6.** 2 cm = mm	**7.** 1.2 km = m	**8.** 7 m = cm
9. 0.58 km = m	**10.** 815 mm = m	**11.** 650 m = km	**12.** 25 mm = cm
13. 5 kg = g	**14.** 4.2 kg = g	**15.** 6.4 kg = g	**16.** 3 kg = g
17. 0.8 kg = g	**18.** 400 g = kg	**19.** 2 t = kg	**20.** 250 g = kg
21. 0.5 t = kg	**22.** 0.62 t = kg	**23.** 7 kg = t	**24.** 1500 g = kg
25. 800 ml = l	**26.** 2 l = ml	**27.** 1000 ml = l	**28.** 4.5 l = ml
29. 6 l = ml	**30.** 3 l = cm^3	**31.** 2 m^3 = l	**32.** 5.5 m^3 = l
33. 0.9 l = cm^3	**34.** 600 cm^3 = l	**35.** 15 m^3 = l	**36.** 240 ml = l
37. 28 cm = m	**38.** 5.5 m = cm	**39.** 305 g = kg	**40.** 0.046 km = m
41. 16 ml = l	**42.** 208 mm = m	**43.** 28 mm = cm	**44.** 27 cm = m
45. 788 m = km	**46.** 14 t = kg	**47.** 1.3 kg = g	**48.** 90 l = m^3
49. 2.9 t = kg	**50.** 19 ml = l		

51. Write down the most appropriate metric unit for measuring:

a) the distance between Madrid and Barcelona
b) the capacity of a wine bottle
c) the mass of raisins needed for a cake
d) the diameter of a small drill
e) the mass of a car
f) the area of a football pitch.

Example

A 1 cm by 1 cm square measures 10 mm by 10 mm. The *area* of the square in mm^2 is therefore $10 \times 10 = 100$ mm^2.

1 cm = 10 mm

1 cm = 10 mm

There are similar area conversions for m^2 into cm^2 and km^2 into m^2:

$1 \text{ m}^2 = 100 \times 100 = 10\,000 \text{ cm}^2$

$1 \text{ km}^2 = 1000 \times 1000 = 1\,000\,000 \text{ m}^2$

A 1 cm by 1 cm by 1 cm cube measures 10 mm by 10 mm by 10 mm. The *volume* of the cube is therefore $10 \times 10 \times 10 = 1000\text{ mm}^3$.

1 cm = 10 mm

1 cm = 10 mm

1 cm = 10 mm

Likewise, $1\text{ m}^3 = 100 \times 100 \times 100 = 1\,000\,000\text{ cm}^3$

Exercise 45

Copy and complete.

1. $2\text{ cm}^2 = \quad\text{mm}^2$

2. $45\text{ cm}^2 = \quad\text{mm}^2$

3. $1600\text{ mm}^2 = \quad\text{cm}^2$

4. $48\text{ mm}^2 = \quad\text{cm}^2$

5. $3\text{ m}^2 = \quad\text{cm}^2$

6. $26\text{ m}^2 = \quad\text{cm}^2$

7. $8600\text{ cm}^2 = \quad\text{m}^2$

8. $760\text{ cm}^2 = \quad\text{m}^2$

9. $5\text{ km}^2 = \quad\text{m}^2$

10. $4\,500\,000\text{ m}^2 = \quad\text{km}^2$

11. $8\text{ cm}^3 = \quad\text{mm}^3$

12. $21\text{ cm}^3 = \quad\text{mm}^3$

13. $48\,000\text{ mm}^3 = \quad\text{cm}^3$

14. $6\text{ m}^3 = \quad\text{cm}^3$

15. $28\,000\,000\text{ cm}^3 = \quad\text{m}^3$

Exercise 46

A school has a machine that can produce centimetre cubes.

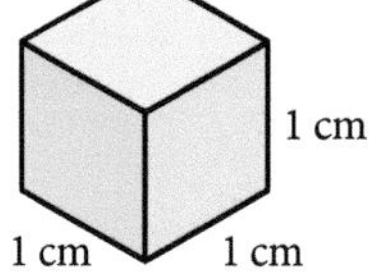

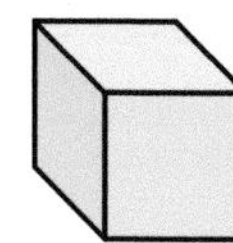

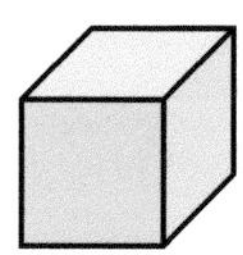

At the end of the afternoon the teacher, Mrs Evans, has one million cubes.

1. The million cubes could be stuck together with super glue to make a tower.
   Would the tower be as tall as:
   a) Nelson's Column
   b) The Empire State Building
   c) Mount Everest?
   [Use the internet to find the relevant heights.]

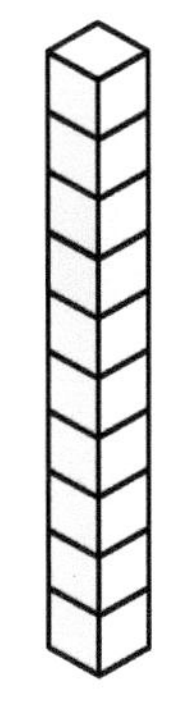

2. If the cubes were placed in a single layer, would there be enough to cover:
   a) the floor of your classroom
   b) a football pitch?

3. If the cubes were in a solid mass, would there be enough:
   a) to fill your classroom
   b) to fill a large fridge-freezer?

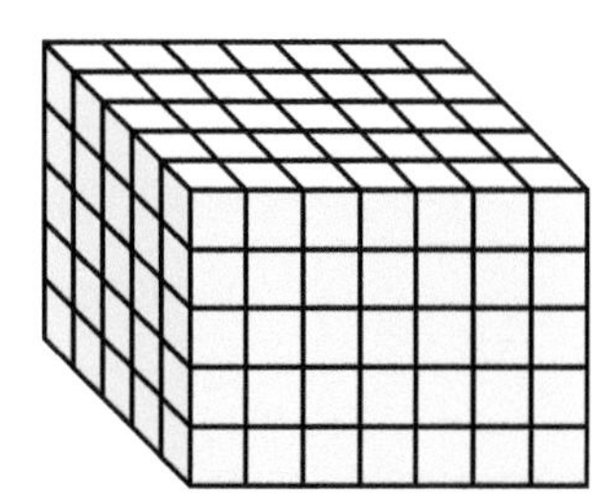

4. Mrs Evans sets out to make a *billion* of the cubes [1 000 000 000].
   a) Would that be enough to fill your classroom?
   b) Placed side by side, roughly how many times would they go around the London ring road (184 km)?

3.16 Problems 1

Making a profit

Example

A shopkeeper buys potatoes at a wholesale price of \$180 per tonne and sells them at a retail price of 22c per kg.

How much profit does he make on one kilogram of potatoes?

He pays \$180 for 1000 kg of potatoes. $\therefore$ he pays \$[180 ÷ 1000] for 1 kg of potatoes.

i.e. he pays 18c for 1 kg

He sells at 22c per kg.

$\therefore$ profit = 4c per kg

Exercise 47

Find the profit in each case.

Commodity	Retail price	Wholesale price	Profit
1. cans of drink	15c each	\$11 per 100	profit per can?
2. rulers	24c each	\$130 per 1000	profit per ruler?
3. pencils	22c each	\$13 per 100	profit per pencil?
4. cans of soup	\$0.27 each	\$8.50 for 50 cans	profit per can?
5. newspapers	22c each	\$36 for 200	profit per newspaper?
6. bars of chocolate	\$0.37 each	\$15.20 for 80	profit per bar?
7. rice	22c per kg	\$160 per tonne	profit per kg?
8. carrots	38c per kg	\$250 per tonne	profit per kg?
9. T-shirts	\$4.95 each	\$38.40 per dozen	profit per T-shirt?
10. eggs	96c per dozen	\$60 per 1200	profit per dozen?
11. lychees	5 for 30c	\$14 for 400	profit per lychee?
12. calculators	\$19.50 each	\$2450 for 200	profit per calculator?
13. fruit juice	55c for 100 ml	\$40 for 10 litres	profit per 100 ml?
14. couscous	\$16 per kg	\$11 000 per tonne	profit per kg?
15. wire	23c per m	\$700 for 10 km	profit per m?
16. cheese	\$2.64 per kg	\$87.50 for 50 kg	profit per kg?
17. string	46c per m	\$160 for 500 m	profit per m?
18. apples	9c each	\$10.08 for 144	profit per apple?
19. grass	\$6.80 per m^2	\$1600 for 500 m^2	profit per m^2?
20. tins of paint	33c per tin	\$72 for 400 tins	profit per tin?

Exercise 48

1. There are 1128 students in a school and there are 36 more girls than boys. How many girls attend the school?
2. A teacher decides to award 1c to the person coming 10th in a test, 2c to the person coming 9th, 4c to the person coming 8th and so on, doubling the amount each time. How much does the teacher award to the person who came 1st?
3. A tree was planted when James Wilkinson was born. He died in 1960, aged 75. How old was the tree in 2015?
4. Washing-up liquid is sold in 200 ml containers. Each container costs 57c. How much will it cost to buy 10 litres of the liquid?

5. A train was supposed to leave Rome at 11:24 and arrive in Milan at 12:40. The train arrived $2\frac{1}{4}$ hours late.
At what time did the train arrive?

6. A clock was stopped for repairs at 17:15 on Tuesday and restarted at 08:20 on Wednesday.
For how long had it been stopped?

7. How much would I pay for nine litres of cola if two litres cost $2.30?

8. A games console was advertised at $282.50 for cash, or in 12 equal instalments of $25.30.
How much would be saved by paying cash?

9. Eggs are packed in boxes of 12. A farmer has enough eggs to fill 316 boxes and he has 62 cracked eggs left over. How many eggs had he to start with?

10. A car travels 9 km on a litre of petrol and petrol costs $1.68 per litre.
Over a period of one year the car travels a distance of 9600 km.
How much does the petrol cost for the whole year?

11. Two bands, 'Inferno' and 'Hotplay', tour Japan. The bar chart shows how many people watched each concert.

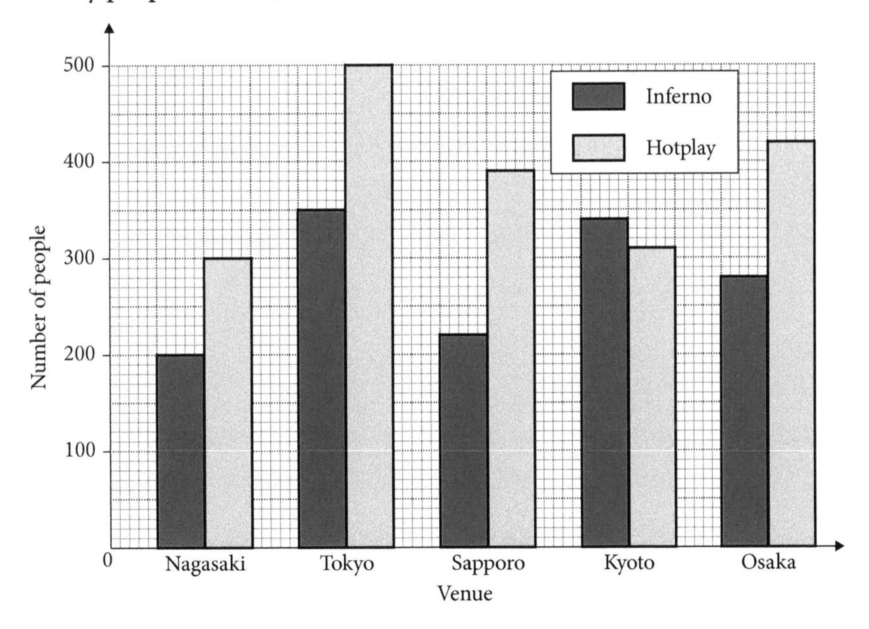

a) How many people watched 'Inferno' in:

i) Tokyo **ii)** Kyoto **iii)** Osaka?

b) Where did 310 people watch 'Hotplay'?

c) In which place did more people watch 'Inferno' than 'Hotplay'?

d) How many *more* people watched 'Hotplay' than 'Inferno' in Nagasaki?

e) How many *more* people watched 'Hotplay' than 'Inferno' in Osaka?

f) What is the total number of people who watched 'Hotplay' in all five venues?

Exercise 49

1. Copy and complete the following bill.

$6\frac{1}{2}$ kg of potatoes at 50c per kg = \$

4 kg of beef at ____ per kg = \$7.20

____ jars of coffee at 95c per jar = \$6.65

Total = \$

2. A hotel manager buys loaves of bread at \$4.44 per dozen. The shop price is 43c per loaf. How much does he save on each loaf? (A 'dozen' means 12.)

3. John Lowe made darts history in 1984 with the first ever perfect game played in a tournament, 501 scored in just nine darts. He won a special prize of \$100 000. His first eight darts were six treble 20s, treble 17 and treble 18.

a) What did he score with the ninth dart?

b) How much did he win per dart thrown, to the nearest dollar?

4. How many 50 ml bottles can be filled from a jar containing 7 litres of liquid?

5. Find two numbers which multiply together to give 60 and which add up to 19.

6. The number z is greater than 10 and the number m is less than 8. Arrange the numbers 9, z and m in order of size, starting with the smallest.

7. One day a third of the class is absent and 16 children are present. How many children are in the class when no one is absent?

8. A boat leaves Antigua at 09:00 and travels towards St. Lucia at 60 km/h. Another boat leaves St. Lucia for Antigua, also at 09:00, and travels at 75 km/h. Which boat is nearer to St. Lucia when they meet?

9. A man is 35 cm taller than his daughter, who is 5 cm shorter than her mother. The man is 1.80 m tall. How tall is his wife?

10. In a simple code A = 1, B = 2, C = 3, . . . Z = 26. Decode the following messages.

   a) 23, 8, 1, 20

   20, 9, 13, 5

   4, 15

   23, 5

   6, 9, 14, 9, 19, 8.

   b) 19, 4^2, (3×7), 18, $(90 - 71)$

   1^3 (9×2), $(2^2 + 1^2)$

   18, $(\frac{1}{5}$ of 105), 2, $(1 \div \frac{1}{2})$, 3^2, 19, 2^3.

   c) 23, $(100 \div 20)$

   1,$(2 \times 3 \times 3)$, $(2^2 + 1^2)$

   21, $(100 - 86)$, $(100 \div 25)$, 5, $(2^4 + 2)$

   1, (5×4), $(10 \div \frac{1}{2})$, 1, $(27 \div 9)$, $(99 \div 9)$.

Exercise 50

1. Twelve calculators cost \$102. How many calculators could be bought for \$76.50?

2. A car travels 35 m in 0.7 seconds. How far does it travel in

   a) 0.1 s **b)** 1 s **c)** 2 minutes?

3. A shape is shown below.

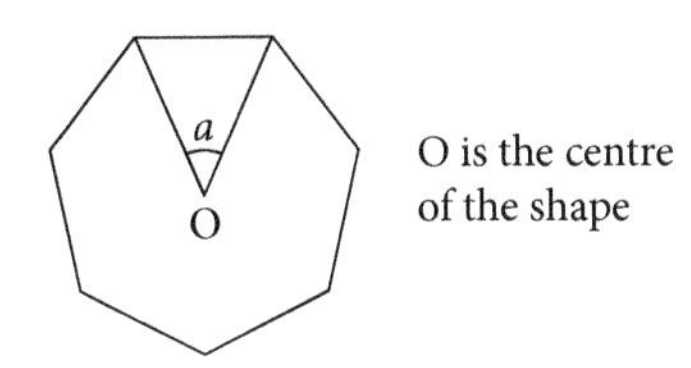

O is the centre of the shape

Calculate the size of the angle, a, to the nearest $\frac{1}{10}$ of a degree.

4. The diagram below shows the map of a farm which grows four different crops in the regions shown.

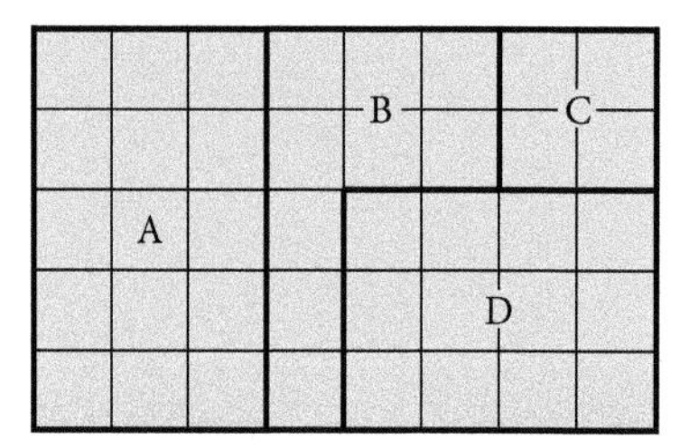

Each square represents one hectare.

a) What is the total area of the farm?

b) What area is used for crop A?

c) What percentage of the farm is used for

i) crop C ii) crop D

iii) crop A iv) crop B?

5. An examination is marked out of a total of 120 marks. How many marks did Imran get if he scored 65% of the marks?

6. A man worked 7 hours per day from Monday to Friday and 4 hours on Saturday. The rate of pay from Monday to Friday is $4.50 per hour and on Saturday it is $6.75. How much did he earn?

7. Aisha spends 69c a day on sweets. How much does she spend on sweets in a whole year of 365 days?

8. Bjorn buys tennis balls at $3.65 for 10 and sells them at 95c each. How much profit does he make per ball?

9. Five 2's can make 25: $25 = 22 + 2 + \frac{2}{2}$

a) Use four 9's to make 100

b) Use three 6's to make 7

c) Use three 5's to make 60

d) Use five 5's to make 61

e) Use four 7's to make 1

f) Use three 8's to make 11

10. Find the missing digits.

a)

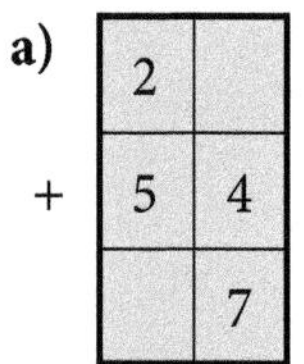

b)

	1	7
+		6
	6	

c)

	5		2
+	1	3	
		1	8

d)

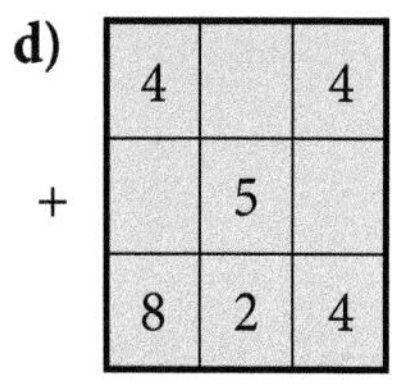

e)

	8	
−		4
	5	2

f)

	8		2
−		5	
	2	3	2

11. The chart below shows the amount of money spent on different items by the average household in New Zealand.

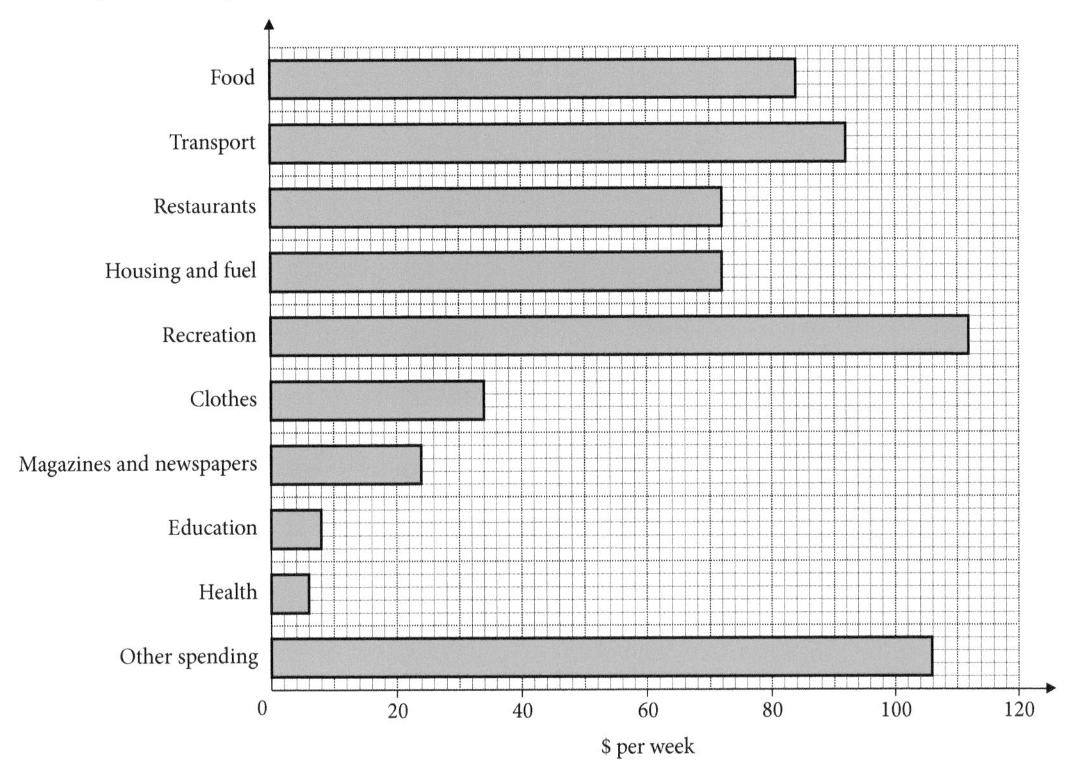

a) How much money was spent on:

i) transport **ii)** education **iii)** clothes?

b) How much *more* money was spent on recreation than on health?

c) What was the total amount of money spent on food and restaurants?

d) What was the total amount spent on everything each week?

Exercise 51

1. A special new cheese is on offer at $3.48 per kilogram. Priti buys half a kilogram. How much change does she receive if she pays with a $5 note?

2. A cup and a saucer together cost $2.80. The cup costs 60c more than the saucer. How much does the cup cost?

3. A garden 9 m by 12 m is to be treated with fertiliser. One cup of fertiliser covers an area of 2 m^2 and one bag of fertiliser gives 18 cups.

a) Find the area of the garden.

b) Find the number of bags of fertiliser needed.

4. Copy and complete the pattern below.

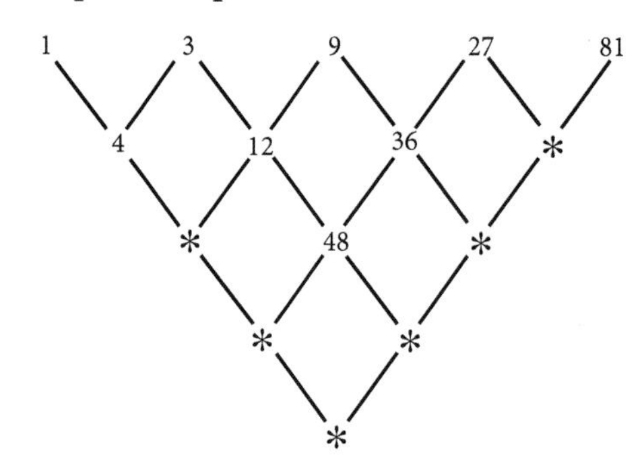

5. Six lamp posts lie at equal distances from each other. If the distance between each pair of lamp posts is 20 m, how far is it from the first lamp post to the sixth?

6. Workers in a company can choose either an 8% increase on their salaries or they can accept a rise of \$3200.

a) A fitter earns \$20 800 a year. Which pay rise should he choose?

b) The manager earns \$46 000 a year. Which pay rise should he choose?

7. A ship's voyage started at 20 : 30 on Tuesday and finished at 07 : 00 on the next day.
How long was the journey in hours and minutes?

8. Work out, without using a calculator:

a) $0.6 - 0.06$ **b)** 0.04×1000

c) $0.4 \div 100$ **d)** $7.2 - 5$

e) 10% of \$90 **f)** 25% of \$160.

9. In 2000 the population of the United States was 281 million. The population was expected to grow by 12% by the end of the century. Find the expected population at the end of the century, correct to the nearest million.

10. Find two numbers which:

a) multiply to give 12 and add up to 7

b) multiply to give 42 and add up to 13

c) multiply to give 32 and add up to 12

d) multiply to give 48 and add up to 26.

Exercise 52

1. In a simple code A = 1, B = 2, C = 3 and so on. When the word 'BAT' is written in code its total score is $(2 + 1 + 20) = 23$.
   a) Find the score for the word 'ZOOM'.
   b) Find the score for the word 'ALPHABET'.
   c) Find a word with a score of 40.
2. How many cubes, each of edge 1 cm, are required to fill a box with internal dimensions 5 cm by 8 cm by 3 cm?
3. A swimming pool 20 m by 12 m contains water to a depth of $1\frac{1}{2}$ m and 1 m^3 of water weighs 1000 kg. What is the weight of the water in the pool?
4. Place the following numbers in order of size, smallest first: 0.12, 0.012, 0.21, 0.021, 0.03.
5. The houses in a street are numbered from 1 to 60. How many times does the number '2' appear?
6. Draw a copy of the square below.

1	2	3	4

   Your task is to fill up all 16 squares using four 1's, four 2's, four 3's and four 4's. Each number may appear only once in any row (↔) or column (↕). The first row has been filled in already.
7. Between the times 11:57 and 12:27 the odometer (distance-counter) of a car changes from 23 793 km to 23 825 km. At what average speed is the car travelling?
8. Which of the shapes below can be drawn without going over any line twice and without taking the pencil from the paper? Write 'yes' or 'no' for each shape.

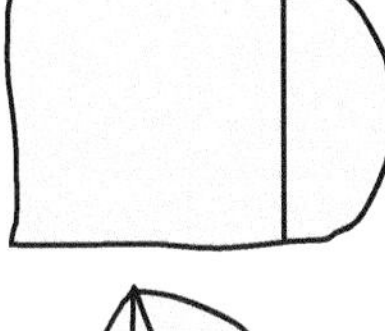

b)
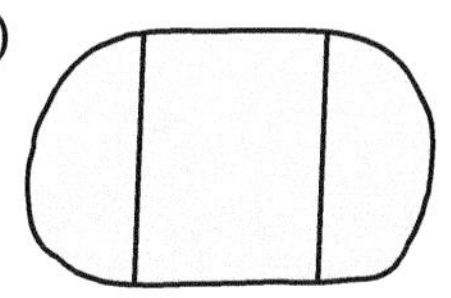

c)
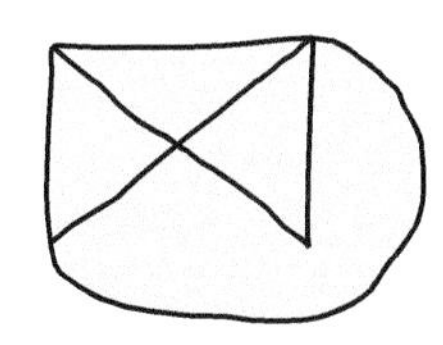

d)
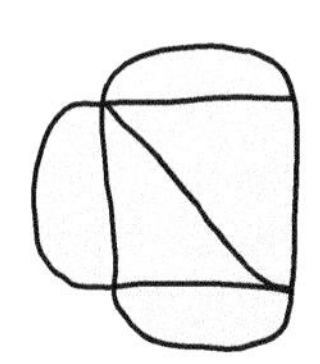

e)

f)

g)

1000 g

Revision exercise 3A

1. A supermarket sells jam in two sizes.

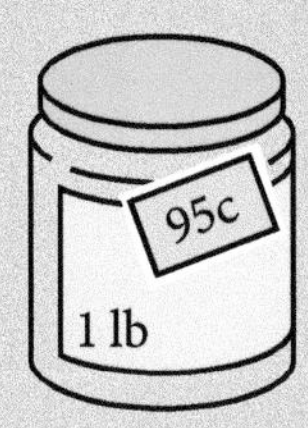

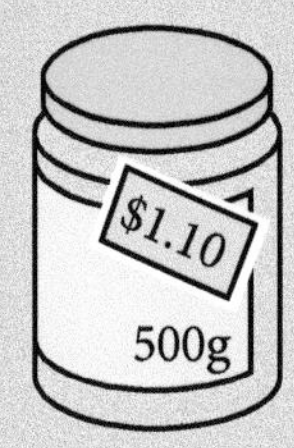

Which jar represents the better value for money? (1 kg = 2.20 lb.)

2. **a)** Calculate the speed (in metres per second) of a slug which moves a distance of 30 cm in 1 minute.

   b) Calculate the time taken for a bullet to travel 8 km at a speed of 5000 m/s.

   c) Calculate the distance flown, in a time of four hours, by a bird which flies at a speed of 12 m/s.

3. The pump shows the price of petrol in a garage.

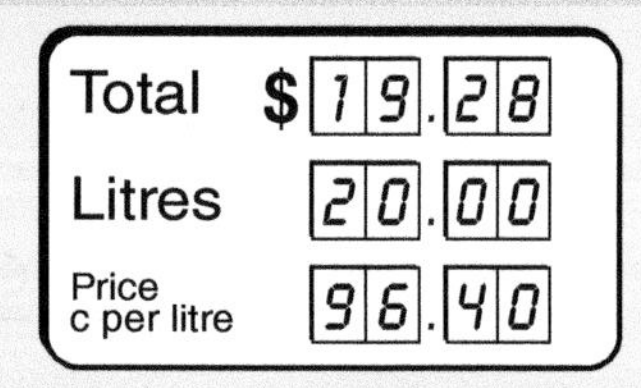

One day I buy $20 worth of petrol: how many litres do I buy?

4. **a)** On a map, the distance between two points is 16 cm. Calculate the scale of the map if the actual distance between the points is 8 km.

   b) On another map, two points are 1.5 cm apart and are actually 60 km apart. Calculate the scale of the map.

5. In December 2015, a factory employed 220 people, each person being paid $650 per week.

   a) Calculate the total weekly wage bill for the factory.

   b) In January 2016, the workforce of 220 was reduced by 10 per cent. Find the number of people employed at the factory after the reduction.

   c) Also in January 2016, the weekly wage of $650 was increased by 10 per cent. Find the new weekly wage.

   d) Calculate the total weekly wage bill for the factory in January 2016.

   e) Calculate the difference between the total weekly wage bills in December 2015 and January 2016.

6. The following are the first six numbers of a pattern.
   4, 13, 28, 49, 76, 109.

   a) Which of these numbers are:

   i) odd numbers

   ii) square numbers

   iii) prime numbers?

   b) The difference between the first and second numbers, 13 – 4, is 9; between the second and the third it is 15, between the third and the fourth it is 21. Work out the difference between

   i) the fourth and the fifth

   ii) the fifth and the sixth.

   c) By considering your answers in part **(b)**, find the seventh and eighth numbers of the pattern.
   Explain how you reached this decision.

d) Use the method you have described to write down the next two terms in the following pattern.
1, 4, 12, 25, 43, 66, —, —.

7. A model of a clock tower is made using a scale of 1 to 20.

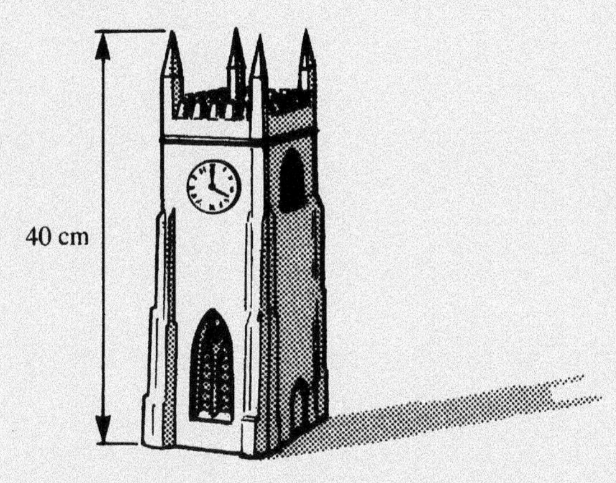

a) The minute hand on the tower clock is 40 cm long. What is the length of the minute hand on the model?

b) The height of the model is 40 cm. What is the height, h, in metres, of the clock tower?

8. A train travels between Milan and Pina, a distance of 108 km, in 45 minutes, at a steady speed. It passes through Rosta 40 minutes after leaving Milan. How far, in km, is it from Rosta to Pina?

9. A school decides to have a disco from 8 p.m. to midnight. The price of the tickets will be $5. The costs are as follows:
Disco and D.J., $250
Hire of hall, $50 an hour
200 cans of soft drinks at $0.50 each
200 packets of crisps at $0.60 each
Printing of tickets, $50

a) What is the total cost of putting on the disco?

b) How many tickets must be sold to cover the cost?

c) If 400 tickets are sold, all the drinks are sold at $0.75 each and all the packets of crisps at $1 each, calculate the profit or loss the school finally makes.

10. Filipe buys 500 marbles at $0.24 each. What change does he receive from $200?

11. Every day at school Omorede buys a roll for 28c, crisps for 22c and a drink for 42c. How much does he spend (in dollars) in the whole school year of 200 days?

12. An athlete runs 25 laps of a track in 30 minutes 10 seconds.

a) How many seconds does he take to run 25 laps?

b) How long does he take to run one lap, if he runs the 25 laps at a constant speed?

13. A pile of 250 tiles is 2 m thick. What is the thickness of one tile in cm?

14. Copy the following bill and complete it by filling in the four blank spaces.

8 rolls of wallpaper at $3.20 each	=	$ …
3 tins of paint at $ … each	=	$ 20.10
… brushes at $2.40 each	=	$ 9.60
Total	=	$ …

15. Work out the difference between one ton and one tonne.

1 tonne = 1000 kg
1 ton = 2240 lb
1 lb = 454 g

Give your answer to the nearest kg.

16. A motorist travelled 200 km in five hours. Her average speed for the first 100 km was 50 km/h. What was her average speed for the second 100 km?

17. Work out

a) 20% of $65

b) 37% of $400

c) 8.5% of $2000.

Examination-style exercise 3B

1. Work out the value of $\frac{12+3\times11}{5}$ [1]

Cambridge IGCSE Mathematics 0580
Paper 12 Q1 June 2008

2. The diameter of the sun is 1 392 530 kilometres.
Write this value correct to 4 significant figures. [1]

Cambridge IGCSE Mathematics 0580
Paper 1 Q1 June 2005

3. Only two of the following five statements are correct.

A $0.07077 \geqslant 0.07707$

B $0.07077 \neq 0.07707$

C $0.07077 = 0.07707$

D $0.07077 < 0.07707$

E $0.07077 > 0.07707$

Write down the letters which correspond to the two correct statements. [2]

Cambridge IGCSE Mathematics 0580
Paper 1 Q12 November 2006

4. 2, 3, 5, 9, 12, 15
From the set of numbers above, write down
(a) a multiple of 6, [1]
(b) a prime factor of 27. [1]

Cambridge IGCSE Mathematics 0580
Paper 1 Q6 June 2005

5. Write down a multiple of 4 and 14 which is less than 30. [1]

Cambridge IGCSE Mathematics 0580
Paper 11 Q1 November 2008

6. p is an integer between 20 and 40.
Write down the value of p when it is
(a) an even square number, [1]
(b) an odd cube number, [1]
(c) a prime factor of 155, [1]
(d) a multiple of 17. [1]

7. A club has 275 members.

(a) 99 members are women. What percentage of the members are women? [2]

(b) If, at the next meeting, more than 12.5% of the members were absent, what is the smallest number of members that could have been absent? [2]

8. In 2016, Lucy paid 589.95 US dollars ($) for a flight from Rome to New York.

The return flight from New York to Rome cost her 402.5 euros (€).

The exchange rate at the time of the return flight was €1 = $1.14.

Calculate the difference, in US dollars, between the costs of the two flights.

Give your answer correct to the nearest dollar. [2]

9. A train leaves Paris at 9:52 and arrives in Marseille at 13:21. How long does the journey take? Give your answer in hours and minutes. [1]

Cambridge IGCSE Mathematics 0580
Paper 12 Q2 June 2008

10.

Wythall	1050	1120	1150	1230
Hollywood	1100	1130	1200	1240
Kings Heath	1125	1155	1225	1305

The table above is part of a bus timetable.

(a) The 1120 bus left Wythall a minute early and arrived at Kings Heath 4 minutes late.

How many minutes did it take to reach Kings Heath? [1]

(b) Zac walked to the bus stop at Hollywood and arrived there at 1151.

The next bus arrived on time.

How many minutes did Zac wait for the bus? [1]

11. (a) Abdul invests $400 for 2 years at 6.05% per year **simple** interest.
Calculate how much **interest** Abdul receives. [2]

(b) Samia invests $400 for 2 years at 6% per year **compound** interest.
Calculate how much **interest** Samia receives.
Give your answer to 2 decimal places. [2]

Cambridge IGCSE Mathematics 0580
Paper 12 Q17 November 2007

12. Nicolas needs to borrow \$6000 for 3 years. The bank offers him choice:

Offer A
Interest rate 7·4% per year Pay the interest at the end of each year

Offer B
Interest rate 7% per year Pay the interest at the end of each year

Nicolas recognises that offer A is simple interest and offer B is compound interest.

(a) If he takes offer A, what is the total amount of interest he will pay? [2]

(b) If he takes offer B, how much **interest** will he pay? Give your answer correct to 2 decimal places. [3]

Cambridge IGCSE Mathematics 0580
Paper 12 Q23 June 2008

13. A bag of balloons costs \$3.15.
Henri and his friend share the cost in the ratio 4:3.
How much does Henri pay? [2]

14. The scale on a map is 1:250 000.
A road is 4.6 centimetres long on the map.
Calculate the actual length of the road in kilometres. [2]

Cambridge IGCSE Mathematics 0580
Paper 11 Q6 November 2008

15. (a) Find the value of

i) 5^0, [1]

ii) the square root of 64, [1]

iii) the cube root of 64, [1]

iv) the integer closest in value to $(1.8)^3$. [1]

(b) Write down

i) a common factor of 15 and 27, which is greater than 1, [1]

ii) a common multiple of 10 and 12. [1]

(c) i) Two of the factors of 2007 are square numbers. One of these is 1. Find the other square number. [1]

ii) Write down the two factors of 2007 which are prime. [2]

Cambridge IGCSE Mathematics 0580
Paper 3 Q1 June 2007

16. (a) i) Write down the number of cm^2 in 2 m^2. [1]

ii) Write down the number of cm^3 in 4000 mm^3. [1]

iii) Write down how many litres there are in 0.1 m^3. [1]

(b) A bath tub measures 1.5 metres by 0.8 metres by 0.7 metres. Work out how long it will take to fill the bathtub if water flows into the tub at a rate of 50 litres per minute. [3]

4 Handling Data 1

C9.1 Collect, classify and tabulate statistical data.
C9.2 Read, interpret and draw simple inferences from tables and statistical diagrams. Compare sets of data using tables, graphs and statistical measures. Appreciate restrictions on drawing conclusions from given data.
C9.3 Construct and interpret bar charts, pie charts, pictograms, stem-and-leaf diagrams, simple frequency distributions, histograms with equal intervals and scatter diagrams.
C9.4 Calculate the mean, median, mode and range for individual and discrete data and distinguish between the purposes for which they are used.
C9.7 Understand what is meant by positive, negative and zero correlation with reference to a scatter diagram.
C9.8 Draw, interpret and use lines of best fit by eye.

4.1 Displaying data

Raw data in the form of numbers is collected when surveys or experiments are conducted. This sort of information is often much easier to understand when either a pie chart or a frequency diagram is drawn.

Pictograms

In a pictogram you represent the frequency by a simple visual symbol that is repeated.

For example, this pictogram shows how many pizzas were sold on four days.

In the pictogram

12 pizzas were sold on Monday
10 pizzas were sold on Tuesday
8 pizzas were sold on Wednesday
17 pizzas were sold on Thursday.

Mon	○○○
Tues	○○◐
Wed	○○
Thur	○○○○◔

Key: ○ represents 4 pizzas

The main problem with a pictogram is showing fractions of the symbol which can sometimes only be approximate.

Exercise 1

1. The pictogram shows the money spent at a school tuck shop by four students.

a) Who spent most?
b) How much was spent altogether?
c) How would you show that someone spent 50c?

Reena	$ $
Sharon	$ $ $ $
Tim	$ $
June	$ $ $

Key: $ represent $1

2. The pictogram shows the make of cars in a car park.

   a) How many cars does the represent?

Make	Number of cars	
Ford	4	
Renault		
Toyota	6	
Audi		

   b) Copy and complete the pictogram.

3. The frequency table shows the number of letters posted to six houses one morning. Draw a pictogram to represent these data.

House 1	House 2	House 3	House 4	House 5	House 6
5	3	2	7	1	4

Stem-and-leaf diagrams

Data can be displayed in groups using a stem-and-leaf diagram.

Here are the ages of 20 people who attended a concert:

25 65 43 16 28 32 57 21 17 61
21 43 36 21 14 35 22 44 52 47

We start by choosing a sensible way to group the data. Here we can use the tens digit of the ages, giving us the groups 10–19, 20–29, 30–39, 40–49, 50–59, 60–69.

We then use the tens digit as the 'stem' and the units digit as the 'leaf'.

First we complete the diagram using the data in the order it appears in the list. Then we make a second diagram, putting the data in numerical order. You also need to include a key, containing a sample piece of data, so that people know how to interpret your diagram.

Stem	Leaf
1	6 7 4
2	5 8 1 1 1 2
3	2 6 5
4	3 3 4 7
5	7 2
6	5 1

Stem	Leaf
1	4 6 7
2	1 1 1 2 5 8
3	2 5 6
4	3 3 4 7
5	2 7
6	1 5

Key
1 | 4 means 14

From this diagram, it is easy to find the mode, the median and the range of the data.

Back-to-back stem plots

Two sets of data can be compared using a back-to-back stem plot.

10 students who received coaching and 10 students who did not receive coaching all took part in a mathematics competition. Their scores are shown in this back-to-back stem plot:

Key (Coached): 9 | 1 means 19

Key (Not coached): 1 | 5 means 15

Coached		Not coached
	0	4 8
9 5 4	1	0 2 5 9
7 6 0	2	4 8
6 5 4 1	3	2 4

Because the two sets of data share the same stem, we can clearly see that, on average, the students who were coached performed better in the competition.

Exercise 2

1. The marks scored by 25 students in a history test are as follows:

   62 45 53 76 60 45 33 64 53 36
   71 42 26 48 62 66 29 37 21 74
   48 56 52 68 62

   a) Draw a stem-and-leaf diagram to display this data.

   b) What was the median score for the students?

   c) Write down the range of the scores.

2. Here is a stem-and-leaf diagram showing the times taken for a group of amateur athletes to run 100 metres, measured to the nearest tenth of a second.

Stem	Leaf
12	9
13	0 1 5 8
14	1 6 8
15	2 2 6 7

Key
13 | 5 means 13.5 seconds

   a) How many athletes' scores were recorded?

   b) What was the median time taken?

   c) What was the range of the times recorded?

   d) What was the modal time?

3. A group containing girls and boys measured their handspans in centimetres.

Here are the results:

Girls	17.4	19.4	18.8	16.7	16.1	21.0	19.3	16.5	20.8	18.5
Boys	17.7	21.0	21.9	18.2	23.1	22.2	18.8	22.7	17.5	19.3

a) Copy and complete the following back-to-back stem plot to display this data.

Girls		Boys
	16	
	17	
	18	
	19	
	20	
	21	
	22	
	23	

Key (Girls)
4 | 17 means 17.4 cm

Key (Boys)
19 | 3 means 19.3 cm

b) What are the median handspans for both girls and boys?

c) What are the ranges of the handspans for girls and boys?

4. The lengths, to the nearest minute, of 10 horror films and 10 action films are collected:

Horror	99	90	94	85	105	92	88	95	89	100
Action	110	88	99	90	119	100	121	106	93	110

a) Display this data in a back-to-back stem plot.

b) What are the median lengths of each type of film?

c) Based on this sample, which type of film is, on average, longer?

Pie charts

Example

The pie chart shows the holiday intentions of 600 people.

a) Number of people camping $= \frac{60^\circ}{360^\circ} \times 600 = 100$

b) Number of people touring $= \frac{72^\circ}{360^\circ} \times 600 = 120$

c) Number of people at seaside $= \frac{102^\circ}{360^\circ} \times 600 = 170$

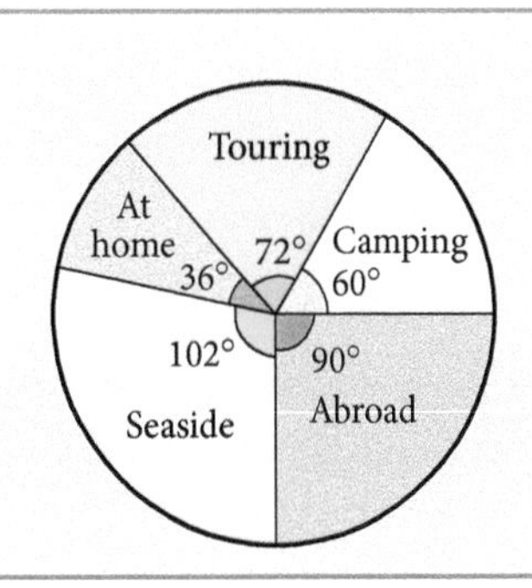

Exercise 3

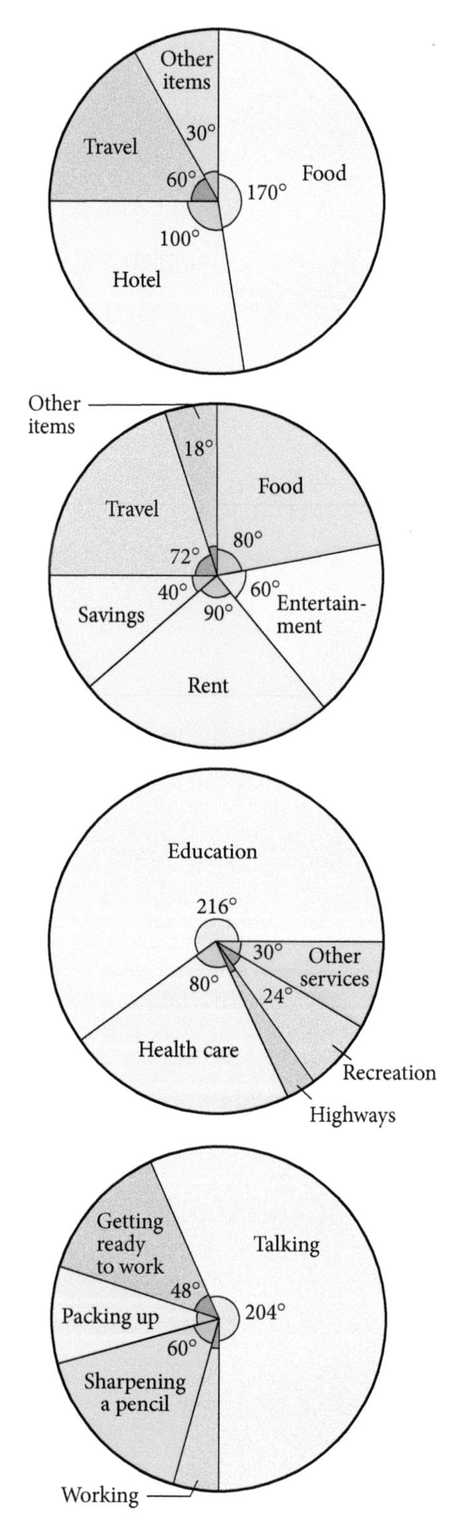

1. The total cost of a holiday was $900. The pie chart shows how this cost was made up.
   - **a)** How much was spent on food?
   - **b)** How much was spent on travel?
   - **c)** How much was spent on the hotel?
   - **d)** How much was spent on other items?

2. Qing-nian has an income of $60 000. The pie chart shows how he uses the money.

   How much does he spend on:
   - **a)** food,
   - **b)** rent,
   - **c)** savings,
   - **d)** entertainment,
   - **e)** travel?

3. The total expenditure of a Council is $36 000 000. The pie chart shows how the money was spent.
   - **a)** How much was spent on:
     - **i)** education **ii)** health care?
   - **b)** What is the angle representing expenditure on highways?
   - **c)** How much was spent on highways?

4. The pie chart shows how a student spends her time in a maths lesson which lasts 60 minutes.
   - **a)** How much time does she spend:
     - **i)** getting ready to work,
     - **ii)** talking,
     - **iii)** sharpening a pencil?
   - **b)** She spends 3 minutes working. What is the angle on the pie chart for the time spent working?

5. Between finishing their dinner and going to bed, Zac and Lucy had 4 hours.

These pie charts show how they spent their time.

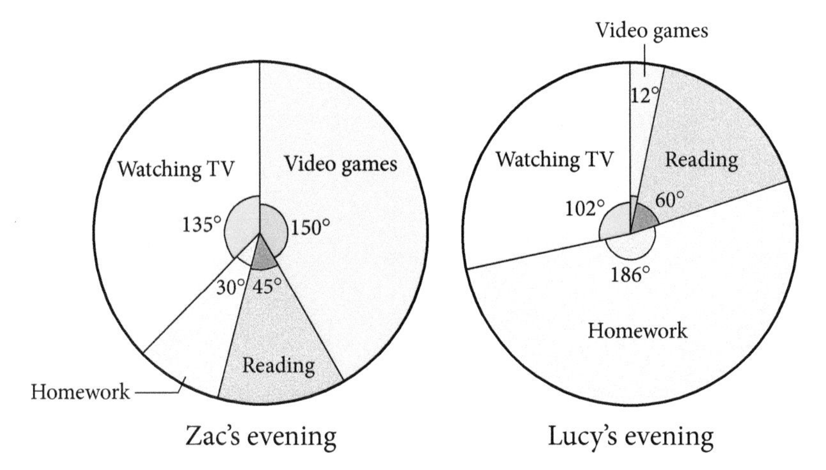

a) Which one of them spent the most time reading?

b) How many minutes did Zac spend doing his homework?

c) How many more minutes did Zac spend watching TV than Lucy?

Exercise 4

1. At the semi-final stage of the UEFA Champions' Cup, 72 neutral referees were asked to predict who they thought would win. Their answers were:

Bayern Munich	9	Real Madrid	22
Manchester United	40	Inter Milan	1

a) Work out

i) $\frac{9}{72}$ of 360° ii) $\frac{40}{72}$ of 360° iii) $\frac{22}{72}$ of 360° iv) $\frac{1}{72}$ of 360°

b) Draw an accurate pie chart to display the predictions of the 72 referees.

2. A survey was carried out to find what 400 students did when they left school:

   120 went into employment

   160 went to university

   80 went to college in another country

   40 were unemployed.

   a) Simplify the following fractions: $\frac{120}{400}$; $\frac{160}{400}$; $\frac{80}{400}$; $\frac{40}{400}$.

   b) Draw an accurate pie chart to show the information above.

3. In a survey on washing powder 180 people were asked to state which brand they preferred. 45 chose Brand A.

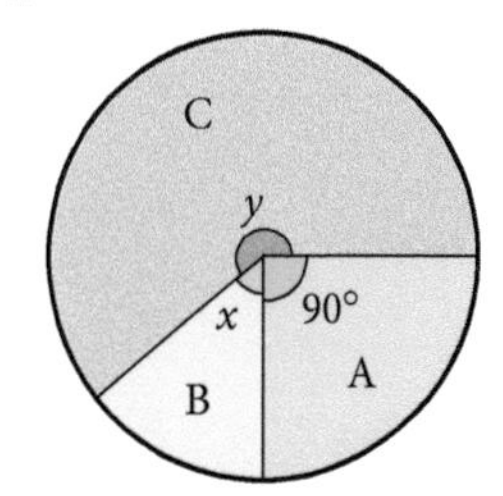

   If 30 people chose brand B and 105 chose Brand C, calculate the angles x and y.

4. A packet of breakfast cereal weighing 600 g contains four ingredients as follows:

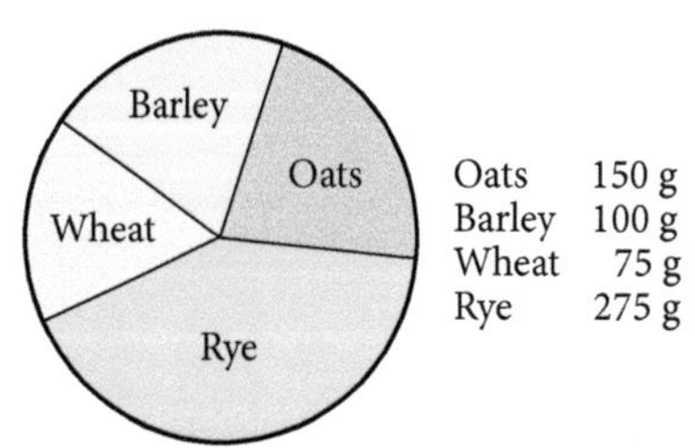

   Calculate the angles on the pie chart shown and draw an accurate diagram.

5. The table below shows the share of car sales achieved by four companies in one year.

Company	A	B	C	D
Share of sales	50%	10%	25%	15%

   In a pie chart to show this information, find the angle of the sectors representing:

   a) Company A
   b) Company B
   c) Company C
   d) Company D.

Frequency diagrams and bar charts

Example

The marks obtained by 36 students in a test were as follows.

1 3 2 3 4 2 1 3 0
5 3 0 1 4 0 4 4 3
3 4 3 1 3 4 3 1 2
1 3 4 0 4 3 2 5 3

Show the data:

a) on a tally chart **b)** on a frequency diagram.

a)

Mark	Tally	Frequency
0	||||	4
1	~~||||~~ |	6
2	||||	4
3	~~||||~~ ~~||||~~ ||	12
4	~~||||~~ |||	8
5	||	2

b)

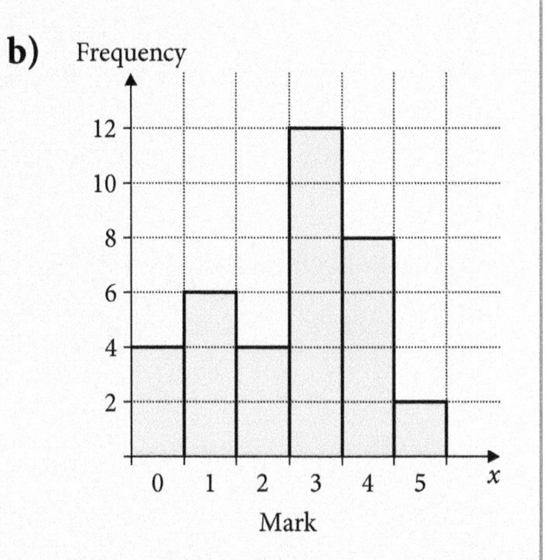

Exercise 5

1. In a survey, the number of occupants in the cars passing a school was recorded.

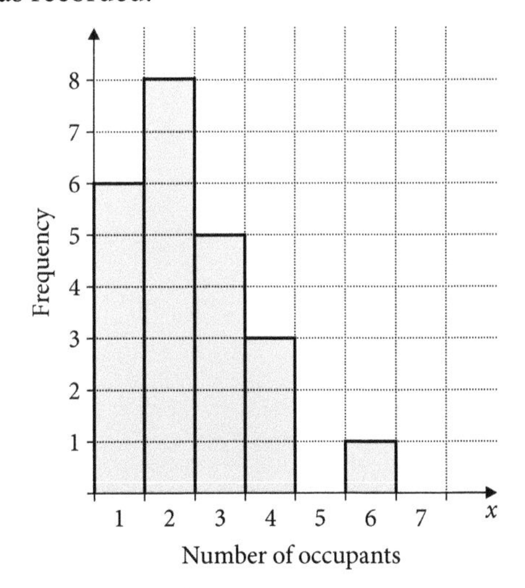

a) How many cars had 3 occupants?

b) How many cars had less than 4 occupants?

c) How many cars were in the survey?

d) What was the total number of occupants in all the cars in the survey?

e) What fraction of the cars had only one occupant?

2. In an experiment, two dice were thrown sixty times and the total score showing was recorded.

2	3	5	4	8	6	4	7	5	10
7	8	7	6	12	11	8	11	7	6
6	5	7	7	8	6	7	3	6	7
12	3	10	4	3	7	2	11	8	5
7	10	7	5	7	5	10	11	7	10
4	8	6	4	6	11	6	12	11	5

a) Draw a tally chart to show the results of the experiment. The tally chart is started below.

Score	Tally marks	Frequency
2	||	2
3	||||	4
4		
.		
.		

b) Draw a frequency graph to illustrate the results. Plot the frequency on the vertical axis.

3. The bar chart shows the profit/loss made by a toy shop from September 2010 to April 2011.

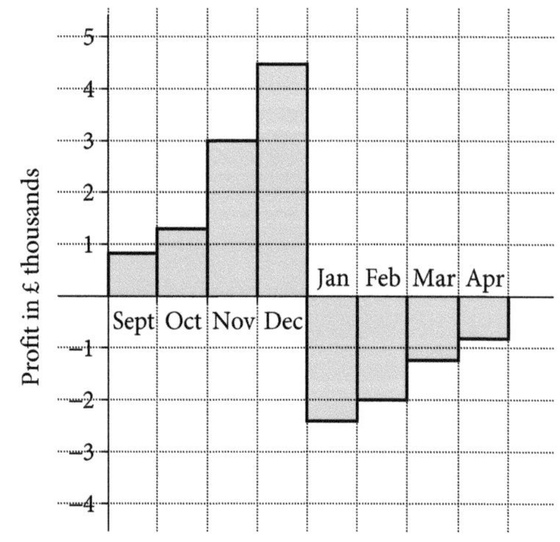

a) Estimate the total profit in this period.

b) Describe what is happening to the shop's profits in this period. Try to think of an explanation for the shape of the bar chart.

Grouped data

Sometimes the data to be displayed can take a wide range of values. In such cases, it is convenient to put the data into groups before drawing a tally chart and frequency diagram.

Example

The hand spans  of 21 children were measured as follows:

14.8	20.0	16.9	20.7	18.1	17.5	18.7
19.0	19.8	17.8	14.3	19.2	21.7	17.4
16.0	15.9	18.5	19.3	16.6	21.2	18.4

Group the data and draw up a tally chart and frequency diagram.

The smallest value is 14.3 cm and the largest is 21.7 cm. The data can be grouped as follows and the frequency diagram drawn.

Class intervals	Tally
$14 \leqslant s < 16$	|||
$16 \leqslant s < 18$	~~||||~~ |
$18 \leqslant s < 20$	~~||||~~ |||
$20 \leqslant s < 22$	||||

Notice that 20.0 goes into the last group $20 \leqslant s < 22$.

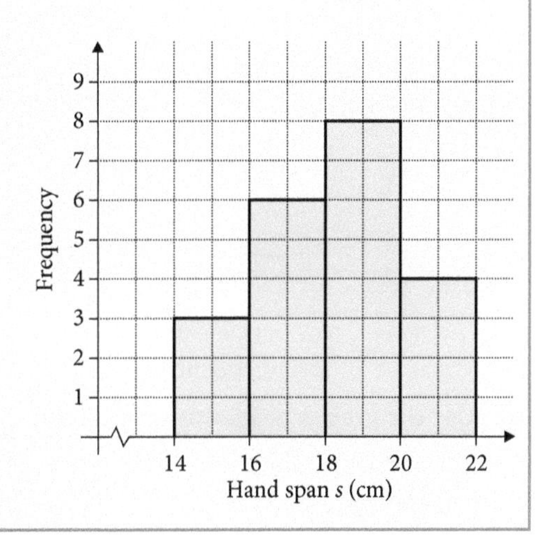

Exercise 6

1. The graph shows the heights of students in a class.

   a) How many students were over 150 cm tall?

   b) How many students had a height between 135 cm and 155 cm?

   c) How many students were in the class?

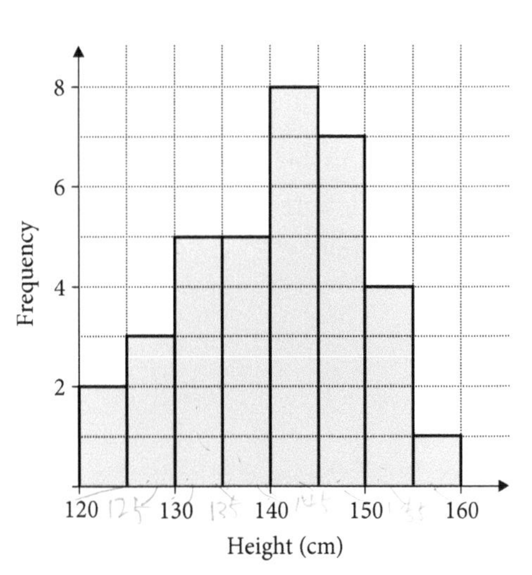

2. In a survey, the heights of children aged 15 were measured in four countries around the world. A random sample of children was chosen, not necessarily the same number from each country.

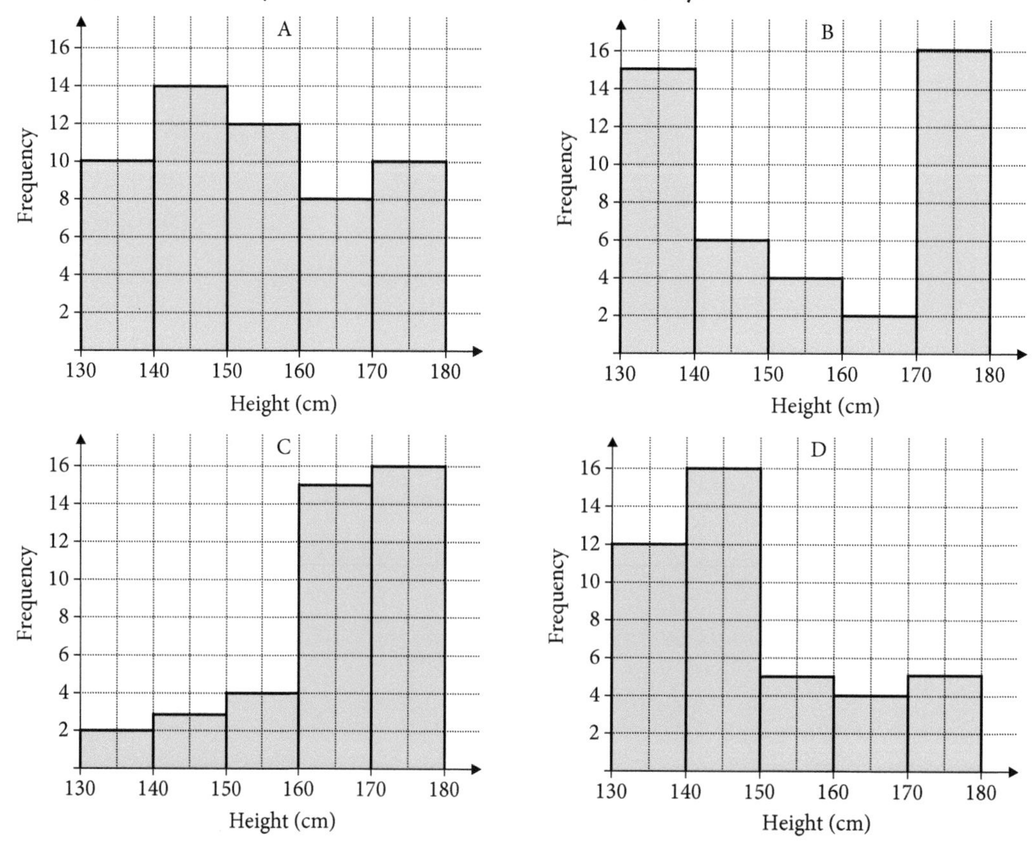

Use the graphs to identify the country in each of the statements below.

a) Two-thirds of the children from Country ____ were less than 150 cm tall.

b) There were 54 children in the sample from Country ____.

c) In Country ____ the heights were spread fairly evenly across the range 130 to 180 cm.

d) The smallest sample of children came from Country ____.

e) In Country ____ three-quarters of the children were either tall or short.

3. A farmer grew carrots in two adjacent fields A and B and treated one of the fields with fertiliser. A random sample of 50 carrots was taken from each field and weighed. Here are the results for Field A (all in grams).

118	91	82	105	72	92	103	95	73	109
63	111	102	116	101	104	107	119	111	108
112	97	100	75	85	94	76	67	93	112
70	116	118	103	65	107	87	98	105	117
114	106	82	90	77	88	66	99	95	103

Make a tally chart using the groups given.

Weight	Tally	Frequency
$60 \leqslant w < 70$		
$70 \leqslant w < 80$		
$80 \leqslant w < 90$		
$90 \leqslant w < 100$		
$100 \leqslant w < 110$		
$110 \leqslant w < 120$		

The frequency graph for Field B is shown below.

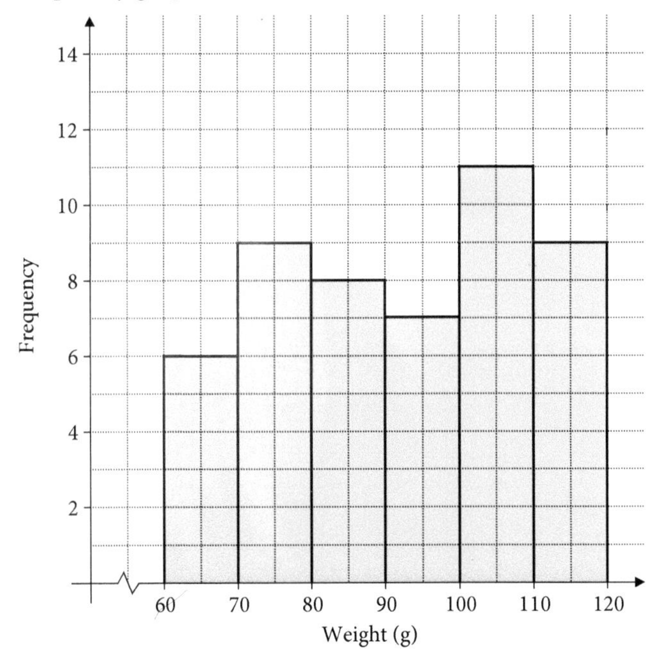

Copy the graph above and, in a different colour, draw the graph for Field A.

Which field do you think was treated with the fertiliser?

4. In an experiment, 52 children took an IQ test before and then after a course of vitamin pills. Here are the results.

Before:

81 107 93 104 103 96 101 102 93 105 82 106 97
108 94 111 92 86 109 95 116 92 94 101 117 102
95 108 112 107 106 124 125 103 127 118 113 91 113
113 114 109 128 115 86 106 91 85 119 129 99 98

After:

93 110 92 125 99 127 114 98 107 128 103 91 104
103 83 125 91 104 99 102 116 98 115 92 117 97
126 100 112 113 85 108 97 101 125 93 102 107 116
94 117 95 108 117 96 102 87 107 94 103 95 96

a) Put the scores into convenient groups between 80 and 130.

b) Draw two frequency graphs to display the results.

c) Write a conclusion. Did the vitamin pills make a significant difference?

Conversion graphs

Exercise 7

Draw the graph and then answer the questions.

1. a) Convert into dollars:

i) £2 **ii)** £1.60 **iii)** £2.40

b) Convert into pounds:

i) \$1 **ii)** \$3.50 **iii)** \$2.50

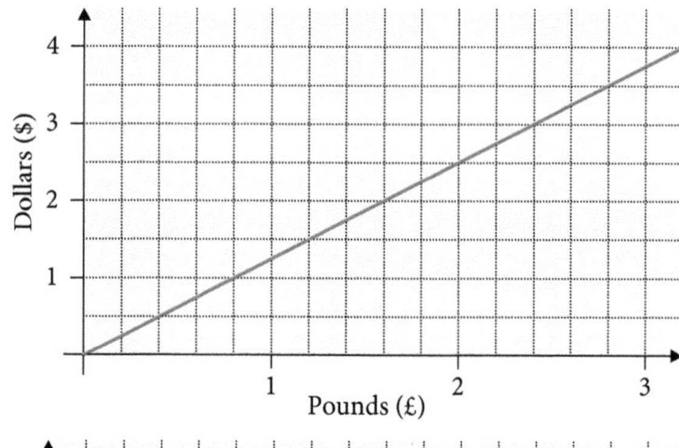

2. Give your answers as accurately as you can. [e.g. 3 lb = 1.4 kg approximately]

a) Convert into kilograms:

i) 5.5 lb **ii)** 8 lb **iii)** 2 lb

b) Convert into pounds:

i) 2 kg **ii)** 3 kg **iii)** 1.5 kg

c) A bag of sugar weighs 1 kg. What is its weight in pounds?

d) A washing machine has a weight limit of 7 lb. What is the weight limit in kilograms?

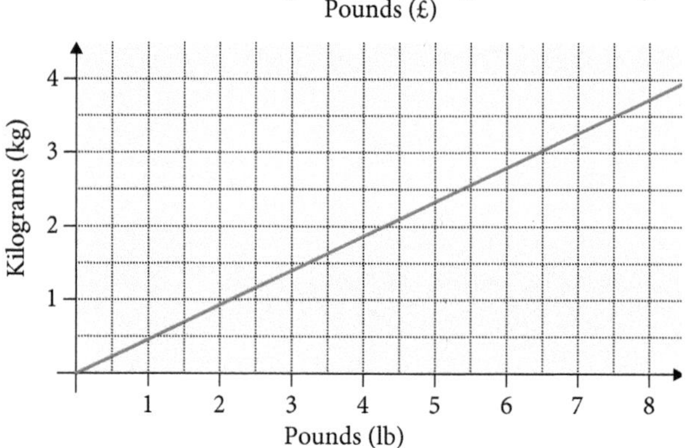

3. Between 1984 and 1994 the value of the British pound against the German mark (DM) changed. How much less in DM did you receive for £1 in 1994 compared with 1984?

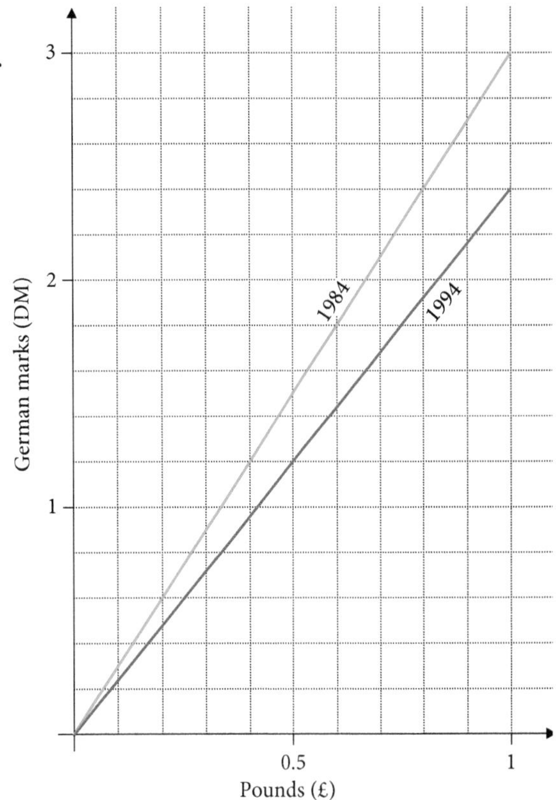

4. Temperature can be measured in °C or in °F. A conversion graph can be constructed using two points as follows:
Draw axes with a scale of 1 cm to 5° as shown.

$$32\,°F = 0\,°C \text{ and } 95\,°F = 35\,°C.$$

Draw a line through these two points.
Use your graph to convert:

a) 50 °F into °C

b) 20 °C into °F

c) 0 °F into °C

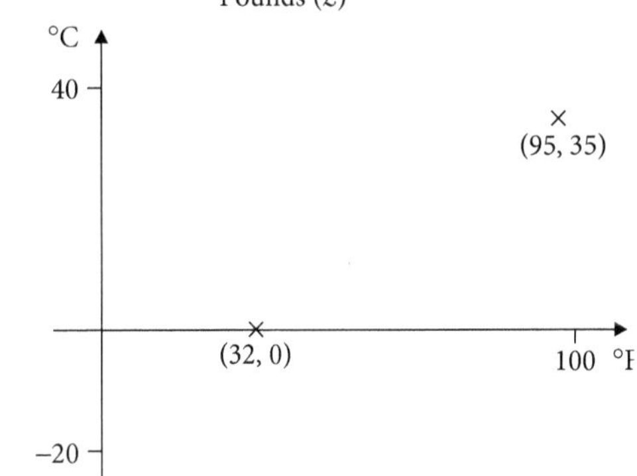

Scatter graphs

Sometimes it is important to discover if there is a connection or relationship between two sets of data.

Examples:

- Are more ice creams sold when the weather is hot?
- Do tall people have higher pulse rates?
- Are people who are good at maths also good at science?
- Does watching TV improve examination results?

If there is a relationship, it will be easy to spot if your data is plotted on a scatter diagram – that is a graph in which one set of data is plotted on the horizontal axis and the other on the vertical axis.

Here is a scatter graph showing the price of pears and the quantity sold.

We can see a *connection* – when the price was high the sales were low and when the price went down the sales increased.

This scatter graph shows the sales of a newspaper and the temperature. We can see there is *no connection* between the two variables.

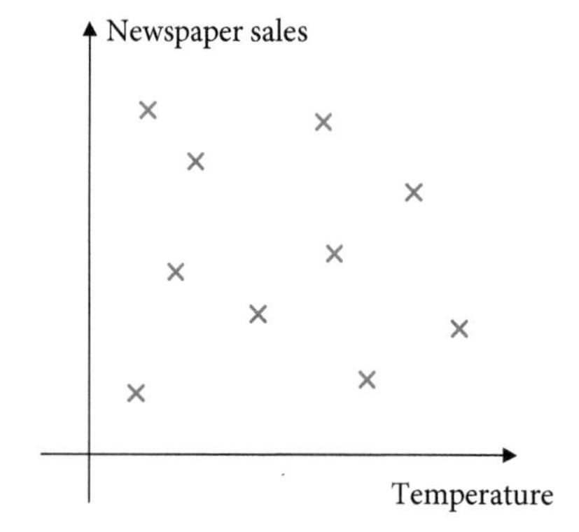

Correlation

The word correlation describes how things *co-relate.* There is correlation between two sets of data if there is a connection or relationship.

The correlation between two sets of data can be positive or negative and it can be strong or weak as indicated by the scatter graphs on the next page.

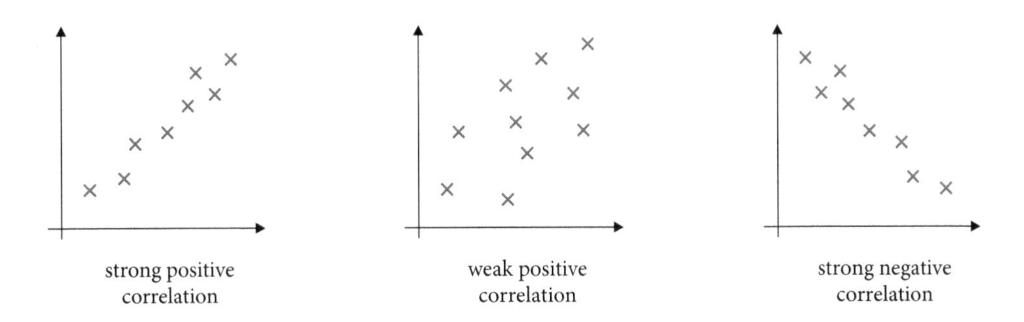

When the correlation is positive the points are around a line which slopes upwards to the right. When the correlation is negative the 'line' slopes downwards to the right.
When the correlation is strong the points are bunched close to a line through their midst. When the correlation is weak the points are more scattered.
It is important to realise that often there is *no* correlation between two sets of data.
If, for example, we take a group of students and plot their maths test results against their time to run 800 m, the graph might look like the one on the right. A common mistake in this topic is to 'see' a correlation on a scatter graph where none exists.

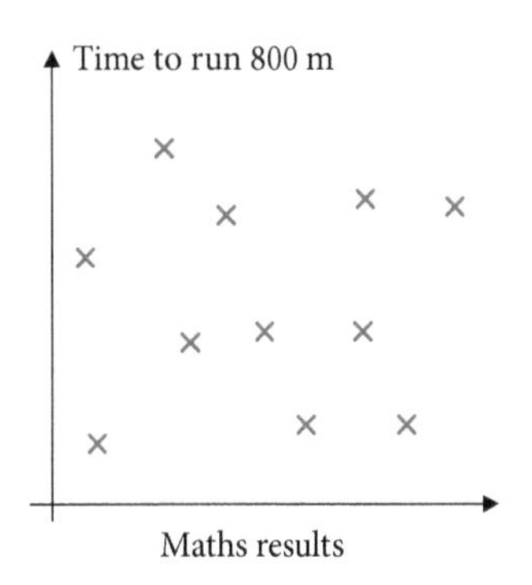

There is also *no* correlation in these two scatter graphs.

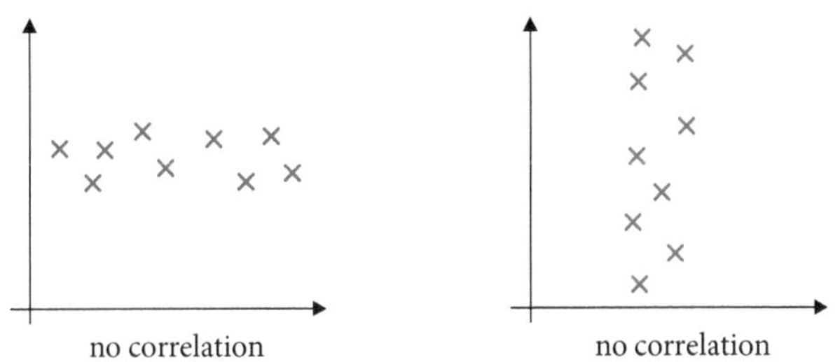

Exercise 8

1. Make the following measurements for everyone in your class:

height	(nearest cm)
arm span	(nearest cm)
head circumference	(nearest cm)
hand span	(nearest cm)
pulse rate	(beats/minute)

Name	Height	Arm span	Head	
Roger	161	165	56	
Liz	150	148	49	
Gill				

Enter all the measurements in a table, either on the board or on a sheet of paper.

a) Draw the scatter graphs shown below:

i) arm span / height

ii) hand span / pulse rate

b) Describe the correlation, if any, in the scatter graphs you drew in part **(a)**.

c) **i)** Draw a scatter graph of two measurements where you think there might be positive correlation.

ii) Was there really a positive correlation?

2. Plot the points given on a scatter graph, with s across the page and p up the page. Draw axes with values from 0 to 20.
Describe the correlation, if any, between the values of s and p [i.e. 'strong negative', 'weak positive' etc.].

a)

s	7	16	4	12	18	6	20	4	10	13
p	8	15	6	12	17	9	18	7	10	14

b)

s	3	8	12	15	16	5	6	17	9
p	4	2	10	17	5	10	17	11	15

c)

s	11	1	16	7	2	19	8	4	13	18
p	5	12	7	14	17	1	11	8	11	5

3. Describe the correlation, if any, in these scatter graphs.

a)

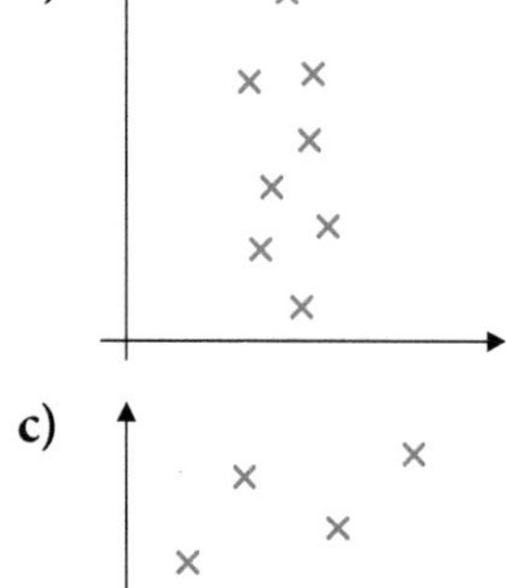

b)

c)

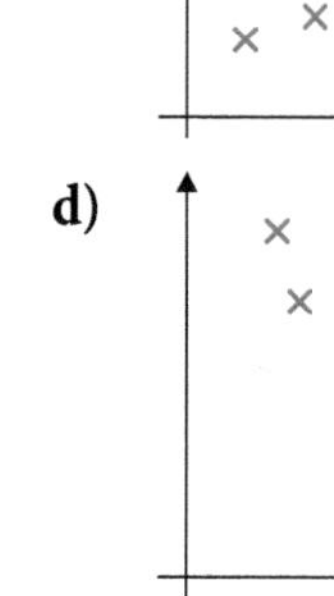

d)

Line of best fit

When a scatter graph shows either positive or negative correlation, a **line of best fit** can be drawn. The sums of the distances to points on either side of the line are equal and there should be an equal number of points on each side of the line. The line is easier to draw when a transparent ruler is used.

Here are the marks obtained in two tests by 9 students.

Student	A	B	C	D	E	F	G	H	I
Maths mark	28	22	9	40	37	35	30	23	?
Physics mark	48	45	34	57	50	55	53	45	52

A line of best fit can be drawn as there is strong positive correlation between the two sets of marks.

The line of best fit can be used to estimate the maths result of student I, who missed the maths test but scored 52 in the physics test.

We can *estimate* that student I would have scored *about* 33 in the maths test. It is not possible to be *very* accurate using scatter graphs. It is reasonable to state that student I 'might have scored between 30 and 36' in the maths test.

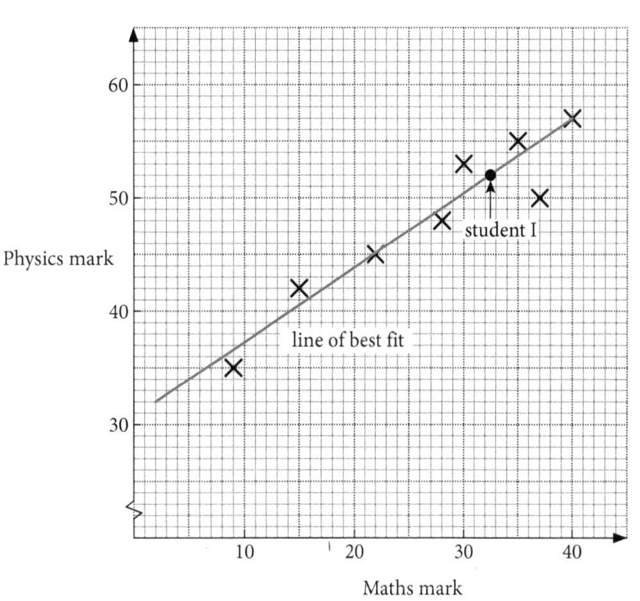

Exercise 9

In Questions **1**, **2** and **3** plot the points given on a scatter graph, with s across the page and p up the page.
Draw axes with the values from 0 to 20.
If possible draw a line of best fit on the graph.
Where possible estimate the value of p on the line of best fit where $s = 10$.

1.

s	2	14	14	4	12	18	12	6
p	5	15	16	6	12	18	13	7

2.

s	2	15	17	3	20	3	6
p	13	7	5	12	4	13	11

3.

s	4	10	15	18	19	4	19	5
p	19	16	11	19	15	3	1	9

4. The following data gives the marks of 11 students in a French test and in a German test.

French	15	36	36	22	23	27	43	22	43	40	26
German	6	28	35	18	28	28	37	9	41	45	17

a) Plot this data on a scatter graph, with French marks on the horizontal axis.

b) Draw the line of best fit.

c) Estimate the German mark of a student who got 30 in French.

d) Estimate the French mark of a student who got 45 in German.

5. The data below gives some information about cars with the same size engine, when driven at different speeds.

Speed (m.p.h.)	30	62	40	80	70	55	75
Petrol consumption (m.p.g.)	38	25	35	20	26	34	22

a) Plot a scatter graph and draw a line of best fit.

b) Estimate the petrol consumption of a car travelling at 45 m.p.h.

c) Estimate the speed of a car whose petrol consumption is 27 m.p.g.

6. The table shows the marks of 7 students in the two papers of a science examination.

Paper 1	35	10	60	17	43	55	49
Paper 2	26	15	40	15	30	34	35

a) Plot the marks on a scatter diagram, using a scale of 1 cm to 5 marks and draw a line of best fit.

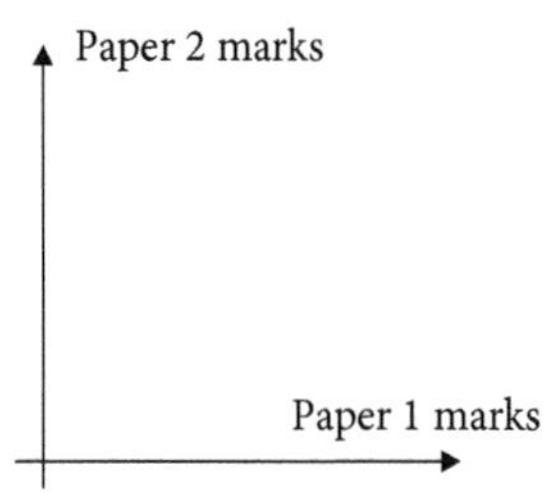

b) A student got a mark of 25 on paper 1 but missed paper 2. What would you expect her to get on paper 2?

Using a spreadsheet on a computer

This section is written for use with Microsoft Excel. Other spreadsheet programs work in a similar way.

Select Microsoft Excel from the desktop.

A spreadsheet appears on your screen as a grid with rows numbered 1, 2, 3, 4, . . . and the columns lettered A, B, C, D, . . . The result should be a window like the one below.

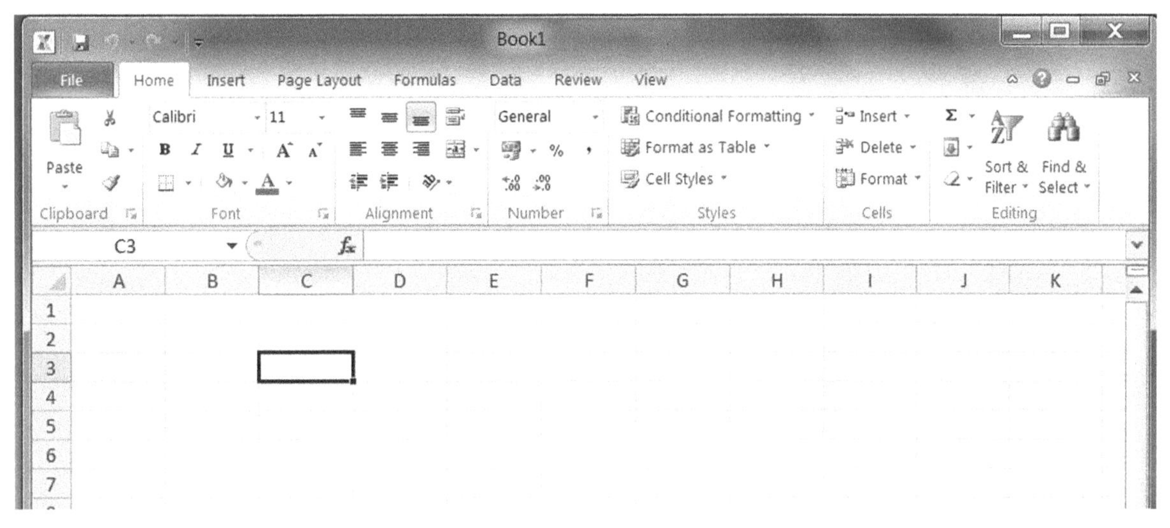

Cell The spaces on the spreadsheet are called cells. Individual cells are referred to as A1, B3, F9, like grid references.
Cells may contain *labels, values* or *formulae.* The current cell has a black border.

Label Any words, headings or messages used to help the layout and organisation of the spreadsheet.

Value A number placed in a cell. It may be used as input to a calculation.

Tasks 1, 2 and 3 are written for you to become familiar with how the main functions of a spreadsheet program work. Afterwards there are sections on different topics where spreadsheets can be used.

Task 1. To generate the whole numbers from 1 to 10 in column A.

a) In cell A1 type '1' and press *Return.* This will automatically take you to the cell below. (Note that you must use the *Return* button and not the arrow keys to move down the column.)

b) In cell A2 type the formula '= A1 + 1' and press *Return.*
[Note that the = sign is needed before any formula.]

c) We now want to copy the formula in A2 down column A as far as A10. Click on A2 again and put the arrow in the bottom right corner of cell A2 (a + sign will appear) and drag down to A10.

Task 2. To generate the odd numbers in column B.

a) In B1 type '1' (press *Return*).

b) In B2 type the formula '= B1 + 2' (press *Return*).

c) Click in B2 and copy the formula down column B as far as B10.

Task 3. To generate the first 15 square numbers.

a) As before generate the numbers from 1 to 15 in cells A1 to A15.

b) In B1 put the formula '= A1 * A1' and press *Return*.

c) Click in B1 and copy the formula down as far as B15.

Pie charts and bar charts using a spreadsheet on a computer

Example

Display the data about the activities in one day.

Enter the headings: *Sleep* in A1, *School* in B1 etc. [Use the *tab* key to move across the page.]

Enter the data: 8 in A2, 7 in B2 etc.

	A	B	C	D	E	F	G	H
1	Sleep	School	TV	Eating	Homework	Other		
2	8	7	1.5	1	1.5	5		
3								
4								

Now highlight all the cells from A1 to F2. [Click on A1 and drag across to F2.]

Choose 'Insert' from the menus and you can select various types of graph.

Select 'Pie' and then choose one of the examples displayed. Follow the on-screen prompts.

Alternatively, for a bar chart, select the bar chart icon. Proceed as above.

You will be able to display your charts with various '3D' effects, possibly in colour. This approach is recommended when you are presenting data that you have collected as part of an investigation.

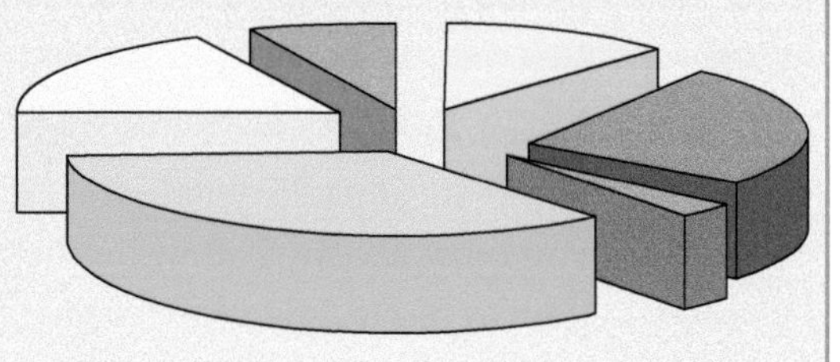

Scatter graphs on a computer

Example

Plot a scatter graph showing the marks of 10 students in Maths and Science.

Enter the headings: *Maths* in A1, *Science* in B1. Enter the data as shown.

Now highlight all the cells from A2 to B11.
[Click on A1 and drag across and down to B11.]

Choose 'Insert' from the tool bar and select the scatter graph icon.

Follow the on-screen prompts.

	A	B
1	**Maths**	**Science**
2	23	30
3	45	41
4	73	67
5	35	74
6	67	77
7	44	50
8	32	41
9	66	55
10	84	70
11	36	32

On 'Titles' enter: Chart title: Maths/Science results
Value (X) axis: Maths
Value (Y) axis: Science

Experiment with 'Axes', 'Gridlines', 'Legend' and 'Data Labels'.

Task. Enter the data on a spreadsheet and print a scatter graph. What does each scatter graph show?

a)

Height	Arm span
162	160
155	151
158	157
142	144
146	148
165	163
171	167
148	150
150	147

b)

Temperature	Sales
23	7
18	14
7	23
20	9
4	30
12	19
15	15
18	15
10	20

4.2 Questionnaires

The material in this section will not be tested in your examinations. Surveys are conducted by organisations for a variety of reasons.

- In the U.S.A., newspapers publish opinion polls about the voting intentions of people or the popularity of the President. They provide interesting stories for the newspaper.

- Car makers conduct surveys to find what features most people want to have in their cars such as CD players, electric windows, sun roofs and so on. They then use the survey results to help with the design of future models.

- Supermarkets conduct surveys to discover what things are most important to their customers. They might want to find out how people felt about ease of car parking, price of food, quality of food, length of time waiting to pay, etc.

- Surveys are made to find the popularity of various TV programmes. Advertisers are prepared to pay a large sum for a 30 second advertisement in a programme with an audience of 10 million people.

Most surveys are conducted using questionnaires. It is very important to design the questionnaire well so that:

a) people will cooperate and will answer the questions honestly

b) the questions are not biased

c) the answers to the questions can be analysed and presented for ease of understanding.

Here is a checklist of five things to improve your questionnaire design:

1. Provide an introduction to the sheet so that people know the purpose of the questionnaire.

   'Proposed new traffic lights'

2. Make the questions easy to understand and specific to answer.
   Do *not* ask vague questions like this. → ~~Did you see much of the Olympics on TV?~~
   The answers could be:

   'Yes, a lot'
   'Not much'
   'Only the best bits'
   'Once or twice a day'

   You will find it hard to analyse this sort of data.

   A *better* question is:

   'How much of the Olympic coverage did you watch?' Tick one box

Not at all	☐
Up to 1 hour per day	☐
1 to 2 hours per day	☐
More than 2 hours per day	☐

3. Make sure that the questions are not *leading* questions. It is human nature not to contradict the questioner. Remember that the survey is to find out opinions of other people, not to support your own.
   Do *not* ask:

   'Do you agree that BBC has the best sports coverage?'

   A better question is:

   'Which of the following has the best sports coverage?'

BBC	ITV	Channel 4	Satellite TV
☐	☐	☐	☐

   You might ask for one tick or possibly numbers 1, 2, 3, 4 to show an order of preference.

4. If you are going to ask sensitive questions (about age or income, for example), design the question with care so as not to offend or embarrass.
   Do not ask:
   'How old are you?'
   or 'Give your date of birth'
   A better question is:

'Tick one box for your age group.'			
15–17	18–20	21–30	31–50
☐	☐	☐	☐

5. Do not ask more questions than necessary and put the easy questions first.

Exercise 10

Criticise the following questions and suggest a better question. Write some questions with 'yes/no' answers and some questions which involve multiple responses.
Remember to word your questions simply.

1. Do you think it is ridiculous to spend money on food 'mountains' in Europe while people in Africa are starving?
2. What do you think of the new head teacher?
3. How dangerous do you think it is to fly in a single-engined aeroplane?

4. How much would you pay to use the new car park?
   ☐ less than $1 ☐ more than $2.50.
5. Do you agree that English and Maths are the most important subjects at school?
6. Do you or your parents often hire DVDs from a shop?
7. Do you think that we get too much homework?
8. Do you think you would still eat meat if you saw the animals being killed?

Analysis

Having conducted the survey, you need to display your results clearly. Diagrams like pie charts, frequency diagrams and scatter graphs are a good idea. Do not be afraid to use colours.

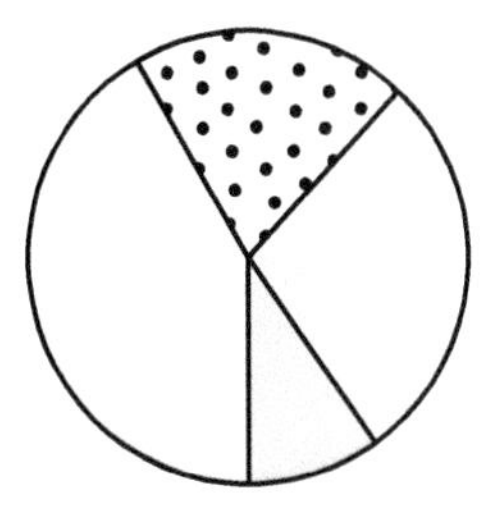

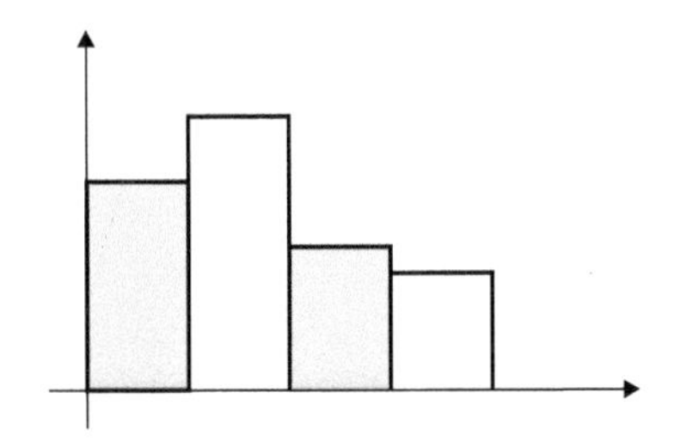

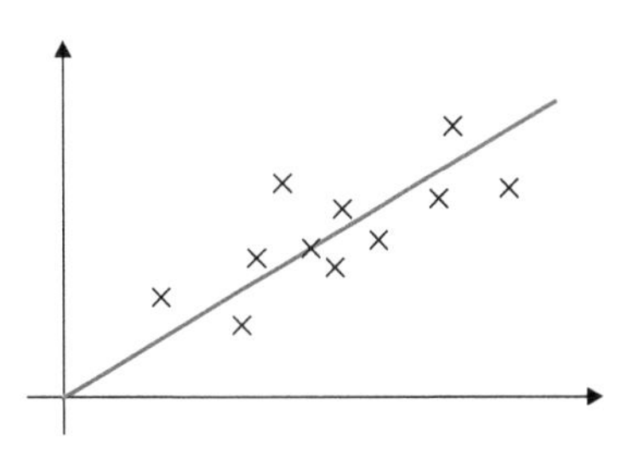

You might want to use a database or spreadsheet program on a computer if you think this would help your work.

Draw *conclusions* from your results but make sure they are justified by the evidence.

The best way to learn about questionnaires is to conduct your own survey on a topic which *you* find interesting.

Hypothesis testing

A hypothesis is defined as 'a statement which may be true, but for which a proof has not been found'. Statisticians are employed to collect and analyse information about a question with the aim of proving or disproving it. Questionnaires are often used for this purpose. Here are some questions:

A 'Is there too much sport on television?'

B 'Are people who are good at spelling also good at arithmetic?'

castle √	$51 \times 17 = 867$ √
elefant ×	$0.4 \times 0.2 = 0.08$ √
necessary √	$5.6 - 4 = 5.2$ ×
tomorrow √	$\frac{1}{6} + \frac{1}{2} = \frac{2}{8}$ ×

C 'Does smoking damage your health?'

D 'Do 11-year-old students watch more TV than 16-year-old students?'

Once you have the question, your first task is to make a hypothesis (make a statement) so that you have something concrete to test.

Hypotheses for the above four questions could be:

A Most people would like TV schedules to contain less coverage of sport.

B People who are good at spelling are also good at arithmetic.

C Smokers have a shorter life span than non-smokers.

D 11-year-old students watch more television than 16-year-old students.

There are several factors which you must consider when making your hypothesis.

1. Can you test it?
In the smokers problem there are many factors which will affect life span – diet, fitness, stress, heredity etc. How can you eliminate these so that it is *only* the smoking which counts?

2. Can you collect enough data to give a reasonable result? Where will you collect your data?
For the spelling/arithmetic problem, you could write your own tests and then ask about 30 students, preferably of different ages, to do them. You should try to get people with a range of abilities in spelling and arithmetic.

3. How will you know if you have proved or disproved the hypothesis?
You need to have some idea of the criteria for proof (or disproof) before you start collecting data.
In the question about sport on television, what do you mean by 'most'? Do you mean over half of those questioned? What about 'don't knows'?

4. Can you collect the type of data which you can analyse?
Consider the techniques at your disposal:
mean, median, mode, scatter diagrams, pie charts, frequency graphs.
The spelling/arithmetic data, for example, could be clearly displayed on a scatter diagram.

5. Do you find it interesting?
If you don't, the whole piece of work will be dull and tedious, both to you and to your teacher.

Almost certainly the best idea for a hypothesis will be an idea which *you* think of because *you* want to know the answer. As a guide, here is a list of questions which some students have looked at. You can use one of these if you find it interesting or if you can't think of a better one yourself.

a) Young people are more superstitious than older people.

b) Given a free choice, most girls would hardly ever wear a dress in preference to something else.

c) More babies are born in the Winter than the Summer.

d) The age for part-time jobs should be reduced from 16 to 14.

e) The school day should start at 08:00 and end at 14:00.

f) Most cars these days use unleaded petrol.

4.3 Averages

If you have a set of data, say exam marks or heights, and are told to find the 'average', just what are you trying to find? The answer is: a single number which can be used to represent the entire set of data. This could be done in three different ways.

a) The median

The data is arranged in order from the smallest to the largest; the middle number is then selected. This is really the central number of the range and is called the median.

If there are two 'middle' numbers, the median is in the middle of these two numbers.

b) The mean

All the data is added up and the total divided by the number of items. This is called the mean and is equivalent to sharing out all the data evenly.

c) The mode

The number of items which occurs most frequently in a frequency table is selected. This is the most popular value and is called the mode (from the French 'à la mode' meaning 'fashionable').

Each 'average' has its purpose and sometimes one is preferable to the others.

The median is fairly easy to find and has an advantage in being hardly affected by untypical values such as very large or very small values that occur at the ends of the distribution.

Consider these exam marks:

20, 21, 21, 22, 23, 23, 25, 27, 27, 27, 29, 98, 98

↑ (under 25)

The median (25) gives a truer picture of the centre of the distribution than the mean (35.5).

The mean takes account of all of the data and is the 'average' which most people readily think of. It does, of course, take a little longer to calculate than either the mode or the median.

The mode of this data is 27. It is easy to calculate and it eliminates some of the effects of extreme values. However, it does have disadvantages, particularly in data which has two 'most popular' values, and it is not widely used.

Range

In addition to knowing the centre of a distribution, it is useful to know the range or spread of the data.

range = (largest value) – (smallest value)

For the examination marks, range = 98 – 20 = 78.

Example

Find the median, the mean, the mode and the range of this set of 10 numbers:

5, 4, 10, 3, 3, 4, 7, 4, 6, 5.

a) Arrange the numbers in order of size to find the median.

3, 3, 4, 4, 4, 5, 5, 6, 7, 10

↑

The median is the 'average' of 4 and 5.

$\therefore$ Median = 4.5

b) $\text{Mean} = \frac{(5+4+10+3+3+4+7+4+6+5)}{10} = \frac{51}{10} = 5.1$

c) Mode = 4 because there are more 4's than any other number.

d) Range = 10 – 3 = 7

Exercise 11

1. Find the mean, median and mode of the following sets of numbers:

a) 3, 12, 4, 6, 8, 5, 4

b) 7, 21, 2, 17, 3, 13, 7, 4, 9, 7, 9

c) 12, 1, 10, 1, 9, 3, 4, 9, 7, 9

d) 8, 0, 3, 3, 1, 7, 4, 1, 4, 4.

2. The temperature in °C on 17 days was:
1, 0, 2, 2, 0, 4, 1, 3, 2, 1, 2, 3, 4, 5, 4, 5, 5.
What was the modal temperature?

3. A dice was thrown 14 times as follows:

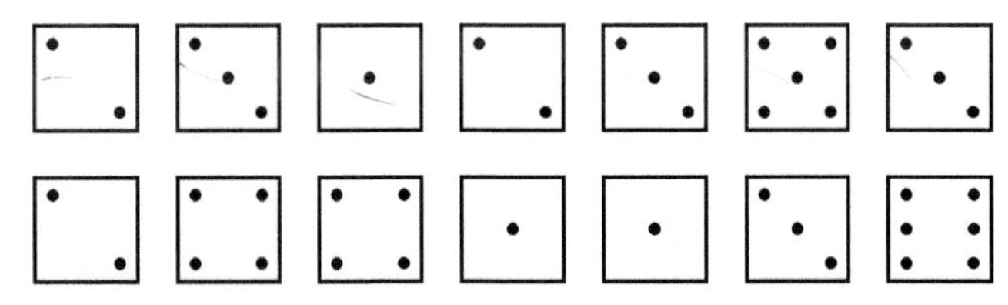

a) What was the modal score?

b) What was the median score?

4. Write down five numbers so that:

the mean is 6
the median is 5
the mode is 4.

5. Louise claims that she is better at maths than her brother Peter.
Louise's last five marks were 63, 72, 58, 84 and 75 and Peter's last four marks were 69, 73, 81 and 70. Find the mean mark for Louise and for Peter. Is Louise better than Peter?

6. The bar chart shows the marks scored in a test. What was the modal mark?

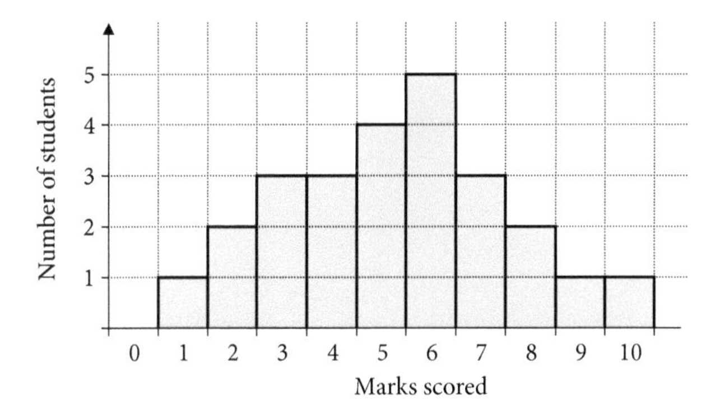

7. Six boys have heights of 1.53 m, 1.49 m, 1.60 m, 1.65 m, 1.90 m and 1.43 m.

a) Find the mean height of the six boys.

b) Find the mean height of the remaining five boys when the shortest boy leaves.

8. Seven women have weights of 44 kg, 51 kg, 57 kg, 63 kg, 48 kg, 49 kg and 45 kg.
   a) Find the mean weight of the seven women.
   b) Find the mean weight of the remaining five women after the lightest and the heaviest women leave.

9. In a maths test the marks for the boys were 9, 7, 8, 7, 5 and the marks for the girls were 6, 3, 9, 8, 2, 2.
   a) Find the mean mark for the boys.
   b) Find the mean mark for the girls.
   c) Find the mean mark for the whole class.

10. The following are the salaries of 5 people:

A	$22 500	**B**	$17 900	**C**	$21 400
D	$22 500	**E**	$155 300.		

   a) Find the mean and the median of their salaries.
   b) Which does *not* give a fair 'average'? Explain why in one sentence.

11. A farmer has 32 cows to sell. The masses of the cows in kg are:

81	81	82	82	83	84	84	85
85	86	86	87	87	88	89	91
91	92	93	94	96	150	152	153
154	320	370	375	376	380	381	390

   [Total mass = 5028 kg]
   On the telephone to a potential buyer, the farmer describes the cattle and says the 'average' mass is 'over 157 kg'.
   a) Find the mean mass and the median mass.
   b) Which 'average' has the farmer used to describe his cows? Does this average describe the cows fairly?

12. A company sells seeds and claims that the average height of the plants after one year's growth will be 85 cm. A sample of 24 of the plants was measured after one year with the following results (in cm):

6	7	7	9	34	56	85	89
89	90	90	91	91	92	93	93
93	94	95	95	96	97	97	99

   [The sum of the heights is 1788 cm.]
   a) Find the mean and the median height of the sample.
   b) Is the magazine's claim about average height justified?

4.4 Frequency polygons

We have seen earlier on page 145 how a frequency distribution can be shown in the form of a bar chart.

The number of peas in 40 pea pods is shown below. Note: Frequency goes on the vertical axis.

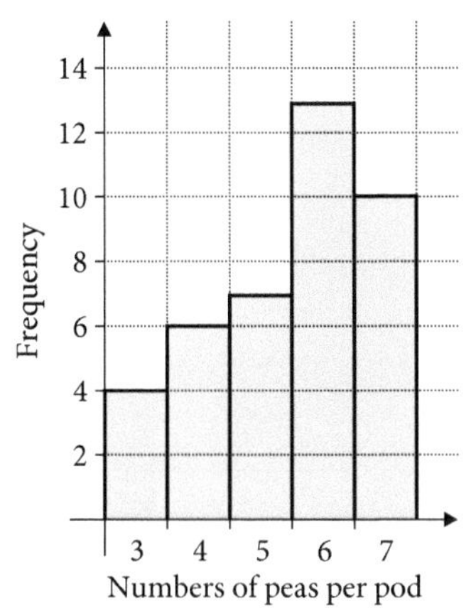

A **frequency polygon** is formed by joining the mid-points of the tops of the bars in a bar chart by straight lines.

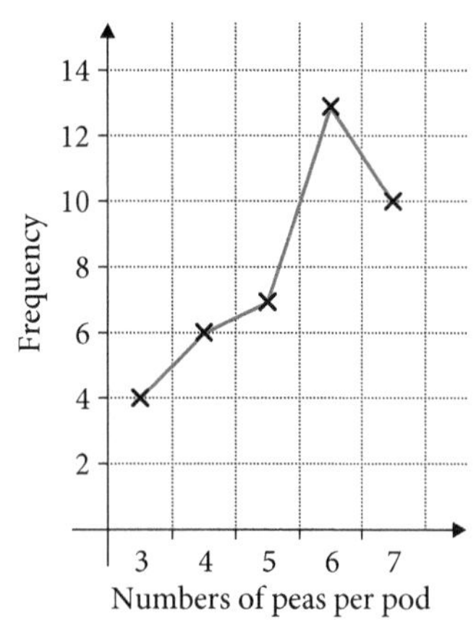

Discrete and continuous data

The data that we record can be either **discrete** or **continuous**.
Discrete data can take only certain values:

- the number of peas in a pod
- the number of children in a class
- shoe sizes.

Continuous data comes from measuring and can take any value:

- height of a child
- weight of an apple
- time taken to boil a kettle.

Class boundaries

The lengths of 36 pea pods were measured and rounded to the nearest mm. So a pea pod which is actually 59.2 mm long is rounded off to 59 mm.

52	80	65	82	77	60	72	83	63
78	84	75	53	73	70	86	55	88
85	59	76	86	73	89	91	76	92
66	93	84	62	79	90	73	68	71

This data can be put into a grouped frequency table.

Length (mm)	Tally	Frequency
$50 \le l < 60$	||||	4
$60 \le l < 70$	~~||||~~ |	6
$70 \le l < 80$	~~||||~~ ~~||||~~ ||	12
$80 \le l < 90$	~~||||~~ ~~||||~~	10
$90 \le l < 100$	||||	4

For the class $50 \le l < 60$, the class boundaries are 50 and 60. The bar will go from 50 to 60 mm.

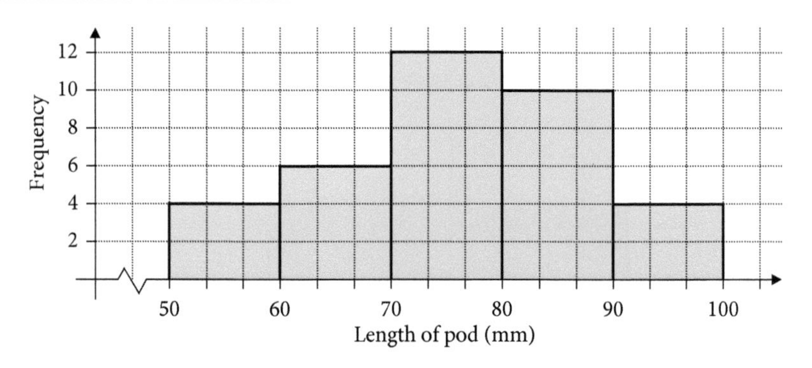

The frequency polygon for this data can be drawn in the same way as with discrete data. Note that you can draw the frequency polygon *without* drawing a bar chart first. You must calculate the mid-points of each group.

For the $50 \le l < 60$ group:

$$\text{mid-point} = \frac{50+60}{2} = 55$$

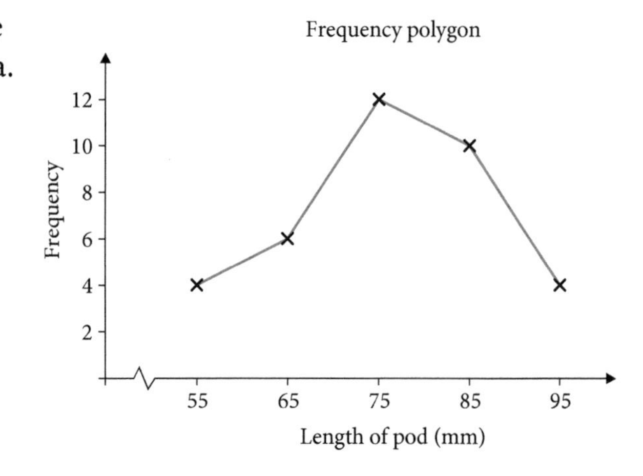

Mid-points

The mid-points of other groups can be calculated as follows:

a)

Mark	Mid-point
0–9	4.5
10–19	14.5

$\left(\frac{0+9}{2}\right)$ $\left(\frac{10+19}{2}\right)$

b)

Height	Mid-point
$150 \leqslant h < 155$	152.5
$155 \leqslant h < 160$	157.5

$\left(\frac{150+155}{2}\right)$ $\left(\frac{155+160}{2}\right)$

Exercise 12

1. In a survey the number of people in 100 cars passing a set of traffic lights was counted. Here are the results:

Number of people in car	0	1	2	3	4	5	6
Frequency	0	10	35	25	20	10	0

a) Draw a bar chart to illustrate this data.

b) On the same graph draw the frequency polygon.

Here we have started the bar chart.
For frequency, use a scale of 1 cm for 5 units.

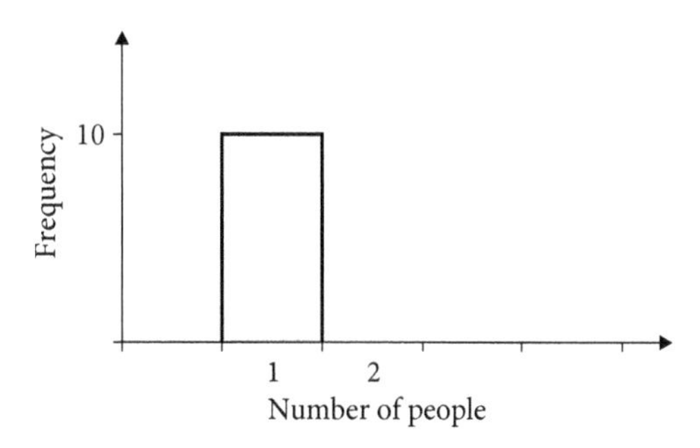

2. The frequency polygon shows the marks obtained by students in a maths test.

a) How many students got 7 marks?

b) How many students were there altogether?

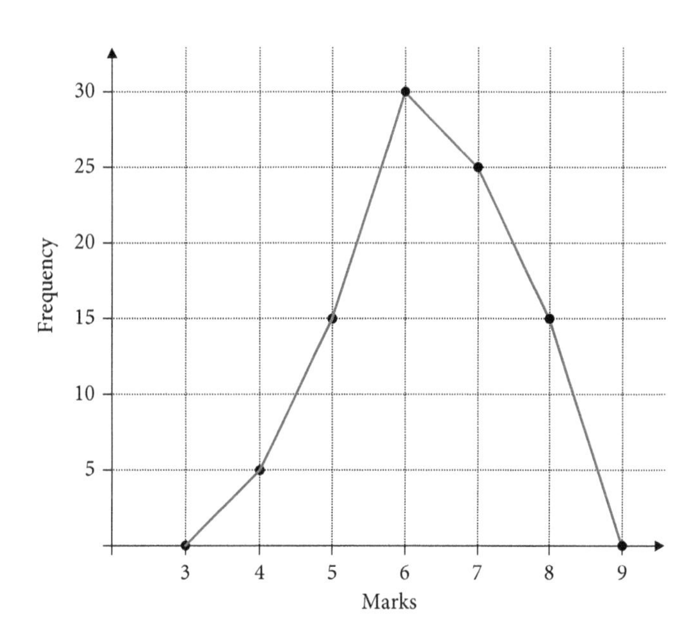

3. The members of several professional basketball teams were measured for their heights. The results were:

Height	Frequency
$180 \leqslant h < 185$	5
$185 \leqslant h < 190$	8
$190 \leqslant h < 195$	15
$195 \leqslant h < 200$	11
$200 \leqslant h < 205$	6
$205 \leqslant h < 210$	2

Draw a bar chart and a frequency polygon to illustrate this data.

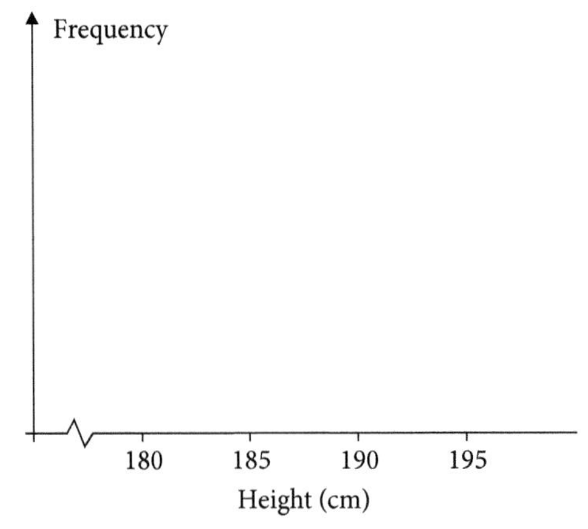

4. Two frequency polygons are shown giving the distribution of the masses of players in two different sports A and B.

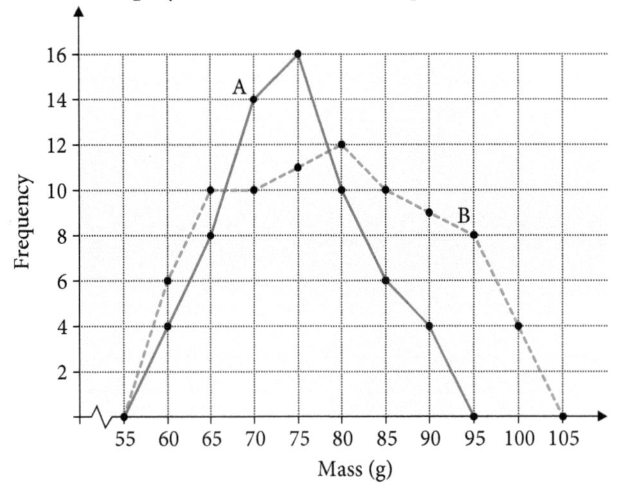

a) How many people played sport A?

b) Comment on two differences between the two frequency polygons.

c) Either for A or for B suggest a sport where you would expect the frequency polygon of mass to have this shape. Explain in one sentence why you have chosen that sport.

5. A scientist measures the heights of some raspberry plants and also the total mass of fruit collected. She does this for two sets of plants: one with fertiliser and one without it. Here are the frequency polygons:

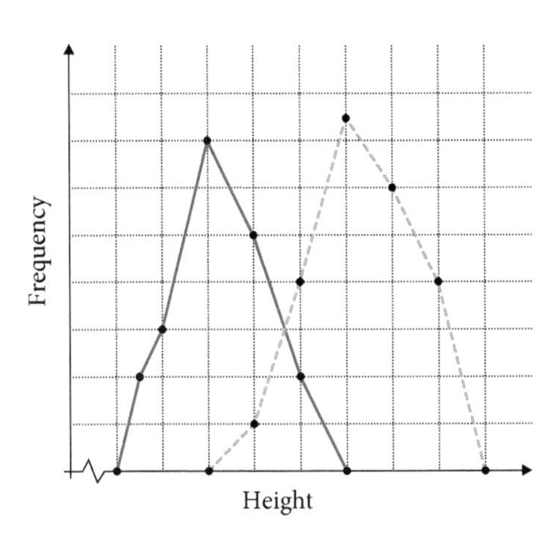

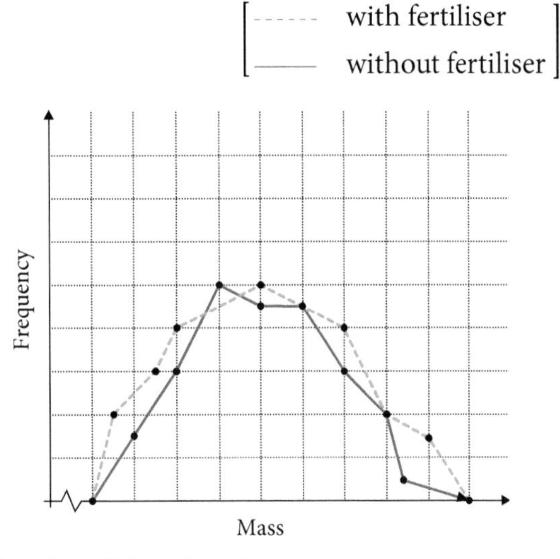

a) What effect did the fertiliser have on the heights of the plants?

b) What effect was there on the mass of fruit collected?

Revision exercise 4A

1. In a test, the marks of nine students were 7, 5, 2, 7, 4, 9, 7, 6, 6. Find
   a) the mean mark
   b) the median mark
   c) the modal mark.

2. The mean height of 10 boys is 1.60 m and the mean height of 15 girls is 1.52 m. Find the mean height of the 25 boys and girls.

3. a) The mean mass of 10 boys in a class is 56 kg.
      i) Calculate the total mass of these 10 boys.
      ii) Another boy, whose mass is 67 kg, joins the group. Calculate the mean mass of the 11 boys.
   b) A group of 10 boys whose mean mass is 56 kg joins a group of 20 girls whose mean mass is 47 kg. Calculate the mean mass of the 30 children.

4. The mean of four numbers is 21.
   a) Calculate the sum of the four numbers.

   Six other numbers have a mean of 18.

   b) Calculate the mean of the ten numbers.

5. The pie chart shows the after school activities of 200 students.

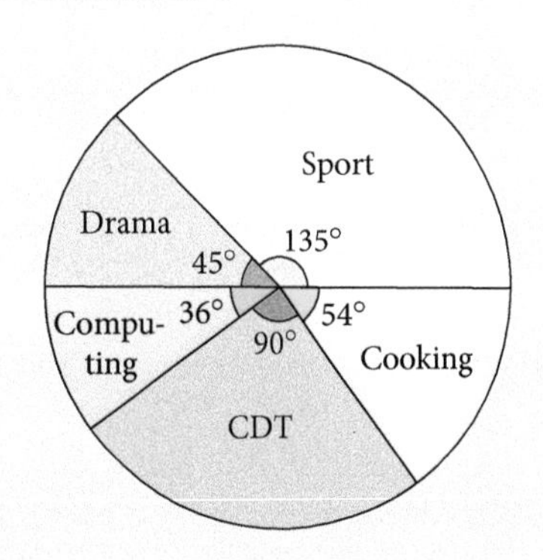

   a) How many students do drama?
   b) How many students do sport?
   c) How many students do computing?

6. Forty teenagers were asked to name their favourite holiday destinations with the following results:

   Spain 12, France 5, Greece 10

   Portugal 4, U.S.A. 9

   Display this information on a pie chart, showing the angles corresponding to each country.

7. The chart shows the rainfall recorded in a village in one month.

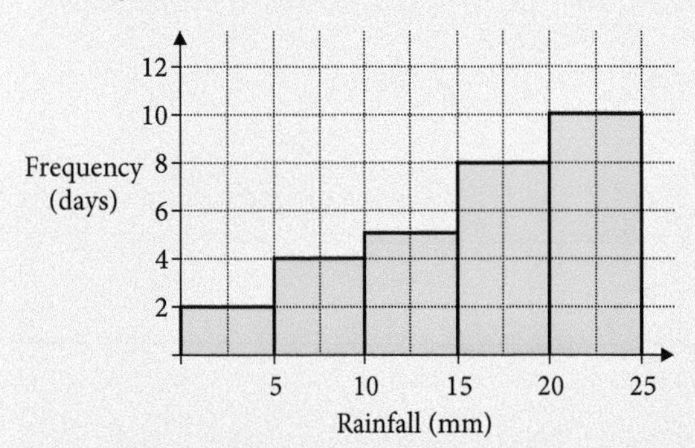

   a) How many days were there in the month?

   b) For how many days were there 10 mm or more of rain?

   c) Chew Ling said 'It rained more at the end of the month'. Explain whether Chew Ling is right or wrong.

8. The *median* age of five people was 11 and the range of their ages was 3. Write each sentence below and write near to it whether it is *True, Possible* or *False*.

   a) Every person was either 10 or 11 years old.

   b) The oldest person in the tent was 14 years old.

   c) The mean age of the people was less than 11 years.

9. During 2016, an amateur weather enthusiast kept a record of the highest temperature in London on the first day of each month. She recorded the temperatures to the nearest 1°C. Here are the results:

   9 12 12 9 14 12 20 17 23 14 13 7

   a) Complete the following stem-and-leaf diagram to display this data.

Stem	Leaf
0	
1	
2	

   Key
   1 | 2 means 12°C

   b) For the first day of the month in London during 2016, what was:

      i) the median temperature?

      ii) the modal temperature?

      iii) the range of the temperatures?

Examination-style exercise 4B

1. A travel brochure contains 24 pictures from different countries. The table shows how many pictures there are from each country.

Country	Number of pictures	Angle in a pie chart
Argentina	6	90°
South Africa	10	150°
Australia	3	
New Zealand		

(a) Complete the table. [3]

(b) Complete the pie chart accurately and label the sectors for South Africa, Australia and New Zealand. [2]

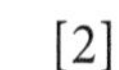

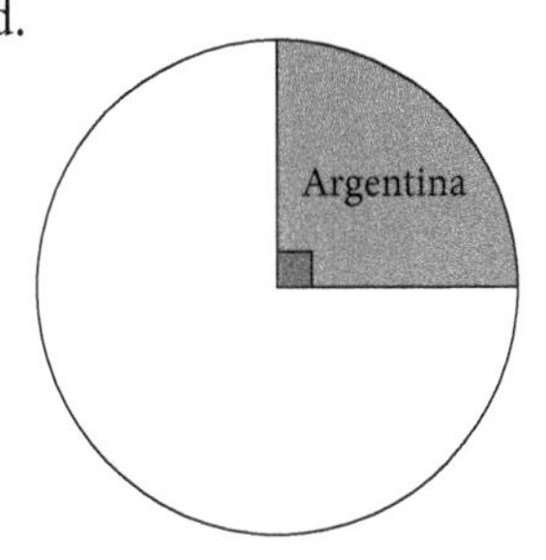

Cambridge IGCSE Mathematics 0580
Paper 11 Q22 November 2008

2. Margarita keeps a record of all her marks for science experiments, as shown in the table below.

Mark	5	6	7	8	9	10
Frequency	1	5	10	9	7	3

(a) i) How many science experiments did Margarita do? [1]

ii) Write down the mode. [1]

iii) Find the median. [1]

iv) Calculate the mean. [3]

(b) Margarita draws a pie chart to show this information. The sectors for her marks of 5, 6, 7 and 8 have already been drawn.

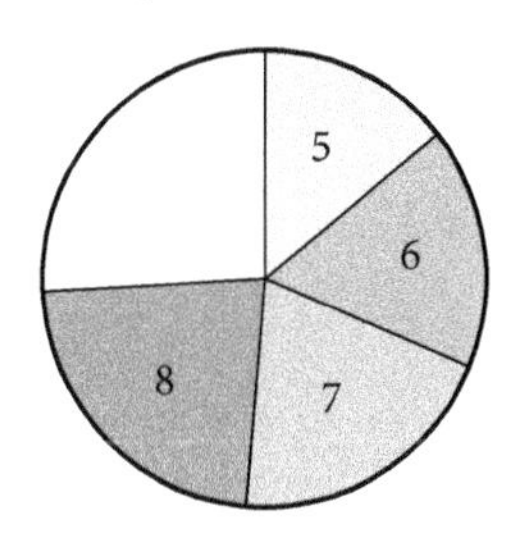

i) Calculate the angle of the sector for her mark of 9. [2]

ii) Complete the pie chart accurately. [1]

Cambridge IGCSE Mathematics 0580
Paper 3 Q1 November 2007

3. Which word describes the correlation in the scatter graph below?

Positive Negative None [1]

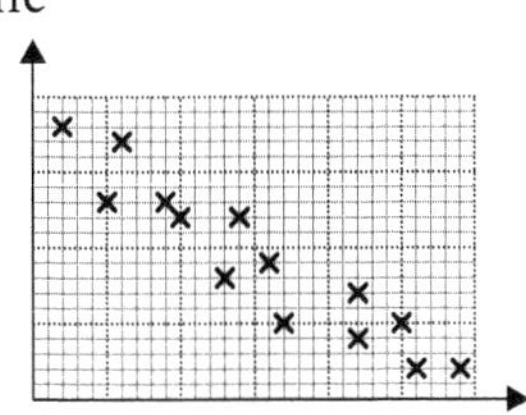

Cambridge IGCSE Mathematics 0580
Paper 1 Q3 November 2006

4. Ann plots a scatter diagram of rate of reaction against temperature.

   As the temperature increases, the rate of reaction also increases.

   Which one of the following types of correlation will her scatter diagram show?

   Positive   Negative   Zero [1]

5. A school has 780 students.

   (a) On the last day of term, 85% of the students were present.

   Calculate how many students were absent. [2]

   (b) The table shows the number of students attending school in one week.

Monday	Tuesday	Wednesday	Thursday	Friday
756	738	760	759	767

   For these values,

   i) calculate the mean, [2]

   ii) find the median, [1]

   iii) find the range. [1]

6. Ahmed selected a sample of 10 students from his school and measured their hand spans and heights. The results are shown in the table below.

Hand span (cm)	15	18.5	22.5	26	19	23	17.5	25	20.5	22
Height (cm)	154	156	164	178	162	170	154	168	168	160

   He calculated the mean hand span to be 20.9 cm and the range of the hand spans to be 11 cm.

   (a) Calculate

   i) the mean **height** in cm, [2]

   ii) the range of the **heights** in cm. [2]

(b) In order to compare the two measures, he used a scatter diagram.
The first three points are plotted on the grid.

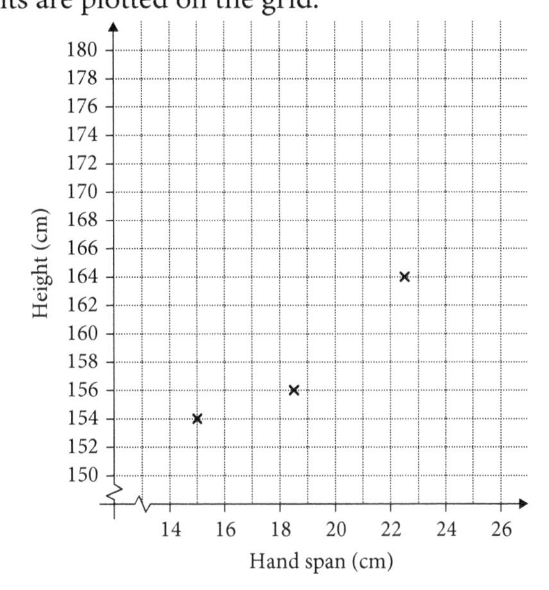

i) Complete the scatter diagram by plotting the remaining 7 points. [2]

ii) Draw the line of best fit on the grid. [1]

iii) Use the line of best fit to estimate the height of a student with hand span 21 cm. [1]

iv) Which one of the following words describes the correlation?

Positive Negative Zero [1]

v) What does this indicate about the relationship between hand span and height? [1]

Cambridge IGCSE Mathematics 0580
Paper 3 Q6 June 2006

7. **(a)** Naomi records the sizes of the 34 pairs of shoes that her shop sells in one day.

4 10 5 6 4 8 6 4 7 3 9 7 4

7 3 5 4 6 5 10 7 5 5 6 4 7

7 6 6 5 5 3 5 6

i) Using the list above complete the frequency table.

Shoe size	3	4	5	6	7	8	9	10
Frequency								

[3]

ii) Calculate the mean of those shoe sizes. [3]

iii) Find the range of these sizes. [1]

iv) Find the mode of these sizes. [1]

v) Work out the median shoe size. [2]

vi) Calculate the percentage of all the pairs of shoes that are size 7. [2]

vii) Naomi orders 306 pairs of shoes to sell in her shop. Estimate how many of these pairs of shoes should be size 7. [2]

(b) Findlay draws a bar chart to show how many pairs of shoes he has sold in his shop in one week.

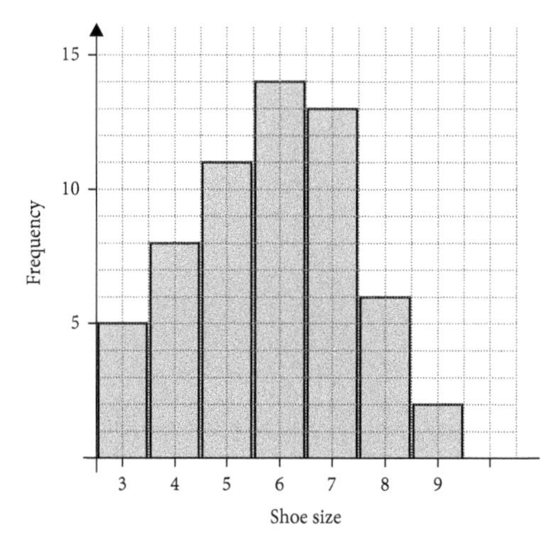

i) Use the information in the bar chart to copy and complete the frequency table below. [2]

Shoe size	3 and 4	5 and 6	7 and 8	9 and 10
Frequency				

ii) Which is the modal class in the frequency table? [1]

Cambridge IGCSE Mathematics 0580
Paper 3 Q8 November 2006

8. The results of the men's 400 metre race from the 2012 and 2016 Olympic Games are displayed in the following stem-and-leaf diagram. The times are given to the nearest tenth of a second.

Key (2012)
5 | 44 means 44.5 sec

2012		2016
9	43	0 8 9
8 8 8 5 5	44	0 3 4 5 6
1 0	45	

Key (2016)
44 | 3 means 44.3 sec

(a) Calculate

i) the median time for each year, [2]

ii) the range of the times for each year. [2]

(b) A newspaper report says 'in 2016 the athletes were both faster and more consistent'. Comment on the accuracy of this statement. [2]

5 Shape and Space 2

C4.1 Use and interpret the geometrical terms: point, line, parallel, bearing, right angle, acute, obtuse and reflex angles, perpendicular, similarity and congruence. Use and interpret vocabulary of triangles, quadrilaterals, circles, polygons and simple solid figures including nets.

C6.1 Interpret and use three-figure bearings.

C6.2 Apply Pythagoras' theorem.

C7.1 Describe a translation by using a vector represented by e.g. $\begin{pmatrix} x \\ y \end{pmatrix}$, $\overrightarrow{AB}$ or **a**. Add and subtract vectors. Multiply a vector by a scalar.

C7.2 Reflect simple plane figures in horizontal or vertical lines. Rotate simple plane figures about the origin, vertices or midpoints of edges of the figures, through multiples of 90°. Construct given translations and enlargements of simple plane figures. Recognise and describe reflections, rotations, translations and enlargements.

5.1 Transforming shapes

Reflection

A′B′C′D′ is the **image** of ABCD after reflection in the broken line (the mirror line).

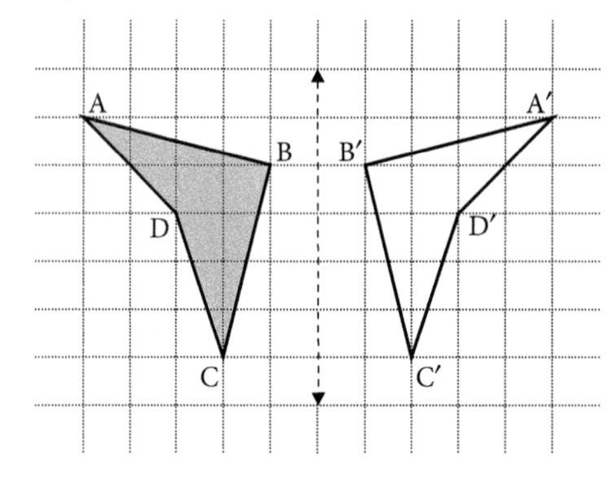

Exercise 1

On squared paper draw the object and its image after reflection in the broken line.

1.

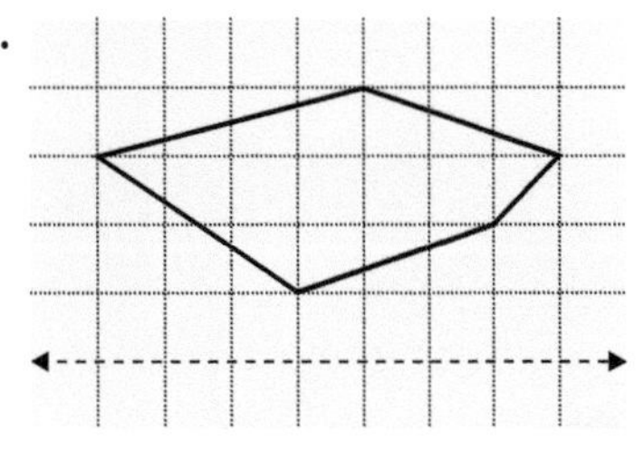

2.

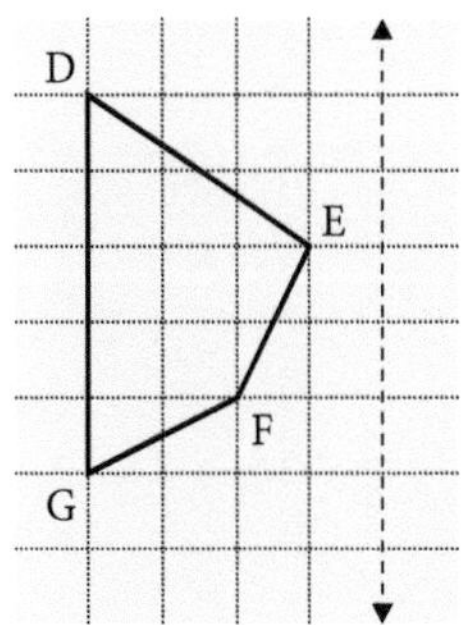

3.

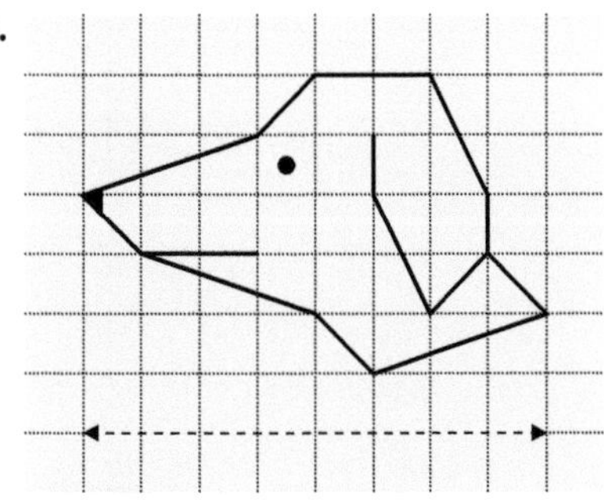

4.

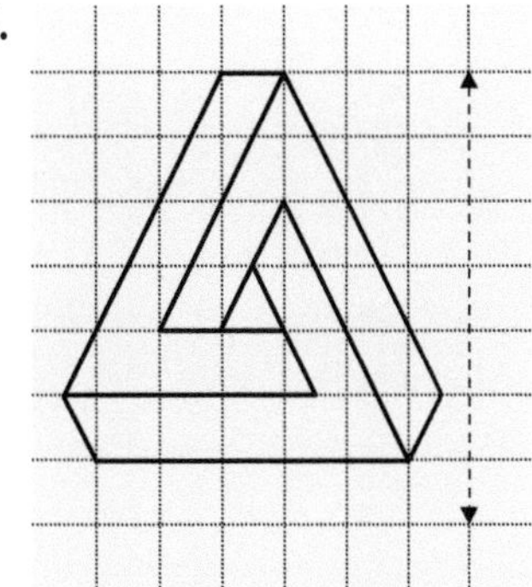

5.

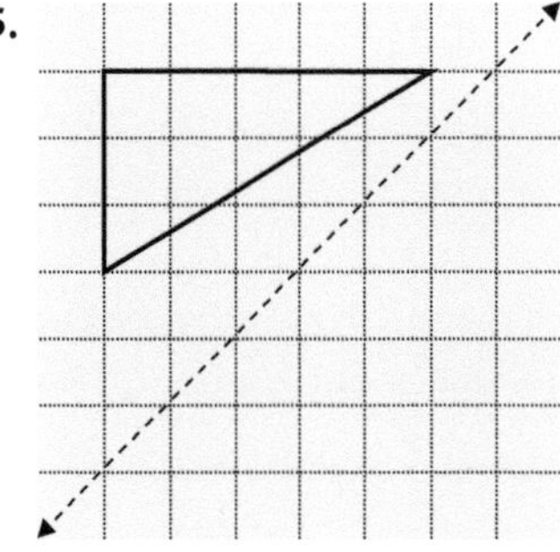

6.

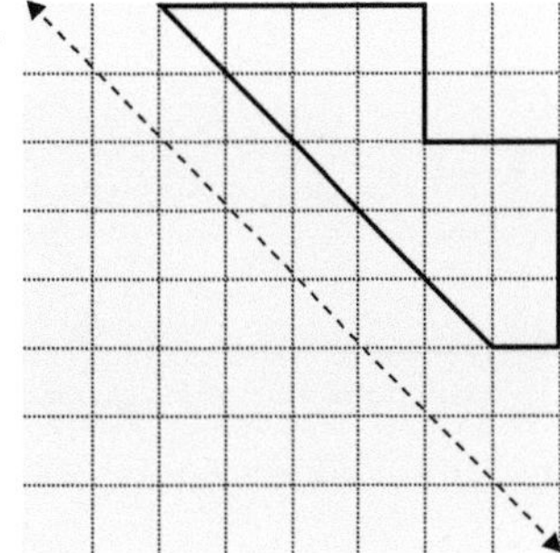

7.

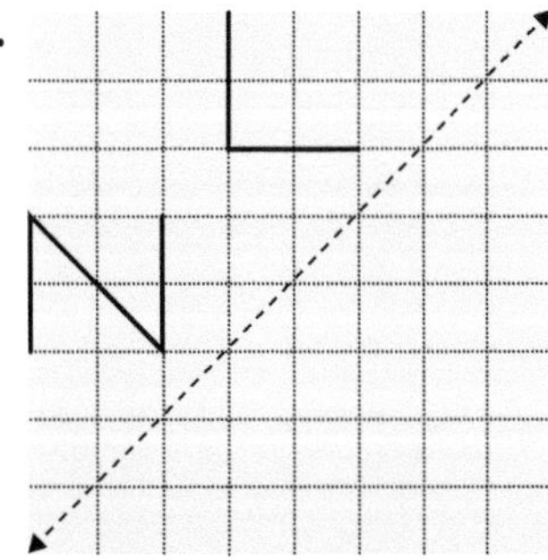

8.

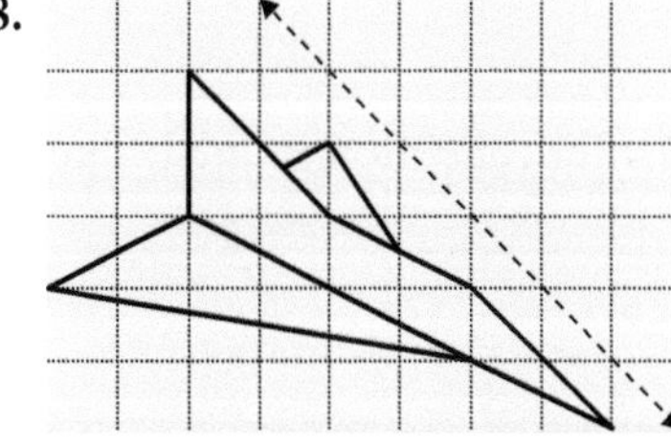

9.

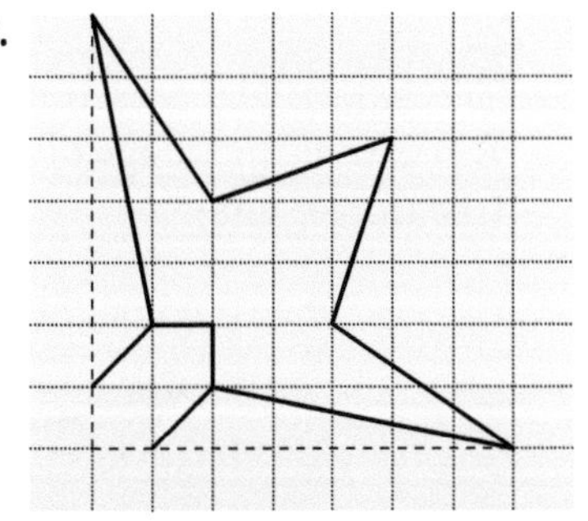

Reflect this shape in *both* of the broken lines.

Exercise 2

1. Copy the diagram below.

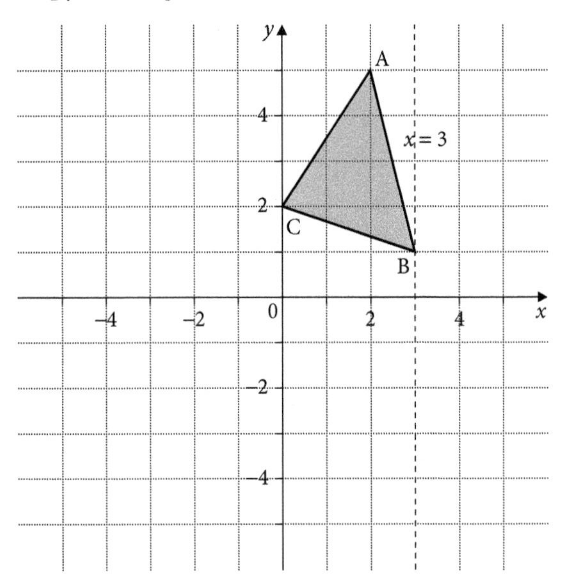

Draw the image of ΔABC after reflection in:

a) the x-axis. Label it $\Delta 1$

b) the y-axis. Label it $\Delta 2$

c) the line $x = 3$. Label it $\Delta 3$.

For Questions **2** to **5** draw a pair of axes so that both x and y can take values from -7 to $+7$.

2. **a)** Plot and label P(7, 5), Q(7, 2), R(5, 2).

b) Draw the lines $y = -1$, $x = 1$ and $y = x$. Use dotted lines.

c) Draw the image of ΔPQR after reflection in:

i) the line $y = -1$. Label it $\Delta 1$

ii) the line $x = 1$. Label it $\Delta 2$

iii) the line $y = x$. Label it $\Delta 3$.

d) Write down the coordinates of the image of point P in each case.

3. **a)** Plot and label L(7, −5), M(7, −1), N(5, −1).

b) Draw the lines $y = x$ and $y = -x$. Use dotted lines.

c) Draw the image of ΔLMN after reflection in:

i) the x-axis. Label it $\Delta 1$

ii) the line $y = x$. Label it $\Delta 2$

iii) the line $y = -x$. Label it $\Delta 3$.

d) Write down the coordinates of the image of point L in each case.

4. **a)** Draw the line $x + y = 7$. [It passes through (0, 7) and (7, 0).]
   b) Draw Δ1 at (−3, −1), (−1, −1), (−1, −4).
   c) Reflect Δ1 in the y-axis onto Δ2.
   d) Reflect Δ2 in the x-axis onto Δ3.
   e) Reflect Δ3 in the line $x + y = 7$ onto Δ4.
   f) Reflect Δ4 in the y-axis onto Δ5.
   g) Write down the coordinates of Δ5.
5. **a)** Draw the lines $y = 2$, $x = -1$ and $y = x$.
   b) Draw Δ1 at (1, −3), (−3, −3), (−3, −5).
   c) Reflect Δ1 in the line $y = x$ onto Δ2.
   d) Reflect Δ2 in the line $y = 2$ onto Δ3.
   e) Reflect Δ3 in the line $x = -1$ onto Δ4.
   f) Reflect Δ4 in the line $y = x$ onto Δ5.
   g) Write down the coordinates of Δ5.
6. Find the equation of the mirror line for the reflection:
   a) Δ1 onto Δ2
   b) Δ1 onto Δ3
   c) Δ1 onto Δ4
   d) Δ1 onto Δ5.

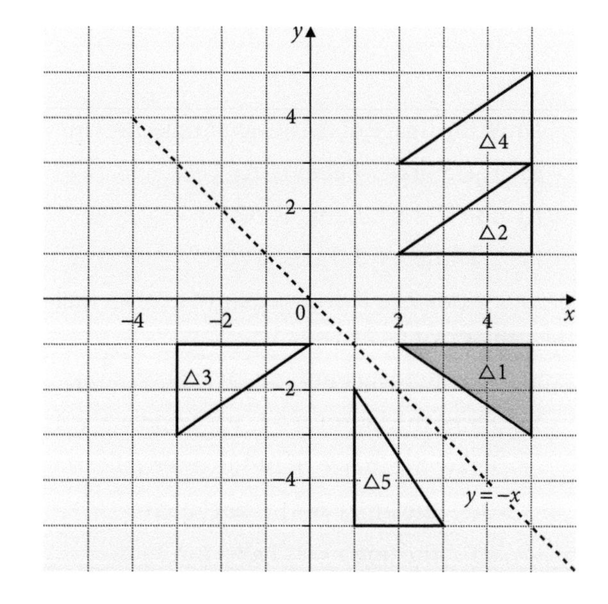

Rotation

ΔA′ B′C′ is the image of ΔABC after a 90° clockwise rotation about centre C.

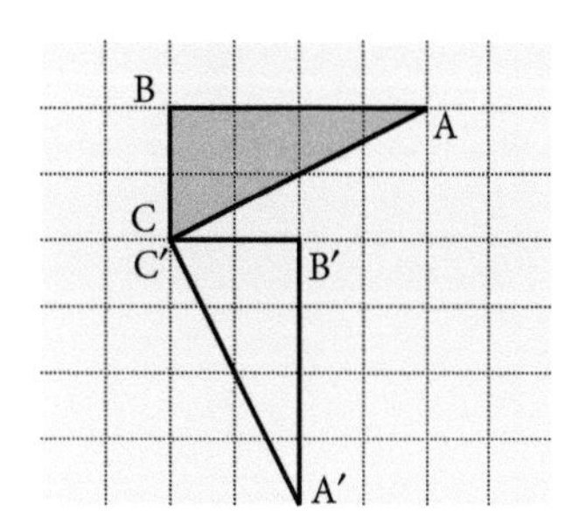

Draw ΔABC on tracing paper and then put the tip of your pencil on C. Turn the tracing paper 90° clockwise about C. The tracing paper now shows the position of ΔA′ B′C′. Notice that you need three things to describe a rotation:

a) the centre
b) the angle
c) the direction (e.g. clockwise).

Exercise 3

Draw the object and its image under the rotation given.

Take O as the centre of rotation in each case.

1.

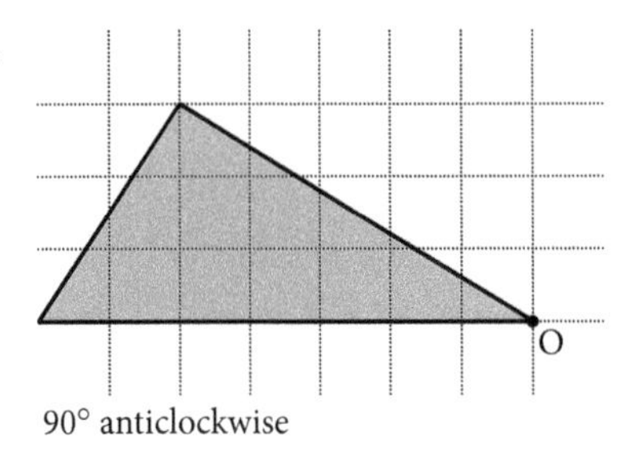

90° anticlockwise

2.

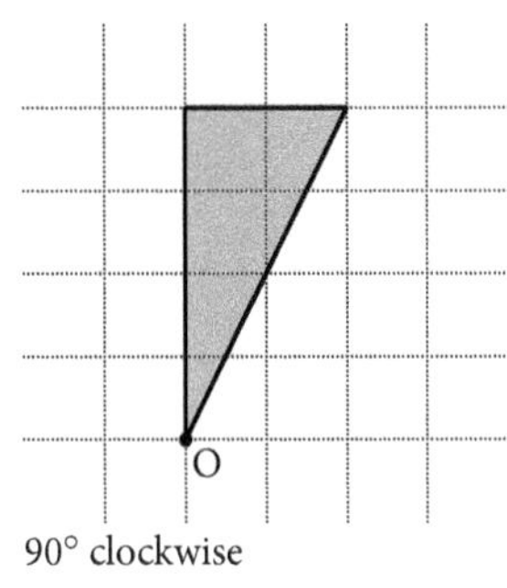

90° clockwise

3.

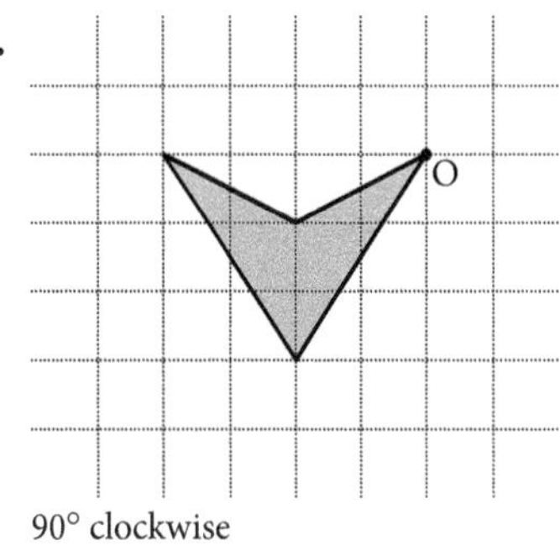

90° clockwise

4.

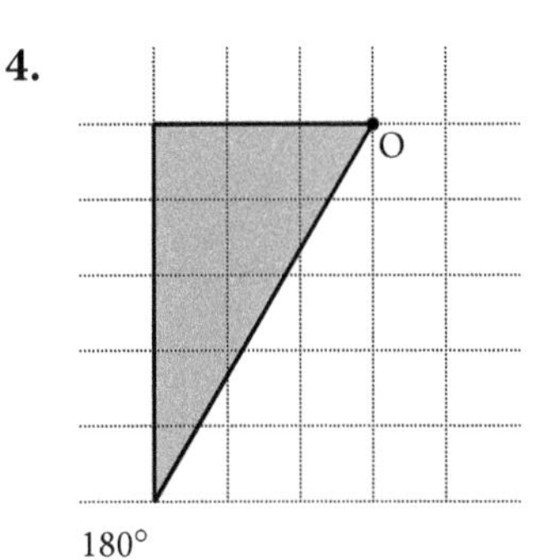

180°

5.

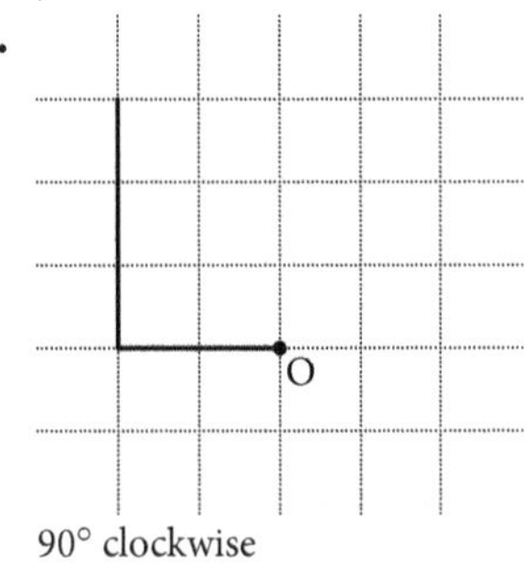

90° clockwise

6.

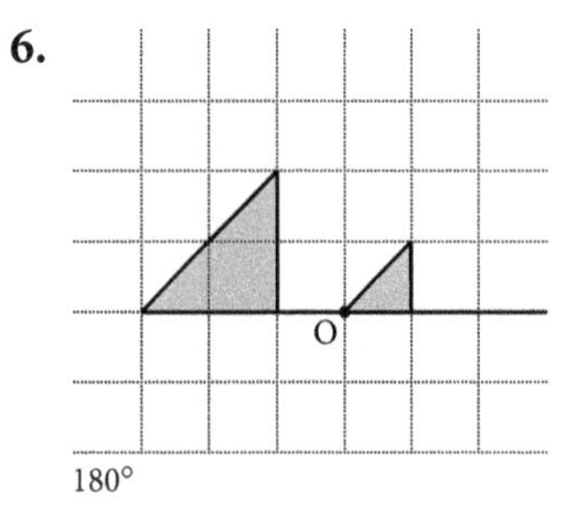

180°

7. The shape on the right has been rotated about several different centres to form the pattern below.

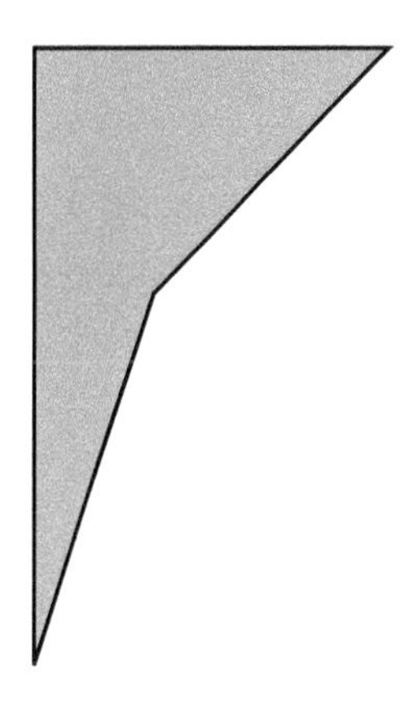

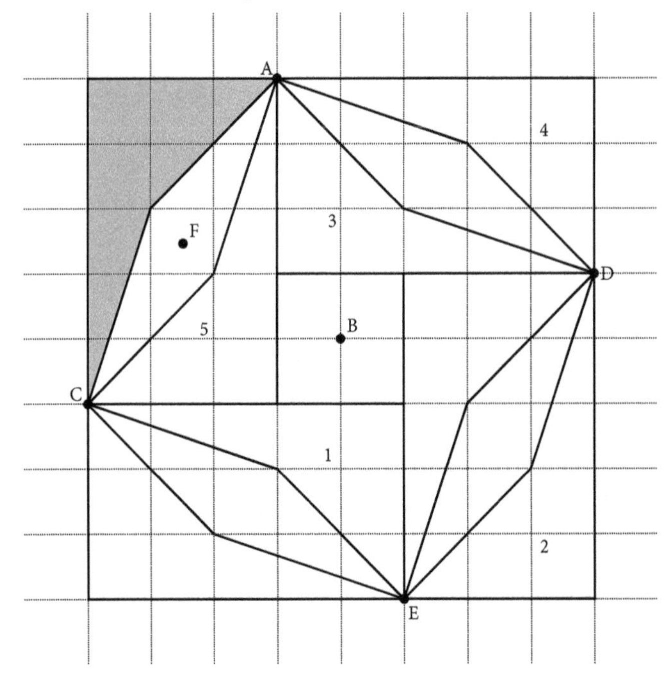

Describe the rotation which takes the shaded shape onto shape 1, shape 2, shape 3, shape 4 and shape 5. For each one, give the centre (A, B, C, D, E or F), the angle and the direction of the rotation. [e.g. 'centre C, 90°, clockwise']

Exercise 4

1. Copy the diagram on the right.
   a) Rotate ΔABC 90° clockwise about (0, 0). Label it Δ1.
   b) Rotate ΔDEF 180° clockwise about (0, 0). Label it Δ2.
   c) Rotate ΔGHI 90° clockwise about (0, 0). Label it Δ3.

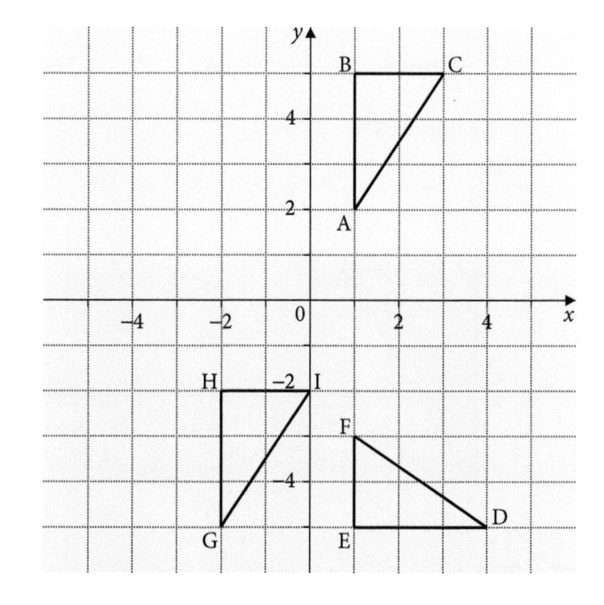

For Questions **2** and **3** draw a pair of axes with values of x and y from −7 to + 7.

2. a) Plot Δ1 at (2, 3), (6, 3), (3, 6).
   b) Rotate Δ1 90° clockwise about (2, 3) onto Δ2.
   c) Rotate Δ2 180° about (0, 0) onto Δ3.
   d) Rotate Δ3 90° anticlockwise about (−2, 1) onto Δ4.
   e) Write down the coordinates of Δ4.
3. a) Plot Δ1 at (4, 4), (6, 6), (2, 6).
   b) Rotate Δ1 90° anticlockwise about (4, 4) onto Δ2.
   c) Rotate Δ2 90° anticlockwise about (2, 2) onto Δ3.
   d) Rotate Δ3 90° clockwise about (−2, 2) onto Δ4.
   e) Write down the coordinates of Δ4.

Finding the centre of a rotation

Exercise 5

In Questions **1** to **3** copy the diagram exactly and then use tracing paper to find the centre of the rotation which takes the shaded shape onto the unshaded shape. Mark the centre of rotation with a cross.

1.

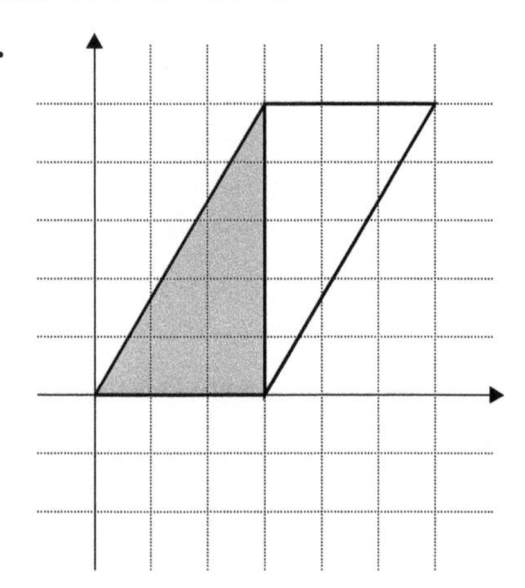

2.

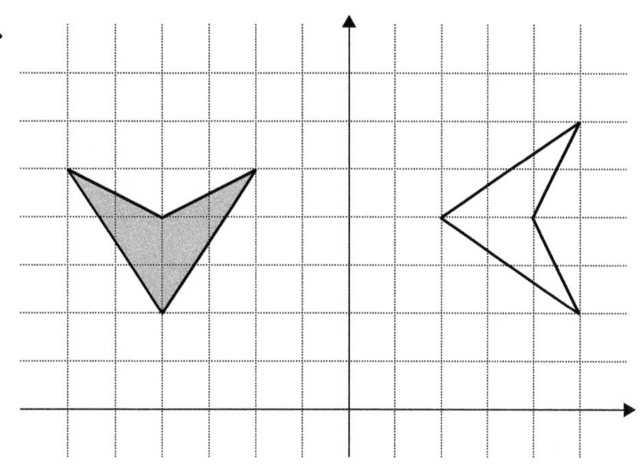

3.

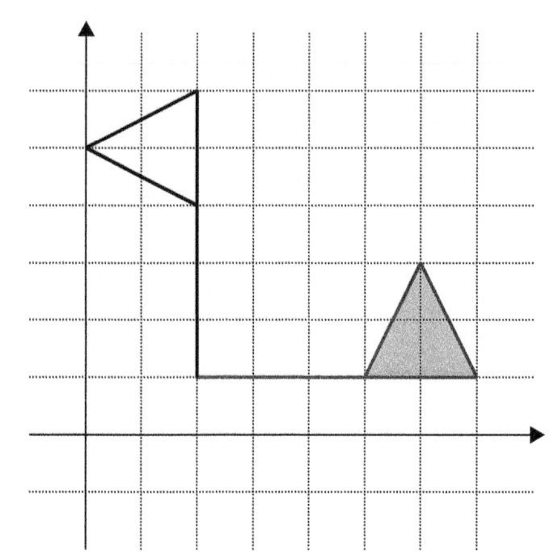

Enlargement

A

B

C

Photo A has been enlarged to give photos B and C.

Notice that the shape of the face is exactly the same in all the pictures.

Photo A measures 22 mm by 27 mm
Photo B measures 44 mm by 54 mm
Photo C measures 66 mm by 81 mm

From A to B both the width and the height have been multiplied by 2. We say B is an enlargement of A with a *scale factor* of 2. Similarly C is an enlargement of A with a scale factor of 3.

Also C is an enlargement of B with a scale factor of $1\frac{1}{2}$.

The scale factor of an enlargement can be found by dividing corresponding lengths on two pictures.

In this enlargement the scale factor is $\frac{21}{14}(=1.5)$

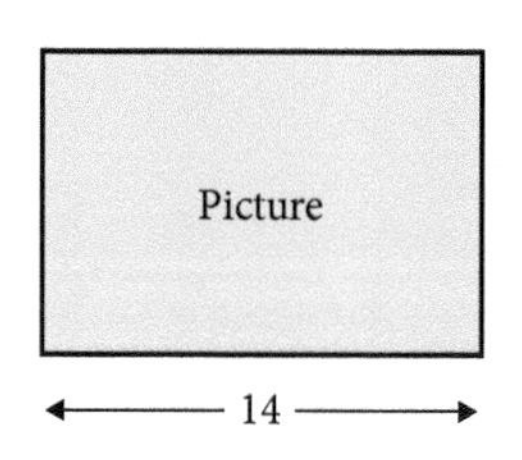

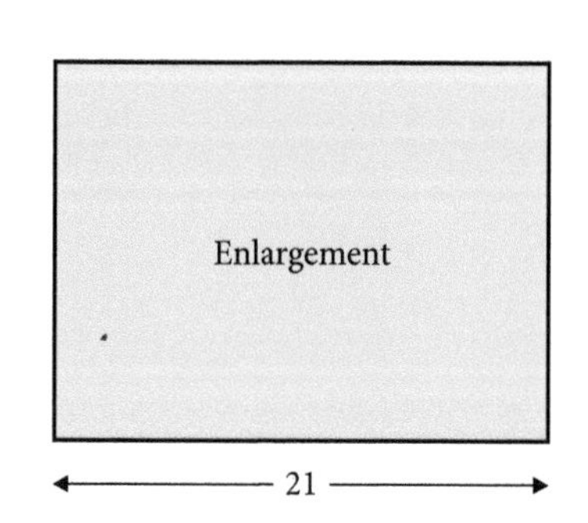

Exercise 6

1. This picture is to be enlarged and we want the enlargement to fit exactly in a frame. Which of the following frames will the picture fit?

   Write 'yes' or 'no'.

   a) 100 mm by 76 mm
   b) 110 mm by 76 mm
   c) 150 mm by 114 mm
   d) 75 mm by 57 mm.

38 mm

50 mm

2. This picture is to be enlarged so that it fits exactly into the frame. Find the length x.

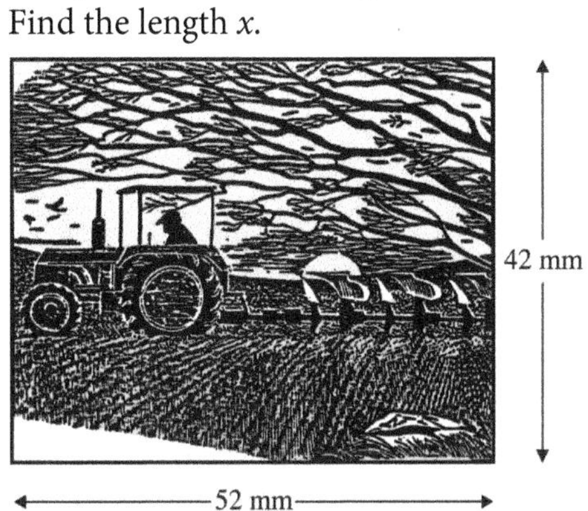

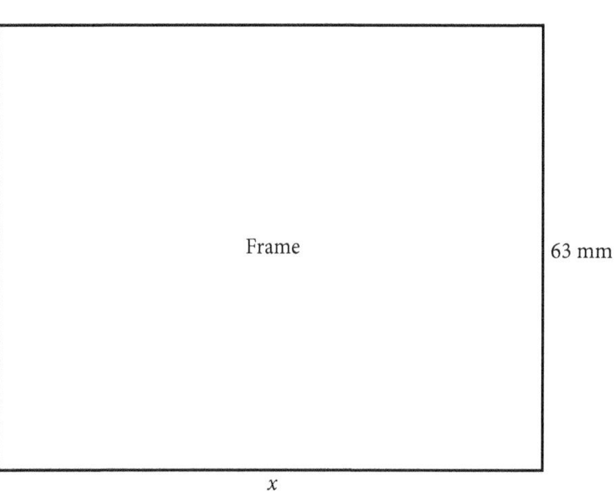

3. This picture is enlarged or reduced to fit into each of the frames shown. Calculate y and z.

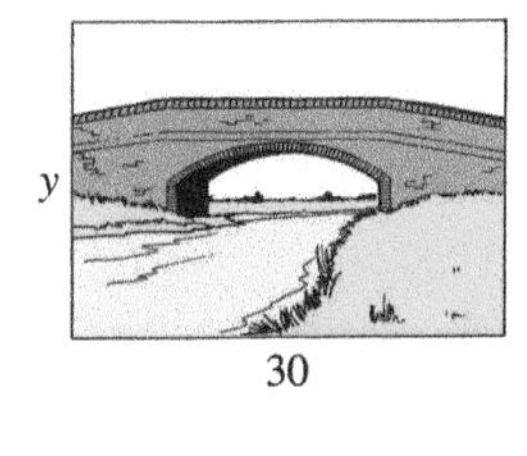

4. Here we have started to draw a two times enlargement of a house using the squares.

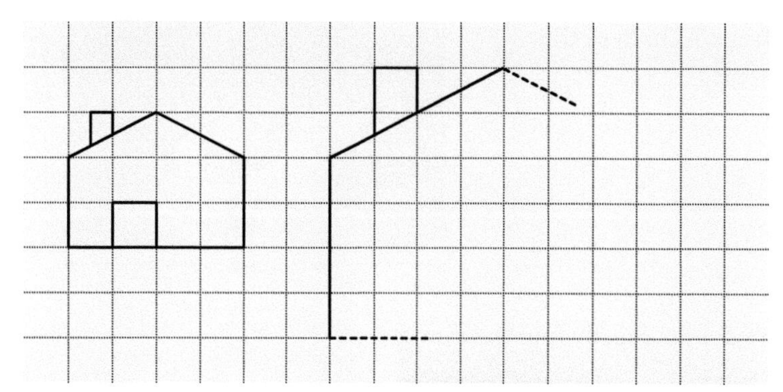

Draw the complete enlargement in your book (use squared paper).

5. Draw a three times enlargement of this figure.

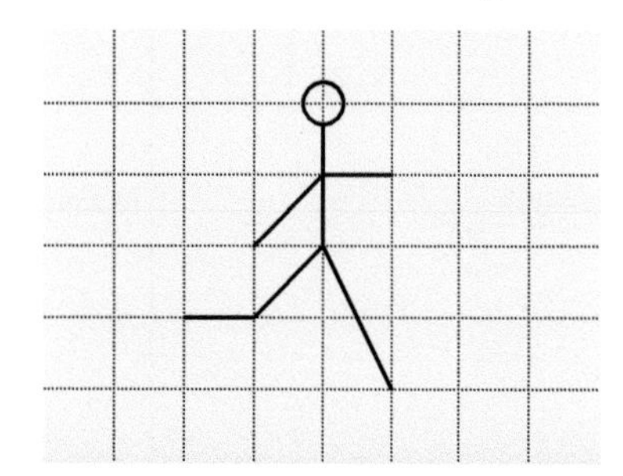

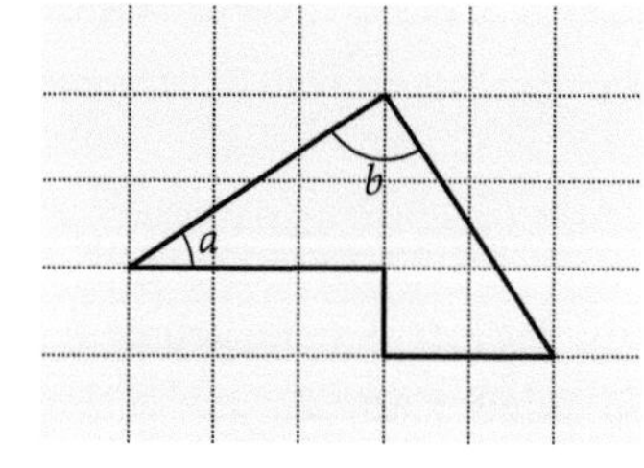

6. Draw a two times and a three times enlargement of this shape. Measure the angles a and b on each enlargement.

   Write the correct version of this sentence: 'In an enlargement, the angles in a shape are changed/unchanged.'

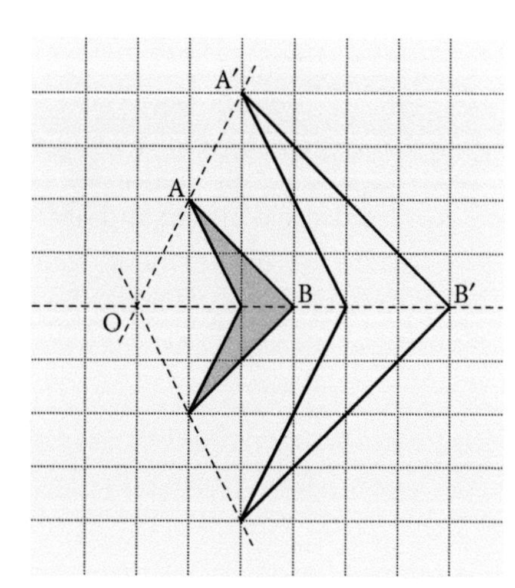

7. This diagram shows an arrowhead and its enlargement. Notice that lines drawn through corresponding points (A, A′ or B, B′) all go through one point O.

   This point is called the centre of enlargement.

   Copy and complete:

   OA′ = ______ × OA

   OB′ = ______ × OB.

8. Copy this shape and its enlargement. Draw construction lines to find the centre of enlargement.

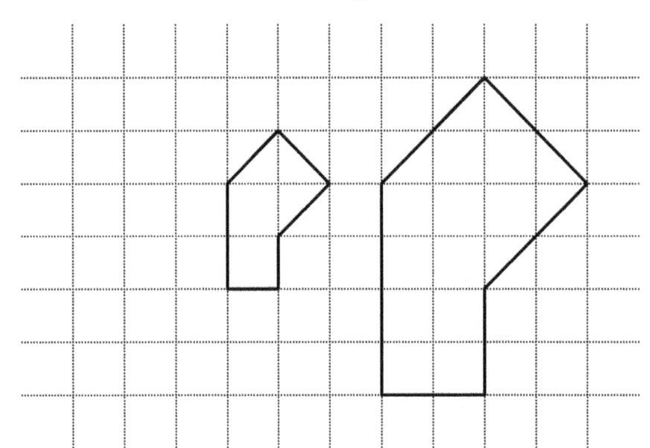

9. In this diagram, $\Delta 1$ is a two times enlargement of the shaded triangle with O_1 as centre of enlargement.

Also $\Delta 2$ is a three times enlargement of the shaded triangle with O_2 as centre of enlargement.

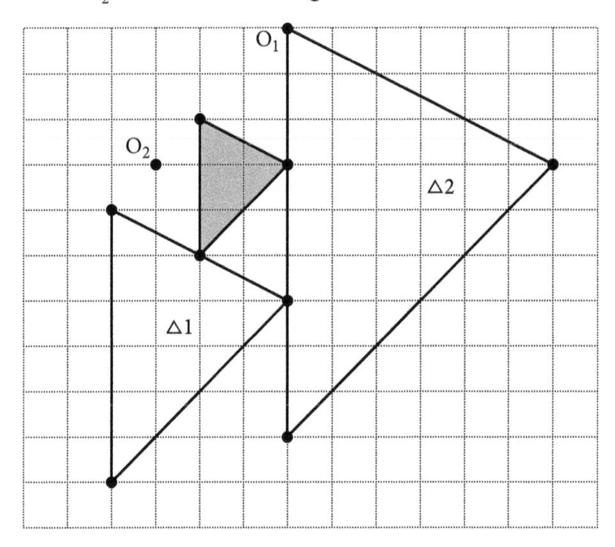

a) Copy the diagram and draw construction lines to find the centre of enlargement from $\Delta 1$ onto $\Delta 2$.

b) What is the scale factor for the enlargement $\Delta 1$ onto $\Delta 2$?

Leave space on the left side of the diagram.

For a mathematical description of an enlargement we need two things:

a) the scale factor **b)** the centre of enlargement.

Example

Enlarge triangle ABC onto triangle A′ B′C′ with a scale factor of 3 and centre O.

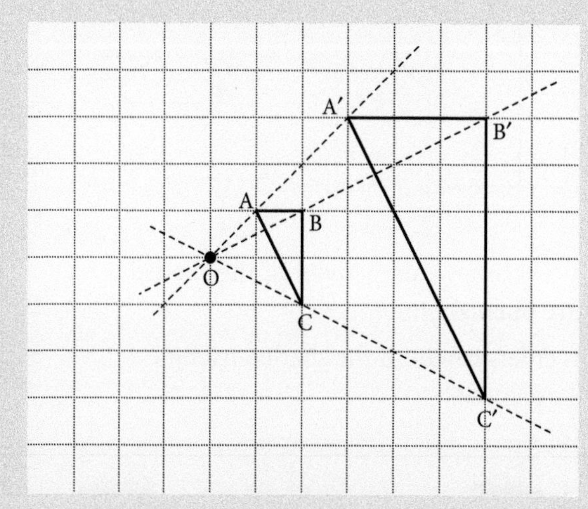

Note: OA′ = 3 × OA; OB′ = 3 × OB; OC′ = 3 × OC.
All lengths are measured from the *centre of enlargement*.

Exercise 7

In Questions **1** to **6** copy the diagram and draw an enlargement using the centre O and the scale factor given.

1.

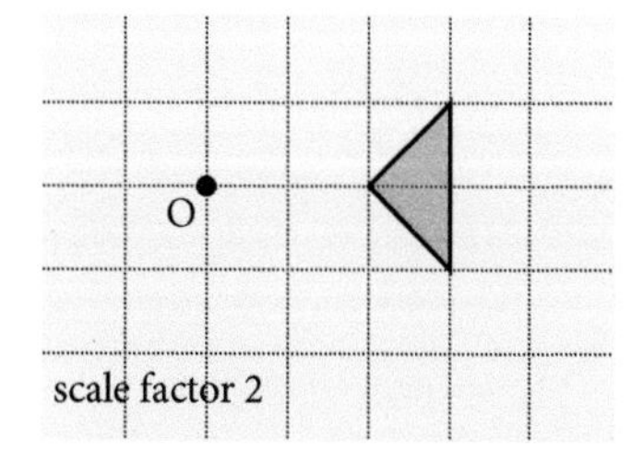

2.

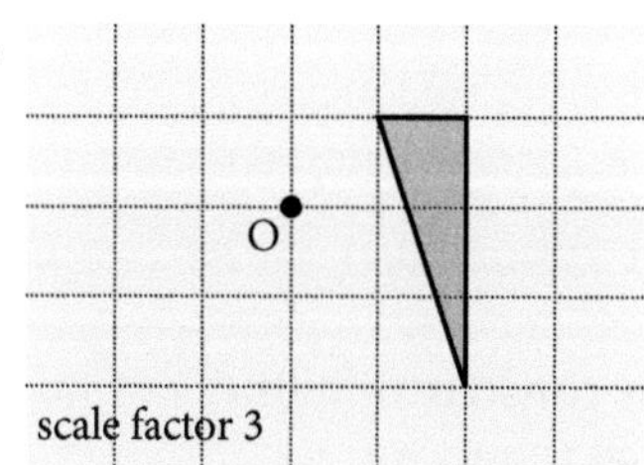

3.

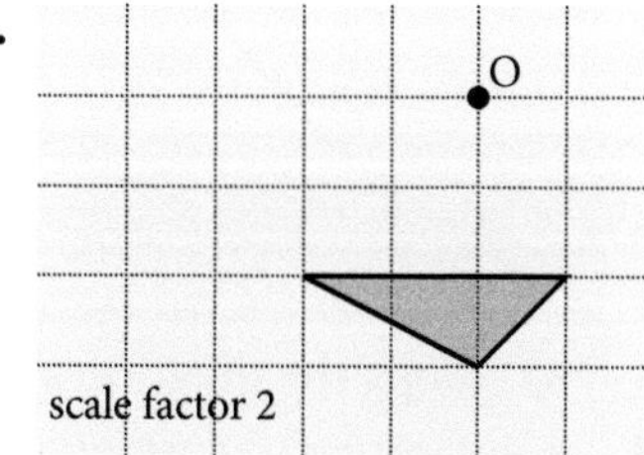

4.

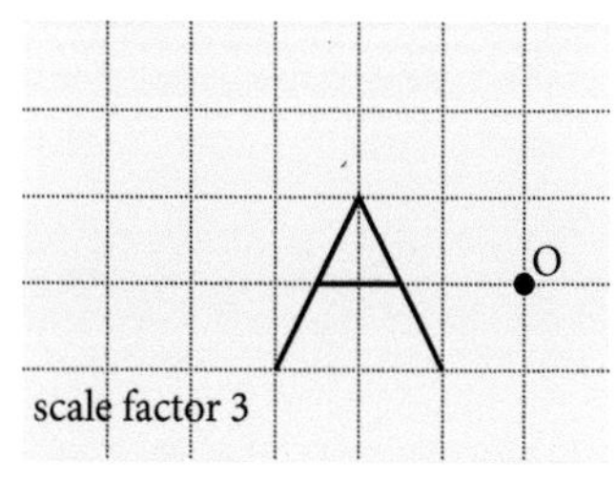

5.

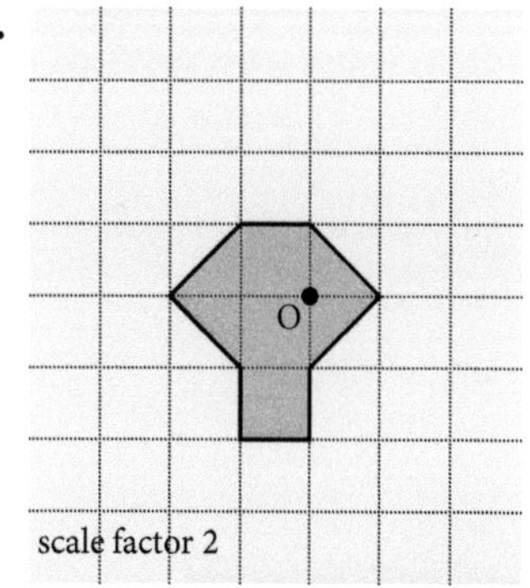

6.

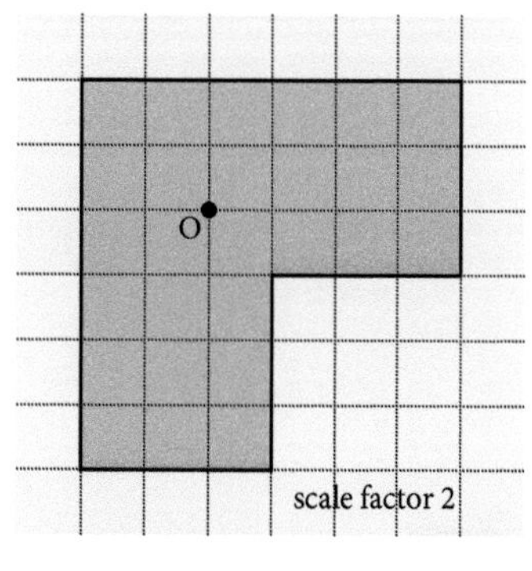

7. **a)** Copy the diagram on the right.

   b) Draw the image of Δ1 after enlargement with scale factor 3, centre (0, 0).
   Label the image Δ4.

   c) Draw the image of Δ2 after enlargement with scale factor 2, centre (−1, 3).
   Label the image Δ5.

   d) Draw the image of Δ3 after enlargement with scale factor 2, centre (−1, −5).
   Label the image Δ6.

   e) Write down the coordinates of the 'pointed ends' of Δ4, Δ5 and Δ6.
   [The 'pointed end' is the vertex of the triangle with the smallest angle.]

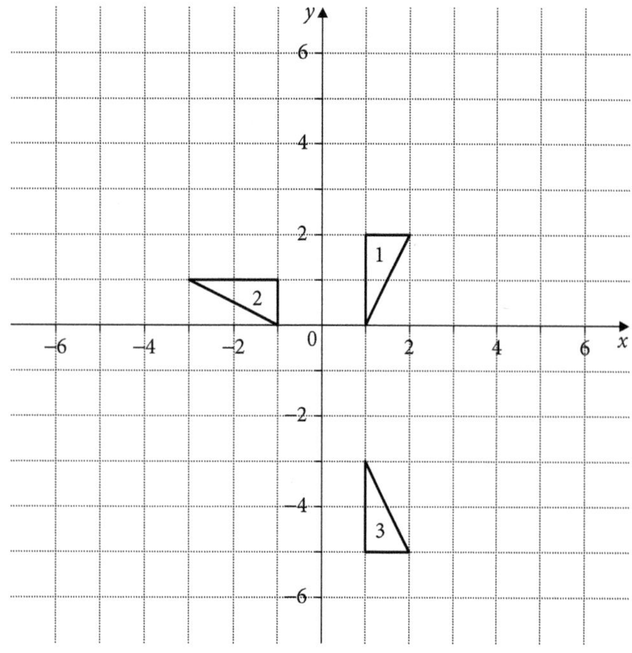

For Questions **8** and **9** draw a pair of axes with values from −7 to +7.

8. **a)** Plot and label the triangles:

   Δ1: (5, 5), (5, 7), (4, 7)
   Δ2: (−6, −5), (−3, −5), (−3, −4)
   Δ3: (1, −4), (1, −6), (2, −6).

   b) Draw the image of Δ1 after enlargement with scale factor 2, centre (7, 7). Label the image Δ4.

   c) Draw the image of Δ2 after enlargement with scale factor 3, centre (−6, −7). Label the image Δ5.

   d) Draw the image of Δ3 after enlargement with scale factor 2, centre (−1, −5). Label the image Δ6.

   e) Write down the coordinates of the 'pointed ends' of Δ4, Δ5 and Δ6.

9. **a)** Plot and label the triangles:

   Δ1: (5, 3), (5, 6), (4, 6)
   Δ2: (4, −3), (1, −3), (1, −2)
   Δ3: (−4, −7), (−7, −7), (−7, −6).

   b) Draw the image of Δ1 after enlargement with scale factor 2, centre (7, 7). Label the image Δ4.

   c) Draw the image of Δ2 after enlargement with scale factor 3, centre (5, −4). Label the image Δ5.

d) Draw the image of Δ3 after enlargement with scale factor 4, centre (−7, −7). Label the image Δ6.

e) Write down the coordinates of the 'pointed ends' of Δ4, Δ5 and Δ6.

Enlargements with fractional scale factors (reductions)

The unshaded shape is the image of the shaded shape after an enlargement with scale factor $\frac{1}{2}$, centre O.

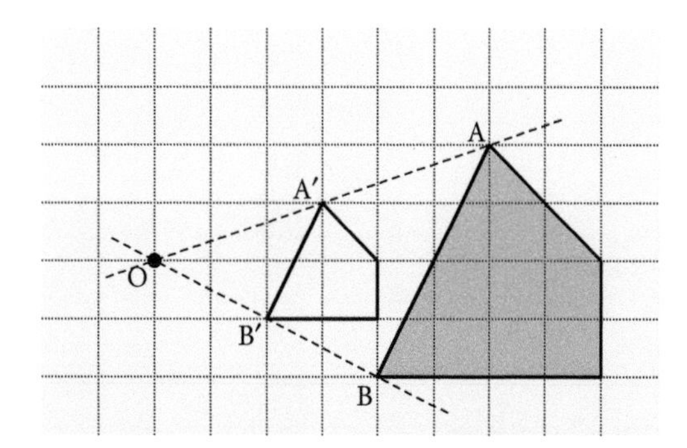

Note: $OA' = \frac{1}{2} \times OA$

$OB' = \frac{1}{2} \times OB$

Even though the shape has undergone a reduction, mathematicians prefer to call it an enlargement with a fractional scale factor.

Exercise 8

In Questions **1** to **3** copy the diagram and draw an enlargement using the centre O and the scale factor given.

1.

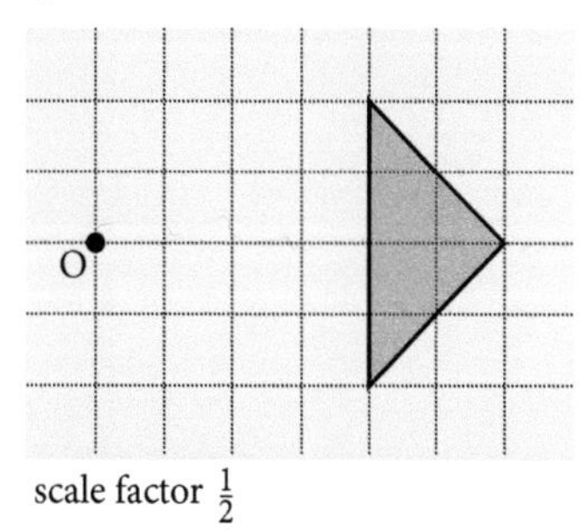

scale factor $\frac{1}{2}$

2.

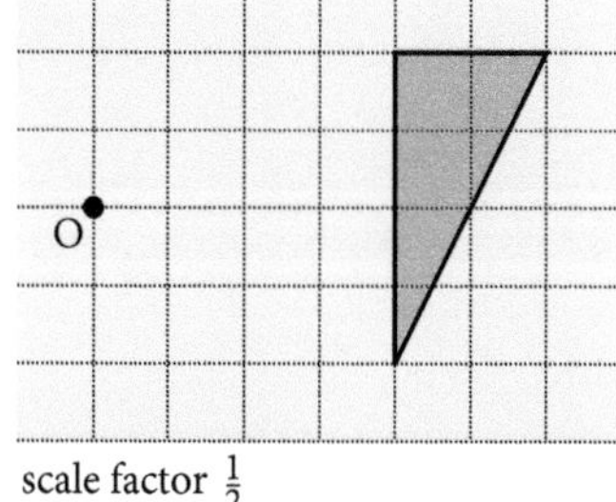

scale factor $\frac{1}{2}$

3.

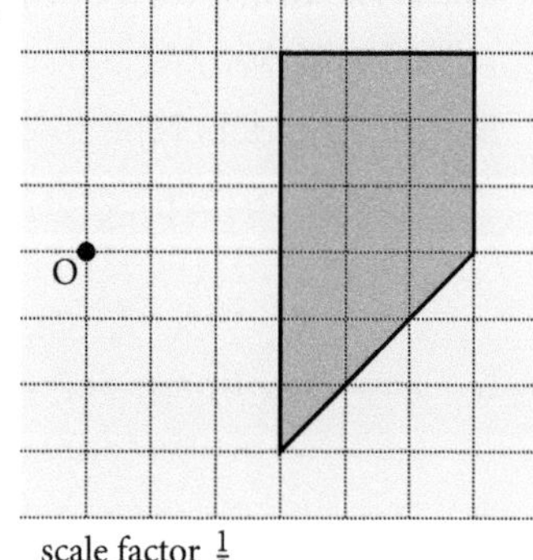

scale factor $\frac{1}{3}$

4. a) Plot and label the triangles:

$\Delta 1$: (7, 6), (1, 6), (1, 3)

$\Delta 2$: (7, −1), (7, −7), (3, −7)

$\Delta 3$: (−5, 7), (−5, 1), (−7, 1).

b) Draw $\Delta 4$, the image of $\Delta 1$ after an enlargement with scale factor $\frac{1}{3}$, centre (−2, 0).

c) Draw $\Delta 5$, the image of $\Delta 2$ after an enlargement with scale factor $\frac{1}{2}$, centre (−5, −7).

d) Draw $\Delta 6$, the image of $\Delta 3$ after an enlargement with scale factor $\frac{1}{2}$, centre (−7, −5).

Translation

A translation is simply a 'shift'. There is no turning or reflection and the object stays the same size.

Example

a) $\Delta 1$ is mapped onto $\Delta 2$ by the translation with vector $\begin{pmatrix} 4 \\ 2 \end{pmatrix}$

b) $\Delta 2$ is mapped onto $\Delta 3$ by the translation with vector $\begin{pmatrix} 2 \\ -3 \end{pmatrix}$

c) $\Delta 3$ is mapped onto $\Delta 2$ by the translation with vector $\begin{pmatrix} -2 \\ 3 \end{pmatrix}$

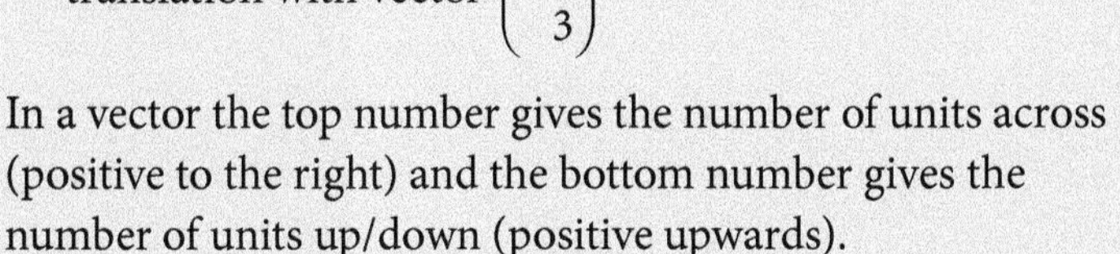

In a vector the top number gives the number of units across (positive to the right) and the bottom number gives the number of units up/down (positive upwards).

So $\begin{pmatrix} 4 \\ 2 \end{pmatrix}$ is 4 across → 2 up ↑ $\begin{pmatrix} -2 \\ 3 \end{pmatrix}$ is 2 across ← 3 up ↑

Exercise 9

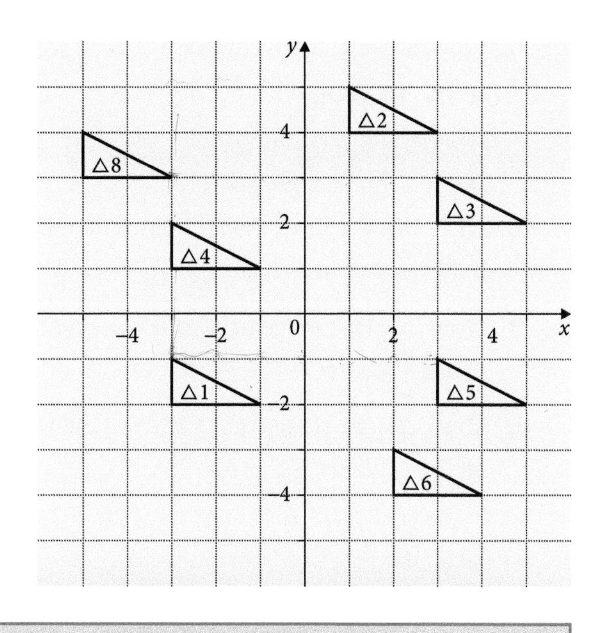

1. Look at the diagram shown.

Write down the vector for each of the following translations:

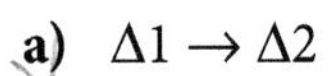

a) $\Delta 1 \rightarrow \Delta 2$ **b)** $\Delta 1 \rightarrow \Delta 3$

c) $\Delta 1 \rightarrow \Delta 4$ **d)** $\Delta 1 \rightarrow \Delta 5$

e) $\Delta 1 \rightarrow \Delta 6$ **f)** $\Delta 6 \rightarrow \Delta 5$

g) $\Delta 1 \rightarrow \Delta 8$ **h)** $\Delta 2 \rightarrow \Delta 3$

i) $\Delta 2 \rightarrow \Delta 4$ **j)** $\Delta 2 \rightarrow \Delta 5$

k) $\Delta 2 \rightarrow \Delta 6$ **l)** $\Delta 2 \rightarrow \Delta 8$

m) $\Delta 3 \rightarrow \Delta 5$ **n)** $\Delta 8 \rightarrow \Delta 2$

Adding vectors

Example

a) Add the vectors $\begin{pmatrix} 4 \\ 1 \end{pmatrix}$ and $\begin{pmatrix} 3 \\ 5 \end{pmatrix}$.

$$\begin{pmatrix} 4 \\ 1 \end{pmatrix} + \begin{pmatrix} 3 \\ 5 \end{pmatrix} = \begin{pmatrix} 7 \\ 6 \end{pmatrix}$$

b) Add the vectors $\begin{pmatrix} 1 \\ -2 \end{pmatrix}$ and $\begin{pmatrix} 6 \\ 2 \end{pmatrix}$.

$$\begin{pmatrix} 1 \\ -2 \end{pmatrix} + \begin{pmatrix} 6 \\ 2 \end{pmatrix} = \begin{pmatrix} 7 \\ 0 \end{pmatrix}$$

Multiplying a vector by a scalar

A 'scalar' is just a number.

Example

Multiply the vector $\begin{pmatrix} 3 \\ 2 \end{pmatrix}$ by 5.

$$5\begin{pmatrix} 3 \\ 2 \end{pmatrix} = \begin{pmatrix} 15 \\ 10 \end{pmatrix}$$

Notice that the vectors $\begin{pmatrix} 3 \\ 2 \end{pmatrix}$ and $\begin{pmatrix} 15 \\ 10 \end{pmatrix}$ are parallel and that $\begin{pmatrix} 15 \\ 10 \end{pmatrix}$ is five times as long as $\begin{pmatrix} 3 \\ 2 \end{pmatrix}$.

In general:

When vector **a** is multiplied by 2, the result is 2**a**.

When **a** is multiplied by –3, the result is –3**a**.

Exercise 10

Work out the following.

1. $\begin{pmatrix}3\\2\end{pmatrix}+\begin{pmatrix}4\\0\end{pmatrix}$ **2.** $\begin{pmatrix}5\\1\end{pmatrix}+\begin{pmatrix}11\\4\end{pmatrix}$ **3.** $\begin{pmatrix}4\\-1\end{pmatrix}+\begin{pmatrix}0\\2\end{pmatrix}$ **4.** $\begin{pmatrix}5\\-5\end{pmatrix}+\begin{pmatrix}1\\6\end{pmatrix}$ **5.** $\begin{pmatrix}10\\-5\end{pmatrix}+\begin{pmatrix}-10\\2\end{pmatrix}$

6. $\begin{pmatrix}8\\3\end{pmatrix}+\begin{pmatrix}2\\1\end{pmatrix}+\begin{pmatrix}-4\\0\end{pmatrix}$ **7.** $6\begin{pmatrix}2\\1\end{pmatrix}$ **8.** $8\begin{pmatrix}2\\-1\end{pmatrix}$ **9.** $5\begin{pmatrix}20\\11\end{pmatrix}$ **10.** $\frac{1}{2}\begin{pmatrix}32\\4\end{pmatrix}$

Describing transformations

Exercise 11

1. a) Reflect shape A in line 1 onto shape B.

b) Reflect shape B in line 2 onto shape C.

c) What single transformation will move shape A onto shape C?

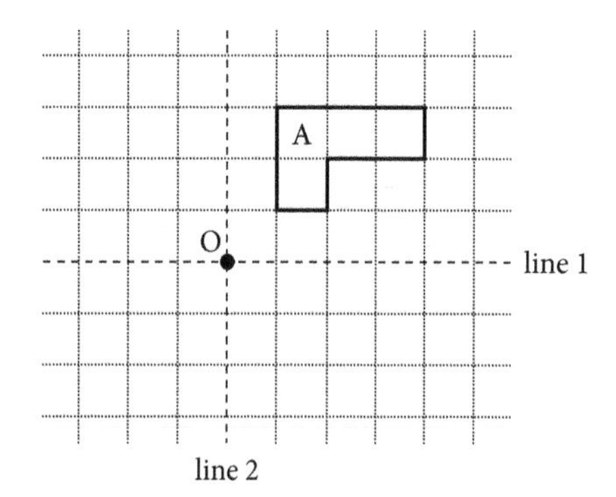

2. a) Rotate ΔD 90° clockwise about (0, 0). Label the image ΔE.

b) Rotate ΔE 90° clockwise about (0, 0). Label the image ΔF.

c) What single transformation will move ΔD onto ΔF?

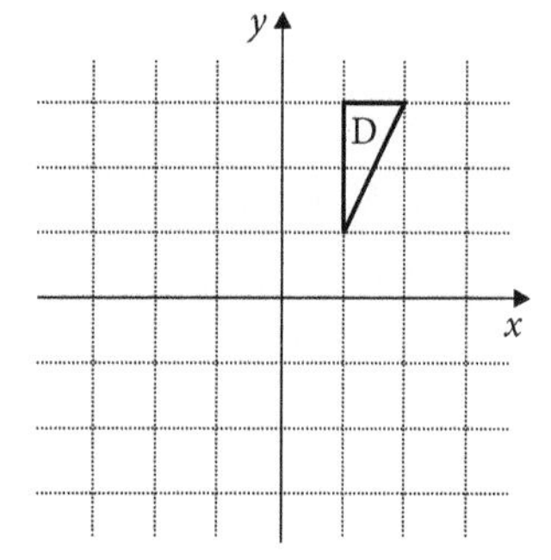

3. a) Draw ΔX.

b) Translate ΔX 4 units right onto ΔY.

c) Translate ΔY 1 unit right and 2 units up onto ΔZ.

d) What single translation will move ΔX onto ΔZ?

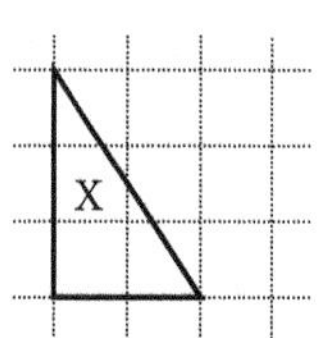

4. Describe the transformations below. Mark any points and lines necessary to write the answers.

   a) ΔA→ΔB in one move.

   b) ΔB→ΔC in one move.

   c) ΔD→ΔC in one move.

5. Describe fully the following transformations.

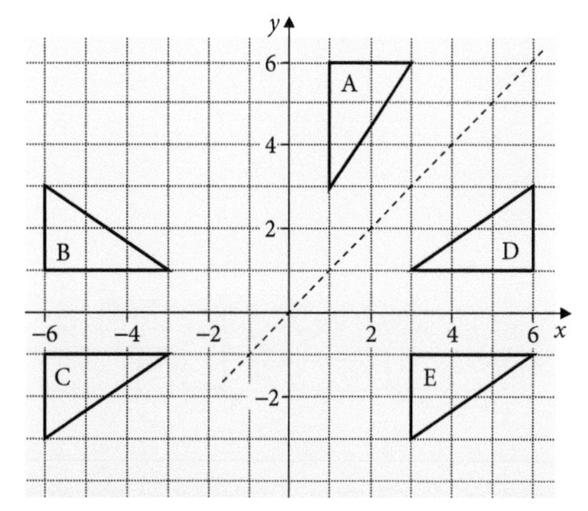

   a) ΔA → ΔB

   b) ΔB → ΔC

   c) ΔA → ΔD

   d) ΔC → ΔE

   e) ΔA → ΔC (in two transformations)

   f) ΔA → ΔE (in two or three transformations).

6. Draw axes with values from –7 to +7 and draw triangles with the following vertices:

   Δ1: (–6, –6) (–2, –6) (–2, –4)

   Δ2: (–6, –6) (–6, –2) (–4, –2)

   Δ3: (6, 2) (2, 2) (2, 0)

   Δ4: (–6, 2) (–2, 2) (–2, 0)

   Δ5: (6, 3) (6, 7) (4, 7)

   Describe fully the following rotations or reflections.
   For rotations, give the angle, direction and centre.
   For reflections, give the equation of the mirror line.

   a) Δ1 → Δ2 b) Δ1 → Δ3

   c) Δ1 → Δ4 d) Δ1 → Δ5

7. Draw axes with values from –7 to +7 and draw triangles with the following vertices:

Δ1: (3, 1)	(7, 1)	(7, 3)
Δ2: (1, 3)	(1, 7)	(3, 7)
Δ3: (7, –1)	(3, –1)	(3, –3)
Δ4: (–1, –7)	(–3, –7)	(–3, –3)
Δ5: (–2, 2)	(–6, 2)	(–6, 0)
Δ6: (3, –4)	(3, –6)	(7, –6)

Describe fully the following rotations or reflections:

a) $\Delta 1 \rightarrow \Delta 2$

b) $\Delta 1 \rightarrow \Delta 3$

c) $\Delta 1 \rightarrow \Delta 4$

d) $\Delta 1 \rightarrow \Delta 5$

e) $\Delta 3 \rightarrow \Delta 6$

8.

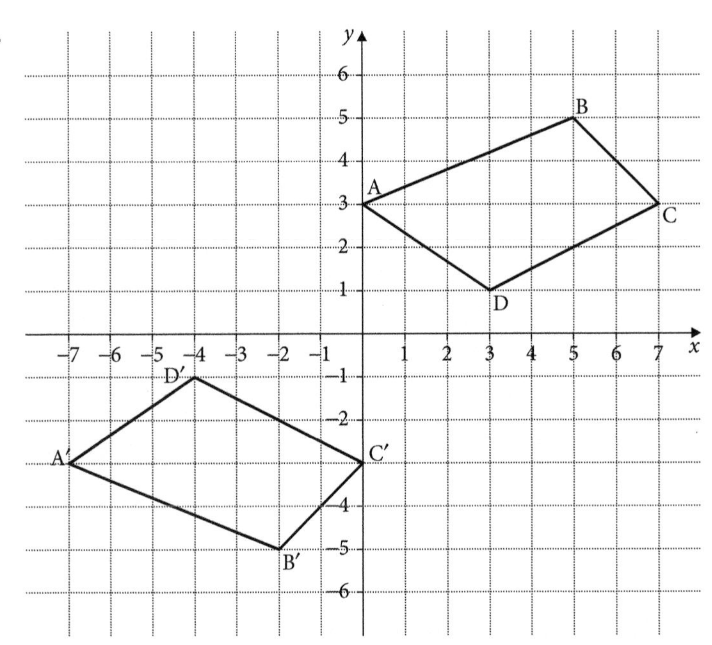

ABCD is mapped onto A′B′C′D′ by a reflection followed by a translation parallel to the x-axis.

a) Describe these two transformations as fully as possible.

b) Would the image be the same if the translation was completed before the reflection?

9. Draw axes for both x and y between −8 and +8.
   Plot the points (1, 1), (3, 1), (3, 2), (2, 2), (2, 4) and (1, 4) and join up to make an 'L' shape.
   This is mapped onto the shape formed by joining (−2, −2), (−2, −6), (−4, −6), (−4, −4), (−8, −4), (−8, −2), by *two* transformations; an enlargement with centre (0, 0) followed by a reflection.
   Describe these transformations as fully as possible.

5.2 Quadrilaterals and other polygons

Properties of quadrilaterals

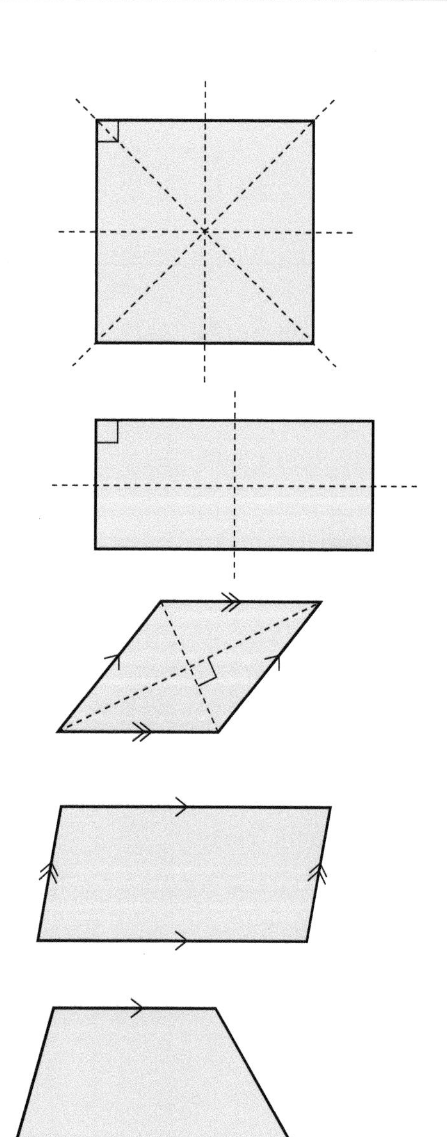

Square:

Four equal sides;

All angles 90°;

Four lines of symmetry.

Rotational symmetry of order 4.

Rectangle (not square):

Two pairs of equal and parallel sides;

All angles 90°;

Two lines of symmetry.

Rotational symmetry of order 2.

Rhombus:

Four equal sides; Opposite sides parallel;

Diagonals bisect at right angles;

Diagonals bisect angles of rhombus;

Two lines of symmetry.

Rotational symmetry of order 2.

Parallelogram:

Two pairs of equal and parallel sides;

Opposite angles equal;

No lines of symmetry (in general).

Rotational symmetry of order 2.

Trapezium:

One pair of parallel sides.

No rotational symmetry.

Kite:

AB = AD, CB =CD;

Diagonals meet at 90°;

One line of symmetry.

No rotational symmetry.

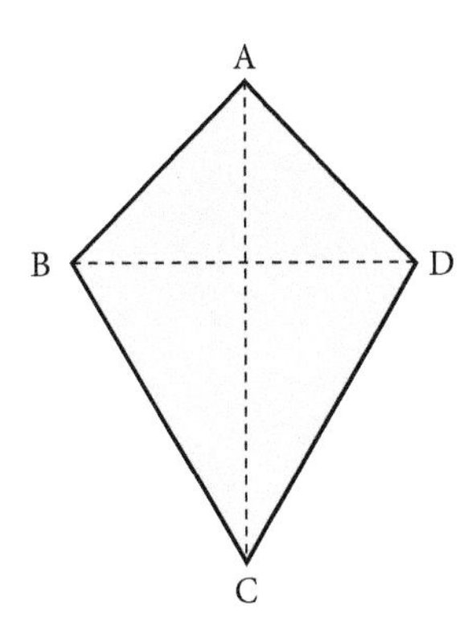

For all quadrilaterals the sum of the interior angles is 360°.

Exercise 12

1. Name each of the following shapes:
   a) ABEH
   b) EFGH
   c) CDFE

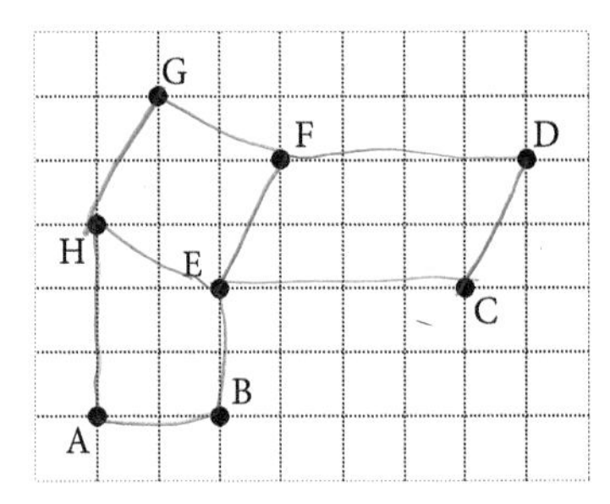

2. a) Write down the coordinates of point D if ABCD is a kite.
   b) Write down the coordinates of point E if ABCE is a parallelogram.
   c) Write down the coordinates of point G if BCGF is an arrowhead.
   [There is more than one possible answer to part **(c)**.]

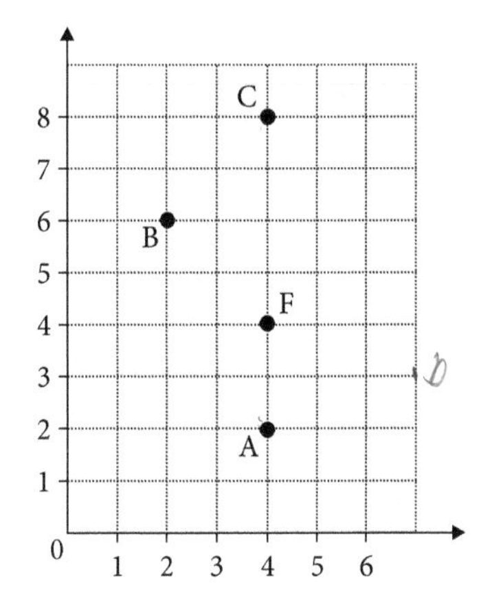

3. Copy the table and fill all the boxes with either 'Yes', 'No' or a number.

	How many lines of symmetry?	How many pairs of opposite sides are parallel?	Diagonals always equal?	Diagonals are perpendicular?
Square				
Rectangle				
Kite				
Rhombus				
Parallelogram				
Arrowhead				

4. Find the angle x.

a)

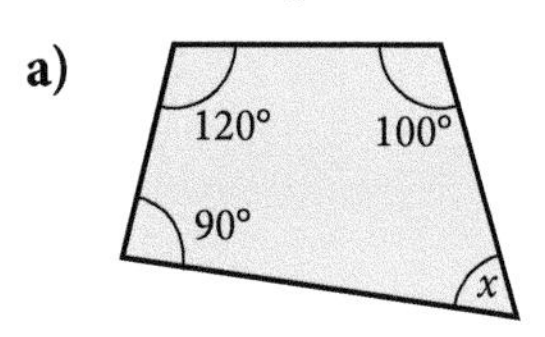

b)

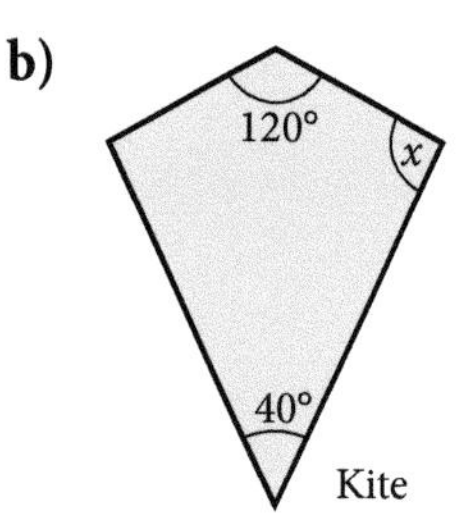

c)

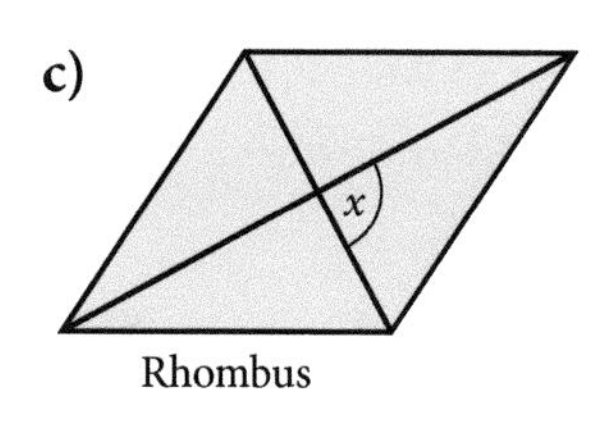

d)

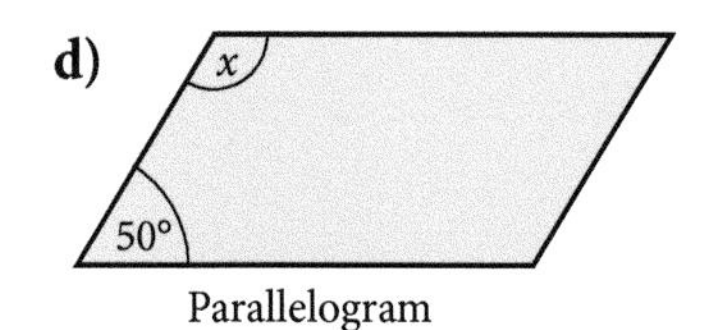

e)

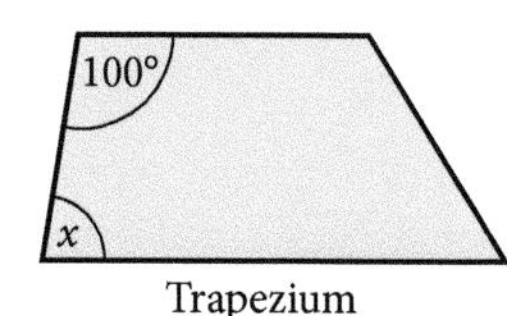

f)

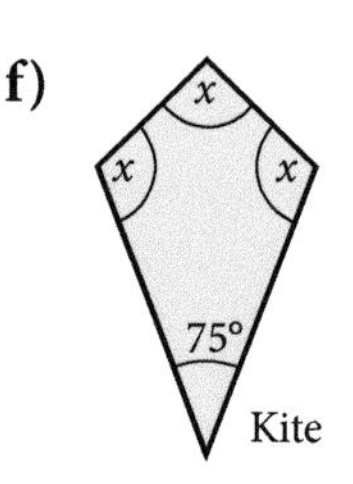

5. The diagram shows three vertices (corners) of a parallelogram. Copy the diagram and mark with crosses the *three* possible positions of the fourth vertex.

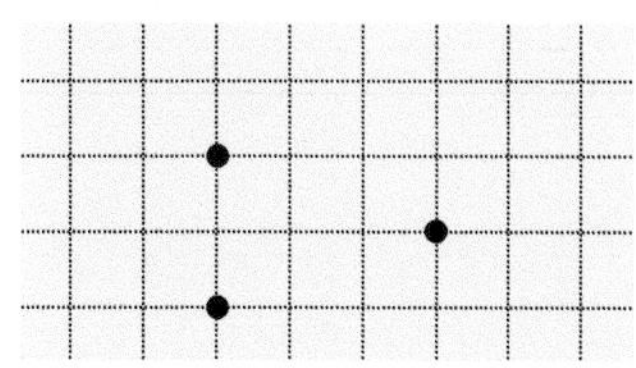

6. Line AC is one *diagonal* of a rhombus ABCD. Draw *two* possible rhombuses ABCD.

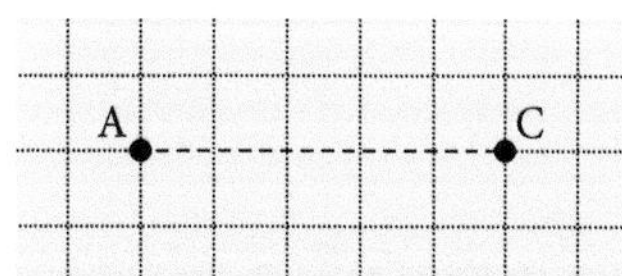

7. Suppose you cut along the diagonal of a rectangle to make two congruent triangles. Join the diagonals together in a different way. What shape is formed?

8. Suppose you had two identical isosceles triangles. Put the equal sides together to make as many different shapes as possible. Name the shapes formed.

9. An equilateral triangle has vertices P, Q, R.

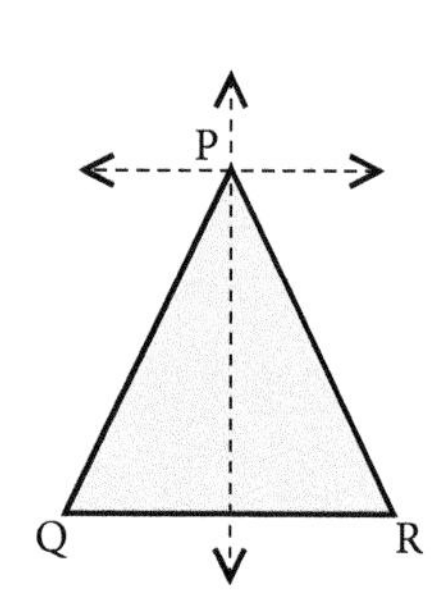

a) Suppose the vertex P moves perpendicular to QR.
What different types of triangle can be made?
Can you make: a right-angled triangle
an obtuse-angled triangle
a scalene triangle?

b) If the vertex P moves *parallel* to QR, what different types of triangle can be made?

Exercise 13

1. ABCD is a rhombus whose diagonals intersect at M. Find the coordinates of C and D.

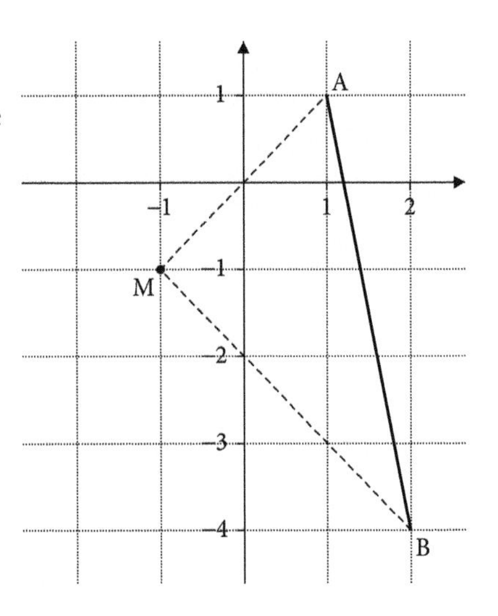

In Questions **2** to **12**, begin by drawing a diagram and remember to put the letters around the shape in alphabetical order.

2. In a rectangle KLMN, angle LNM = 34°.
   Calculate:

   a) angle KLN **b)** angle KML

3. In a trapezium ABCD, angle ABD = 35°, angle BAD = 110° and AB is parallel to DC. Calculate:

   a) angle ADB **b)** angle BDC

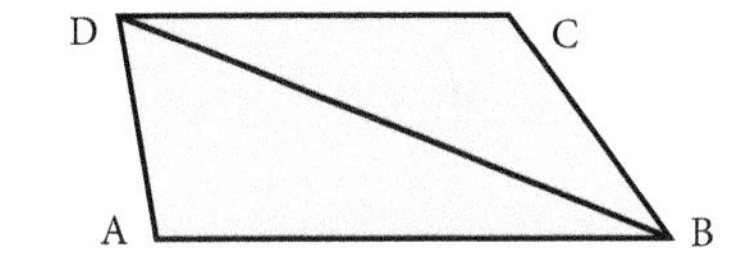

4. In a parallelogram WXYZ, angle WXY = 72°, angle ZWY = 80°. Calculate:

   a) angle WZY **b)** angle XWZ **c)** angle WYX

5. In a kite ABCD, AB = AD, BC = CD, angle CAD = 40° and angle CBD = 60°. Calculate:

   a) angle BAC **b)** angle BCA **c)** angle ADC

6. In a rhombus ABCD, angle ABC = 64°. Calculate:

   a) angle BCD **b)** angle ADB **c)** angle BAC

7. 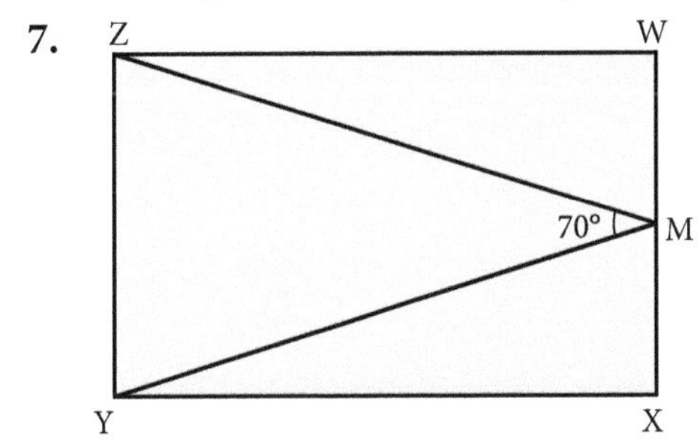

   In a rectangle WXYZ, M is the mid-point of WX and angle ZMY = 70°.
   Calculate:

   a) angle MZY **b)** angle YMX

8. In a trapezium ABCD, AB is parallel to DC, AB = AD, BD = DC and angle BAD = 128°. Find:

   a) angle ABD **b)** angle BDC **c)** angle BCD

9. 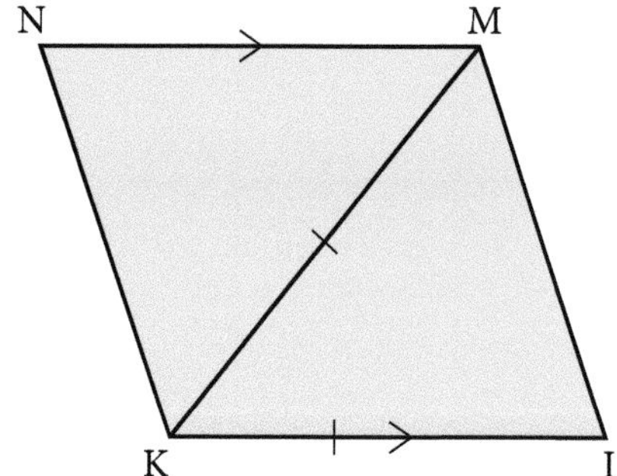

In a parallelogram KLMN, KL = KM and angle KML = 64°.

Find:

a) angle MKL **b)** angle KNM **c)** angle LMN

10. In a kite PQRS with PQ = PS and RQ = RS, angle QRS = 40° and angle QPS = 100°. Find angle PQR.

11. In a rhombus PQRS, angle RPQ = 54°. Find:

a) angle PRQ **b)** angle PSR **c)** angle RQS

12. In a kite PQRS, angle RPS is twice the angle PRS, PQ = QS = PS and QR = RS.

Find:

a) angle QPS **b)** angle PRS **c)** angle QSR

Polygons

A polygon is a flat shape/figure with three or more sides.

A quadrilateral is the name given to a polygon with four sides.

The table on page 8 shows the names of the more common polygons.

A **regular** polygon has sides of equal length and all its interior angles are equal.

Exercise 14

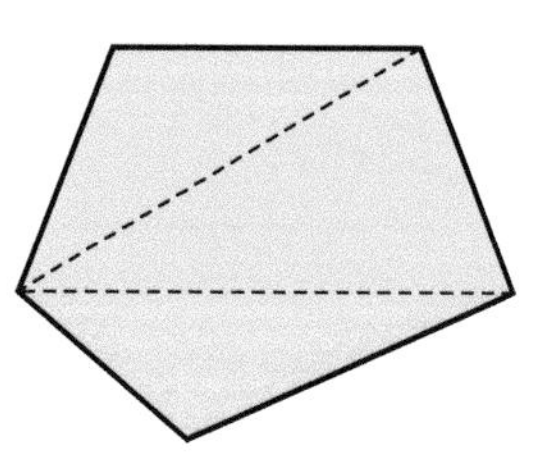

1. The diagram shows a pentagon in which we have started to draw in the diagonals. Draw your own diagram of a pentagon and find how many diagonals there are altogether.
2. Draw a hexagon and show that it has nine diagonals.
3. How many lines of symmetry has a regular pentagon?
4. How many lines of symmetry has a regular hexagon?
5. What is the name for a regular polygon with

   a) four sides

   b) three sides?

6. This shape has one pair of parallel sides.

   Draw three *pentagons* with:

   a) one pair of parallel sides

   b) two pairs of parallel sides

   c) three right angles.

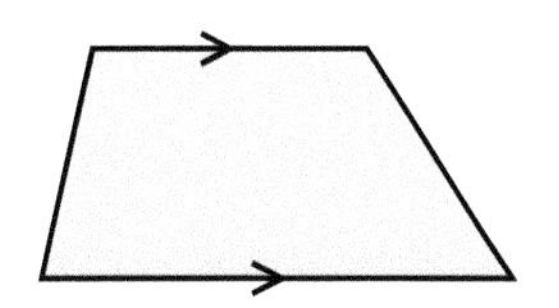

7. Sketch a diagram of a regular hexagon. Are all the diagonals the same length?

5.3 Bearings

Bearings are used where there are no roads to guide the way. Ships, aircraft and mountaineers use bearings to work out where they are.

Bearings are measured *clockwise from North*.

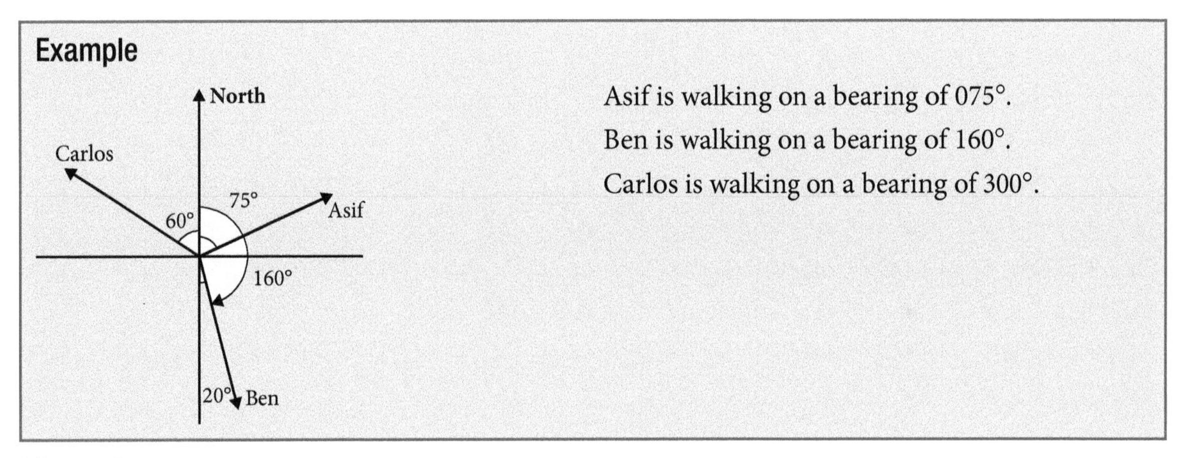

Exercise 15

The diagrams show the directions in which several people are travelling. Work out the bearing for each person.

1.

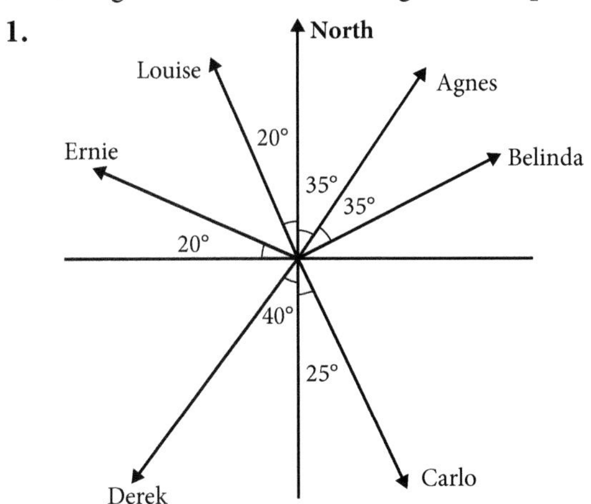

2.

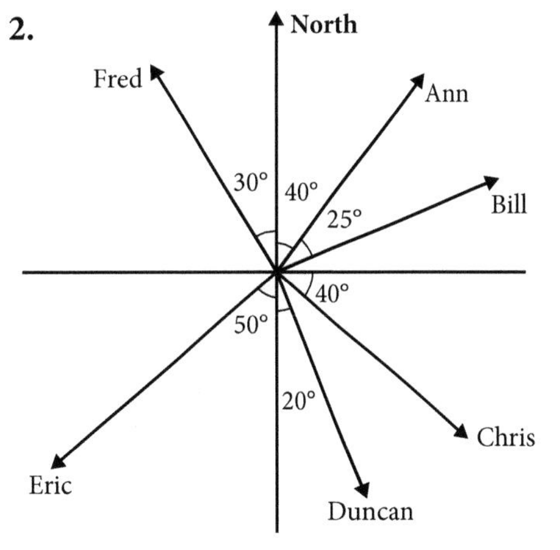

Relative bearings

The bearing of A from B is the direction in which you travel to get to A from B.

It helps to show the journey with an arrow, as in the example below.

Example

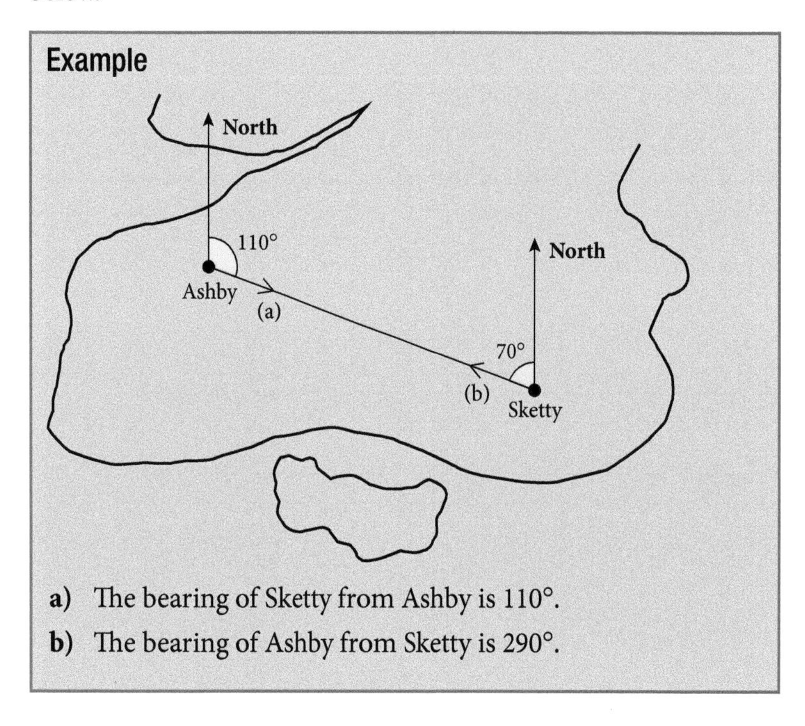

a) The bearing of Sketty from Ashby is 110°.

b) The bearing of Ashby from Sketty is 290°.

Exercise 16

The map of North America shows six radar tracking stations, A, B, C, D, E, F.

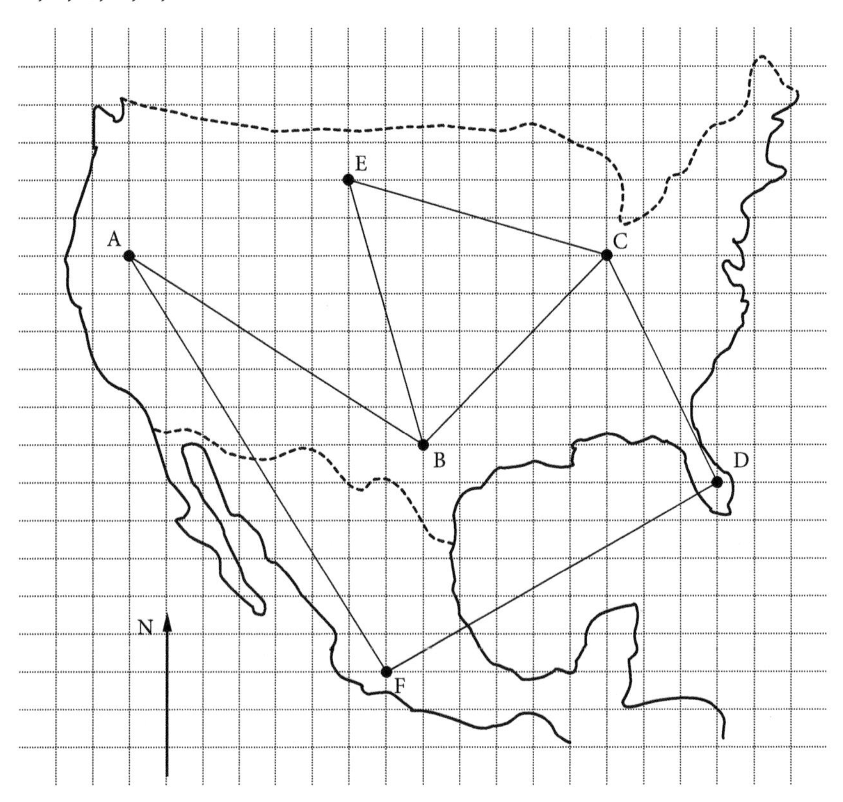

1. From A, measure the bearing of **a)** F **b)** B **c)** C.
2. From C, measure the bearing of **a)** E **b)** B **c)** D.
3. From F, measure the bearing of **a)** D **b)** A.
4. From B, measure the bearing of **a)** A **b)** E **c)** C.

Ships or aircraft can be located when their bearings from two places are known.

Example

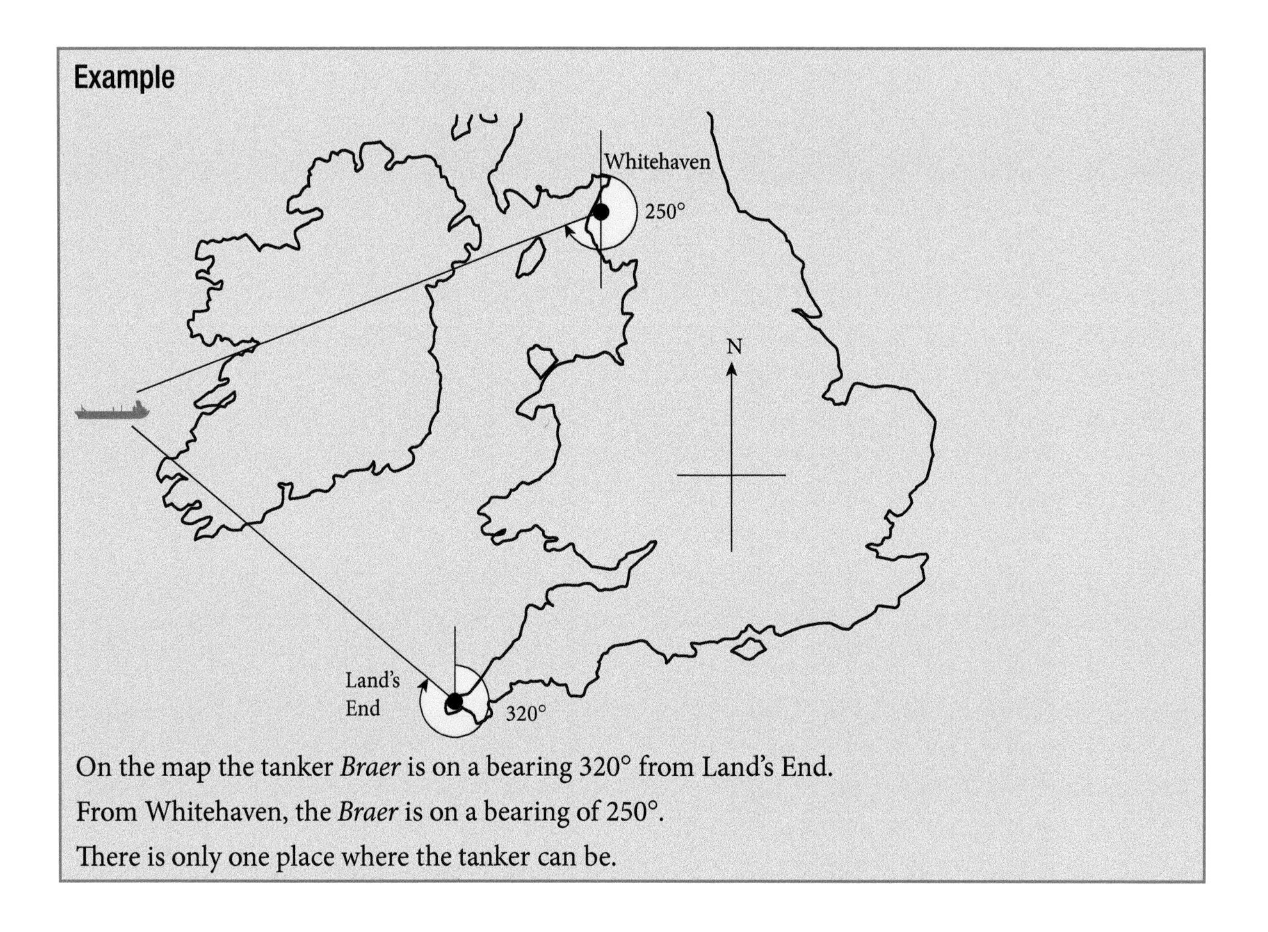

On the map the tanker *Braer* is on a bearing 320° from Land's End.

From Whitehaven, the *Braer* is on a bearing of 250°.

There is only one place where the tanker can be.

Exercise 17

Draw the points P and Q as shown in the middle of a clean page of squared paper. Mark the points A, B, C, D and E accurately, using the information given.

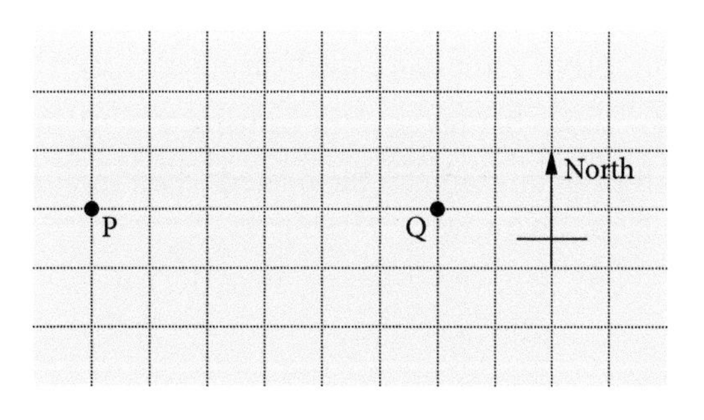

1. A is on a bearing of 040° from P and 015° from Q.
2. B is on a bearing of 076° from P and 067° from Q.
3. C is on a bearing of 114° from P and 127° from Q.
4. D is on a bearing of 325° from P and 308° from Q.
5. E is on a bearing of 180° from P and 208° from Q.

Exercise 18

Draw the points X and Y as shown in the middle of a clean page of squared paper. Mark the points K, L, M, N and, O accurately using the information given.

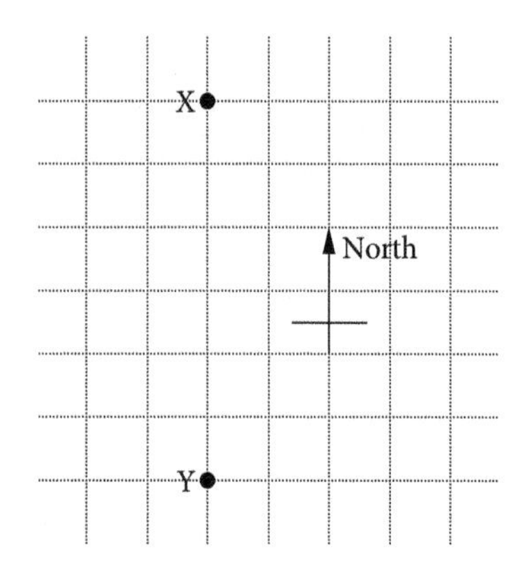

1. K is on a bearing of 041° from X and 025° from Y.
2. L is on a bearing of 090° from X and 058° from Y.
3. M is on a bearing of 123° from X and 090° from Y.
4. N is on a bearing of 203° from X and 215° from Y.
5. O is on a bearing of 288° from X and 319° from Y.

Exercise 19

Make accurate scale drawings with a scale of 1 cm to 1 km, unless told otherwise. Use squared paper and begin each question by drawing a small sketch of the journey.

1. A ship sails 8 km due North and then a further 7 km on a bearing 080°, as in the diagram (which is not drawn to scale).

   How far is the ship now from its starting point?

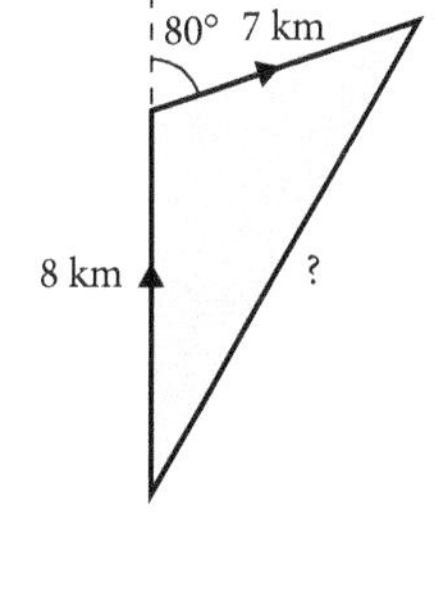

2. A ship sails 9 km on a bearing 090° and then a further 6 km on a bearing 050°, as shown in the diagram. How far is the ship now from its starting point?

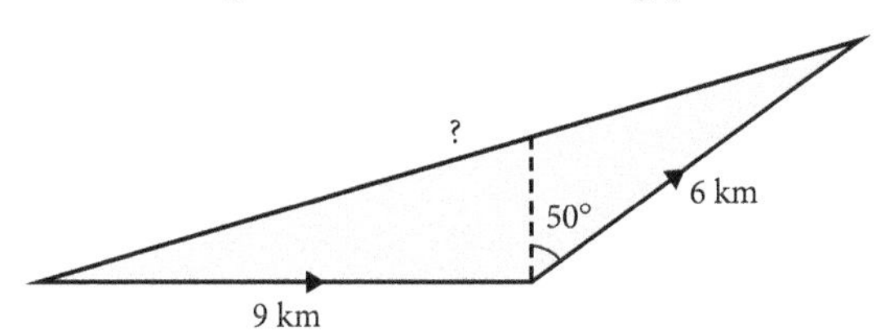

3. A ship sails 6 km on a bearing 160° and then a further 10 km on a bearing 240°, as shown.

   a) How far is the ship from its starting point?

   b) On what bearing must the ship sail so that it returns to its starting point?

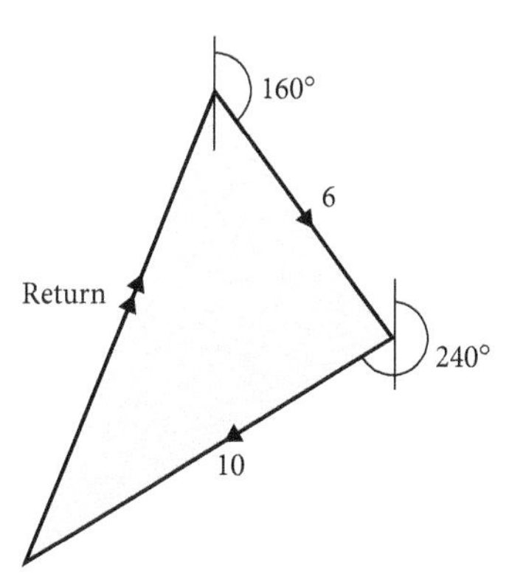

4. A ship sails 5 km on a bearing 030°, then 3 km on a bearing 090° and finally 4 km on a bearing 160°. How far is the ship now from its starting point?

5. Point B is 8 km from A on a bearing 140° from A.
   Point C is 9 km from A on a bearing 200° from A.

   a) How far is B from C?

   b) What is the bearing of B from C?

6. Point Q is 10 km from P on a bearing 052° from P. Point R is 4 km from P on a bearing 107° from P.

   a) How far is Q from R?

   b) What is the bearing of Q from R?

7. A laser beam L is 120 km from P on a bearing 068°.
   The laser beam is directed on a bearing 270° from L.

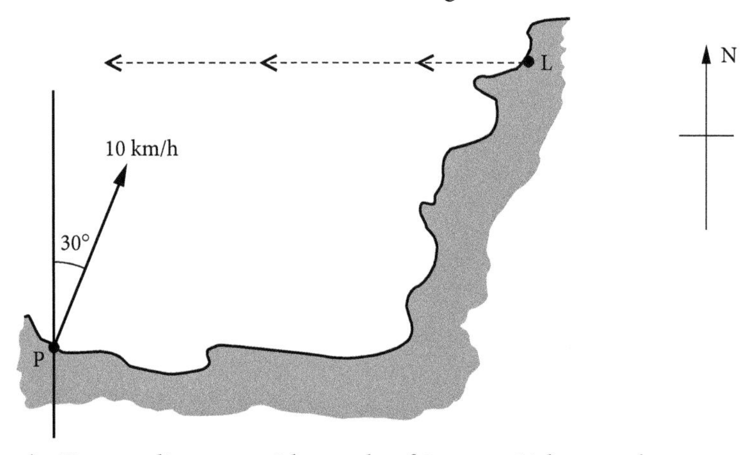

   a) Draw a diagram, with a scale of 1 cm to 10 km, to show the positions of P and L.

   b) A ship sails from P at a speed of 10 km/h on a bearing 030°. For how long does the ship sail before it cuts the beam?

8. Robinson Crusoe is on a tiny island R. There is an airport at A which is 150 km from R on a bearing 295° from R.

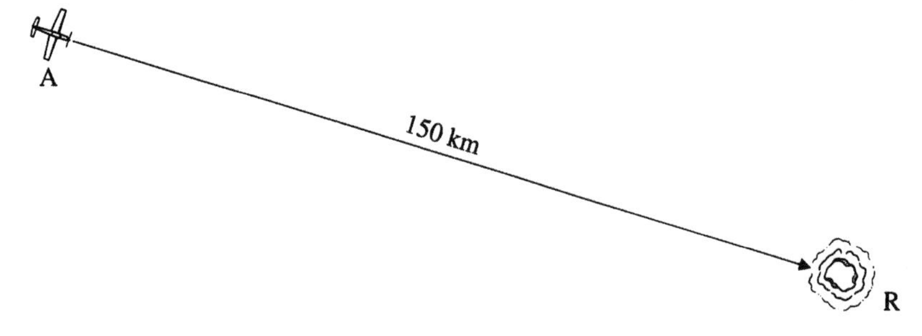

   An aircraft flies from A. If the aircraft gets within 40 km of R, the pilot will see Robinson's bonfire and he will be saved.
   Will he be saved if the plane flies on a bearing of 098°?

5.4 Pythagoras' theorem

In a right-angled triangle the square on the hypotenuse is equal to the sum of the squares on the other two sides.

$$a^2 + b^2 = c^2$$

The *converse* is also true:
'If the square on one side of a triangle is equal to the sum of the squares on the other two sides, then the triangle is right-angled.'

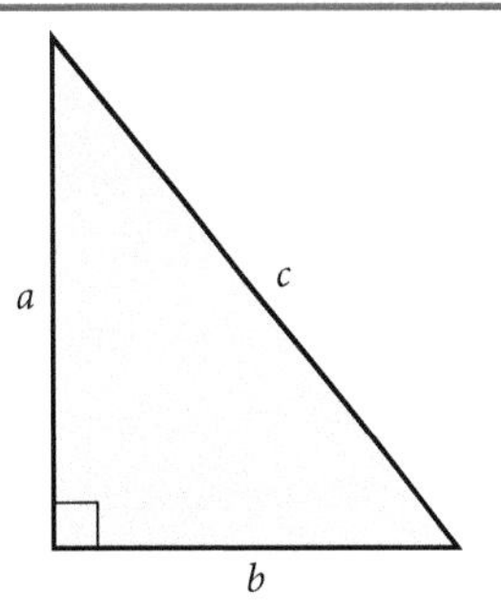

Example

Find the side marked *d*.

$d^2 + 4^2 = 7^2$

$d^2 = 49 - 16$

$d = \sqrt{33} = 5.74$ cm (3 s.f.)

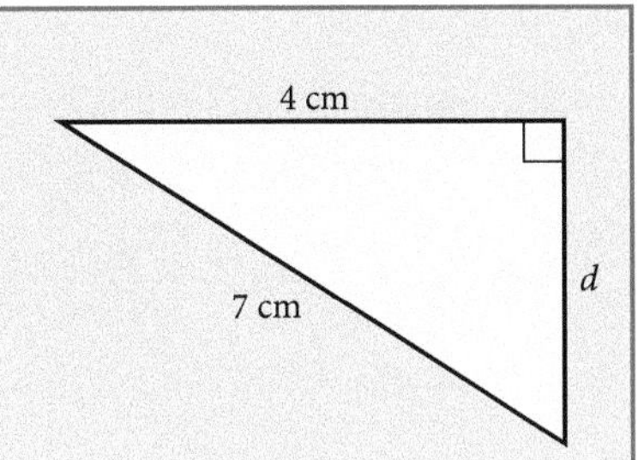

Exercise 20

In Questions **1** to **8**, find x. All the lengths are in cm.

1.

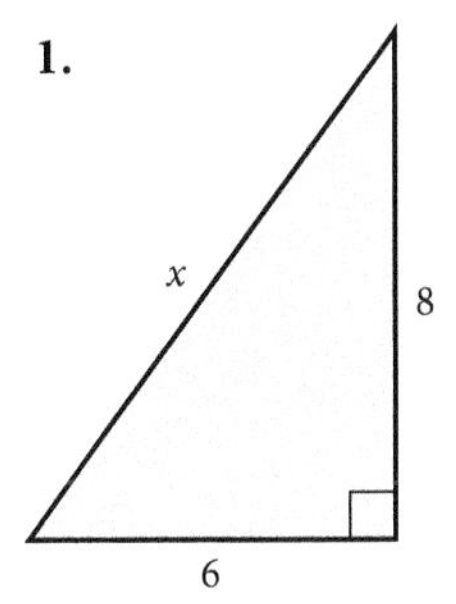

2.

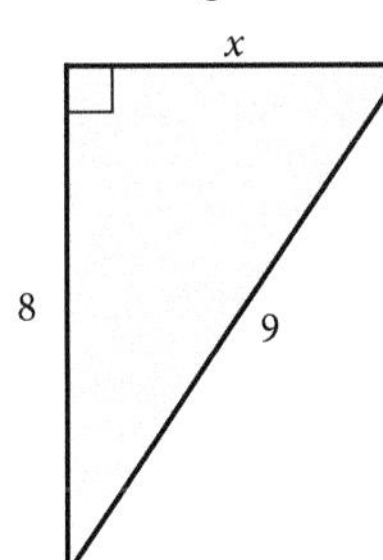

3.

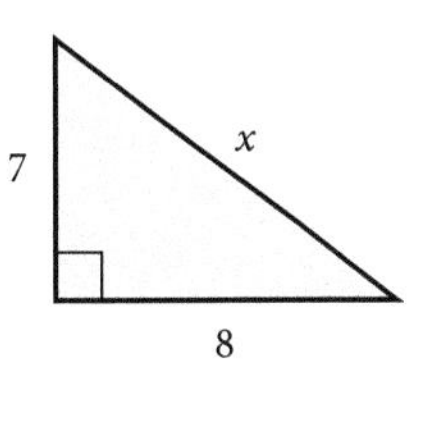

4.

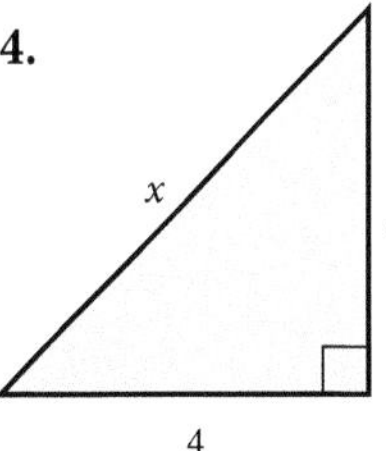

5.

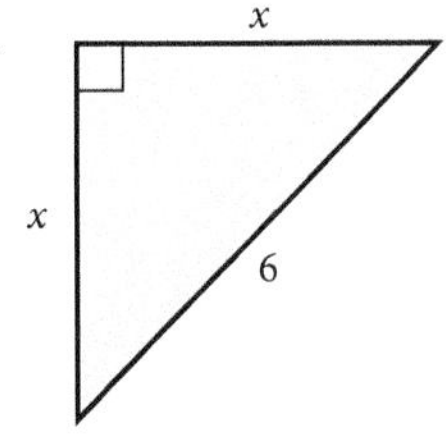

6.

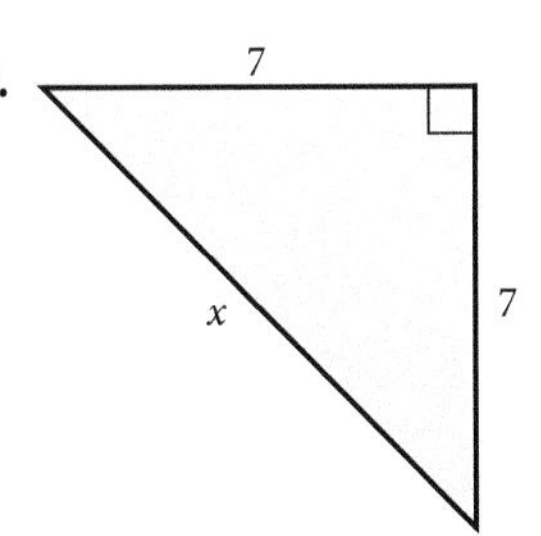

7.

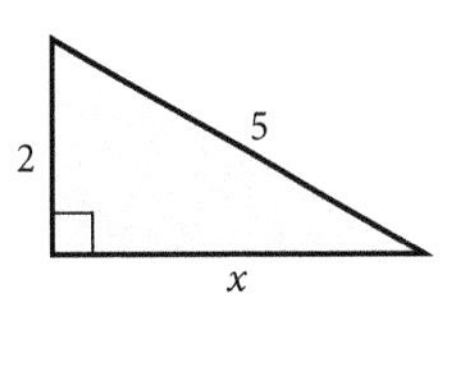

8.

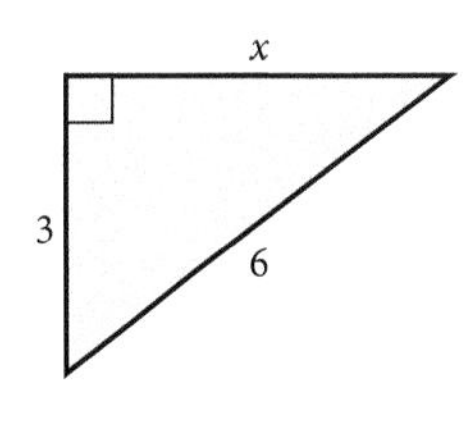

9. Find the length of a diagonal of a rectangle of length 9 cm and width 4 cm.

10. A square has diagonals of length 10 cm. Find the length of the sides of the square.

11. A 4 m ladder rests against a vertical wall with its foot 2 m from the wall. How far up the wall does the ladder reach?

12. A ship sails 20 km due North and then 35 km due East. How far is it from its starting point?

13. A thin wire of length 18 cm is bent in the shape shown. Calculate the direct distance from A to B.

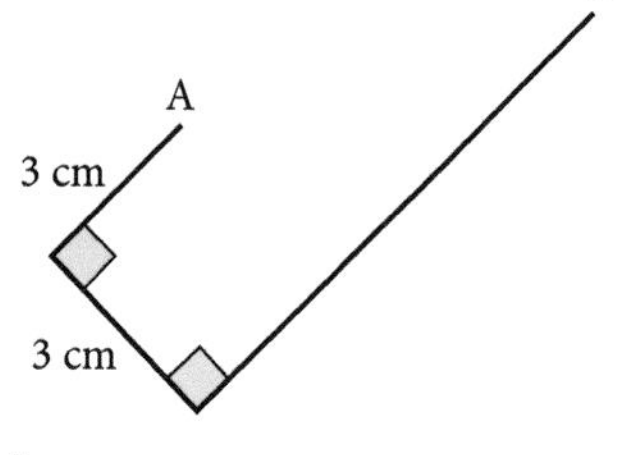

14. A paint tin is a cylinder of radius 12 cm and height 22 cm. Leonardo, the painter, drops his stirring stick into the tin and it disappears. Work out the maximum length of the stick.

15. In the diagram A is (1, 2) and B is (6, 4). Work out the length AB. [First find the length of AN and BN.]

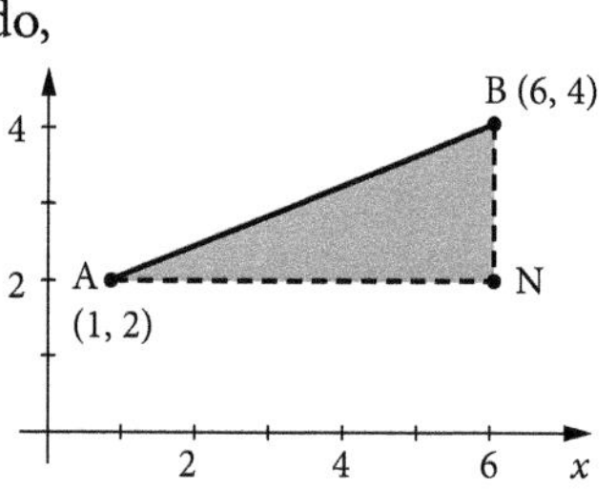

16. On squared paper plot P(1, 3), Q(6, 0), R(6, 6). Find the lengths of the sides of triangle PQR. Is the triangle isosceles?

Questions **17** to **22** are more difficult. In each case, find x.

17.

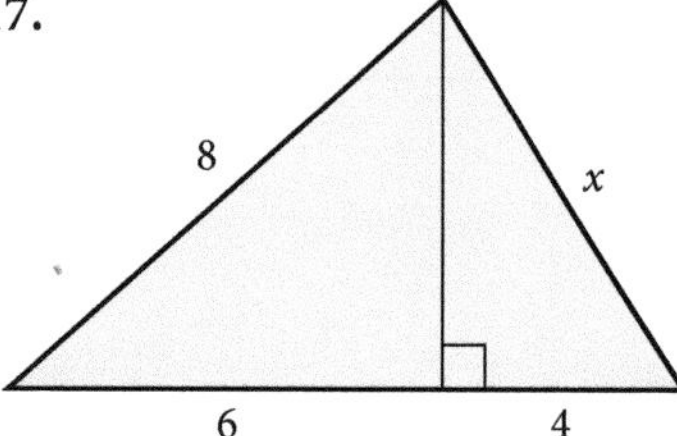

18.

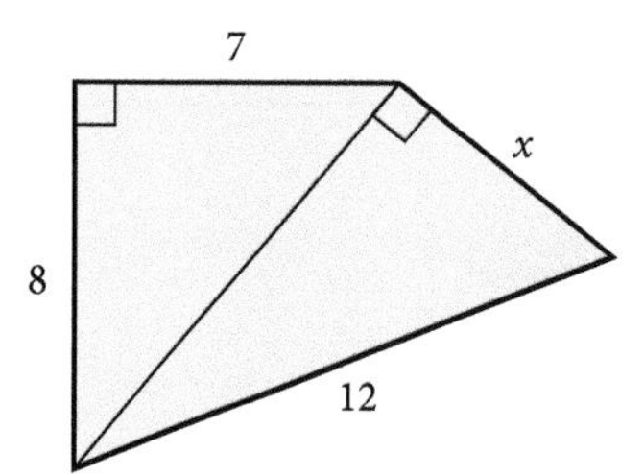

19.

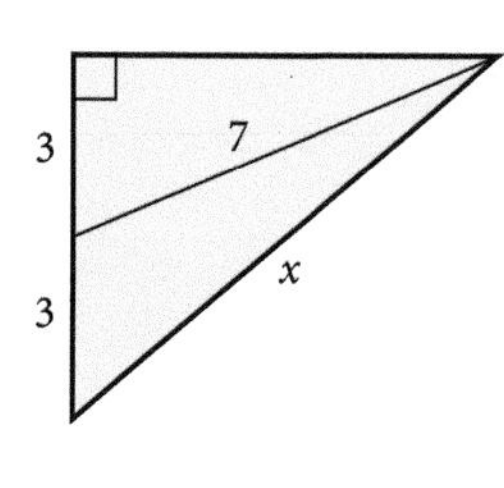

20.

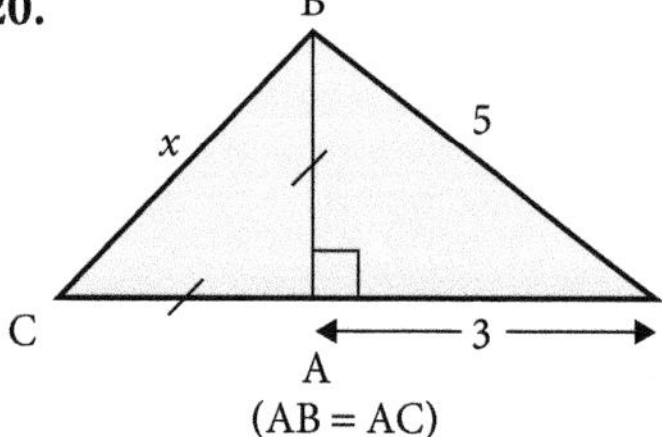

21.

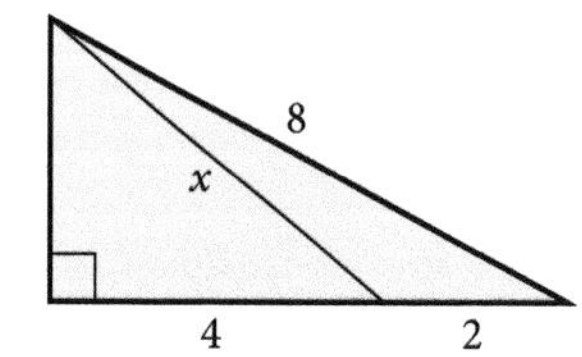

22.

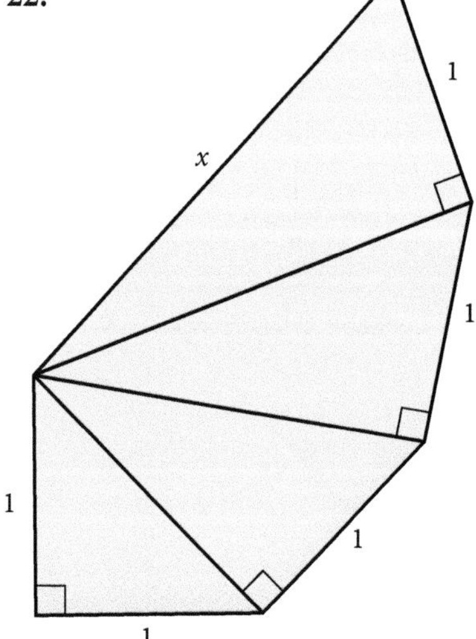

23. The most well known right-angled triangle is the 3, 4, 5 triangle $[3^2 + 4^2 = 5^2]$.
It is interesting to look at other right-angled triangles where all the sides are whole numbers.

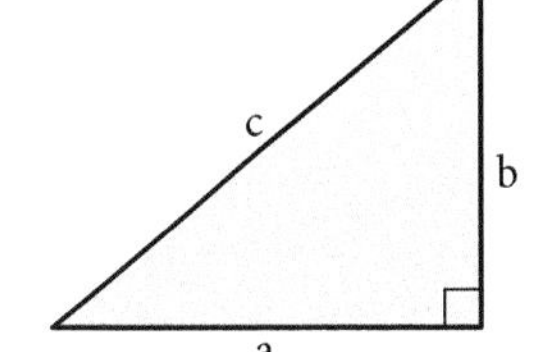

a) i) Find c if $a = 5$, $b = 12$

ii) Find c if $a = 7$, $b = 24$

iii) Find a if $c = 41$, $b = 40$

b) Write the results in a table.

a	b	c
3	4	5
5	12	?
7	24	?
?	40	41

c) Look at the sequences in the 'a' column and in the 'b' column. Also write down the connection between b and c for each triangle.

d) Predict the next three sets of values of a, b, c. Check to see if they really do form right-angled triangles.

24. The diagram shows a rectangular block.

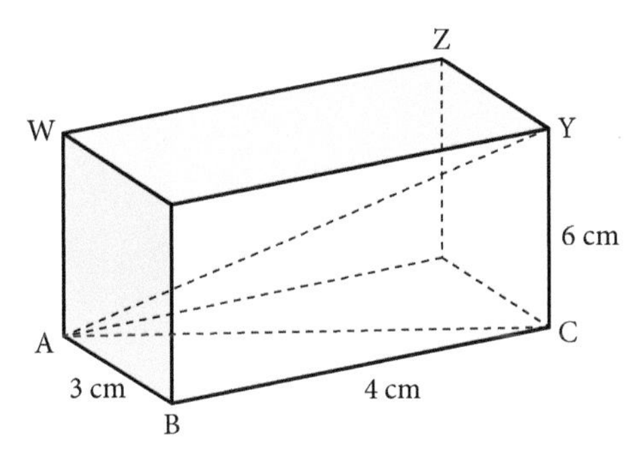

Use the triangles below to calculate: **a)** AC **b)** AY

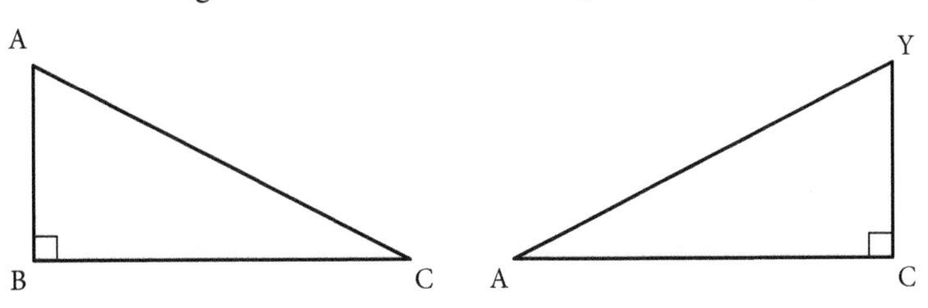

25. Alexis and Philip were arguing about a triangle that had sides 10 cm, 11 cm and 15 cm. Alexis said the triangle had a right angle, and Philip said that it did not. Who was correct?

5.5 Problems 2

Exercise 21

1. Find the capacity in litres of the oil drum shown below. ($1000\text{ cm}^3 = 1$ litre)

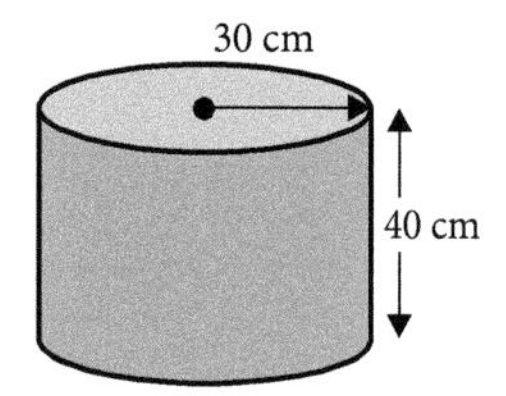

2. Find the volume in litres of a cylinder of height 55 cm and diameter 20 cm.

3. The diagram shows a square ABCD in which DX = XY = YC = AW.

   The area of the square is 45 cm^2.

   a) What is the fraction $\frac{DX}{DC}$?

   b) What fraction of the square is shaded?

   c) Find the area of the unshaded part.

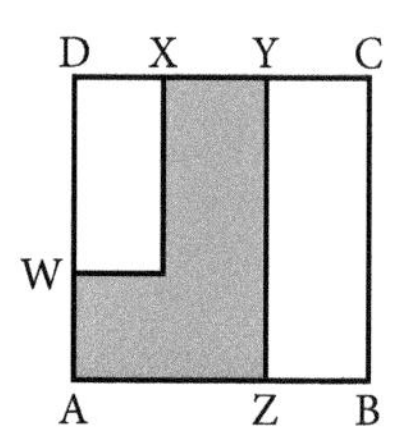

4. A floor 5 m by 20 m is covered by square tiles of side 20 cm. How many tiles are needed?

5. A rectangular field, 400 m long, has an area of 6 hectares. Calculate the perimeter of the field. [1 hectare = $10\,000\text{ m}^2$]

6. Find the shaded area. The lengths are in centimetres.

   (a)

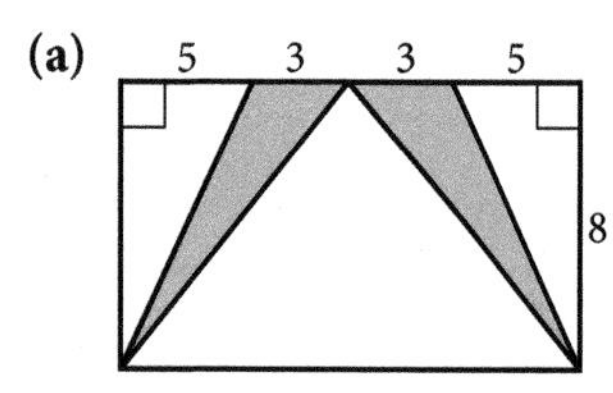

   (b)

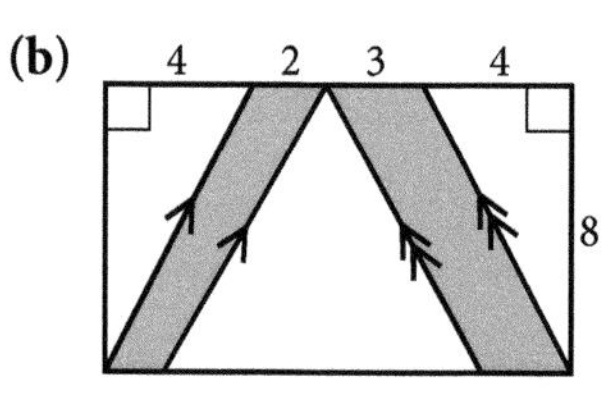

7. Calculate the volume of the object below. The lengths are in centimetres.

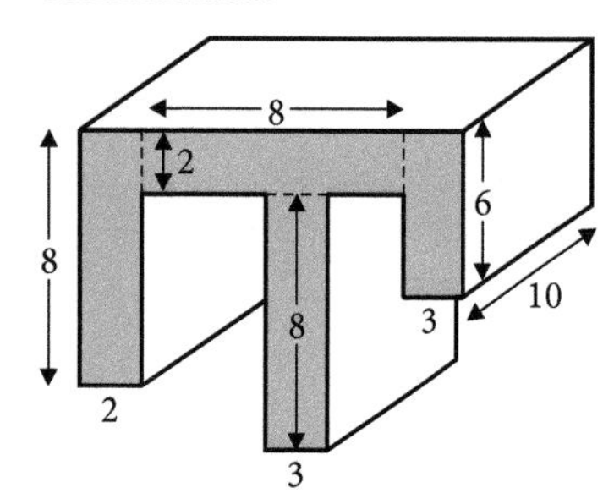

8. The arrowhead has an area of 3.6 cm^2.
Find the length x.

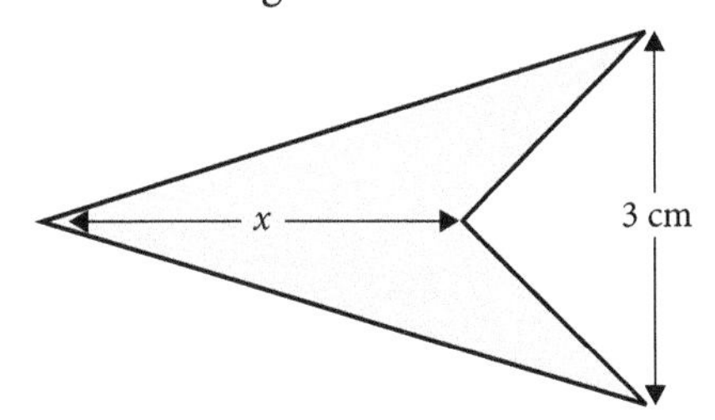

9. Find the length x.

a)

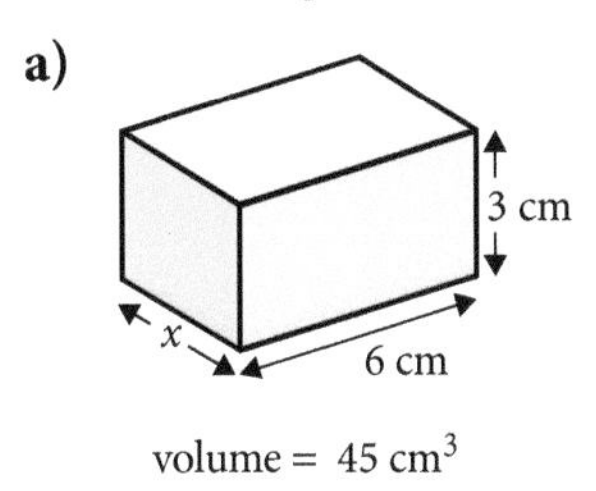

b)

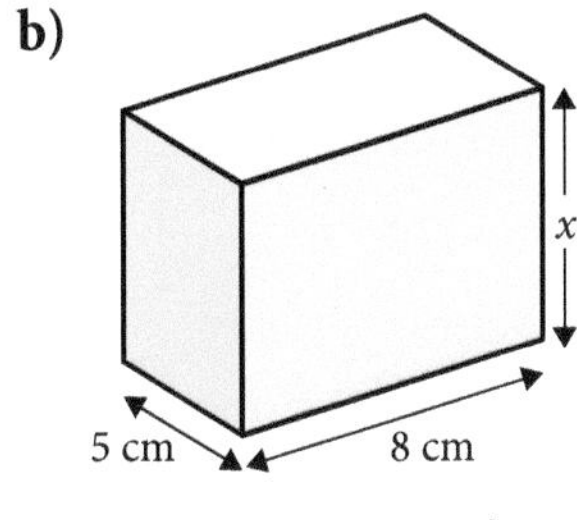

volume = 130 cm^3

10. A rectangular block of metal has dimensions 20 cm × 16 cm × 8 cm.
It is melted down and recast into cubes of edge length 4 cm.
How many cubes will be cast?

11. A freezer makes ice cubes which are rectangular blocks 5 cm × 3 cm × 2 cm.
How many ice cubes can be made from 3 litres of water?

12. A wall, 12 m long, 150 cm high and 15 cm thick is constructed using bricks which measure 20 cm × 15 cm × 10 cm.
How many bricks are needed (ignoring the cement)?

13. The diagonals of a rhombus measure 24 cm and 32 cm.
   a) Work out the area of the rhombus.
   b) Work out the perimeter of the rhombus.

14. The solid object shown is made from 27 small cubes each 1 cm by 1 cm by 1 cm. The small cubes are glued together and then the outside is painted red.
Calculate:
   a) the number of cubes with one face painted
   b) the number of cubes with two faces painted
   c) the number of cubes with three faces painted
   d) the number of cubes with no faces painted.

   (Check that the answers to **(a)**, **(b)**, **(c)** and **(d)** add up to the correct number.)

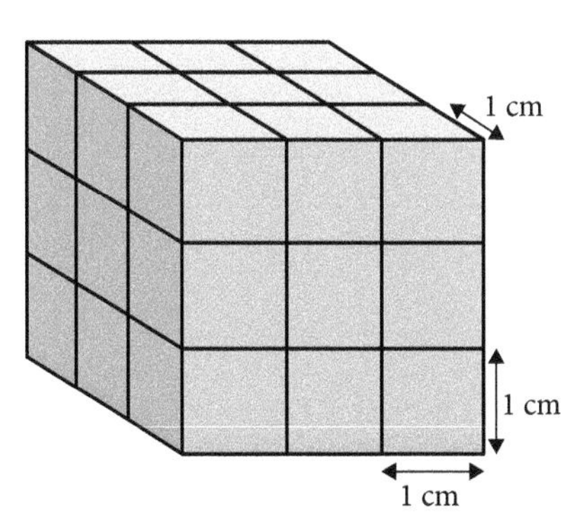

Revision exercise 5A

1. Find x.

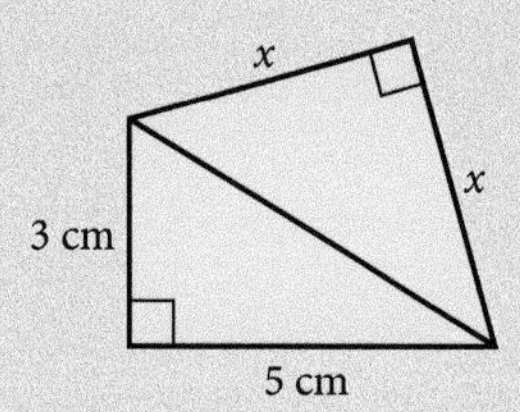

2. In the quadrilateral PQRS, PQ = QS = QR; PS is parallel to QR and angle QRS = 70°. Calculate

   a) angle RQS

   b) angle PQS.

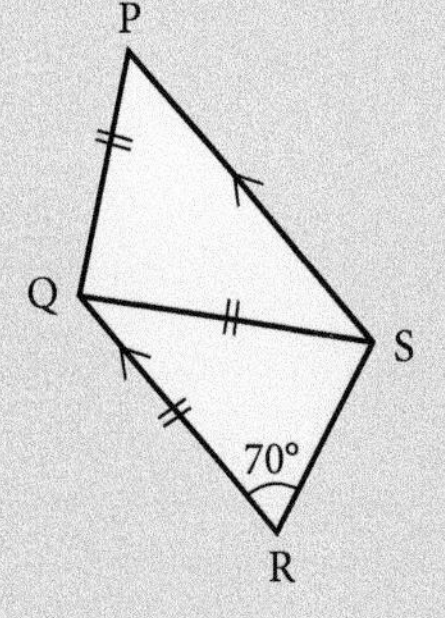

3. A regular octagon of side length 20 cm is to be cut out of a square card.

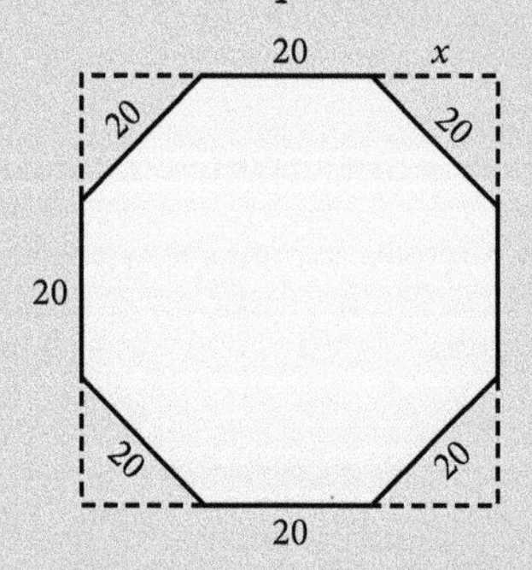

   a) Find the length x and hence find the size of the smallest square card from which this octagon can be cut.

   b) Calculate the area of the octagon (to 3 s.f.).

4. A photo 21 cm by 12 cm is enlarged as shown.

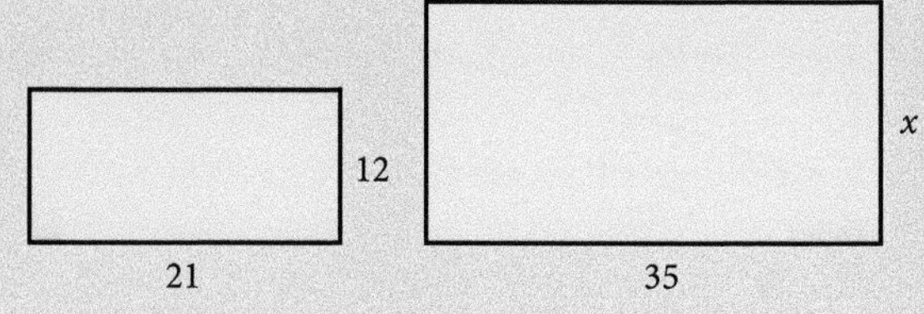

   a) What is the scale factor of the enlargement?

   b) Work out the length x.

5. Look at the diagram below.

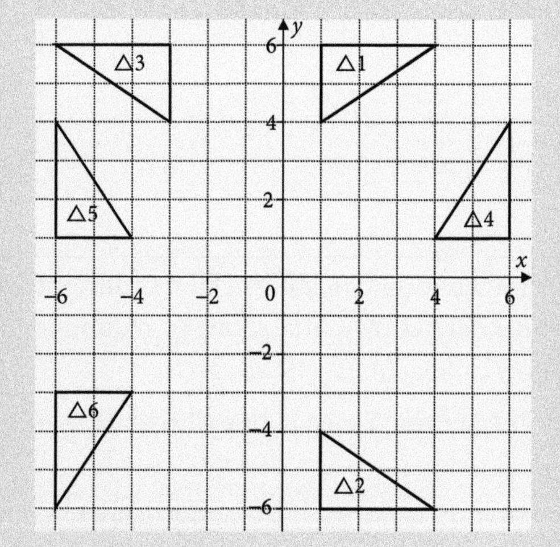

   Describe fully the following transformations.

   a) $\Delta1 \rightarrow \Delta2$

   b) $\Delta1 \rightarrow \Delta3$

   c) $\Delta1 \rightarrow \Delta4$

   d) $\Delta5 \rightarrow \Delta1$

   e) $\Delta5 \rightarrow \Delta6$

   f) $\Delta4 \rightarrow \Delta6$

6. Plot and label the following triangles.

$\Delta 1$: (−3, −6), (−3, −2), (−5, −2)

$\Delta 2$: (−5, −1), (−5, −7), (−8, −1)

$\Delta 3$: (−2, −1), (2; −1), (2, 1)

$\Delta 4$: (6, 3), (2, 3), (2, 5)

$\Delta 5$: (8, 4), (8, 8), (6, 8)

$\Delta 6$: (−3, 1), (−3, 3), (−4, 3)

Describe fully the following transformations.

a) $\Delta 1 \to \Delta 2$ **b)** $\Delta 1 \to \Delta 3$

c) $\Delta 1 \to \Delta 4$ **d)** $\Delta 1 \to \Delta 5$

e) $\Delta 1 \to \Delta 6$ **f)** $\Delta 3 \to \Delta 5$

g) $\Delta 6 \to \Delta 2$

7. **a)** Plot and label

$\Delta 1$: (−3, 4), (−3, 8), (−1, 8)

$\Delta 5$: (−8, −2), (−8, −6), (−6, −2)

b) Draw the triangles $\Delta 2$, $\Delta 3$, $\Delta 4$, $\Delta 6$ and $\Delta 7$ as follows:

i) $\Delta 1 \to \Delta 2$: translation $\begin{pmatrix} 9 \\ -4 \end{pmatrix}$.

ii) $\Delta 2 \to \Delta 3$: translation $\begin{pmatrix} -4 \\ -8 \end{pmatrix}$.

iii) $\Delta 3 \to \Delta 4$: reflection in the line $y = x$.

iv) $\Delta 5 \to \Delta 6$: rotation 90° anticlockwise, centre (−4, −1).

v) $\Delta 6 \to \Delta 7$: rotation 180°, centre (0, −1).

c) Write down the coordinates of the 'pointed ends' of triangles $\Delta 2$, $\Delta 3$, $\Delta 4$, $\Delta 6$ and $\Delta 7$.

8. Point B is on a bearing 120° from point A. The distance from A to B is 110 km.

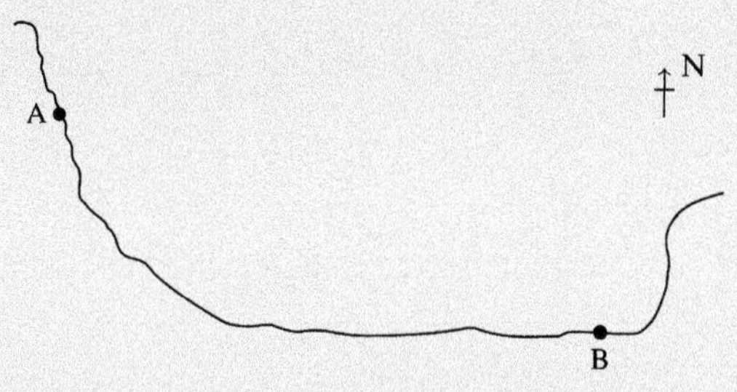

a) Draw a diagram showing the positions of A and B. Use a scale of 1 cm to 10 km.

b) Ship S is on a bearing 072° from A. Ship S is on a bearing 325° from B. Show S on your diagram and state the distance from S to B.

9. Copy the diagrams and then calculate x, correct to 2 s.f.

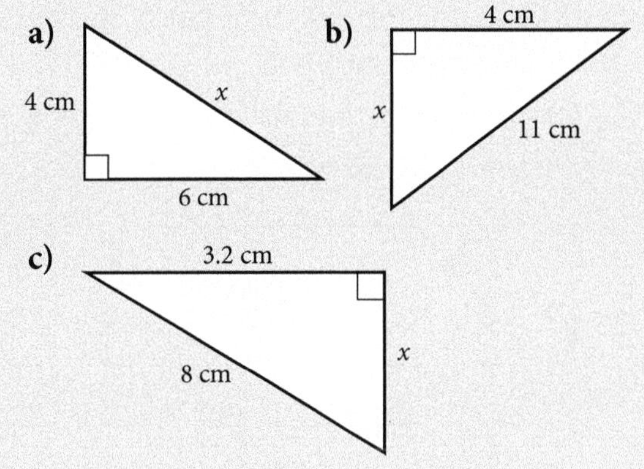

10. **a)** A lies on a bearing of 040° from B. Calculate the bearing of B from A.

b) The bearing of X from Y is 115°. Calculate the bearing of Y from X.

Examination-style exercise 5B

1.

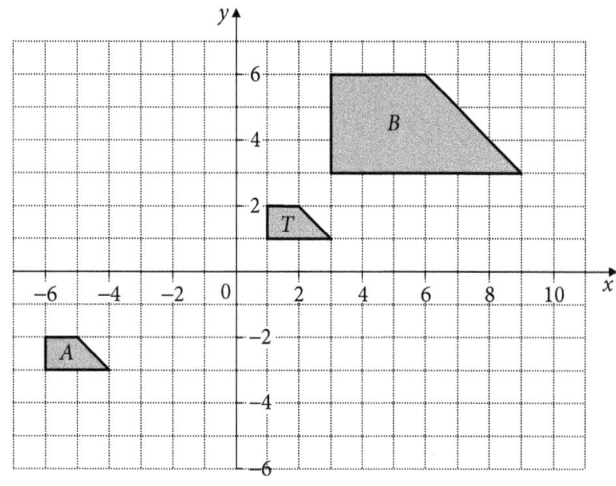

(a) In each case describe fully the **single** transformation which maps

i) T onto A, [3]

ii) T onto B. [3]

(b) Draw on the grid the rotation of T by 90° anticlockwise about (0, 0).
Label your answer R. [2]

(c) Draw on the grid the reflection of T in the line $y = -2$.
Label your answer M. [2]

Cambridge IGCSE Mathematics 0580
Paper 3 Q1 June 2006

2.

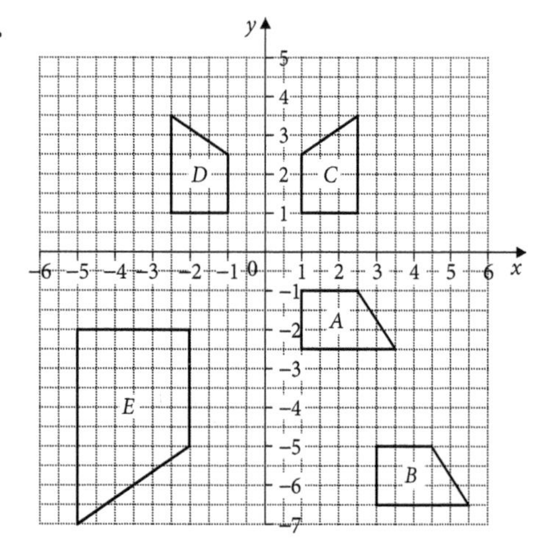

Describe fully the **single** transformation which maps

(a) A onto B, [3]

(b) C onto D, [2]

(c) A onto C. [3]

Cambridge IGCSE Mathematics 0580
Paper 3 Q2 June 2008

3. The points A and B are marked on the diagram.

(a) Write $\overrightarrow{AB}$ as a column vector. [1]

(b) $\overrightarrow{BC} = \begin{pmatrix} -3 \\ -2 \end{pmatrix}$.

Write down the coordinates of C. [1]

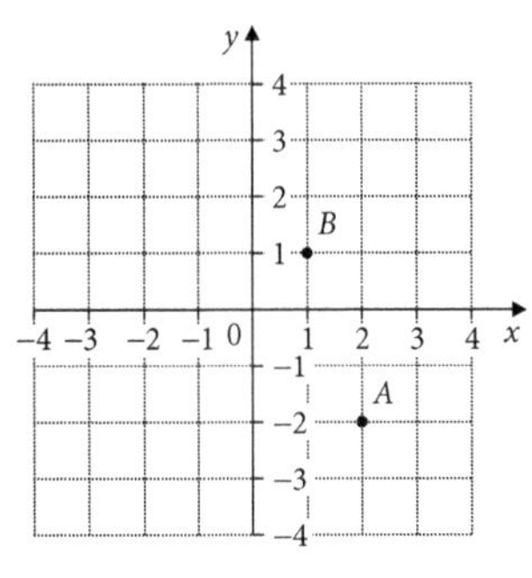

Cambridge IGCSE Mathematics 0580
Paper 11 Q8 June 2007

4. Points A, B and C are shown on the grid.

(a) Plot the point D on the grid so that $ABCD$ is a parallelogram. [1]

(b) Write $\overrightarrow{DB}$ as a column vector. [2]

(c) M is the mid-point of BD.

Write $\overrightarrow{AM}$ as a column vector. [1]

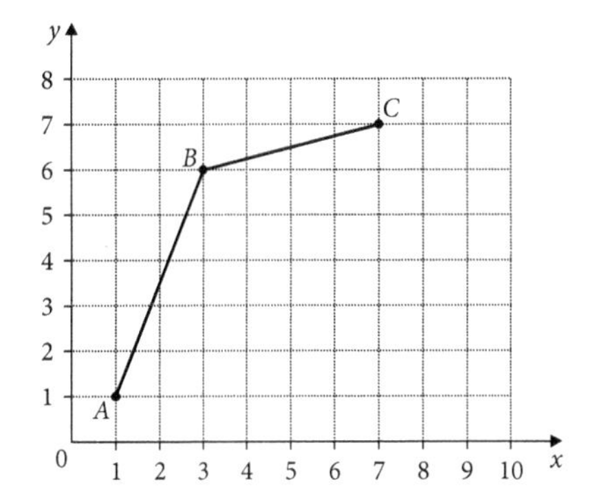

5.

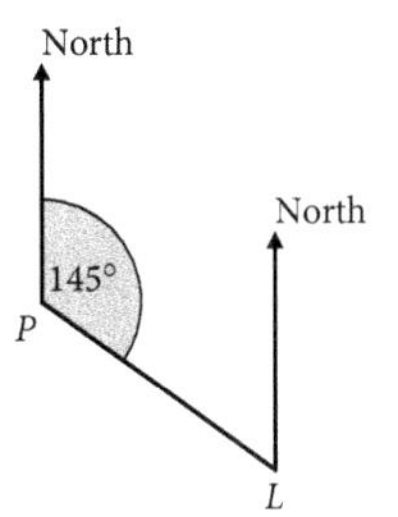

The bearing of a lighthouse, L, from a port, P, is 145°.

Find the bearing of P from L. [2]

Cambridge IGCSE Mathematics 0580
Paper 11 Q7 June 2007

6. The diagram shows the route of an aeroplane.

The plane flies from A to B on a bearing of $120°$ and then from B to C on a bearing of $085°$.

$AB = BC$

North
North
North
120°
A
85°
C
B

(a) Show that angle $ABC = 145°$. [1]

(b) Work out the bearing of A from C. [2]

7. $\mathbf{a} = \begin{pmatrix} 3 \\ -2 \end{pmatrix}$ and $\mathbf{b} = \begin{pmatrix} -1 \\ 2 \end{pmatrix}$.

(a) Work out

i) $\mathbf{a} + 3\mathbf{b}$, [2]

ii) $\mathbf{b} - \mathbf{a}$. [2]

(b) $\overrightarrow{PQ} = 2\mathbf{b}$.

The point P is marked on the grid below.

Draw the vector $\overrightarrow{PQ}$ on the grid. [2]

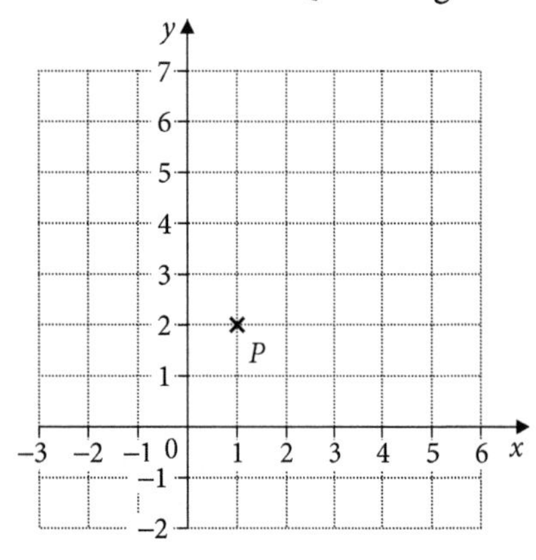

Cambridge IGCSE Mathematics 0580
Paper 12 Q24 June 2008

8. *ABC* is a right-angled triangle.

$AB = 0.5$ m and $AC = 1.3$ m.

Calculate the length of *BC*. [2]

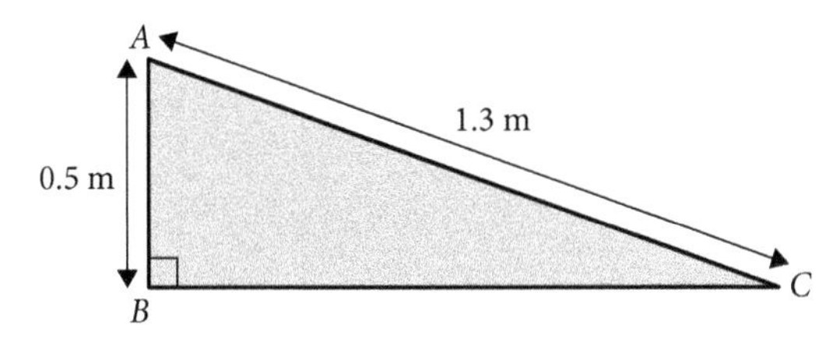

9. Triangle *ABC* is drawn on the grid.

(a) i) Write down the coordinates of *A*. [1]

ii) Write $\overrightarrow{AB}$ and $\overrightarrow{BC}$ as column vectors. [2]

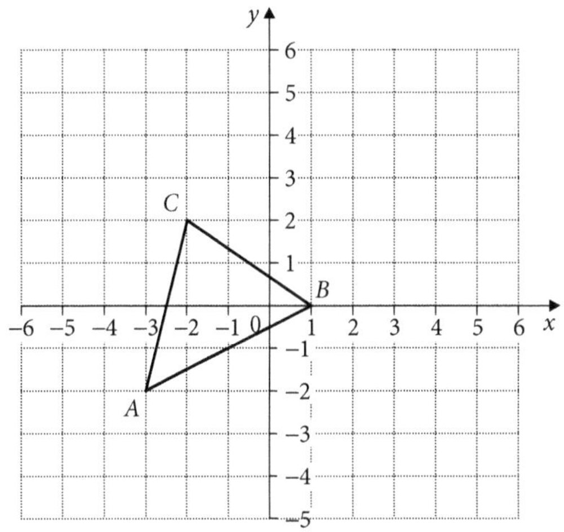

(b) Translate triangle *ABC* by the vector $\begin{pmatrix} 4 \\ -3 \end{pmatrix}$. Label the image *T*.

(c) $\overrightarrow{AP} = 2\overrightarrow{AB}$ and $\overrightarrow{AQ} = 2\overrightarrow{AC}$

i) Plot the points *P* and *Q* on the grid. [2]

ii) Describe fully the single transformation which maps triangle *ABC* onto triangle *APQ*. [3]

(d) Rotate triangle *ABC* through 180° about the mid-point of the side *AB*. Label the image *R*. [2]

Cambridge IGCSE Mathematics 0580
Paper 3 Q8 November 2008

10.

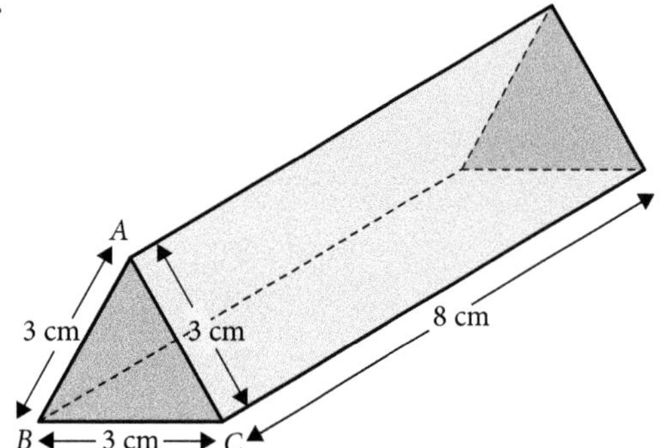

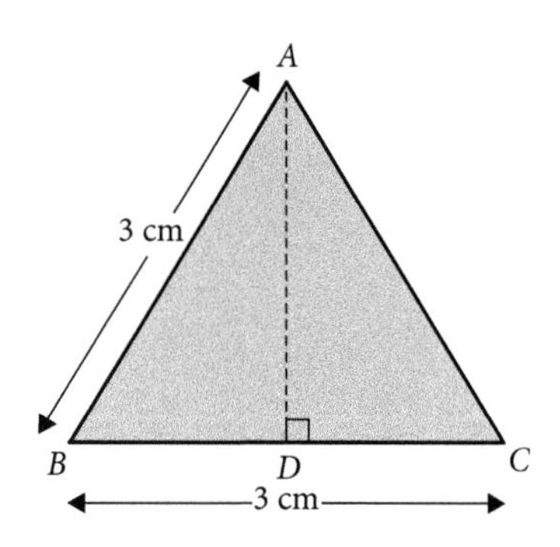

A physics teacher uses a set of identical triangular glass prisms in a lesson.

Diagram 1 shows one of the prisms.

Diagram 2 shows the cross-section of one prism.

The triangle *ABC* is equilateral, with sides of length 3 cm and height *AD*.

(a) **i)** Calculate the length of *AD*. [2]

ii) Calculate the area of triangle *ABC*. [2]

iii) The length of the prism is 8 cm. Calculate the volume of the prism. [2]

(b) After the lesson, the glass prisms are put into a box, which is also a triangular prism.

The cross-section is an equilateral triangle, with sides of length 9 cm. The length of the box is 16 cm.

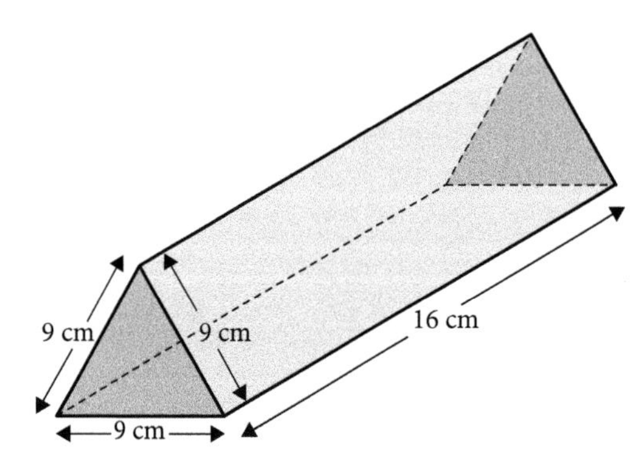

i) Work out the largest number of glass prisms that can fit into the box. [2]

ii) Sketch a net of the box. (Accurate construction is **not** required.) [1]

iii) Calculate the surface area of the box. [6]

iv) The box was made out of plastic, which cost 6 cents per square centimetre.
To make the box, 540 cm^2 of plastic was bought.
Calculate the total cost of the plastic, giving your answer in dollars. [2]

Cambridge IGCSE Mathematics 0580
Paper 3 Q7 November 2007

6 Algebra 2

C2.1 Rearrange simple formulae.
C2.2 Use brackets and extract common factors. Expand products of algebraic expressions.
C2.5 Derive and solve simultaneous linear equations in two unknowns.
C2.7 Continue a given number sequence. Recognise patterns in sequences including the term-to-term rule and relationships between different sequences. Find and use the nth term of sequences.
C2.10 Interpret and use graphs in practical situations including travel graphs and conversion graphs.

6.1 Finding a rule

For the sequence 3, 8, 13, 18, . . . the term-to-term rule is 'add 5'. We draw a mapping diagram with a column for 5 times the term number (i.e. $5n$).

n	$5n$	term
1	5	3
2	10	8
3	15	13
4	20	18

We see that each term is 2 less than $5n$.

So, the 10th term is $(5 \times 10) - 2 = 48$

the 20th term is $(5 \times 20) - 2 = 98$

the nth term is $5 \times n - 2 = 5n - 2$

Exercise 1

1. Look at the sequence 5, 8, 11, 14, . . .
The difference between terms is 3.
Copy the table, which has a column for $3n$.
Copy and complete: 'The nth term of the sequence is $3n + \square$.'

n	$3n$	term
1	3	5
2	6	8
3	9	11
4	12	14

2. Look at the sequence and the table underneath.
Find the nth term in each case.

a) Sequence 5, 9, 13, 17, . . .

n	$4n$	term
1	4	5
2	8	9
3	12	13
4	16	17

nth term = $\square$

b) Sequence 2, 8, 14, 20, . . .

n	$6n$	term
1	6	2
2	12	8
3	18	14
4	24	20

nth term = $\square$

3. In the sequence 6, 11, 16, 21, . . .
the difference between terms is 5.
Copy and complete the table and write an expression for the nth term of the sequence.

n	☐	term
1	☐	6
2	☐	11
3	☐	16
4	☐	21

4. Look at the sequence 6, 10, 14, 18, . . .
Write down the difference between terms.
Make a table like the one in Question **3** and use it to find an expression for the nth term.

5. Write down each sequence in a table and then find the nth term.
   a) 5, 7, 9, 11, . . .
   b) 3, 7, 11, 15, . . .
   c) 2, 8, 14, 20, . . .

6. Make a table for each sequence and write the nth term.
   a) 2, 10, 18, 26, . . .
   b) 7, 10, 13, 16, . . .
   c) 21, 30, 39, 48, . . .

In Questions **7** to **18** you are given a sequence in a table. Copy the table and make an extra column. Find an expression for the nth term of each sequence. [t stands for 'term'.]

7.

n	t
1	3
2	8
3	13
4	18
5	23

8.

n	t
1	3
2	6
3	9
4	12
5	15

9.

n	t
1	7
2	13
3	19
4	25
5	31

10.

n	t
1	6
2	8
3	10
4	12
5	14

11.

n	t
1	6
2	7
3	8
4	9
5	10

12.

n	t
1	1
2	4
3	7
4	10
5	13

13.

n	t
1	5
2	13
3	21
4	29
5	37

14.

n	t
1	7
2	12
3	17
4	22
5	27

15.

n	t
6	14
7	17
8	20
9	23
10	26

16.

n	t
8	83
9	93
10	103
11	113
12	123

17.

n	t
4	15
5	18
6	21
7	24

18.

n	t
12	61
13	66
14	71
15	76

Here is a sequence of 'houses' made from matches.

The table on the right records the number of houses h and the number of matches m.

h	m
1	5
2	9
3	13
4	17

If the number in the h column goes up one at a time, look at the number in the m column. If it goes up (or down) by the same number each time, the function connecting m and h is linear. This means that there are no terms in h^2 or anything more complicated.

In this case, the numbers in the m column go up by 4 each time. This suggests that a column for $4h$ might help.

h	m	$4h$
1	5	4
2	9	8
3	13	12
4	17	16

Now it is fairly clear that m is one more than $4h$.

So the formula linking m and h is: $m = 4h + 1$

The table shows how r changes with n.

What is the formula linking r with n?

n	r
2	3
3	8
4	13
5	18

Because r goes up by 5 each time, try writing another column for $5n$.

The table shows that r is always 7 less than $5n$, so the formula linking r with n is: $r = 5n - 7$

n	r	$5n$
2	3	10
3	8	15
4	13	20
5	18	25

Unfortunately if the numbers on the left do not go up by one each time, this method does not work. In that case you have to think of something clever!

Exercise 2

1. Below is a sequence of diagrams showing blue tiles b and white tiles w with the related table.

b	w
1	5
2	6
3	7
4	8

What is the formula for w in terms of b ? [i.e. write '$w = \ldots$']

2. This is a different sequence with blue tiles b and white tiles w and the related table.

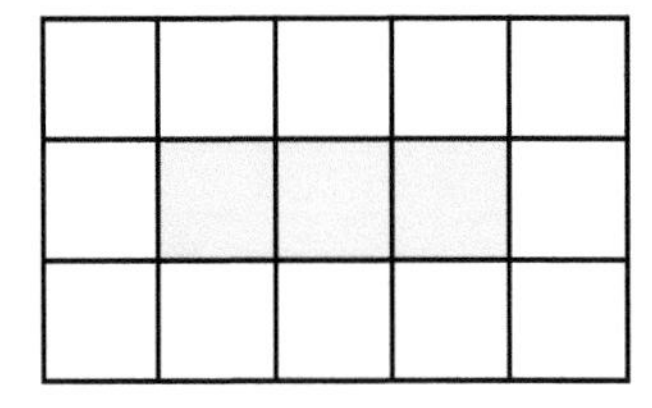

b	w
2	10
3	12
4	14
5	16

What is the formula? Write it as '$w = \ldots$'.

3. Here is a sequence of I's.

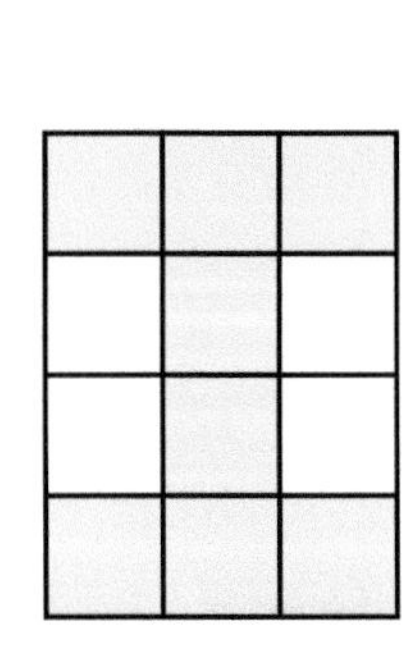

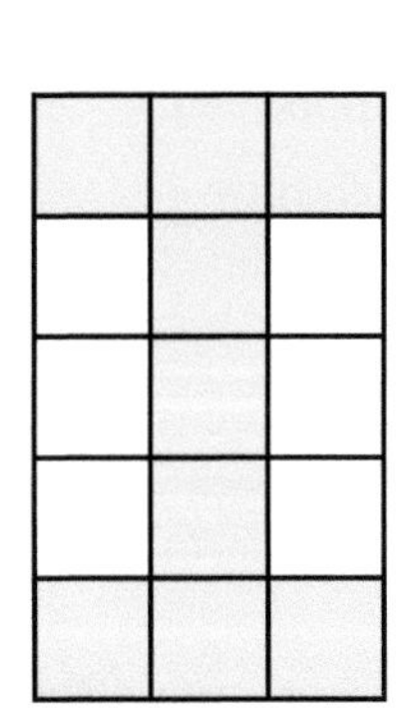

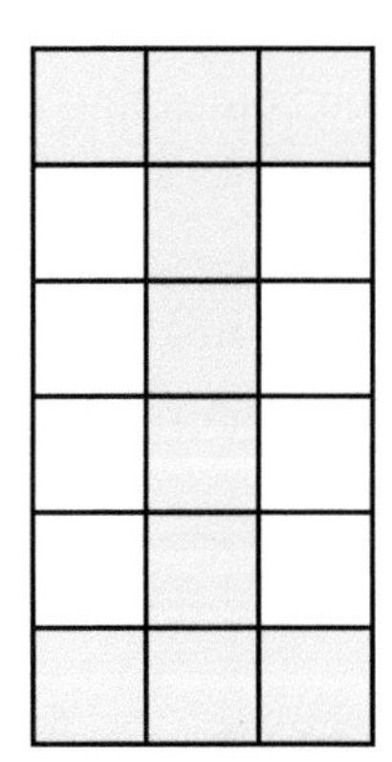

Make your own table for blue tiles b and white tiles w.
What is the formula for w in terms of b ?

4. In this sequence we have matches (m) and triangles (t).

Make a table for t and m. It starts like this:

Continue the table and find a formula for m in terms of t.

Write '$m = \ldots$'.

t	m
1	3
2	5
⋮	⋮

5. Here is a different sequence of matches and triangles.

Make a table and find a formula connecting m and t.

6. In this sequence there are triangles (t) and squares (s) around the outside.

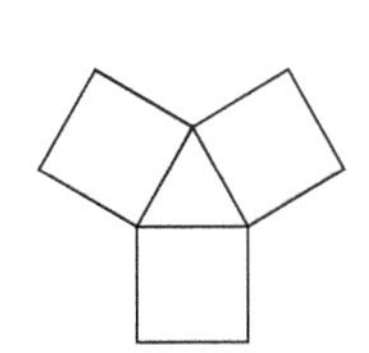 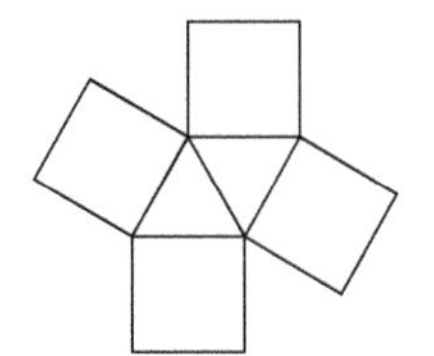 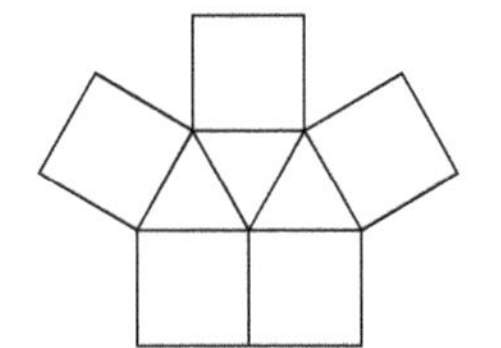 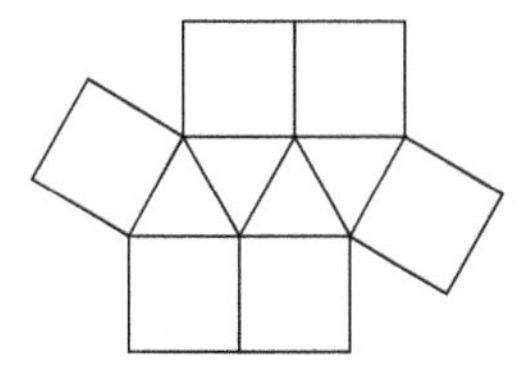

What is the formula connecting t and s ?

7. Look at the tables below. In each case, find a formula connecting the two letters.

a)

n	p
1	3
2	8
3	13
4	18

write '$p = \ldots$'

b)

n	k
2	17
3	24
4	31
5	38

write '$k = \ldots$'

c)

n	w
3	17
4	19
5	21
6	23

write '$w = \ldots$'

8. In these tables it is harder because the numbers on the left do not go up by one each time. Try to find a formula in each case.

a)

n	y
1	4
3	10
7	22
8	25

b)

n	h
2	5
3	9
6	21
10	37

c)

n	k
3	14
7	26
9	32
12	41

9. This is one member of a sequence of cubes (c) made from matches (m).

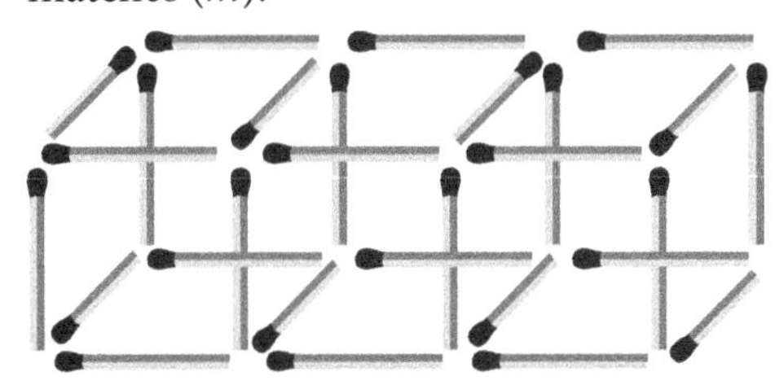

Find a formula connecting m and c.

Example

The sequence 1, 4, 9, 16, 25, . . . does not have a common difference between terms but it is the sequence of *square numbers*.
We can write this as $t = n^2$.

Find the nth term of the following sequence: 3, 6, 11, 18, . . .

We see that each term is 2 more than n^2 so the nth term formula is $t = n^2 + 2$.

n	n^2	t
1	1	3
2	4	6
3	9	11
4	16	18

Exercise 3

Find an expression for the nth term of each sequence.

1. 4, 7, 12, 19, . . .

2. 2, 8, 18, 32, . . .

3. 0, 3, 8, 15 . . .

4. 0.5, 2, 4.5, 8, . . .

5. −6, −3, 2, 9, . . .

6. −1, −4, −9, −16, . . .

7. 0, −3, −8, −15, . . .

8. 2, 9, 28, 65, . . .

9. 2, 16, 54, 128, . . .

10. −1, 6, 25, 62, . . .

Write out the sequence of *cube* numbers and compare . . .

6.2 Simultaneous equations

Graphical solution

Louise and Philip are two children and Louise is 5 years older than Philip.

The sum of their ages is 12 years.

How old is each child?

Let Louise be x years old and Philip be y years old.

We can say $\quad x + y = 12 \quad$ [sum = 12]

and $\quad x - y = 5 \quad$ [difference = 5]

Suppose we draw on the same page the graphs of $\quad x + y = 12$

and $\quad x - y = 5$

$x + y = 12$ goes through (0, 12), (2, 10), (6, 6), (12, 0).

$x - y = 5$ goes through (5, 0), (7, 2), (10, 5).

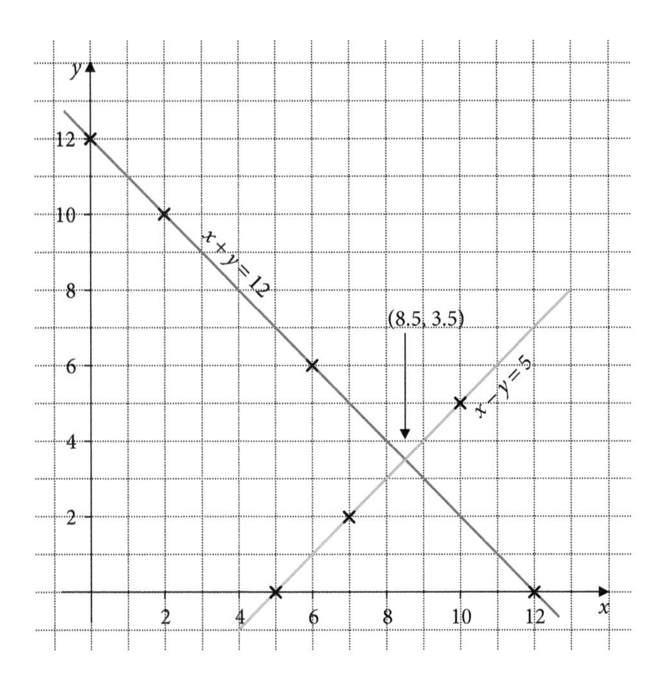

The point (8.5, 3.5) lies on both lines at the same time.

We say that $x = 8.5$, $y = 3.5$ are the solutions of the **simultaneous** equations $x + y = 12$, $x - y = 5$.

So Louise is $8\frac{1}{2}$ years old and Philip is $3\frac{1}{2}$ years old.

Exercise 4

1. Use the graphs to solve these equations.

Solve

a) $x + y = 10$
$y - 2x = 1$

b) $2x + 5y = 17$
$y - 2x = 1$

c) $x + y = 10$
$2x + 5y = 17$

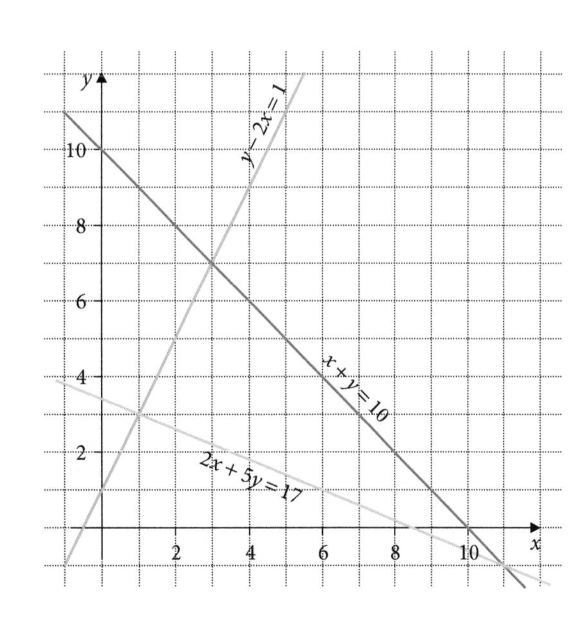

In Questions **2** to **6**, solve the simultaneous equations by drawing graphs. Use a scale of 1 cm to 1 unit on both axes.

2. $x + y = 6$

$2x + y = 8$

Draw axes with x and y from 0 to 8.

3. $x + 2y = 8$

$3x + y = 9$

Draw axes with x and y from 0 to 9.

4. $x + 3y = 6$

$x - y = 2$

Draw axes with x from 0 to 8 and y from -2 to 4.

5. $5x + y = 10$

$x - y = -4$

Draw axes with x from -4 to 4 and y from 0 to 10.

6. $a + 2b = 11$

$2a + b = 13$

In this one the unknowns are a and b. Draw the a-axis across the page from 0 to 13 and the b-axis up the page also from 0 to 13.

7. There are four lines drawn here.

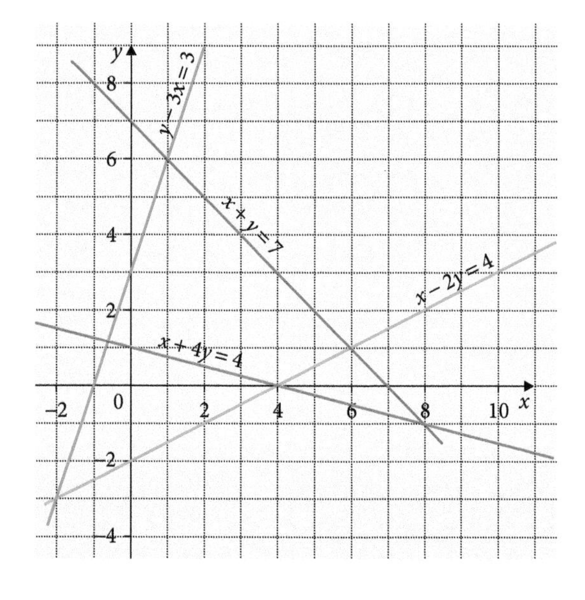

Write down the solutions to the following:

a) $x - 2y = 4$
$x + 4y = 4$

b) $x + y = 7$
$y - 3x = 3$

c) $y - 3x = 3$
$x - 2y = 4$

d) $x + 4y = 4$
$x + y = 7$

e) $x + 4y = 4$
$y - 3x = 3$ (For this one give x and y correct to 1 d.p.)

Simultaneous equations: algebraic solution

We can also solve simultaneous equations without drawing graphs.

There are two methods: substitution and elimination.

You can choose for yourself which one to use in any question.

a) Substitution method

This method is used when one equation contains a single 'x' or 'y', as in equation [2] of the example below.

Example

Solve the simultaneous equations

$3x - 2y = 0$ ... [1]

$2x + y = 7$ ... [2]

From [2] $2x + y = 7$

$y = 7 - 2x$

Substituting for y in [1]

$3x - 2(7 - 2x) = 0$

$3x - 14 + 4x = 0$

$7x = 14$

$x = 2$

Substituting for x in [2]

$2 \times 2 + y = 7$

$y = 3$

The solutions are $x = 2$, $y = 3$.

These values of x and y are the only pair which simultaneously satisfy *both* equations.

Exercise 5

Use the substitution method to solve the following:

1. $2x + y = 5$
$x + 3y = 5$

2. $x + 2y = 8$
$2x + 3y = 14$

3. $3x + y = 10$
$x - y = 2$

4. $2x + y = -3$
$x - y = -3$

5. $4x + y = 14$
$x + 5y = 13$

6. $x + 2y = 1$
$2x + 3y = 4$

7. $2x + y = 5$
$3x - 2y = 4$

8. $2x + y = 13$
$5x - 4y = 13$

9. $7x + 2y = 19$
$x - y = 4$

10. $b - a = -5$
$a + b = -1$

11. $a + 4b = 6$
$8b - a = -3$

12. $a + b = 4$
$2a + b = 5$

13. $3m = 2n - 6\frac{1}{2}$
$4m + n = 6$

14. $2w + 3x - 13 = 0$
$x + 5w - 13 = 0$

15. $x + 2(y - 6) = 0$
$3x + 4y = 30$

16. $2x = 4 + z$
$6x - 5z = 18$

17. $3m - n = 5$
$2m + 5n = 7$

18. $5c - d - 11 = 0$
$4d + 3c = -5$

It is useful, at this point, to revise the operations of addition and subtraction with negative numbers.

Simplify:

a) $-7 + -4 = -7 - 4 = -11$

b) $-3x + (-4x) = -3x - 4x = -7x$

c) $4y - (-3y) = 4y + 3y = 7y$

d) $3a + (-3a) = 3a - 3a = 0$

b) Elimination method

Use this method when the first method is unsuitable (some prefer to use it for every question).

Example

	$2x + 3y = 5$	... [1]
	$5x - 2y = -16$	... [2]
[1] × 5	$10x + 15y = 25$	... [3]
[2] × 2	$10x - 4y = -32$	... [4]
[3] – [4]	$15y - (-4y) = 25 - (-32)$	
	$19y = 57$	
	$y = 3$	
Substitute in [1]	$2x + 3 \times 3 = 5$	
	$2x = 5 - 9 = -4$	
	$x = -2$	

The solutions are $x = -2$, $y = 3$.

Exercise 6

Use the elimination method to solve the following:

1. $2x + 5y = 24$
$4x + 3y = 20$

2. $5x + 2y = 13$
$2x + 6y = 26$

3. $3x + y = 11$
$9x + 2y = 28$

4. $x + 2y = 17$
$8x + 3y = 45$

5. $3x + 2y = 19$
$x + 8y = 21$

6. $2a + 3b = 9$
$4a + b = 13$

7. $2x + 3y = 11$
$3x + 4y = 15$

8. $3x + 8y = 27$
$4x + 3y = 13$

9. $2x + 7y = 17$
$5x + 3y = -1$

10. $5x + 3y = 23$
$2x + 4y = 12$

11. $7x + 5y = 32$
$3x + 4y = 23$

12. $3x + 2y = 4$
$4x + 5y = 10$

13. $3x + 2y = 11$
$2x - y = -3$

14. $3x + 2y = 7$
$2x - 3y = -4$

15. $x - 2y = -4$
$3x + y = 9$

16. $5x - 7y = 27$
$3x - 4y = 16$

17. $3x - 2y = 7$
$4x + y = 13$

18. $x - y = -1$
$2x - y = 0$

19. $y - x = -1$
$3x - y = 5$

20. $x - 3y = -5$
$2y + 3x + 4 = 0$

Problems solved by simultaneous equations

Exercise 7

Solve each problem by forming a pair of simultaneous equations.

1. Find two numbers with a sum of 15 and a difference of 4.

   [Let the numbers be x and y.]

2. Twice one number added to three times another gives 21.

   Find the numbers, if the difference between them is 3.

3. The average of two numbers is 7, and the difference between them is 6. Find the numbers.

4. Here is a puzzle from a newspaper. The ? and * stand for numbers which are to be found. The totals for the rows and columns are given.

   Write down two equations involving ? and * and solve them to find the values of ? and *

?	*	?	*	36
?	*	*	?	36
*	?	*	*	33
?	*	?	*	36
36	33	36	33	

5. The line with equation $y + ax = c$ passes through the points (1, 5) and (3, 1). Find a and c.

   For the point (1, 5) put $x = 1$ and $y = 5$ into $y + ax = c$, etc.

6. The line $y = mx + c$ passes through (2, 5) and (4, 13).

   Find m and c.

7. A stone is thrown into the air and its height, h metres above the ground, is given by the equation
   $h = at - bt^2$.

   From an experiment we know that $h = 40$ when $t = 2$ and that $h = 45$ when $t = 3$.

   Show that $a - 2b = 20$
   and $a - 3b = 15$.

   Solve these equations to find a and b.

8. A shop owner can buy either two televisions and three DVD players for \$1750 or four televisions and one DVD player for \$1250. Find the cost of one of each. Let the cost of a television be x and the cost of a DVD player be y.

9. A spider can lay either white or brown eggs. Three white eggs and two brown eggs weigh 13 grams, while five white eggs and four brown eggs weigh 24 grams. Find the weight of a brown egg and of a white egg.

10. A bag contains forty coins, all of them either 2c or 5c coins. Let there be x 2c coins and y 5c coins. If the value of the money in the bag is \$1.55, find the number of each kind.

11. A slot machine takes only 10c and 50c coins and contains a total of twenty-one coins altogether. If the value of the coins is \$4.90, find the number of coins of each value.

6.3 Interpreting graphs

Travel graphs

Exercise 8

1. The graph shows a return journey by car from Grenoble to Sisteron.

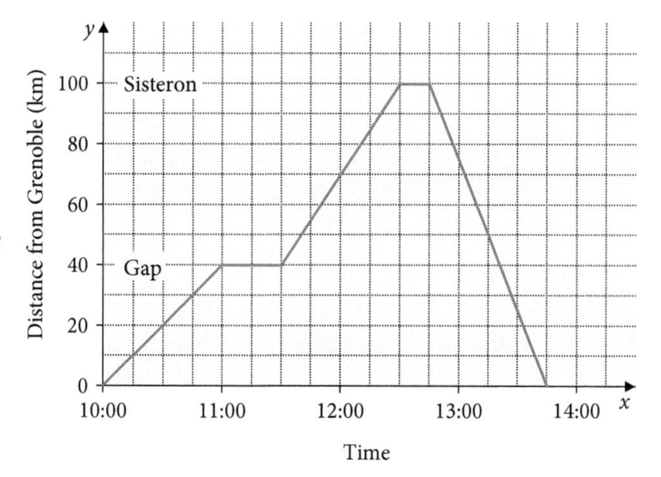

   a) How far is it from Grenoble to Gap?
   b) How far is it from Gap to Sisteron?
   c) At which two places does the car stop?
   d) How long does the car stop at Sisteron?
   e) When does the car
      i) arrive in Gap,
      ii) arrive back in Grenoble?
   f) What is the speed of the car
      i) from Grenoble to Gap,
      ii) from Gap to Sisteron,
      iii) from Sisteron to Grenoble?

2. Yousef cycles to a friend's house but on the way his bike breaks, and he has to walk the remaining distance.
   At his friend's house, he repairs the bike and then returns home. On the way back, he stops at a shop.

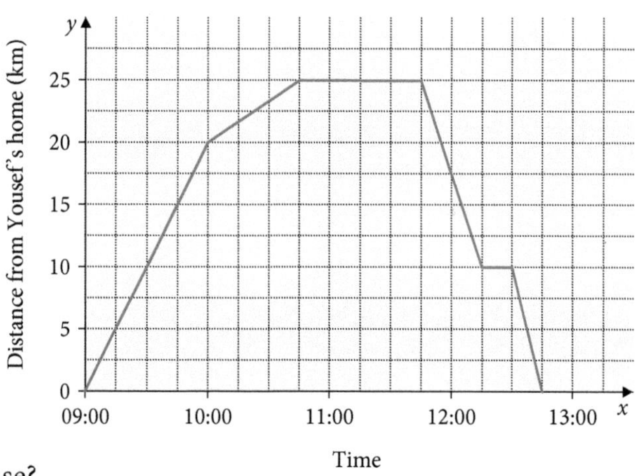

   a) How far is it to his friend's house?
   b) How far is it from his friend's house to the shop?
   c) At what time did his bike break?
   d) How long did he stay at his friend's house?

e) At what speed did he travel:

   i) from home until the bike broke,

   ii) after the bike broke to his friend's house,

   iii) from his friend's house to the shop,

   iv) from the shop back to his own home?

3. Eberto and Markus use the same road to travel between Aston and Borton.

   a) At what time did:

      i) Eberto arrive in Borton,

      ii) Markus leave Aston?

   b) i) When did Eberto and Markus pass each other?

      ii) In which direction was Eberto travelling?

   c) Find the following speeds:

      i) Markus from Aston to Stanley,

      ii) Eberto from Aston to Borton,

      iii) Markus from Stanley to Borton,

      iv) Eberto from Borton back to Aston.

   d) (More difficult) When did Markus arrive in Borton?

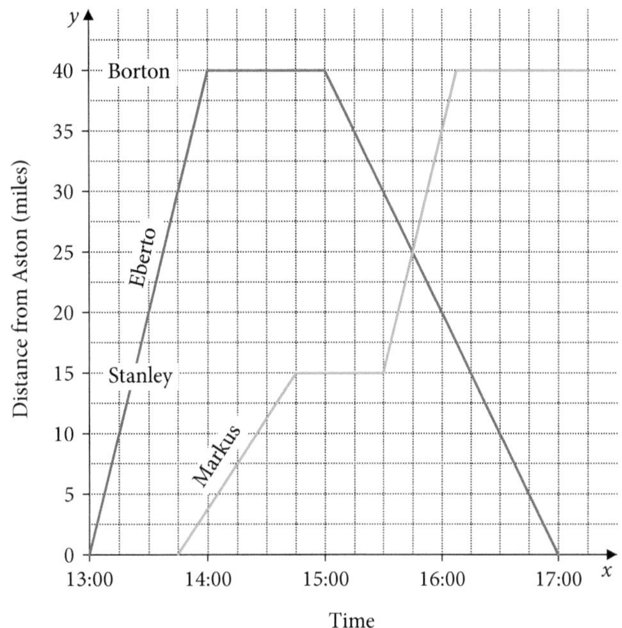

4. The graph shows the journeys made by a van and a car starting at Toledo, travelling to Madrid and returning to Toledo.

   a) For how long was the van stationary during the journey?

   b) At what time did the car first overtake the van?

   c) At what speed was the van travelling between 09:30 and 10:00?

   d) What was the greatest speed attained by the car during the entire journey?

   e) What was the average speed of the car over its entire journey?

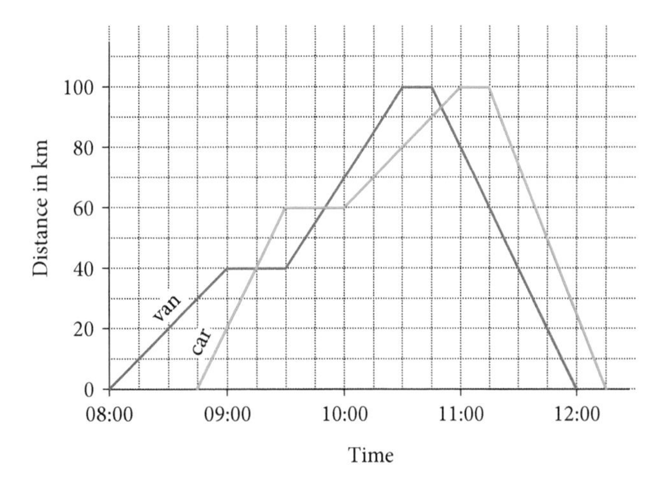

5. The graph shows the journeys of a bus and a car along the same road. The bus goes from Bangkok to Tainan and back to Bangkok. The car goes from Tainan to Bangkok and back to Tainan.

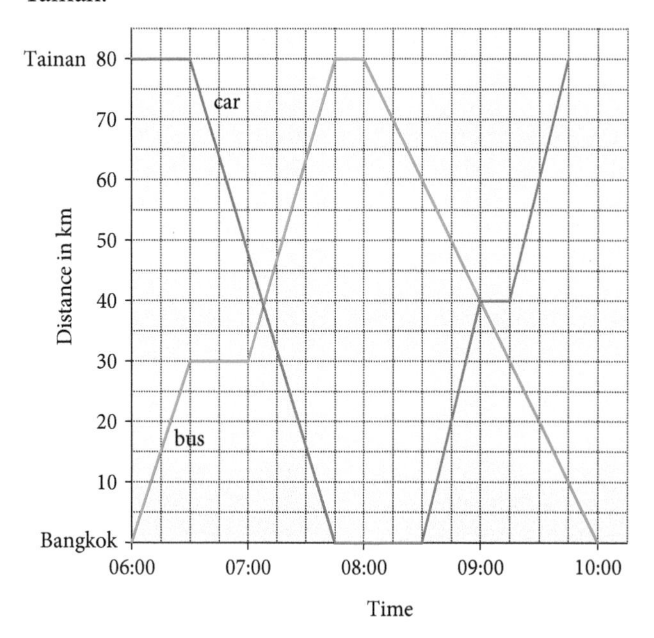

a) When did the bus and the car meet for the second time?

b) At what speed did the car travel from Tainan to Bangkok?

c) What was the average speed of the bus over its entire journey?

d) Approximately how far apart were the bus and the car at 09:45?

e) What was the greatest speed attained by the car during its entire journey?

In Questions **6**, **7** and **8**, draw a travel graph to illustrate the journey described. Draw axes with similar scales to Question **5**.

6. Mrs Chuong leaves home at 08:00 and drives at a speed of 50 km/h. After $\frac{1}{2}$ hour she reduces her speed to 40 km/h and continues at this speed until 09:30. She stops from 09:30 until 10:00 and then returns home at a speed of 60 km/h.

Use a graph to find the approximate time at which she arrives home.

7. Cillian leaves home at 09:00 and drives at a speed of 20 km/h. After $\frac{3}{4}$ hour he increases his speed to 45 km/h and continues at this speed until 10:45. He stops from 10:45 until 11:30 and then returns home at a speed of 50 km/h.

   Use a graph to find the approximate time at which he arrives home.

8. At 10:00 Akram leaves home and cycles to his grandparents' house which is 70 km away. He cycles at a speed of 20 km/h until 11:15, at which time he stops for $\frac{1}{2}$ hour. He then completes the journey at a speed of 30 km/h. At 11:45 Akram's sister, Hameeda, leaves home and drives her car at 60 km/h. Hameeda also goes to her grandparents' house and uses the same road as Akram. At approximately what time does Hameeda overtake Akram?

Real-life graphs

Exercise 9

1. The graph shows how the share price of a chemical firm varied over a period of weeks. The share price is the price in cents paid for one share in the company.

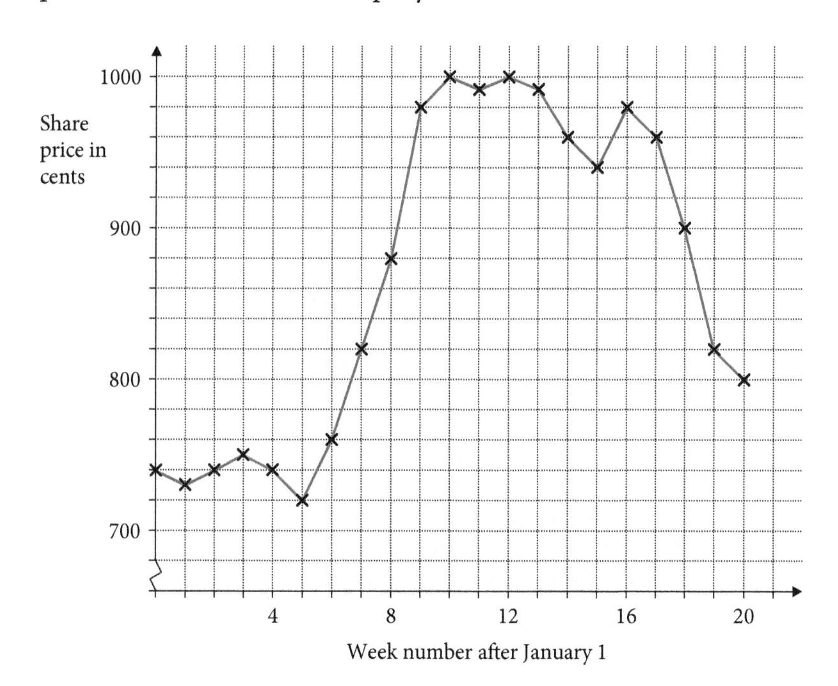

a) What was the share price in Week 4?

b) Kasia bought 200 shares in Week 6 and sold them all in week 18. How much profit did she make?

c) Nhean can buy (and then sell) 5000 shares. He consults a very accurate fortune teller who can predict the share price over the coming weeks. What is the maximum profit he could make?

d) When there is a full moon the fortune teller's predictions can be fairly disastrous. What is the maximum *loss* Nhean could make?

2. The graph shows the number of students in a school on one day.

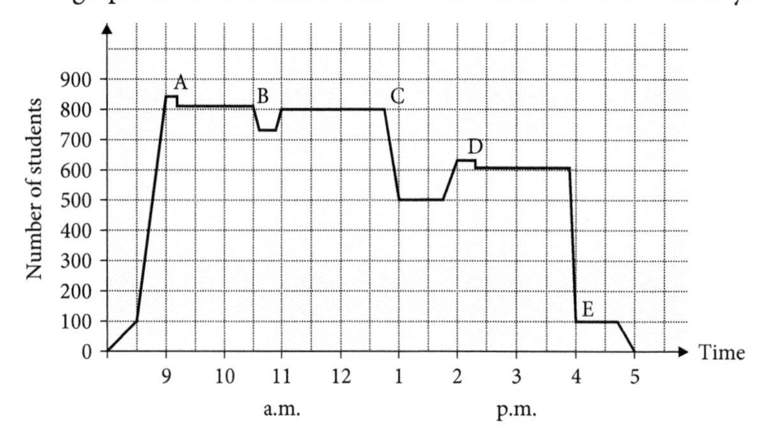

The graph tells you some interesting things. Referring to the points A, B, C, D, E, describe briefly what happened during the day. Give an explanation of what you think might have happened.

3. The graph below shows average television and radio audiences throughout a typical day.

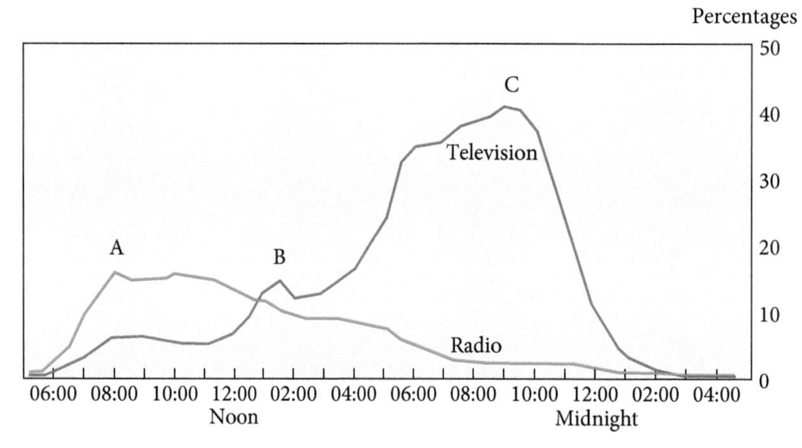

a) When are the 'peak times' for

i) radio audiences ii) television audiences?

b) Give reasons which explain the shapes of the graphs at times A, B and C.

4. The graph below shows how to convert miles into kilometres.

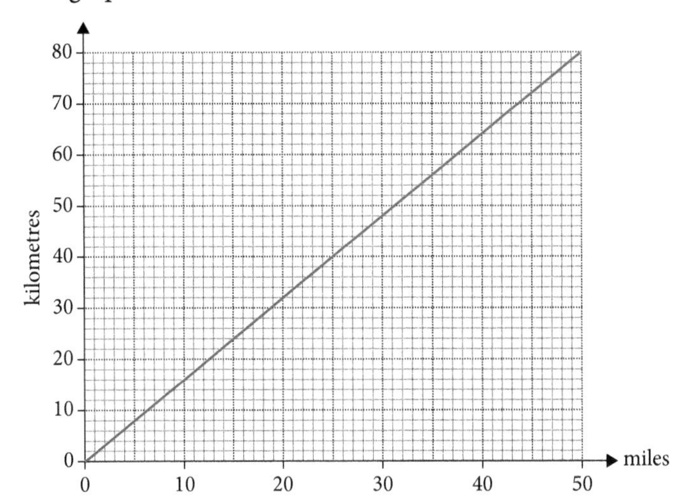

a) How many kilometres is one small square worth on the vertical axis?

b) Use the graph to find how many kilometres are the same as:

i) 25 miles **ii)** 15 miles **iii)** 45 miles **iv)** 5 miles

c) Use the graph to find how many miles are the same as:

i) 64 km **ii)** 56 km **iii)** 16 km **iv)** 32 km

5. The graph below shows how to convert dollars into euros.

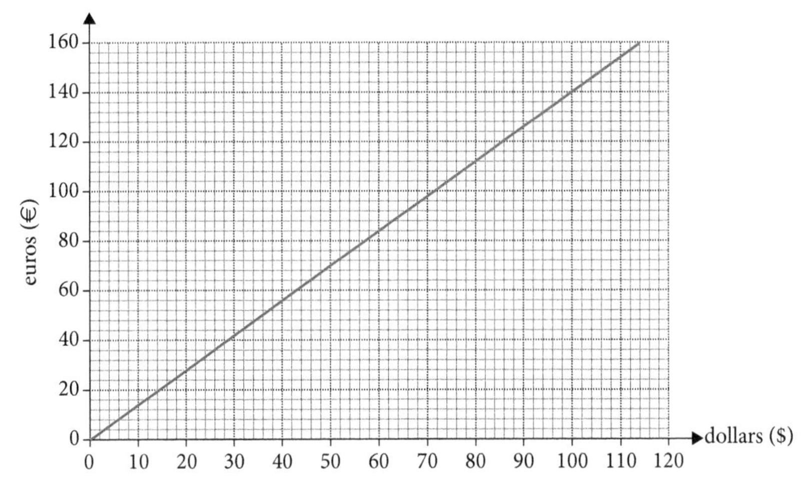

a) Use the graph to find how many euros are the same as:

i) $20 **ii)** $80 **iii)** $50

b) Use the graph to find how many dollars are the same as:

i) €56 **ii)** €84 **iii)** €140

c) Tim spends €154 on clothes in Paris. How many dollars has he spent?

6. A car travels along a motorway and the amount of petrol in its tank is monitored as shown on the graph.

   a) How much petrol was bought at the first stop?

   b) What was the petrol consumption in km per litre:

      i) before the first stop,

      ii) between the two stops?

   c) What was the average petrol consumption over the 200 km?

   d) After it leaves the second service station the car's petrol consumption is reduced to 4 km per litre for 20 km. After that, the car travels a further 80 km during which time the consumption is 8 km per litre. Draw the graph on the right and extend it to show the next 100 km. How much petrol is in the tank at the end of the journey?

7. Kendal Motors hires out vans.

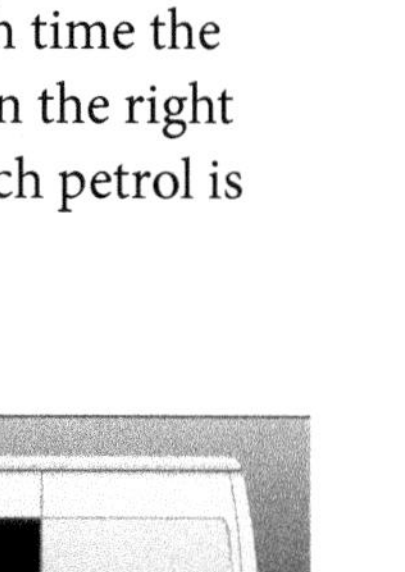

Copy and complete the table where x is the number of km travelled and C is the total cost in dollars.

x	0	50	100	150	200	250	300
C	35			65			95

Draw a graph of C against x, using scales of 2 cm for 50 km on the x-axis and 1 cm for \$10 on the C-axis.

Use the graph to find the number of km travelled when the total cost was \$71.

8. Jeff sets up his own business as a plumber.

Copy and complete the table where C stands for his total charge and h stands for the number of hours he works.

h	0	1	2	3
C		33		

Draw a graph with h across the page and C up the page.
Use scales of 2 cm to 1 hour for h and 2 cm to \$10 for C.

Use your graph to find how long he worked if his charge was \$55.50.

Sketch graphs

Exercise 10

1. Which of the graphs A to D below best fits the following statement:
'Unemployment is still rising but by less each month.'

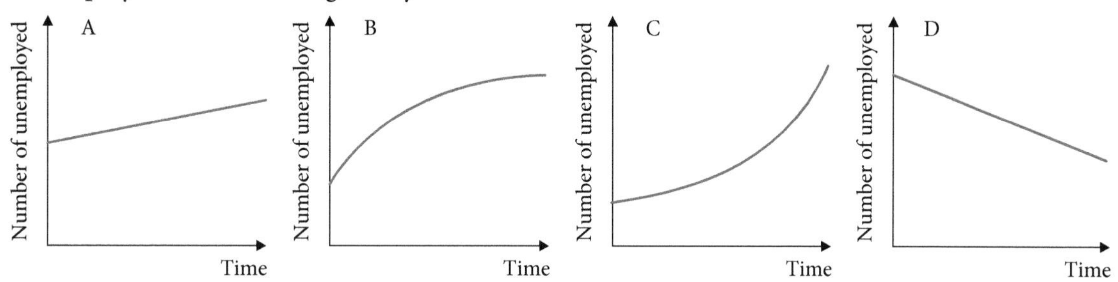

2. Which of the graphs A to D best fits the following statement:
'The price of oil was rising more rapidly in 2015 than at any time in the previous ten years.'?

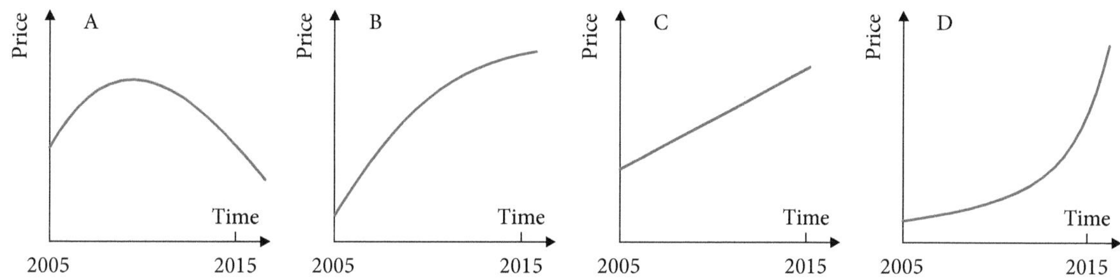

3. Which of the graphs A to D below best fits each of the following statements:

a) The birthrate was falling but is now steady.

b) Unemployment, which rose slowly until 2012, is now rising rapidly.

c) Inflation, which has been rising steadily, is now beginning to fall.

d) The price of gold has fallen steadily over the last year.

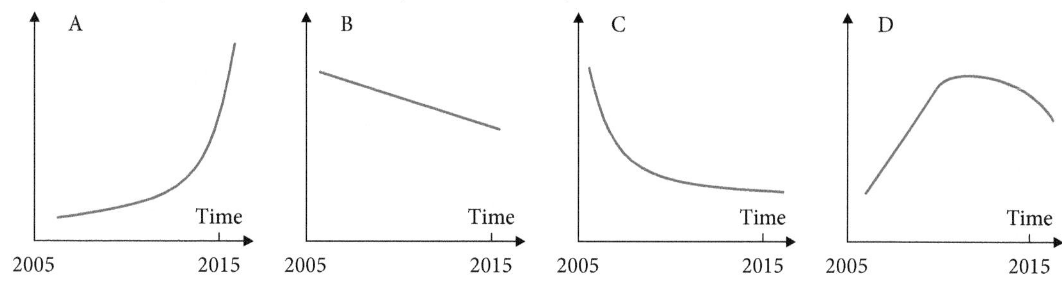

4. The graph shows the motion of three cars A, B and C along the same road.

   Answer the following questions giving estimates where necessary.

   a) Which car is in front after

      i) 10 s, ii) 20 s?

   b) When is B in front?

   c) When are B and C going at the same speed?

   d) When are A and C going at the same speed?

   e) Which car is going fastest after 5 s?

   f) Which car starts slowly and then goes faster and faster?

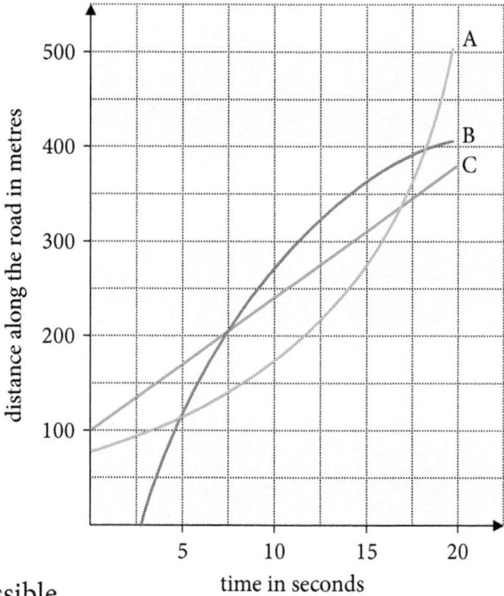

5. Three girls Hanna, Fateema and Carine took part in an egg and spoon race.
   Describe what happened, giving as many details as possible.

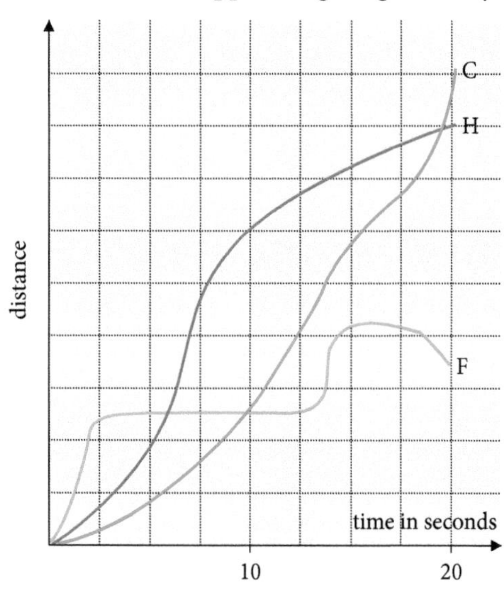

6. The graph shows the speed of the baton during a 4×100 m relay race.

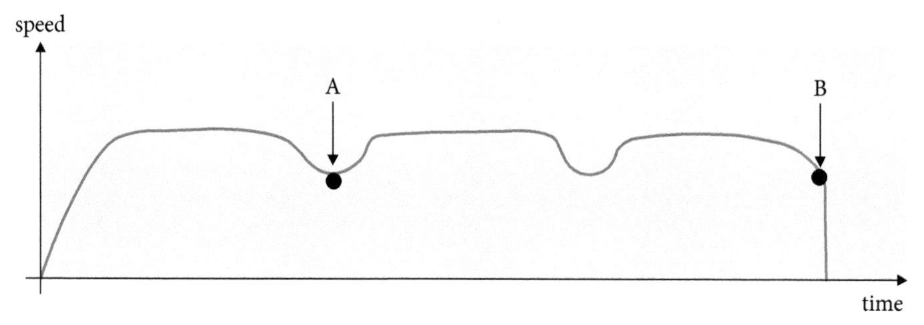

   a) Describe what is happening at point A.

   b) Describe what is happening at point B.

6.4 Brackets and factors

Example

a) Expand $2x(3 + 4x)$

$$2x(3 + 4x) = 2x \times 3 + 2x \times 4x = 6x + 8x^2$$

b) Expand $(x + 3)(x + 2)$

$$(x + 3)(x + 2) = x \times x + 3 \times x + 2 \times x + 3 \times 2 = x^2 + 3x + 2x + 6$$
$$= x^2 + 5x + 6$$

c) Expand $(x - 4)(x + 7)$

$$(x - 4)(x + 7) = x \times x - 4 \times x + 7 \times x - 4 \times 7 = x^2 - 4x + 7x - 28$$
$$= x^2 + 3x - 28$$

Exercise 11

Multiply out the brackets.

$2(3x + 2) = 6x + 4$

1. $3(x + 3)$ **2.** $4(x - 2)$ **3.** $5(2x + 1)$

4. $4(a + 7)$ **5.** $6(2x + 1)$ **6.** $10(5 - x)$

7. $3(4x + 5)$ **8.** $9(3 + x)$ **9.** $5(y - 2)$

10. $7(a - 2)$ **11.** $11(2x - y)$ **12.** $8(3x + 2y)$

Multiply out the brackets.

13. $x(4 + 2x)$ **14.** $x(3x - 2)$ **15.** $y(4y + 7)$

16. $a(2a - 6)$ **17.** $3x(4 - 6x)$ **18.** $4y(3y + 5)$

19. $5a(3a - 4)$ **20.** $7p(6 - 7p)$ **21.** $3x(4x + x^2)$

22. $4x(x^2 - 3x)$

Multiply out the brackets.

23. $(x + 2)(x + 1)$ **24.** $(x + 4)(x + 6)$ **25.** $(x + 3)(x - 2)$

26. $(x - 2)(x + 6)$ **27.** $(x + 5)(x - 7)$ **28.** $(x - 8)(x + 3)$

29. $(x - 2)(x - 1)$ **30.** $(x - 5)(x - 3)$ **31.** $(x - 8)(x - 9)$

32. $(2x + 1)(x + 2)$ **33.** $(3x + 2)(x - 1)$ **34.** $(2x - 3)(x + 4)$

35. $(2x + 1)(2x + 3)$

Factors

Example

Factorise the following: **a)** $12a - 15b$ **b)** $3x^2 - 2x$ **c)** $2xy + 6y^2$

d) $x^2 + 3x$ **e)** $6x + 2x^2$

a) $12a - 15b = 3(4a - 5b)$

b) $3x^2 - 2x = x(3x - 2)$

c) $2xy + 6y^2 = 2y(x + 3y)$

d) The Highest Common Factor is now the letter, x, so we can factorise as follows:

$x^2 + 3x = x(x + 3)$

e) The Highest Common Factor for the numbers is 2 and for the letters, x, so we can factorise as follows:

$6x + 2x^2 = 2x(3 + x)$

Note we can check our factorisations by multiplying out our answers.

Exercise 12

In Questions **1** to **10** copy and complete the statement.

1. $6x + 4y = 2(3x + \square)$

2. $9x + 12y = 3(\square + 4y)$

3. $10a + 4b = 2(5a + \square)$

4. $4x + 12y = 4(\square + \square)$

5. $10a + 15b = 5(\square + \square)$

6. $18x - 24y = 6(3x - \square)$

7. $8u - 28v = \square(\square - 7v)$

8. $15s + 25t = \square(3s + \square)$

9. $24m + 40n = \square(3m + \square)$

10. $27c - 72d = \square(\square - 8d)$

In Questions **11** to **30** factorise the expression.

11. $20a + 8b$

12. $30x - 24y$

13. $27c - 33d$

14. $35u + 49v$

15. $12s - 32t$

16. $40x - 16t$

17. $24x + 84y$

18. $12x + 8y + 16z$

19. $12a - 6b + 9c$

20. $10x - 20y + 25z$

21. $20a - 12b - 28c$

22. $48m + 8n - 24x$

23. $42x + 49y - 21z$

24. $6x^2 + 15y^2$

25. $20x^2 - 15y^2$

26. $7a^2 + 28b^2$

27. $27a + 63b - 36c$

28. $12x^2 + 24xy + 18y^2$

29. $64p - 72q - 40r$

30. $36x - 60y + 96z$

In Questions **31** to **42** factorise the expression.

31. $a^2 + 4a$

32. $3x + 4x^2$

33. $4x^2 - x$

34. $7x - 3x^2$

35. $2x^2 + 4x$

36. $6x - 3x^2$

37. $12x + 16x^3$

38. $25x^2 - 15x^3$

39. $30x^3 + 10x^2$

40. $80y^3 - 30y^2$

41. $12x + 15x^2 - 18x^3$

42. $4a^3 - 6a + 8a^2$

6.5 Changing the subject of a formula

Example

Make x the subject in the formulae below.

a) $ax - p = t$

$ax = t + p$

$x = \frac{t + p}{a}$

b) $y(x + y) = v^2$

$yx + y^2 = v^2$

$yx = v^2 - y^2$

$x = \frac{v^2 - y^2}{y}$

Exercise 13

Make x the subject.

1. $x + b = e$
2. $x - t = m$
3. $x - f = a + b$
4. $x + h = A + B$
5. $x + t = y + t$
6. $a + x = b$
7. $k + x = m$
8. $v + x = w + y$
9. $ax = b$
10. $hx = m$
11. $mx = a + b$
12. $kx = c - d$
13. $vx = e + n$
14. $3x = y + z$
15. $xp = r$
16. $xm = h - m$
17. $ax + t = a$
18. $mx - e = k$
19. $ux - h = m$
20. $ex + q = t$
21. $kx - u^2 = v^2$
22. $gx + t^2 = s^2$
23. $xa + k = m^2$
24. $xm - v = m$
25. $a + bx = c$
26. $t + sx = y$
27. $y + cx = z$
28. $a + hx = 2a$
29. $mx - b = b$
30. $kx + ab = cd$
31. $a(x - b) = c$
32. $c(x - d) = e$
33. $m(x + m) = n^2$
34. $k(x - a) = t$
35. $h(x - h) = k$
36. $m(x + b) = n$
37. $a(x - a) = a^2$
38. $c(a + x) = d$
39. $m(b + x) = e$

Formulae involving fractions

Example

Make x the subject in the formulae below.

a) $\frac{x}{a} = p$

$x = ap$

b) $\frac{m}{x} = t$

$m = xt$

$\frac{m}{t} = x$

c) $v = \frac{a^2}{x}$

$vx = a^2$

$x = \frac{a^2}{v}$

Exercise 14

Make x the subject.

1. $\frac{x}{t}=m$
2. $\frac{x}{e}=n$
3. $\frac{x}{p}=a$
4. $am=\frac{x}{t}$
5. $bc=\frac{x}{a}$
6. $e=\frac{x}{y^2}$
7. $\frac{x}{a}=(b+c)$
8. $\frac{x}{t}=(c-d)$
9. $\frac{x}{m}=s+t$
10. $\frac{x}{k}=h+i$
11. $\frac{x}{b}=\frac{a}{c}$
12. $\frac{x}{m}=\frac{z}{y}$
13. $\frac{x}{h}=\frac{c}{d}$
14. $\frac{m}{n}=\frac{x}{e}$
15. $\frac{b}{e}=\frac{x}{h}$
16. $\frac{x}{(a+b)}=c$
17. $\frac{x}{(h+k)}=m$
18. $\frac{x}{u}=\frac{m}{y}$
19. $\frac{x}{(h-k)}=t$
20. $\frac{x}{(a+b)}=(z+t)$
21. $t=\frac{e}{x}$
22. $a=\frac{e}{x}$
23. $m=\frac{h}{x}$
24. $\frac{a}{b}=\frac{c}{x}$
25. $\frac{u}{x}=\frac{c}{d}$
26. $\frac{m}{x}=t^2$
27. $\frac{a^2}{b^2}=\frac{c^2}{x}$

Mixed questions

Exercise 15

Make the letter in square brackets the subject.

1. $ax-d=h$ [x]
2. $zy+k=m$ [y]
3. $d(y+e)=f$ [y]
4. $m(a+k)=d$ [k]
5. $a+bm=c$ [m]
6. $a+e=b$ [e]
7. $yt=z$ [t]
8. $x-c=e$ [x]
9. $my-n=b$ [y]
10. $a(z+a)=b$ [z]
11. $\frac{a}{x}=d$ [x]
12. $\frac{k}{m}=t$ [k]

13. $\frac{u}{m} = n$ [u]

14. $\frac{y}{x} = d$ [x]

15. $\frac{a}{m} = t$ [m]

16. $\frac{d}{g} = n$ [g]

17. $\frac{t}{k} = (a + b)$ [t]

18. $y = \frac{v}{e}$ [e]

19. $c = \frac{m}{y}$ [y]

20. $\frac{a}{m} = b$ [a]

21. $g(m + a) = b$ [m]

22. $h + g = x^2$ [g]

23. $y - t = z$ [t]

24. $2me = c$ [e]

25. $a(y + x) = t$ [x]

26. $uv - t^2 = y^2$ [v]

27. $3k + t = c$ [k]

28. $k - w = m$ [w]

29. $b + an = c$ [n]

30. $m(a + y) = c$ [y]

31. $pq - x = ab$ [x]

32. $a^2 - k = t$ [k]

33. $v^2z = w$ [z]

34. $c = t + u$ [u]

35. $xc + t = 2t$ [c]

36. $n + w = k$ [w]

Revision exercise 6A

1. Here are three diagrams with lines and dots.

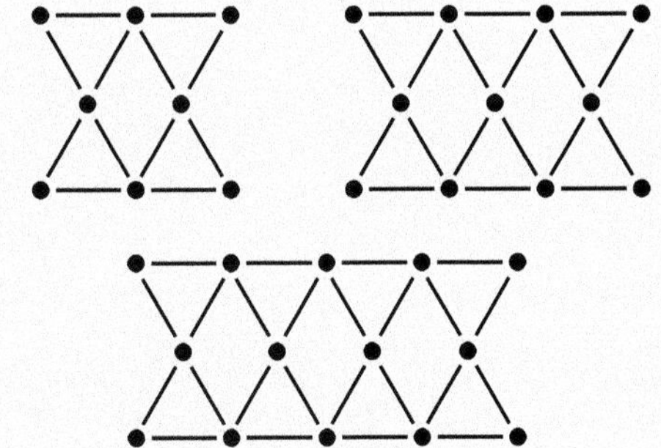

   a) Find a formula connecting the number of lines l and the number of dots d.

   b) How many dots are there in a diagram with 294 lines?

2. A factory cafeteria contains a vending machine which sells drinks. On a typical day:

   - the machine starts half full,
   - no drinks are sold before 9 a.m. and after 5 p.m.,
   - drinks are sold at a slow rate throughout the day, except during the morning and lunch breaks (10.30–11 a.m. and 1–2 p.m.) when there is a greater demand,
   - the machine is filled up just before the lunch break. (It takes about 10 minutes to fill.)

   Sketch a graph showing how the number of drinks in the machine may vary from 8 a.m. to 6 p.m.

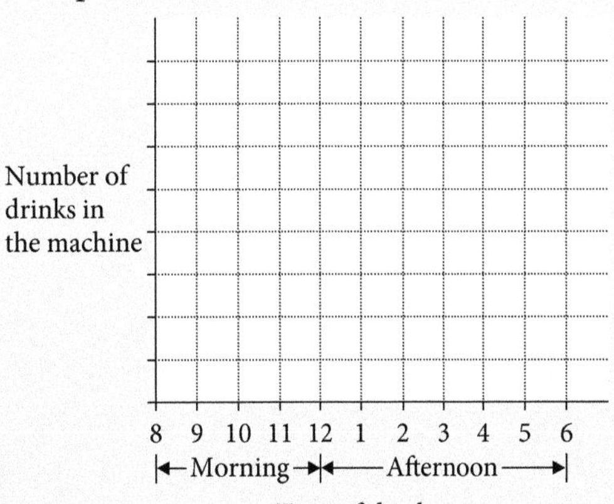

3. The distance–time graphs for several objects are shown. Decide which line represents each of the following:
   - hovercraft from Dover
   - car ferry from Dover
   - cross-channel swimmer
   - marker buoy outside harbour
   - train from Dover
   - car ferry from Calais

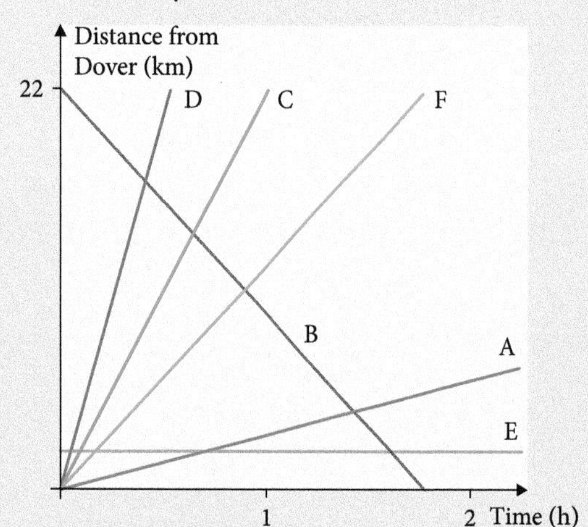

4. Given that $s - 3t = rt$, express:
   a) s in terms of r and t
   b) r in terms of s and t

5.

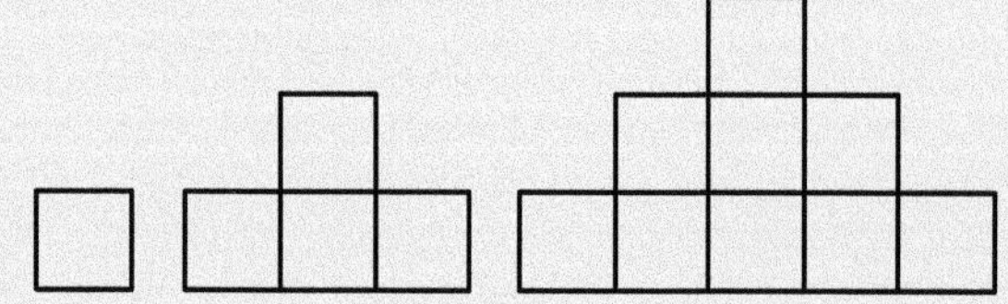

   a) Draw the next diagram in this sequence.
   b) Write down the number of squares in each diagram.
   c) Describe in words the sequence you obtained in part **(b)**.
   d) How many squares will there be in the diagram which has 13 squares on the base?

6. Solve the simultaneous equations:
   a) $7c + 3d = 29$
   $5c - 4d = 33$
   b) $2x - 3y = 7$
   $2y - 3x = -8$

7. This graph shows a car journey from Gateshead to Middlesbrough and back again.

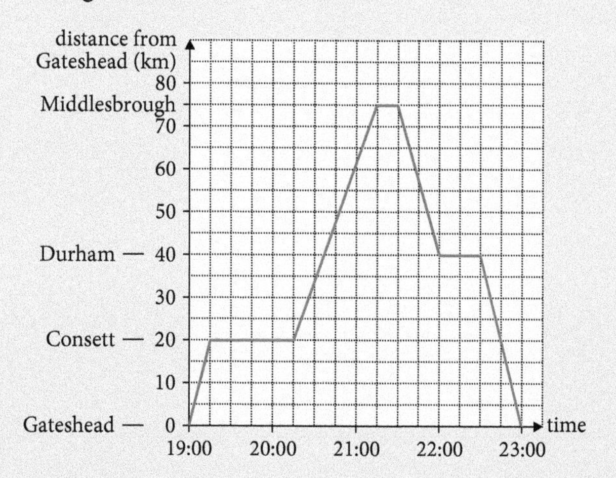

   a) Where is the car
      i) at 19:15 h
      ii) at 22:15 h
      iii) at 22:45 h?
   b) How far is it
      i) from Consett to Middlesbrough
      ii) from Durham to Gateshead?
   c) At what speed does the car travel
      i) from Gateshead to Consett
      ii) from Consett to Middlesbrough
      iii) from Middlesbrough to Durham
      iv) from Durham to Gateshead?
   d) For how long is the car stationary during the journey?

8. Each diagram in the sequence below consists of a number of dots.

Diagram number	1	2	3
	●●● ●●●	●●●● ●　　● ●●●●	●●●●● ●　　　● ●　　　● ●●●●●

a) Draw diagram number 4, diagram number 5 and diagram number 6.

b) Copy and complete the table below:

Diagram number	Number of dots
1	6
2	10
3	
4	
5	
6	

c) Without drawing the diagrams, state the number of dots in:

i) diagram number 10

ii) diagram number 15

d) If we write x for the diagram number and n for the number of dots, write down a formula involving x and n.

Examination-style exercise 6B

1. Factorise $3xy - 2x$. [1]

Cambridge IGCSE Mathematics 0580
Paper 1 Q2 November 2005

2. Expand the brackets and simplify $3x(x - y) + 2x^2$. [2]

3. (a) Expand and simplify $5(3c - 4d) - 8c$. [2]

(b) Factorise $pq - q^2$. [1]

Cambridge IGCSE Mathematics 0580
Paper 11 Q10 June 2009

4. Look at the sequence of numbers 7, 11, 15, 19, ...

(a) Write down the next number in the sequence. [1]

(b) Find the 10th number in the sequence. [1]

(c) Write an expression, in terms of n, for the nth number in the sequence. [1]

Cambridge IGCSE Mathematics 0580
Paper 1 Q16 June 2005

5. In the pattern below each diagram shows a letter E formed by joining dots.

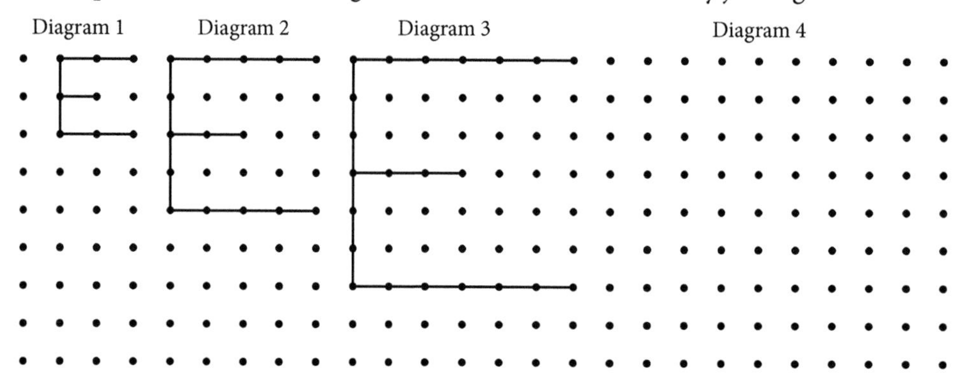

(a) Draw the next letter E in the pattern. [1]

(b) Complete the table showing the number of dots in each letter E.

Diagram	1	2	3	4	5
Dots	8	15			

[3]

(c) How many dots make up the letter E in

i) Diagram 10, [2]

ii) Diagram n? [2]

(d) The letter E in Diagram n has 113 dots.
Write down an equation in n and use it to find the value of n. [3]

Cambridge IGCSE Mathematics 0580
Paper 3 Q9 June 2007

6. (a) The first four terms of a sequence are 12, 7, 2, –3.

i) Write down the next two terms of the sequence. [2]

ii) State the rule for finding the next term of the sequence. [1]

iii) Write down an expression for the nth term of this sequence. [2]

(b) The first four terms of another sequence are –3, 2, 7, 12.
Write down an expression for the nth term of this sequence. [2]

(c) Add together the expressions for the nth terms of both sequences.
Write your answer as simply as possible. [1]

Cambridge IGCSE Mathematics 0580
Paper 3 Q9 June 2009

7. **(a)** Garcia and Elena are each given x dollars.

i) Elena spends 4 dollars.
Write down an expression in terms of x for the number of dollars she has now. [1]

ii) Garcia doubles his money by working and then is given another 5 dollars.
Write down an expression in terms of x for the number of dollars he has now. [1]

iii) Garcia now has three times as much money as Elena.
Write down an equation in x to show this. [1]

iv) Solve the equation to find the value of x. [3]

(b) Solve the simultaneous equations

$$3x - 2y = 3,$$
$$x + 4y = 8.$$

[3]

Cambridge IGCSE Mathematics 0580
Paper 3 Q4 June 2009

8.

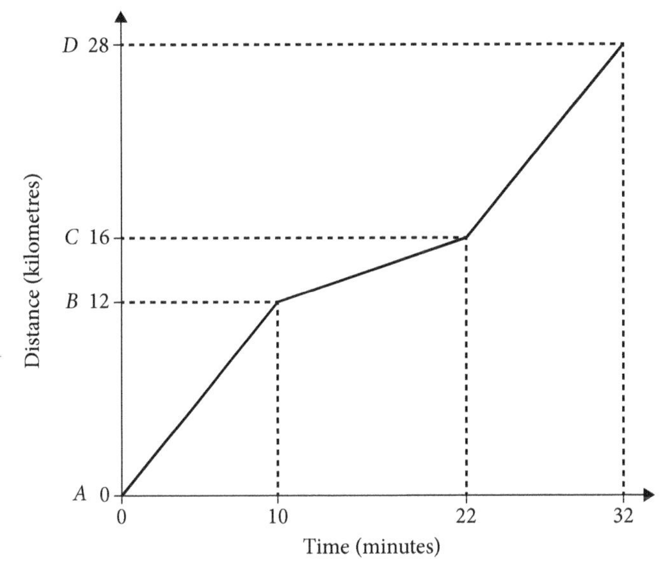

The diagram shows the graph of Mark's journey to visit his mother for her birthday.

Starting at A, he drove 12 kilometres to B at a constant speed.

Between B and C, he had to drive slowly, due to an accident.

From C, he drove a further distance D at his original speed.

(a) For how many minutes was he driving slowly due to the accident? [1]

(b) At what speed did he drive during this slower part of his journey? [2]

(c) What is the total distance from A to D? [2]

9.

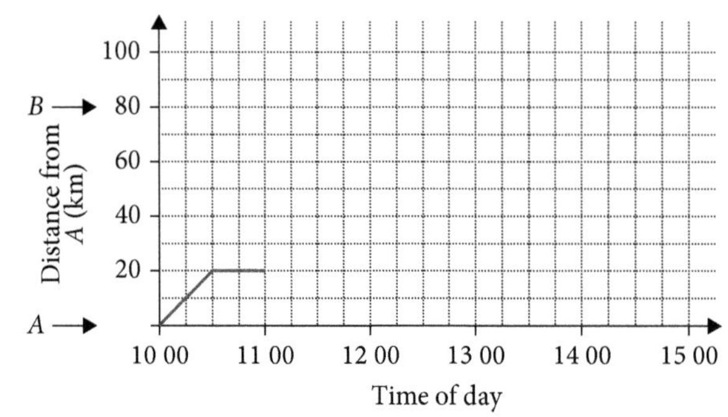

(a) Carla drives from town A to a supermarket.

At 11 00 she continues her journey to town B, driving at 80 km/h.
The first part of the journey is shown on the grid above.

i) How many minutes is Carla at the supermarket? [1]

ii) Draw the rest of her journey to town B on the grid. [1]

(b) Carla spends 1 hour in town B and then drives back to town A, at a constant speed, arriving at 14 30.

Show this information on the grid. [2]

Cambridge IGCSE Mathematics 0580
Paper 1 Q18 November 2006

10.

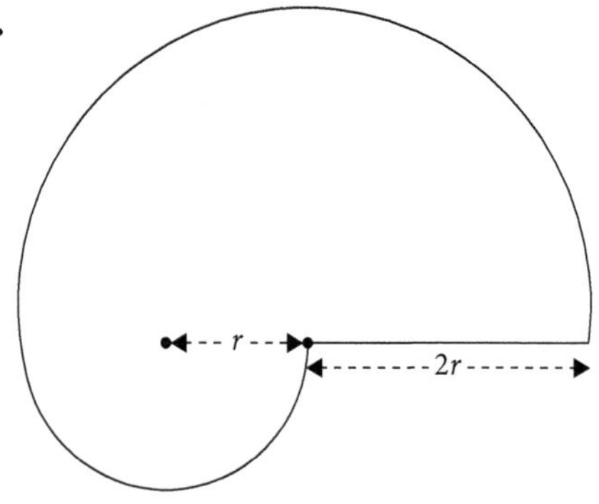

The area of the shape is given by the formula $A = \dfrac{5\pi r^2}{2}$.

(a) Calculate the area when $r = 3$ cm. [2]

(b) Calculate the value of r when $A = 200$ cm^2. [3]

(c) Make r the subject of the formula. [3]

Cambridge IGCSE Mathematics 0580
Paper 3 Q4 November 2007

11. (a) Solve the equations

i) $3x - 4 = 14$, [2]

ii) $\frac{y+1}{5} = 2$, [2]

iii) $3(2z - 7) - 2(z - 3) = -9$. [3]

(b) Donna sent p postcards and q letters to her friends.

i) The total number of postcards and letters she sent was 12.

Write down an equation in p and q. [1]

ii) A stamp for a postcard costs 25 cents and a stamp for a letter costs 40 cents.
She spent 375 cents on stamps altogether. Write down another equation in p and q. [1]

iii) Solve these equations to find the values of p and q. [3]

Cambridge IGCSE Mathematics 0580
Paper 3 Q4 June 2008

12. (a) Kinetic energy, E, is related to mass, m, and velocity, v, by the formula

$$E = \frac{1}{2}mv^2.$$

i) Calculate E when $m = 5$ and $v = 12$. [2]

ii) Calculate v when $m = 8$ and $E = 225$. [2]

iii) Make m the subject of the formula. [2]

(b) Factorise completely $xy^2 - x^2y$. [2]

(c) Solve the equation
$3(x - 5) + 2(14 - 3x) = 7$. [3]

(d) Solve the simultaneous equations

$$4x + y = 13,$$
$$2x + 3y = 9.$$ [3]

Cambridge IGCSE Mathematics 0580
Paper 3 Q3 June 2007

13. **(a)**

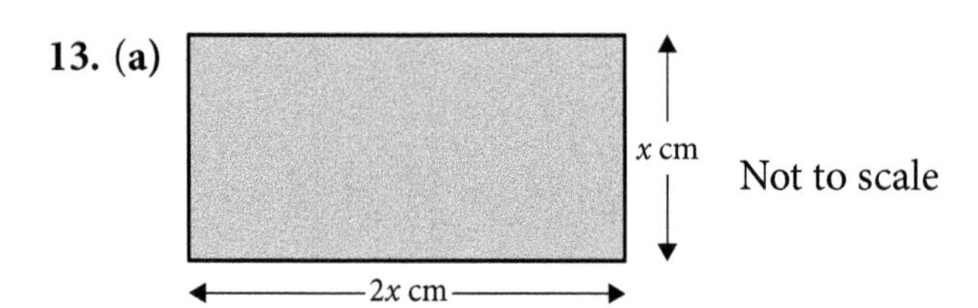

The perimeter of the rectangle in the diagram above is 36 centimetres.

i) Find the value of x. [2]

ii) Using this value of x, calculate the area of the rectangle.
Give your answer in cm^2. [2]

(b)

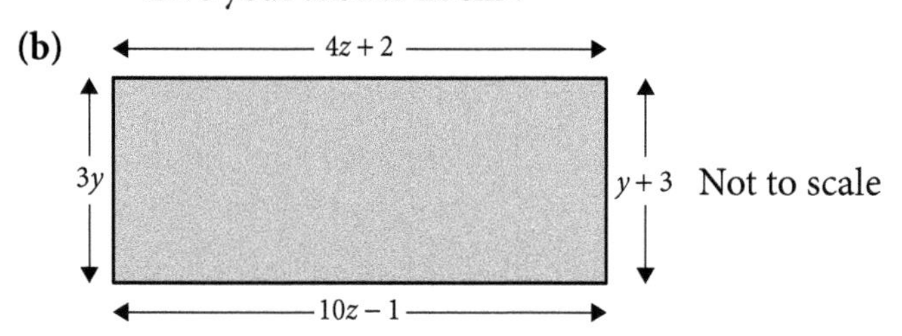

The diagram above shows another rectangle.

i) In this rectangle $3y = y + 3$.
Solve the equation to find y. [2]

ii) Write down an equation in z. [1]

iii) Solve the equation in part **(b)(ii)** to find z. [3]

(c)

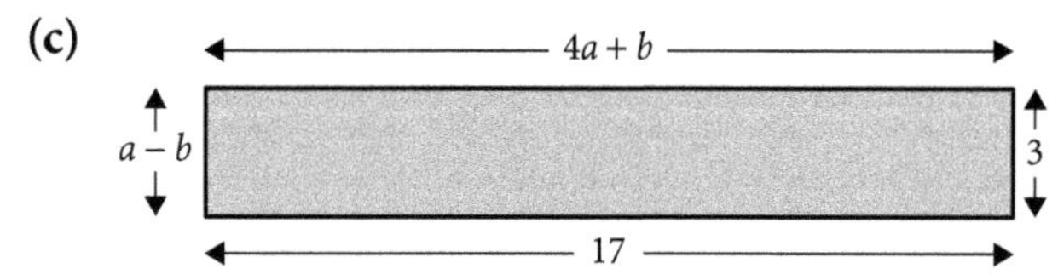

The diagram above shows another rectangle.

i) Write down two equations in a and b. [2]

ii) Solve these two equations simultaneously to find a and b. [3]

Cambridge IGCSE Mathematics 0580
Paper 3 Q6 June 2005

14. Look at this sequence: 3, 8, 15, 24, …

(a) Write down the next term. [1]

(b) Write down the 10th term. [1]

(c) Write down an expression for the nth term of the sequence. [2]

7 Number 2

C1.5 Use the language and notation of simple vulgar and decimal fractions and percentages in appropriate contexts. Recognise equivalence and convert between these forms.

C1.9 Make estimates of numbers, quantities and lengths, give approximations to specified numbers of significant figures and decimal places and round off answers to reasonable accuracy in the context of a given problem.

C1.10 Give appropriate upper and lower bounds for data given to a specified accuracy.

C1.12 Calculate a given percentage of a quantity. Express one quantity as a percentage of another. Calculate percentage increase or decrease.

C1.13 Use a calculator efficiently. Apply appropriate checks of accuracy.

7.1 Percentage change

Price changes are sometimes more significant when expressed as a percentage of the original price. For example if the price of a car goes up from \$7000 to \$7070, this is only a 1% increase. If the price of a jacket went up from \$100 to \$170 this would be a 70% increase!
In both cases the actual increase is the same: \$70.

$$\text{Percentage increase} = \frac{\text{(actual increase)}}{\text{(original value)}} \times \frac{100}{1}$$

Example

The price of a car is increased from \$6400 to \$6800.

Find the percentage increase.

$$\text{Percentage increase} = \frac{400}{6400} \times \frac{100}{1} = 6\frac{1}{4}\%$$

For a *decrease:*

$$\text{Percentage decrease} = \frac{\text{(actual decrease)}}{\text{(original value)}} \times \frac{100}{1}$$

Exercise 1

In Questions **1** to **10** calculate the percentage increase.

	Original price	Final price
1.	\$50	\$54
2.	\$80	\$88
3.	\$180	\$225
4.	\$100	\$102
5.	\$75	\$78
6.	\$400	\$410
7.	\$5000	\$6000
8.	\$210	\$315
9.	\$600	\$690
10.	\$4000	\$7200

In Questions **11** to **20** calculate the percentage decrease.

	Original price	Final price
11.	\$800	\$600
12.	\$50	\$40
13.	\$120	\$105
14.	\$420	\$280
15.	\$6000	\$1200
16.	\$880	\$836
17.	\$15 000	\$14 100
18.	\$7.50	\$6.00
19.	\$8.20	\$7.79
20.	\$16 000	\$15 600

Exercise 2

Find the percentage profit/loss using either the formula:

$$\text{percentage profit} = \frac{(\text{actual profit})}{(\text{cost price})} \times \frac{100}{1} \text{ or percentage loss} = \frac{(\text{actual loss})}{(\text{cost price})} \times \frac{100}{1}$$

Give the answers correct to one decimal place.

	Cost price	Selling price
1.	\$11	\$15
2.	\$21	\$25
3.	\$36	\$43
4.	\$41	\$50
5.	\$411	\$461
6.	\$5.32	\$5.82
7.	\$6.14	\$7.00
8.	\$2.13	\$2.50
9.	\$6.11	\$8.11
10.	\$18.15	\$20

	Cost price	Selling price
11.	\$20	\$18.47
12.	\$17	\$11
13.	\$13	\$9
14.	\$211	\$200
15.	\$8.15	\$7
16.	\$2.62	\$3
17.	\$1.52	\$1.81
18.	\$13.50	\$13.98
19.	\$3.05	\$4.00
20.	\$1705	\$1816

Exercise 3

1. The number of people employed by a company increased from 250 to 280. Calculate the percentage increase.
2. During the first four weeks of her life a baby's weight increases from 3000 g to 3870 g. Calculate the percentage increase.
3. Before cooking, a joint of meat weighs 2.5 kg. After cooking it only weighs 2.1 kg. Calculate the percentage decrease in the weight.
4. When cold, an iron rod is 200 cm long. After being heated, the length increases to 200.5 cm. Calculate the percentage increase.
5. Juan buys a car for $4000 and sells it for $4600. Calculate his percentage profit.
6. Melanie buys berets for $6.20 and sells them for $9.99. Calculate her percentage profit correct to one decimal place.
7. Wei Wei buys rice at 20c per kg but has to sell it at only 17c per kg. Calculate her percentage loss.
8. Before a service, the petrol consumption of a car was 5.1 km per litre. After the service, the consumption improved to 5.8 km per litre. Calculate the percentage improvement, correct to one decimal place.

9. The population of a town went down from 22 315 to 21 987. Calculate the percentage reduction, correct to one decimal place.
10 In 2015 a tennis player earned $2 530 700. In 2016 the same player earned $3 133 010. Calculate the percentage increase in her income, correct to one decimal place.

Exercise 4

This exercise is more difficult.

1. Gabir bought 40 articles for \$10 and sold them at 32c each.

   Calculate:

   a) the cost price of each article
   b) the total selling price of the 40 articles
   c) the total profit
   d) the percentage profit.

2. Ivan bought a box of 40 packets of sweets at 25c per packet.

   a) Find the total cost of the box of sweets.
   b) He sold 10 packets at 37c per packet, and the rest of the crate at 35c per packet.
      i) How much profit did he make?
      ii) Express this profit as a percentage of his total cost price.

3. ABCD is a square of side 100 cm. Side AB is increased by 20% and side AD is reduced by 25% to form rectangle APQR.

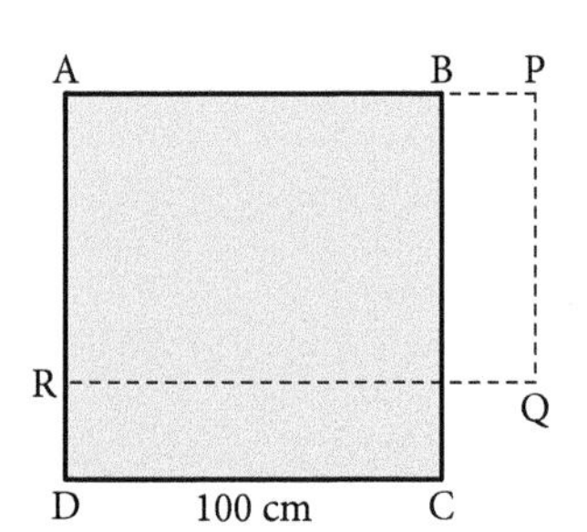

   a) Calculate: i) the length of AP
      ii) the length of AR
      iii) the area of square ABCD
      iv) the area of rectangle APQR.
   b) By what percentage has the area of the square been reduced?

4. When a house was built in 2015 the total cost was made up of the following:

   wages \$35 000
   materials \$18 000
   overheads \$4 500

   a) Find the total cost of the house in 2015.
   b) In 2016 the cost of wages increased by 10%, the cost of materials increased by 5% and the overheads remained at their previous cost.
      i) Find the total cost of the house in 2016, correct to one decimal place.
      ii) Calculate the percentage increase from 2015 to 2016.

5. This question is more difficult. Four maths teachers calculate the area of the shape given and they all get different answers, Beatriz is wrong by 20% and Saghir is wrong by 5%.

   Here are the four answers:

   237.5 m^2, 250 m^2, 260 m^2, 300 m^2

   Which is the correct answer?

7.2 Fractions, ratio, decimals and percentage

Percentages are simply a convenient way of expressing fractions or decimals. '50% of \$60' is the same as '$\frac{1}{2}$ of \$60'. You should be able to convert readily from one form to another.

Example

a) Change $\frac{7}{8}$ to a decimal.

Divide 8 into 7 $\quad 8\overline{)7.000}$ giving 0.875

$\frac{7}{8} = 0.875$

b) Change 0.35 to a fraction.

$0.35 = \frac{35}{100} = \frac{7}{20}$

c) Change $\frac{3}{8}$ to a percentage.

Multiply this fraction by 100.

$\frac{3}{8} = \frac{3}{8} \times 100\% = 37\frac{1}{2}\%$

d) Work out $\frac{1}{6} + 0.72$

$\frac{1}{6} = 0.1666\ldots$ [divide 6 into 1]

$\therefore \frac{1}{6} + 0.72 = 0.1666\ldots$

$$\begin{array}{r} 0.1666\ldots \\ 0.7200+ \\ \hline 0.8866\ldots \\ \hline \end{array}$$

$\frac{1}{6} + 0.72 = 0.89$ (2 d.p.)

Exercise 5

1 Change the fractions to decimals.

a) $\frac{1}{4}$ **b)** $\frac{2}{5}$ **c)** $\frac{3}{8}$

d) $\frac{5}{12}$ **e)** $\frac{1}{6}$ **f)** $\frac{2}{7}$

2. Change the decimals to fractions and simplify.

a) 0.2 **b)** 0.45 **c)** 0.36

d) 0.125 **e)** 1.05 **f)** 0.007

3. Change to percentages.

a) $\frac{1}{4}$ **b)** $\frac{1}{10}$ **c)** 0.72

d) 0.075 **e)** 0.02 **f)** $\frac{1}{3}$

4. Two shops had sale offers on an article which previously cost \$69.

One shop had '$\frac{1}{3}$ off' and the other had '70% of old price'.

Which price is lower?

5. Shareholders in a company can choose either '$\frac{1}{6}$ of \$5000' or '15% of \$5000'. Which is the greater amount?

6. A photocopier increases the sides of a square in the ratio 4 : 5. By what percentage are the sides increased?

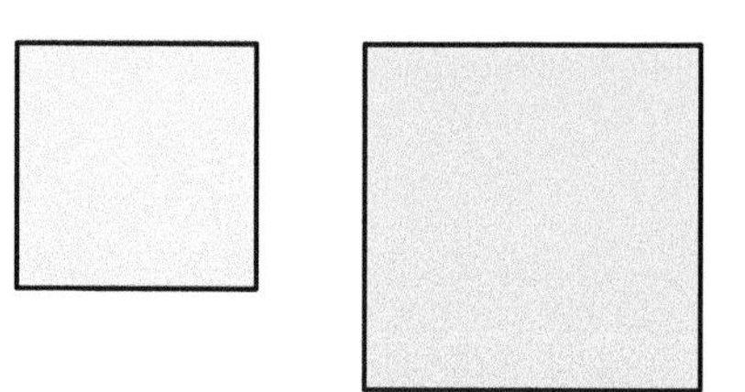

7. In an alloy the ratio of copper to iron to lead is 5 : 7 : 3. What percentage of the alloy is lead?

8. Copy and complete the table:

	Fraction	Decimal	Percentage
a)	$\frac{1}{4}$		
b)		0.2	
c)			80%
d)	$\frac{1}{100}$		
e)			30%
f)	$\frac{1}{3}$		

9. Work out **a)** $\frac{3}{4}$ of 65% of 0.3

   b) 11% of $\frac{3}{5}$ of \$240

10. Arrange in order of size (smallest first)

   a) $\frac{1}{2}$; 45%; 0.6 **b)** 0.38; $\frac{6}{16}$; 4% **c)** 0.111; 11%; $\frac{1}{9}$

In Questions **11** to **18**, evaluate, giving the answer to 2 decimal places:

11. $\frac{1}{4}+\frac{1}{3}$ **12.** $\frac{2}{3}+0.75$ **13.** $\frac{8}{9}-0.24$

14. $\frac{7}{8}+\frac{5}{9}+\frac{2}{11}$ **15.** $\frac{1}{3}\times 0.2$ **16.** $\frac{5}{8}\times\frac{1}{4}$

17. $\frac{8}{11}\div 0.2$ **18.** $\left(\frac{4}{7}-\frac{1}{3}\right)\div 0.4$

19. Pure gold is 24 carat gold. What percentage of 15 carat gold is pure gold?

7.3 Estimating

In some circumstances it is unrealistic to work out the exact answer to a problem. It might be quite satisfactory to give an estimate for the answer.

For example a builder does not know *exactly* how many bricks a new garage will require. He may estimate that he needs 2500 bricks and place an order for that number. In practice he may need only 2237.

Exercise 6

Estimate which answer is closest to the actual answer.

1. The height of a double-decker bus:

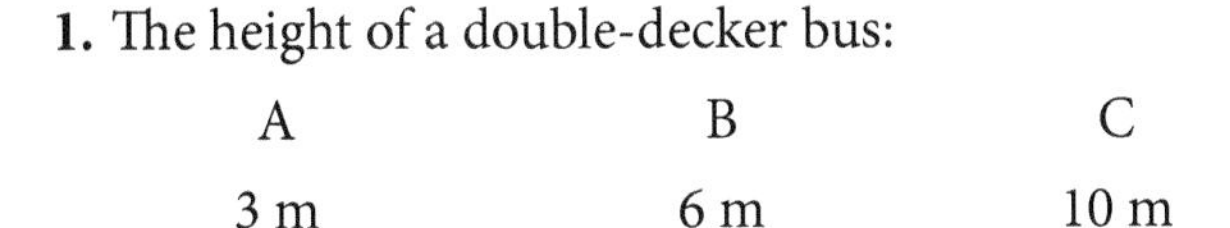

A	B	C
3 m	6 m	10 m

2. The height of the tallest player in the Olympic basketball competition:

A	B	C
1.8 m	3.0 m	2.2 m

3. The height of the Eiffel Tower:

A	B	C
30 m	300 m	1000 m

4. The weight of half a litre of milk in a cardboard carton:

A	B	C
500 g	1000 g	5000 g

5. The volume of your classroom:

A	B	C
100 m^3	1000 m^3	10 000 m^3

6. The top speed of a Grand Prix racing car:

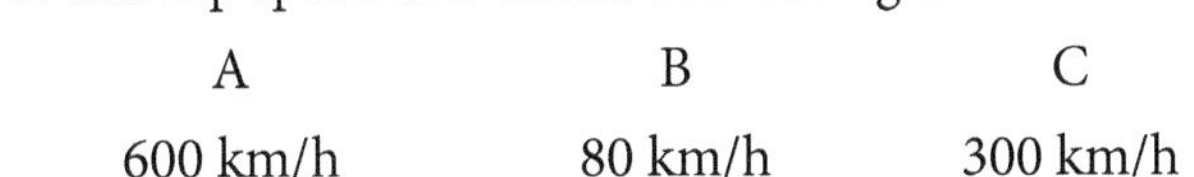

A	B	C
600 km/h	80 km/h	300 km/h

7. The number of times your heart beats in one day (24 h):

A	B	C
10 000	100 000	1 000 000

8. The thickness of one page in this book

A	B	C
0.01 cm	0.001 cm	0.0001 cm

9. The number of cars in a traffic jam 10 km long on a 3-lane motorway:

A	B	C
4000	40 000	200 000

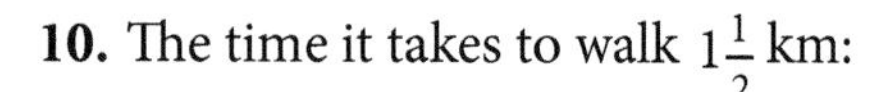

10. The time it takes to walk $1\frac{1}{2}$ km:

A	B	C
10 minutes	20 minutes	60 minutes

11. The area of a standard postcard:

A	B	C
150 cm^2	1000 cm^2	0.1 m^2

12. The weight of an ordinary apple is:

A	B	C
100 g	250 g	400 g

13. The telephone charge to Australia is 70c per minute. The number of words you will be able to say in a call costing $4 is:

A	B	C
120	500	1200

14. The speed at which the hair on your head grows in km/h is:

A	B	C
0.0001	0.000 01	0.000 001

[To answer this question, estimate the rate in centimetres per day, then multiply your estimate by (365 ÷ 100 000) to convert the speed to km/h.]

15. A maths teacher decides to give a rather unusual prize for the person who comes top in his next test. The prize winner receives his or her own weight in coins and they can choose to have either 1c, 5c, 10c, 25c, 50c or $1 coins. All the coins must be the same.

Shabeza is the winner and she weighs 47 kg.
Use the table on the right to find the highest value of her prize.
Give your answer correct to the nearest $100.

Approximate masses	
1c	2.5 g
5c	5.0 g
10c	2.3 g
25c	5.7 g
50c	11.3 g
$1	8.1 g

16. The largest tree in the world has a diameter of 11 m.
Estimate the number of 'average' 15-year-olds required to circle the tree so that they form an unbroken chain.

17. When you multiply by a number greater than 1 you make it bigger.

so **5.3** × 1.03 > **5.3** and **6.75** × 0.89 < **6.75**

When you divide by a number greater than 1 you make it smaller.

so **8.9** ÷ 1.13 < **8.92** and **11.2** ÷ 0.73 > **11.2**

State whether true or false:

a) $3.72 \times 1.3 > 3.72$ **b)** $253 \times 0.91 < 253$ **c)** $0.92 \times 1.04 > 0.92$

d) $8.5 \div 1.4 > 8.5$ **e)** $113 \div 0.73 < 113$ **f)** $17.4 \div 2.2 < 17.4$

g) $0.73 \times 0.73 < 0.73$ **h)** $2511 \div 0.042 < 2511$ **i)** $614 \times 0.993 < 614$

Example

Estimate the answers to the following questions:

a) $9.7 \times 3.1 \approx 10 \times 3$. About 30.

b) $81.4 \times 98.2 \approx 80 \times 100$. About 8000.

c) $19.2 \times 49.1 \approx 20 \times 50$. About 1000.

d) $102.7 \div 19.6 \approx 100 \div 20$. About 5.

Exercise 7

Write down each question and decide (by estimating) which answer is correct. Do not do the calculations exactly.

	Question	Answer A	Answer B	Answer C
1.	7.79 ÷ 1.9	8.2	4.1	1.9
2.	27.03 ÷ 5.1	5.3	0.5	8.7
3.	59.78 ÷ 9.8	12.2	2.8	6.1
4.	58.4 × 102	600.4	5956.8	2450.4
5.	6.8 × 11.4	19.32	280.14	77.52
6.	97 × 1.08	104.76	55.66	1062.3
7.	972 × 20.2	2112.4	19 634.4	8862.4
8.	7.1 × 103	74.3	731.3	7210.3
9.	18.9 × 21	396.9	58.7	201.9
10.	1.078 ÷ 0.98	6.4	10.4	1.1
11.	1250.5 ÷ 6.1	21.4	205	66.2
12.	20.48 ÷ 3.2	6.4	12.2	2.8
13.	25.11 ÷ 3.1	8.1	15.1	19.3
14.	216 ÷ 0.9	56.3	24.3	240
15.	19.2 + 0.41	23.3	8.41	19.61

(Continued)

(*Continued*)

	Question	Answer A	Answer B	Answer C
16.	$207 + 18.34$	25.34	225.34	1248
17.	$68.2 - 1.38$	97.82	48.82	66.82
18.	$7 - 0.64$	6.36	1.48	0.48
19.	974×0.11	9.14	107.14	563.14
20.	$551.1 \div 11$	6.92	50.1	5623
21.	$207.1 + 11.65$	310.75	23.75	218.75
22.	664×0.51	256.2	338.64	828.62
23.	$(5.6 - 0.21) \times 39$	389.21	210.21	20.51
24.	$\frac{17.5 \times 42}{2.5}$	294	504	86
25.	$(906 + 4.1) \times 0.31$	473.21	282.131	29.561
26.	$\frac{543 + 472}{18.1 + 10.9}$	65	35	85
27.	$\frac{112.2 \times 75.9}{6.9 \times 5.1}$	242	20.4	25.2

28. The petrol consumption of a car is 4 km per litre and petrol costs $1.52 per litre.

Jasper estimates that the petrol costs of a round trip of about 1200 km will be $150. Is this a reasonable estimate?

29. 44 teachers buy 190 books at $24.20 each. They share the cost equally between them.

The headmaster used a calculator to work out the cost per teacher and got an answer of $10.50 to the nearest cent. *Without* using a calculator, work out an estimate for the answer to check whether or not he got it right. Show your working.

30. Each year about 150 million trees are cut down to make paper. One tree is enough to make about 650 kg of paper.

a) Weigh several newspapers (large and small) and estimate the number of newspapers which can be made from one tree.

b) Estimate the number of newspapers which could be made from all the trees cut down each year.

c) Weigh some of the exercise books you use at school. Estimate the number of books your class will use in a whole year and estimate the number of trees required to supply the paper for your class for one year.

7.4 Errors in measurement

Whenever a quantity is measured the measurement is never *exact.* If you measure the thickness of a wire with a ruler, you might read the thickness as 2 mm. If you use a more accurate device for measuring you might read the thickness as 2.3 mm. An even more accurate device might read the thickness as 2.31 mm. None of these figures is precise.

They are all approximations to the actual thickness. This means that there is always an error in making any kind of measurement such as length, weight, time, temperature and so on. An error of this kind is not the same as making a mistake in a calculation!

Bounds of accuracy

a) Suppose the length of a book is measured at 22 cm to the nearest cm. The actual length could be from 21.5 to *almost* 22.5. We say 'almost' 22.5 because a length of 22.4999999... would be rounded off to 22 cm. The number 22.499999... is effectively 22.5 and we take 22.5 as the **upper bound.**

21.5 cm $\leqslant$ length $<$ 22.5 cm

b) Using a ruler, the length of a nail is measured as 3.8 cm to the nearest 0.1 cm. In this case the bounds of accuracy are 3.75 cm and 3.85 cm.

3.75 cm $\leqslant$ length $<$ 3.85 cm

c) Sometimes measurements are given 'to the nearest 10, 100, etc.' Suppose the length of a lake is measured as 4200 m to the nearest 100 m. The bounds of accuracy are 4150 m and 4250 m.

In **(a)**, **(b)** and **(c)** above the maximum possible error is always half of the level of accuracy.

In part **(b)** the level of accuracy is the nearest 0.1 cm. The maximum possible error is 0.05 cm.

d) Here are some further examples:

i) The weight of an apple is 43 g to the nearest gram.

ii) The temperature of a room is 22.9 °C to one decimal place.

iii) The length of a road is 780 m to the nearest 10 m.

iv) The capacity of a mug is 115 ml to the nearest 5 ml.

v) The weight of a lorry is 23 000 kg to two significant figures.

lower bound	upper bound
42.5 g	43.5 g
22.85 °C	22.95 °C
775 m	785 m
112.5 ml	117.5 ml
22 500 kg	23 500 kg

Exercise 8

1. Copy and complete each statement. Part **(a)** is done as an example.
   a) A length d is 42 m, to the nearest m, so $41.5 \leqslant d < 42.5$.
   b) A volume V is 8 m^3, to the nearest cubic metre, so $7.5 \leqslant V < \square$
   c) A mass m is 72 kg, to the nearest kg, so $\square \leqslant m < \square$
   d) A time t is 3.2 h, to the nearest 0.1 h, so $\square \leqslant t < 3.25$
   e) A radius r is 5.8 cm, to the nearest 0.1 cm, so $\square \leqslant r < \square$
2. The height of a table is measured at 84 cm to the nearest cm. Write down the lower bound for the height of the table.
3. A man weighs a parcel at 5.2 kg to the nearest 0.1 kg. Write down the upper bound for the weight of the parcel.
4. The length and width of a rectangle are measured to the nearest 0.1 cm, as shown.

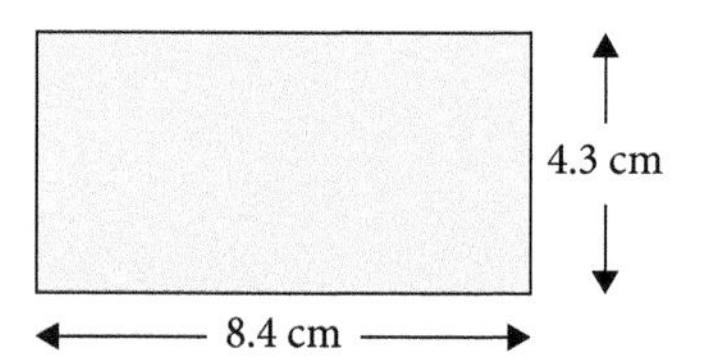

   a) Write down the upper bound for the length of the rectangle.
   b) Write down the lower bound for the width of the rectangle.
5. The height of a man is measured at 173 cm, to the nearest cm. Write down the upper bound for the height of the man.
6. A scientist weighs a sea shell at 3.7 g, correct to one decimal place. What is the least possible weight of the shell?
7. A book states that the distance from the Earth to the Sun is 93 million miles correct to two significant figures. What is the shortest possible distance?

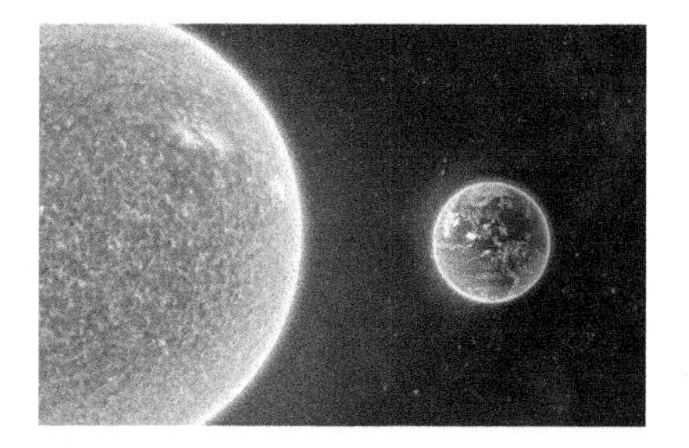

8. In a 200 m race a sprinter is timed at 20.63 seconds to the nearest 0.01 seconds. Write down the least possible time.
9. The weight of an egg is 17.8 g, correct to one decimal place. What is the greatest possible weight of the egg?
10. Copy and complete the table:
   a) length of nail = 5.6 cm, to nearest mm
   b) height of lighthouse = 37 m, to nearest m
   c) weight of insect = 0.27 mg, to 2 d.p.
   d) temperature in oven = 230 °C to nearest 10 °C
   e) length of oil pipeline = 315 km, to nearest km

lower bound	upper bound
a)	
b)	
c)	
d)	
e)	

7.5 Mental arithmetic

Ideally these questions should be read out by a teacher or friend and you should not be looking at them. Each question should be repeated once and then the answer, and only the answer, should be written down.

Each test should take about 30 minutes.

If you do not have anyone to read out the questions for you, try to do the test without writing down any detailed working.

Test 1

1. Find the cost in dollars of ten books at 35 cents each.
2. Add together \$4.20 and 75 cents.
3. What number divided by six gives an answer of eight?
4. I spend \$1.60 and pay with \$2. My change consists of three coins. What are they?
5. Find the difference between $13\frac{1}{2}$ and 20.
6. Write one centimetre as a fraction of one metre.
7. How many ten cents coins are there in a pile worth \$5.60?
8. Ten per cent of the students in a school play hockey, 15% play basketball and the rest play football. What percentage play football?
9. In a room of 20 people, three quarters were women. What was the number of women?
10. Four lemons costing 11 cents each are bought with a \$1 bill. What is the change?
11. I arrive at the railway station at 5.20 p.m. and my train is due at 6.10 p.m. How long do I have to wait?
12. What number is ten times a big as 0.65?
13. A hockey pitch measures 25 metres by 40 metres. Find the distance around the pitch.
14. Write the number 768 correct to the nearest ten.
15. By how many does a half of 62 exceed 20?
16. How many 2c coins are worth the same as ten 5c coins?
17. What number must be added to $1\frac{1}{4}$ to make $2\frac{1}{2}$?
18. Three books cost \$6. How much will five books cost?
19. An eraser costs 20 cents. How many can be bought for \$2?

20. What number is a hundred times as big as 0.605?
21. How many millimetres are there in $5\frac{1}{2}$ cm?
22. Find the average of 12 and 20.
23. A car travelling at 80 kilometres per hour takes 30 minutes for a journey. How long will the car take at 40 kilometres per hour?
24. A certain number multiplied by itself gives 81 as the answer. What is half of that number?
25. The difference between two numbers is 15. One of the numbers is 90. What is the other?
26. How many half-litre glasses can be filled from a vessel containing ten litres?
27. How much will a dozen oranges cost at 20 cents each?
28. On a coach forty-one out of fifty people are men. What percentage is this?
29. A prize of \$400 000 is shared equally between one hundred people. How much does each person receive?
30. If electric cable is 6 cents for 50 cm, how much will 4 metres cost?

Test 2

1. What are 48 twos?
2. How many fives are there in ninety-five?
3. What is 6.30 a.m. on the 24-hour clock?
4. Add together \$2.25 and 50 cents.
5. I go shopping with \$2.80 and buy a magazine for 90 cents. How much money have I left?
6. Two angles of a triangle are 65° and 20°. What is the third angle?
7. Write in figures the number 'five million, eighteen thousand and one'.
8. How many 20 cent biros can be bought for \$3?
9. Work out 1% of \$600.
10. A packet of 10 small cakes costs 35 cents. How much does each cake cost?
11. Add eight to 9 fives.

12. A packet of flour weighing 2400 grams is divided into three equal parts. How heavy is each part?
13. Add together 7, 23 and 44.
14. A car does 4 km per litre of petrol. How far does the car travel on seven litres of petrol?
15. How many twenty cents coins are needed to make eight dollars?
16. A certain butterfly lives for just 96 hours. How many days is this?
17. What number is 25 more than 37?
18. Find the average of 2, 5 and 8.
19. Footballs cost $11 each. How many can I buy for $60?
20. How many minutes are there in eight hours?
21. What number is twice as big as seventy-nine?
22. How many minutes are there between 6.25 p.m. and 8.00 p.m.?
23. Write one-fifth as a decimal.
24. Which is the larger: 0.7, or 0.071?
25. If a woman earns $8.40 per hour, how much does she earn in ten hours?
26. A car costing $2500 is reduced by $45. What is the new price?
27. How many half kilogram packets of sugar can be filled from a large sack containing 32 kilograms?
28. My daily paper costs 15 cents and I buy the paper six days a week. What is my weekly bill?
29. A car journey of 110 km took two hours. What was the average speed of the car?
30. How many days will there be in February 2018?

Test 3

1. What number is fifteen more than fifty-five?
2. What is a tenth of 2400?
3. What is twenty times forty-five?
4. Write in figures the number ten thousand, seven hundred and five.
5. A play lasting $2\frac{1}{4}$ hours starts at half-past eight. When does it finish?
6. What number is fifty-five less than 300?

7. How many twelves are there in 240?
8. A book costs $1.95. How much change do I receive from five dollars?
9. Find the cost of eight biros at 22 cents each.
10. What four coins make 61 cents?
11. Work out $\frac{1}{2}$ plus $\frac{1}{4}$ and give the answer as a decimal.
12. A box holds 16 cans. How many boxes are needed for 80 cans?
13. If the 25th of December is a Tuesday, what day of the week is the first of January?
14. By how much is two kilos more than 500 g?
15. Write down fifteen thousand and fifty cents in dollars and cents.
16. The sides of a square field measure 160 metres. Find the total distance around the field.
17. A mountain bike costing $970 is reduced by $248. What is the new price?
18. A prize of $150 000 is shared equally between six people. How much does each person receive?
19. Ice creams cost twenty-four cents each. How many can I buy with $1?
20. A bag contains 22 five cent coins. How much is in the bag?
21. How many metres are there in twelve kilometres?
22. A wine merchant puts 100 bottles in crates of 12. How many crates does he need?
23. Add together 73 and 18.
24. What is 5% of $120?
25. Peaches cost fourteen cents each. How much do I pay for seven peaches?
26. A toy costs 54 cents. Find the change from five dollars.
27. A boy goes to and from school by bus and a ticket costs 33 cents each way. How much does he spend in a five-day week?
28. In your purse, you have two ten dollar notes, three five dollar notes and seven one dollar notes. How much have you got altogether?
29. What are eighty twelves?
30. True or false: $\frac{1}{10}$ is greater than 0.2?

Test 4

1. What is the change from a \$10 note for goods costing \$1.95?
2. Add 12 to 7 nines.
3. How many 20 cent coins are needed to make \$5?
4. A pile of 100 sheets of paper is 10 cm thick. How thick is each sheet?
5. Lemons cost 7 cents each or 60 cents a dozen. How much is saved by buying a dozen instead of 12 separate lemons?
6. How many weeks are there in two years?
7. What is 1% of \$40?
8. How much more than \$92 is \$180?
9. My watch reads five past 6. It is 15 minutes fast. What is the correct time?
10. If a litre of cola costs 82c, how much does a boy pay for 10 litres?
11. A cycle track is 800 metres long. How far do I go in kilometres if I complete 5 laps of the track?
12. A train travels at an average speed of 30 km/h for $1\frac{1}{2}$ hours. How far does it travel?
13. I go shopping with \$5 and buy 3 items at 25 cents each. How much money have I left?
14. From one thousand and seven take away nine.
15. If I can cycle 1 km in 3 minutes, how many km can I cycle in one hour?
16. How many millimetres are there in 20 cm?
17. A metal rod 90 cm long is cut into four equal parts. How long is one part?
18. Find the cost of fifteen items at \$5 each.
19. A 2 cent coin is about 2 mm thick. How many coins are in a pile which is 2 cm high?
20. Add up the first four odd numbers.
21. Add up the first four even numbers.
22. My daily paper costs 18 cents. I pay for it with a \$10 note. What change do I receive?
23. A film starts at 8.53 p.m. and finishes at 9.15 p.m. How long is the film?
24. We finish school at twenty to four. What is that on the 24-hour clock?

25. Add together \$2.34 and \$5.60.
26. What is 10% of \$7?
27. How many 2 cent coins are needed to make \$4?
28. There are four TV channels. 35% of a class prefer Channel 1 and 30% prefer Channel 3. What percentage prefer the other two channels?
29. How many minutes are there between 6.20 p.m. and 8.00 p.m.?
30. What is the cost of 1000 books at \$2.50 each?

The questions in the next three tests are a little harder.

Test 5

1. A car travels at a speed of 50 km/h for 30 minutes. How far does it travel?
2. I bought two books costing \$2.50 and \$1.90. How much did I spend altogether?
3. What is the cost of six items at \$35 each?
4. Tickets for a concert cost \$6.50 each. What is the cost of four tickets?
5. It takes me 24 minutes to walk to school. I cycle three times as fast as I walk. How long do I take to cycle to school?
6. Work out as a single number, four squared plus three squared.
7. Write down an approximate value for forty-nine times eleven.
8. Write one metre as a fraction of one kilometre.
9. What number is exactly half-way between 2.5 and 2.8?
10. The First World War started in 1914. How long ago was that?
11. Lottery tickets cost \$2.50 each. How much is raised from the sale of six thousand tickets?
12. Train fares are increased by ten per cent. If the old fare was \$3.50, what is the new fare?
13. Mattie earns \$5.50 per hour, how much does he earn in five hours?
14. A box holds twelve eggs. How many boxes are needed for 90 eggs?
15. When playing darts you score double ten, double twenty and treble eight. What is your total score?
16. How many cm are there in twelve metres?

17. A petrol pump delivered $2\frac{1}{2}$ litres in 5 seconds. How many litres will it deliver in one minute?
18. A square has sides of length 5 cm. How long is a diagonal to the nearest centimetre?
19. How much more than 119 is 272?
20. What is the cube root of 64?
21. Find the average of 4, 8 and 9.
22. A rectangular lawn is 7 m wide and 15 m long. What area does it cover?
23. How many centimetres are there in 20 km?
24. A ship was due at noon on Tuesday, but arrived at 15:00 on Thursday. How many hours late was it?
25. A litre of lemonade fills 9 glasses. How many litre bottles are needed to fill 50 glasses?
26. Work out 15% of $40.
27. A cake weighs 2.3 kg. How many grams is that?
28. How many seconds are there in $2\frac{1}{2}$ minutes?
29. How many days are there altogether in 19 weeks?
30. If the eighth of May is a Monday, what day of the week is the seventeenth?

Test 6

1 What is the angle between the hands of a clock at two o'clock?
2 What is a half of a half of 0.2?
3 In a test Paul got 16 out of 20. What percentage is that?
4 Work out $2 \times 20 \times 200$.
5. Two friends share a bill for $33.80. How much does each person pay?
6. Work out $\frac{1}{2}$ plus $\frac{1}{5}$ and give the answer as a decimal.
7. How long will it take a car to travel 320 km at an average speed of 60 km/h?
8. What is $\frac{1}{8}$ as a percentage?
9. What is the height of a triangle with base 12 cm and area 36 cm^2?
10. Work out 0.1 cubed.

11. Between which two consecutive whole numbers does the square root of 58 lie?
12. What is eight per cent of $25?
13. A car has a 1795 c.c. engine. What is that approximately in litres?
14. The mean of four numbers is 12.3. What is their sum?
15. Find the cost of eating 4 cakes a day for five days if 2 cakes cost $1.25.
16. How many minutes are there in $2\frac{3}{4}$ hours?
17. A pie chart has a red sector representing 20% of the whole chart. What is the angle of the sector?
18. How many five cent coins are needed to make $12?
19. I buy three kg of oranges for $1.02. How much do they cost per kg?
20. A rectangular pane of glass is 3 m long and 2 m wide. Glass costs $1.50 per square metre. How much will the pane cost?
21. A car journey of 150 km took $2\frac{1}{2}$ hours. What was the average speed?
22. Add 218 to 84.
23. Pencils cost 50 cents each. How many can I buy with $250?
24. Write down the next prime number after 31.
25. A ruler costs 37 cents. What is the total cost of three rulers?
26. A salesman receives commission of $1\frac{1}{2}$% on sales. How much commission does he receive when he sells a computer for $1000?
27. How many edges does a cube have?
28. Between which two consecutive whole numbers does the square root of 80 lie?
29. A baseball cap is marked at a sale price of $12 after a reduction of 25%. What was the original price?
30. One boomerang costs $3.45. How much will four cost?

Test 7

1. Two angles of a triangle are 42° and 56°. What is the third angle?
2. Telephone charges are increased by 20%. What is the new charge for a call which previously cost 60 cents?

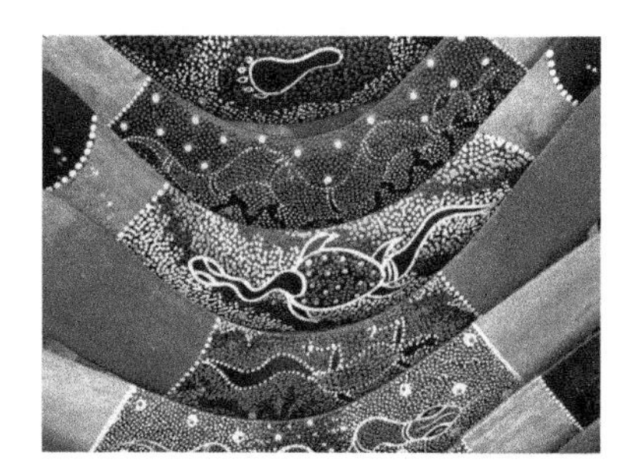

3. What number is exactly half way between 0.1 and 0.4?
4. A boat sails at a speed of 18 knots for five hours. How far does it go?
5. How many 23c stamps can be bought for $2?
6. The mean age of three girls is 12 years. If two of the girls are aged 9 and 16 years, how old is the third girl?
7. Multiply $3\frac{1}{4}$ by 100.
8. What is a quarter of a third?
9. A prize of five million dollars is shared equally between 200 people. How much does each person receive?
10. The attendance at an athletics meeting was forty-eight thousand, seven hundred and eleven. Write this number correct to two significant figures.

11. Work out 0.1 multiplied by 63.
12. Find the cost of 6 bars of chocolate at $1.45 per bar.
13. Three people agree to share a bill equally. The cost comes to $7.20. How much does each person pay?
14. A pump removes water at a rate of 6 litres per minute. How many hours will it take to remove 1800 litres?
15. Work out three-eighths of $100.
16. A metal rod of length 27.1 cm is cut exactly in half. How long is each piece?
17. A square has sides of length 7 cm. How long is a diagonal to the nearest centimetre?
18. The cost of five vegeburgers is $7.50. How much will six cost?
19. What number is a thousand times as big as 0.2?
20. Pencils cost five cents each. How much will two dozen pencils cost?
21. How many fours are there in a thousand?
22. Work out the area, in square metres, of a rectangular field of width twenty metres and length twenty-five metres.
23. A packet of peanuts costs 65 cents. I buy two packets and pay with a ten dollar note. Find the change.
24. What is a half of a half of 0.1?
25. I bought three kilograms of flour and I used four hundred and fifty grams of it. How many grams of flour do I have left?

26. A prize of two hundred thousand dollars is shared equally between five people. How much does each person receive?
27. What is the angle between the hands of a clock at 5 o' clock?
28. Five boys and three girls share $240. How much do the boys get altogether?
29. How many 17c stamps can I buy for $2?
30. A milk crate has space for 24 bottles. How many crates are needed for 200 bottles?

Mathematical magic

Here is a trick which you can perform to demonstrate that you can add even quicker than a calculator!

a) Ask someone to give a five-digit number with the figures all jumbled up to make it more 'difficult'.

b) Ask for two more five-digit numbers. You may now have:

47563 ...A
25608 ...B
87265 ...C

c) Pretend to add two more five-digit numbers at random. In fact choose the fourth number so that when added to number B it makes 99999. Similarly the fifth number is chosen so that when added to number C it also makes 99999. We now have:

47563
25608
87265
74391
12734

d) You now add them together 'in your head' and write down the answer. (Check this on a calculator.)

Answer = 247561

How does it work?

The first digit is always a '2'.

The next five digits are simply 2 less than number A.
i.e. $47563 - 2 = 47561$.

Here is another example.

Can you work out why it works?

Now challenge your friends or relatives to an addition race: your brain versus their calculator.

58627
43817
38065
56182
+ 61934
258625

7.6 Using a calculator

Order of operations

All calculators work differently so it is important that you are confident using yours before the examination. Calculators cannot think for themselves. *You* have to decide in which order the buttons have to be pressed.

Always perform operations in the following order:

a) Brackets

b) Divide and multiply

c) Add and subtract.

Example

a) $7+6\div 3=7+2$
$=9$

b) $6\times 4-8\div 2=24-4$
$=20$

c) $5+(28+5)\div 3=5+33\div 3$
$=5+11$
$=16$

d) $\dfrac{4.2}{1.2-0.7}=\dfrac{4.2}{0.5}$
$=8.4$

Notice that the division line ——— acts like a pair of brackets so that we work out 1.2 – 0.7 first.

Exercise 9

Work out, without a calculator:

1. $11+8\div 1$ **2.** $60-7\times 8$ **3.** $15-2\times 6$

4. $15\div 5-3$ **5.** $30+15\div 3$ **6.** $9\times 5+15$

7. $40-3\times 8$ **8.** $12-36\div 6$ **9.** $3+20\div 2$

10. $13+8\div 8$ **11.** $2\times 4+3\times 5$ **12.** $6\times 6+7\times 5$

13. $1\times 6+7\times 2$ **14.** $2\times 8+2\times 10$ **15.** $3\times 5-12\div 2$

16. $3\times 5-28\div 4$ **17.** $7\times 4+2\times 2$ **18.** $30\div 3+5\times 4$

19. $20\div 2-3\times 2$ **20.** $8\div 8-1\times 1$ **21.** $\dfrac{27+3\times 3}{(3\times 2)}$

22. $\dfrac{6+8\times 3}{(8\times 2-10)}$ **23.** $\dfrac{13-12\div 4}{4+3\times 2}$ **24.** $\dfrac{11+6\times 6}{5-8\div 2}$

25. $\dfrac{12+3\times 6}{4+3\div 3}$ **26.** $\dfrac{24-18\div 3}{1.5+4.5}$

27. $(42 - 5 \times 6) \times (8 - 4 \times 2) + (7 + 3 \times 3)$

28. $(10 - 24 \div 3) + (8 + 3 \times 4) \div (8 - 6 \times 1)$

29. $7 + 9 \times (8 - 6 \div 2)$

30. $[(7 - 2) \times 5] - (6 \times 3 - 2 \times 4)$

31. $[(60 - 7 \times 5) \div 5] + (12 + 7 \times 10)$

32. $(15 - 3 \times 4) \times 4 + [60 \div (24 \div 2)]$

33. $[(9 - 7) \times 12] - (7 \times 3 - 5 \times 4)$

34. $(50 - 8 \times 6) \times 2 + [40 \div (5 \times 2)]$

35. $[(12 - 8) \times 4 \div (11 - 3 \times 1)$

36. $(7 \times 2 - 6) + (7 + 16 \div 8) \times (10 - 4 \times 2)$

Exercise 10

This exercise is more difficult. Write down each question and find the missing signs. (+, –, ×, ÷).
There are no brackets.

1. 7 5 4 = 27
2. 3 5 10 = 25
3. 4 2 3 = 5
4. 11 3 3 = 20
5. 31 10 2 = 11
6. 10 6 5 = 40
7. 4 8 7 = 25
8. 12 9 2 = 30
9. 18 4 4 = 2
10. 28 10 2 = 8
11. 21 3 5 = 2
12. 7 3 3 = 16
13. 10 2 3 = 8
14. 10 3 12 = 42
15. 18 3 7 = 13
16. 31 40 5 = 39
17. 15 16 4 = 11
18. 15 8 9 = 87
19. 37 35 5 = 44
20. 11 5 9 = 64
21. 8 3 2 4 = 10
22. 12 3 3 1 = 4
23. 11 4 1 6 = 9
24. 15 5 2 4 = 11
25. 7 2 3 3 = 5
26. 12 2 3 4 = 22
27. 8 9 6 11 = 6
28. 20 20 9 0 = 1
29. 20 30 10 8 = 25
30. 30 6 11 11 = 85

Calculator

Example

a) Work out $8.43 + \frac{9.72}{3.3}$ correct to four significant figures.

[8.43] [+] [9.72] [÷] [3.3] [=]

Answer = 11.38 (to 4 s.f.)

b) Work out $(5.2 - 4.737)^2$.

[5.2] [–] [4.737] [=] [x^2]

Answer = 0.2144 (to 4 s.f.)

Exercise 11

Work out, correct to four significant figures:

1. 85.3×21.7
2. $18.6 \div 2.7$
3. $10.074 \div 8.3$
4. 0.112×3.74
5. $8 - 0.111\ 11$
6. $19 + 0.3456$
7. $0.841 \div 17$
8. 11.02×20.1
9. $18.3 \div 0.751$
10. 0.982×6.74
11. $\frac{8.3 + 2.94}{3.4}$
12. $\frac{6.1 - 4.35}{0.76}$

13. $\dfrac{19.7+21.4}{0.985}$

14. $7.3+\left(\dfrac{8.2}{9.5}\right)$

15. $\left(\dfrac{6.04}{18.7}\right)-0.214$

16. $\dfrac{2.4\times 0.871}{4.18}$

17. $19.3+\left(\dfrac{2.6}{1.95}\right)$

18. $6.41+\dfrac{9.58}{2.6}$

19. $\dfrac{19.3\times 0.221}{0.689}$

20. $8.3+\dfrac{0.64}{0.325}$

21. $2.4+(9.7\times 0.642)$

22. $11.2+(9.75\times 1.11)$

23. $0.325+\dfrac{8.6}{11.2}$

24. 8.35^2-25

25. $6.71^2+0.64$

26. $3.45^3+11.8$

27. $2.93^3-2.641$

28. $\dfrac{7.2^2-4.5}{8.64}$

29. $\dfrac{13.9+2.97^2}{4.31}$

30. $(3.3-2.84)^2$

Using the memory

Example

a) Work out $\dfrac{4.2+1.75}{3.63-2.14}$, correct to 4 s.f., using the memory buttons.

Find the bottom line first:

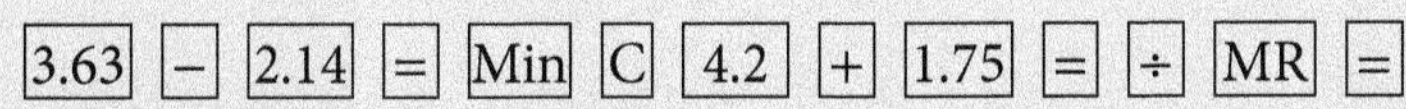

The calculator reads 3.993288591

∴ Answer = 3.993 (to 4 s.f.)

b) Work out $18.75-2.11^3$.

[2.11] [x^y] [3] [=] [Min] [C] [18.75] [–] [MR] [=]

Answer = 9.356 (to 4 s.f.)

Alternative method

It is even quicker to use brackets:

(4.2 + 1.75) ÷ (3.63 – 2.14) =

Using the [ANS] button

The [ANS] button can be used as a 'short-term memory'. It holds the answer from the previous calculation.

Example

Work out $\dfrac{5}{1.2-0.761}$, correct to 4 s.f., using the [ANS] button.

Find the bottom line first:

[1.2] [–] [0.761] [EXE] [5] [÷] [ANS] [EXE]

The calculator reads 11.38952164

∴ Answer = 11.39 (to 4 s.f.)

Notice that the [EXE] button works the same as the [=] button.

Exercise 12

Work out the following, correct to four significant figures.

Use the memory buttons, the ANS button or the brackets buttons.

1. $\dfrac{7.3+2.14}{3.6-2.95}$

2. $\dfrac{2.3+0.924}{1.3+0.635}$

3. $\dfrac{5.89}{7-3.83}$

4. $\dfrac{102}{58.1+65.32}$

5. $\dfrac{18.8}{3.72\times1.86}$

6. $\dfrac{904}{65.3\times2.86}$

7. $12.2-\left(\dfrac{2.6}{1.95}\right)$

8. $8.047-\left(\dfrac{6.34}{10.2}\right)$

9. $1.42-\left(\dfrac{1.7}{2.4}\right)$

10. $\dfrac{9.75-8.792}{4.31-3.014}$

11. $\dfrac{19.6\times3.01}{2.01-1.958}$

12. $3.7^2-\left(\dfrac{8.59}{24}\right)$

13. $8.27-1.56^2$

14. $111.79-5.04^2$

15. $18.3-2.841^2$

16. $(2.93+71.5)^2$

17. $(8.3-6.34)^4$

18. $54.2-2.6^4$

19. $(8.7-5.95)^4$

20. $\sqrt{68.4}+11.63$

21. $9.45-\sqrt{8.248}$

22. $3.4^2-\sqrt{1.962}$

23. $\dfrac{3.54+2.4}{8.47^2}$

24. $2065-\sqrt{44\,000}$

25. $\sqrt{(5.69-0.0852)}$

26. $\sqrt{(0.976+1.03)}$

27. $\sqrt{\dfrac{17.4}{2.16-1.83}}$

28. $\sqrt{\left(\dfrac{28.9}{\sqrt{8.47}}\right)}$

29. $257-\dfrac{6.32}{0.059}$

30. $75\,000-5.6^4$

31. $\dfrac{11.29\times2.09}{2.7+0.082}$

32. $85.5-\sqrt{105.8}$

33. $\dfrac{4.45^2}{8.2^2-51.09}$

34. $\left(\dfrac{8.53+7.07}{6.04-4.32}\right)^4$

35. $2.75+\dfrac{5}{8.2}+\dfrac{11.2}{4.3}$

36. $8.2+\dfrac{6.3}{0.91}+\dfrac{2.74}{8.4}$

37. $\dfrac{18.5}{1.6}+\dfrac{7.1}{0.53}+\dfrac{11.9}{25.6}$

38. $\dfrac{83.6}{105}+\dfrac{2.95}{2.7}+\dfrac{81}{97}$

39. $\left(\dfrac{98.76}{103}+\dfrac{4.07}{3.6}\right)^2$

40. $\dfrac{(5.843-\sqrt{2.07})^2}{88.4}$

41. $\left(\dfrac{1}{7.6}-\dfrac{1}{18.5}\right)^3$

42. $\dfrac{\sqrt{(4.79)}+1.6}{9.63}$

43. $\dfrac{(0.761)^2-\sqrt{(4.22)}}{1.96}$

44. $\sqrt[3]{\left(\dfrac{1.74\times0.761}{0.0896}\right)}$

45. $\left(\dfrac{8.6\times1.71}{0.43}\right)^3$

46. $\dfrac{\sqrt[3]{(86.6)}}{\sqrt[4]{(4.71)}}$

47. $\dfrac{1}{8.2^2}-\dfrac{3}{19^2}$

48. $\dfrac{100}{11^3}+\dfrac{100}{12^3}$

Negative numbers

To enter a negative number on a calculator, press the [(–)] or [+/–] button and then the number.

Example

a) Work out -4.2×6

Press [(–)] [4.2] [×] [6] [EXE] Answer: -25.2

b) Work out $-3 \times (-8.45)$

Press [(–)] [3] [×] [(–)] [8.45] [EXE] Answer: 25.35

Exercise 13

Work out the following. Give the answer correct to one decimal place where appropriate.

1. -7×3

2. $-5 \times (-2)$

3. $8 \div (-4)$

4. $10 \times (-4)$

5. $-2 \times (-2)$

6. $-12 \div 3$

7. $-5 \times (-4)$

8. $-8 - 11$

9. $-7 + 2$

10. $-9 + 30$

11. $-20 \div 4$

12. $-16 - 15$

13. $-3.4 \times (-2.5)$

14. -0.5×6.8

15. $12.5 - (-2.5)$

16. $-1.1 \times (-1.1)$

17. $-8 \div (-0.25)$

18. $-6.8 \div 0.1$

19. $\dfrac{-8 \times (-3)}{4}$

20. $\dfrac{12}{(3 \times (-2))}$

21. $\dfrac{20}{(-2)} + 8$

22. $-11.4 + 1.71$

23. $-9.2 - 7.4 + 15.2$

24. $-4.74 - (-13.08)$

25. $\dfrac{(-8.23) \times (-1.24)}{3.6}$

26. $\dfrac{5.1 \times (-1.42)}{(-1.7)}$

27. $\dfrac{-2.3 \times (-2.8)}{(-3.5)}$

28. $(-3.6)^2 + 2.7$

29. $(-3.91)^2 - 7$

30. $17.4 - (-7.2)^2$

Checking answers

Here are five calculations, followed by sensible checks.

a) 22.2 [÷] 6 = 3.7 check: 3.7 [×] 6 = 22.2

b) 31.7 [–] 4.83 = 26.87 check: 26.87 [+] 4.83 = 31.7

c) 42.8 [×] 30 = 1284 check: 1284 [÷] 30 = 42.8

d) $\sqrt{17} = 4.1231$ check: $4.1231^2 = 17$

e) $3.7 + 17.6 + 13.9 = 35.2$ check: $13.9 + 17.6 + 3.7 = 35.2$ (add in reverse order)

Calculations can also be checked by rounding numbers to a given number of significant figures.

f) $\dfrac{6.1 \times 32.6}{19.3} = 10.3 \text{ (to 3 s.f.)}$

Check this answer by rounding each number to one significant figure and estimating.

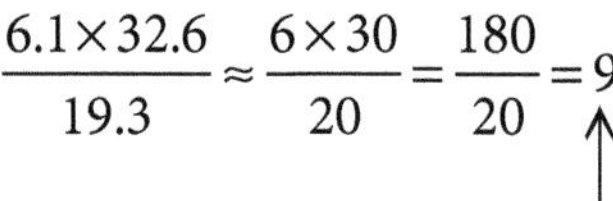

$$\frac{6.1 \times 32.6}{19.3} \approx \frac{6 \times 30}{20} = \frac{180}{20} = 9$$

This is close to 10.3 so the actual answer probably is 10.3

'≈' means 'approximately equal to'

Exercise 14

1. Use a calculator to work out the following, then check the answers as indicated.

a) $92.5 \times 20 = \square$ check: $\square \div 20 = \square$

b) $14 \times 328 = \square$ check: $\square \div 328 = \square$

c) $63 - 12.6 = \square$ check: $\square + 12.6 = \square$

d) $221.2 \div 7 = \square$ check: $\square \times 7 = \square$

e) $384.93 \div 9.1 = \square$ check: $\square \times 9.1 = \square$

f) $13.71 + 25.8 = \square$ check: $\square - 25.8 = \square$

g) $95.4 \div 4.5 = \square$ check: $\square \times 4.5 = \square$

h) $8.2 + 3.1 + 19.6 + 11.5 = \square$ check: $11.5 + 19.6 + 3.1 + 8.2 = \square$

i) $\sqrt{39} = \square$ check: $\square^2 = 39$

j) $3.17 + 2.06 + 8.4 + 16 = \square$ check: $16 + 8.4 + 2.06 + 3.17 = \square$

2. The numbers below are rounded to one significant figure to *estimate* the answer to each calculation. Match each question below to the correct estimated answer.

A	21.9×1.01	***P***	10
B	$\dfrac{19.8^2}{(18.61 + 22.3)}$	***Q***	5
C	7.8×1.01	***R***	0.5
D	$\dfrac{\sqrt{98.7}}{8.78 + 11.43}$	***S***	8
E	$\dfrac{21.42 + 28.6}{18.84 - 8.99}$	***T***	20

3. Do *not* use a calculator.

   $281 \times 36 = 10\,116$

   Work out

   a) $10\,116 \div 36$ **b)** $10\,116 \div 281$ **c)** 28.1×3.6

4. Noor is paid a salary of \$49 620 per year. Work out a rough estimate for her weekly pay. (Give your answer correct to one significant figure).

5. In 2010, the population of France was 62 793 432 and the population of Greece was 11 306 183. Roughly how many times bigger was the population of France compared to the population of Greece?

   Round the numbers to one significant figure.

6. *Estimate*, correct to one significant figure:

   a) $41.56 \div 7.88$ **b)** $\frac{5.13 \times 18.777}{0.952}$ **c)** $\frac{1}{5}$ of \$14 892

   d) $\frac{0.0974 \times \sqrt{104}}{1.03}$ **e)** 52% of 0.394 kg **f)** $\frac{6.84^2 + 0.983}{5.07^2}$

   g) $\frac{2848.7 + 1024.8}{51.2 - 9.98}$ **h)** $\frac{2}{3}$ of \$3124 **i)** $18.13 \times (3.96^2 + 2.07^2)$

Exercise 15

If we work out $25 \times 503 \times 4 + 37$ on a calculator we should obtain the number 50 337. If we turn the calculator upside down (and use a little imagination) we see the word 'LEEDS'.

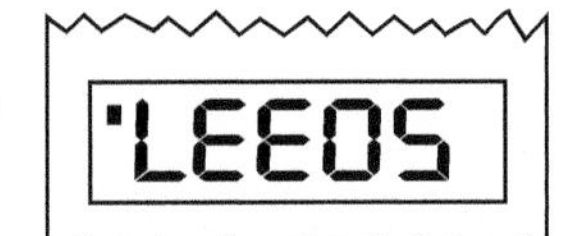

Find the words given by the clues below.

1. $83 \times 85 + 50$ (Lots of this in the garden)
2. $211 \times 251 + 790$ (Tropical or Scilly)
3. $19 \times 20 \times 14 - 2.66$ (Not an upstanding man)
4. $(84 + 17) \times 5$ (Dotty message)
5. $0.014\,43 \times 7 \times 4$ (Three times as funny)
6. $79 \times 9 - 0.9447$ (Greasy letters)
7. $50.19 - (5 \times 0.0039)$ (Not much space inside)
8. $2 \div 0.5 - 3.295$ (Rather lonely)
9. $0.034 \times 11 - 0.002\,92$; $9^4 - (8 \times 71)$ (two words) (Nice for breakfast)
10. $7420 \times 7422 + 118^2 - 30$ (Big Chief)
11. $(13 \times 3 \times 25 \times 8 \times 5) + 7$ (Gatekeeper's house)
12. $71^2 - 11^2 - 5$ (Sad gasp)
13. $904^2 + 89\,62\,1\,818$ (Prickly customer)

14. $(559 \times 6) + (21 \times 55)$ (What a surprise!)

15. $566 \times 711 - 23\,617$ (Bolt it down)

16. $\dfrac{9999+319}{8.47+2.53}$ (Sit up and plead)

17. $\dfrac{2601 \times 6}{4^2+1^2}$; $(401 - 78) - 5^2$ (two words) (Not a great man)

18. $0.4^2 - 0.1^2$ (Little Sidney)

19. $\dfrac{(27 \times 2000 - 2)}{(0.63 \div 0.09)}$ (Not quite a mountain)

20. $(5^2 - 1^2)^4 - 14\,239$ (Just a name)

21. $48^4 + 102^2 - 4^2$ (Pursuits)

22. $615^2 + (7 \times 242)$ (Almost a goggle)

23. $6.2 \times 0.987 \times 1\,000\,000 - 860^2 + 118$ (Flying ace)

24. $(426 \times 474) + (318 \times 487) + 22\,018$ (Close to a bubble)

25. $\dfrac{36^3}{4} - 1530$ (Swiss girl's name)

26. $(594 \times 571) - (154 \times 132) - 38$ (Female Bobby)

27. $(7^2 \times 100) + (7 \times 2)$ (Lofty)

28. $240^2 + 134$; $241^2 - 7^3$ (two words) (Devil of a chime)

29. $1384.5 \times 40 - 1.991$ (Say this after sneezing)

30. $(2 \times 2 \times 2 \times 2 \times 3)^4 + 1929$ (Unhappy ending)

31. $141\,918 + 83^3$ (Hot stuff in France)

Mixed questions

Exercise 16

1. Four dozen bags of grain weigh 2016 kg. How much does each bag weigh?
2. An office building has twelve floors and each floor has twenty windows.

   A window cleaner charges 50c per window. How much will he charge to clean all the windows in the building?
3. Write the following to the degree of accuracy stated:

   a) 7.243 (to 1 d.p.) **b)** 11.275 (to 2 d.p.)

   c) 0.115 (to 1 d.p.) **d)** 0.0255 (to 3 d.p.)

   e) 28.21 (to 1 d.p.) **f)** 0.0072 (to 2 d.p.)

4. Work out, without using a calculator.

a) $0.6 + 2.72$ **b)** $3.21 - 1.6$

c) $2.8 - 1.34$ **d)** $8 - 3.6$

e) 100×0.062 **f)** $27.4 \div 10$

5. A rectangular wheat field is 200 m by 400 m. One hectare is 10 000 m^2 and each hectare produces 3 tonnes of wheat.

a) What is the area of the field in hectares?

b) How much wheat is produced in this field?

6. A computer is hired out at a rate of 50c per minute. How much will it cost to hire the computer from 06:30 to 18:00?

7. An old sailor has ten pounds of gold. One day the price of gold goes up by \$40 an ounce to \$520 an ounce.

a) By how much did his gold rise in value?

b) How much was it worth after the rise? (1 pound = 16 ounces)

8. This packet of wooden blocks costs \$4.50.

How much would you have to pay for this packet?

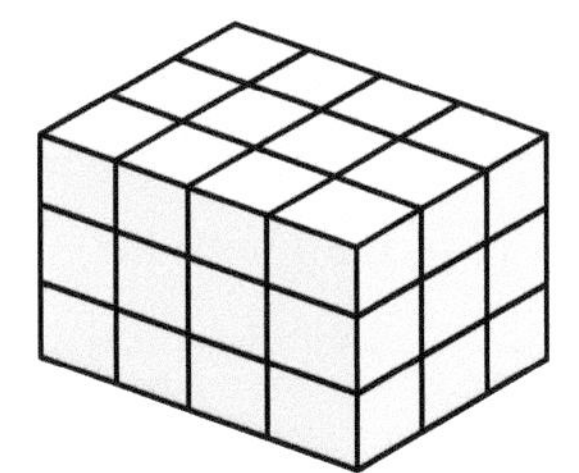

9. A wall measuring 3 m by 2 m is to be covered with square tiles of side 10 cm.

a) How many tiles are needed?

b) If the tiles cost \$3.40 for ten, how much will it cost?

10 Draw the next member of the sequence.

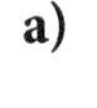

a)

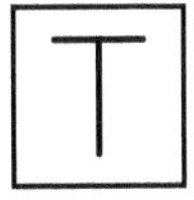
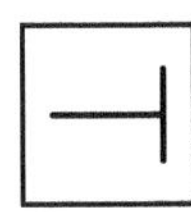
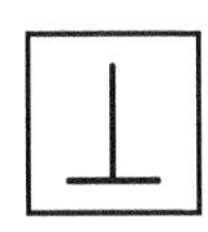

b)

c)

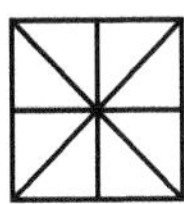
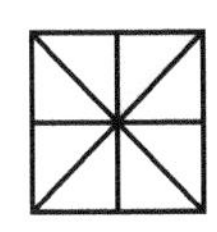
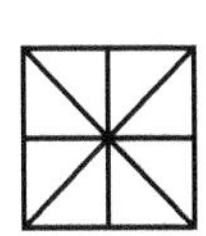

Exercise 17

1. The results of a test given to 50 students are shown below.

Mark	0	1	2	3	4	5
Number of students	1	4	10	12	15	8

a) How many students scored less than 3 marks?

b) Find the percentage of the students who scored:

i) 2 marks

ii) 5 marks

iii) 3 marks or more

iv) no marks.

2. The thirteenth number in the sequence 1, 3, 9, 27, … is 531 441.
What is

a) the twelfth number

b) the fourteenth number?

3. 6 sacks of corn will feed 80 hens for 12 days.

Copy and complete the following:

a) 18 sacks of corn will feed 80 hens for … days.

b) 6 sacks of corn will feed 40 hens for … days.

c) 60 sacks of corn will feed 40 hens for … days.

d) 30 sacks of corn will feed 80 hens for … days.

4. Calculate the area of the shape below. Take $\pi = 3$.

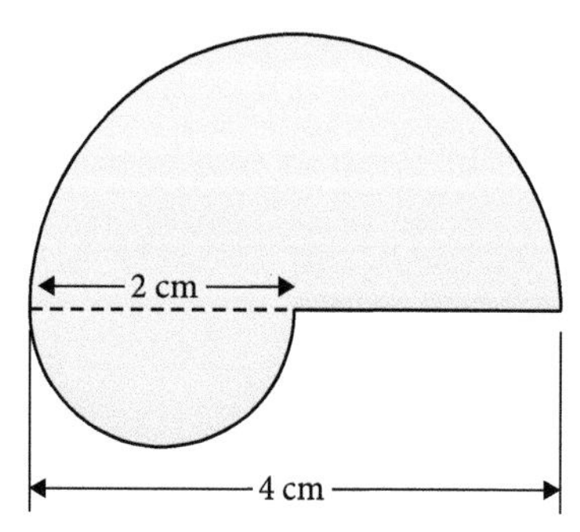

5. The odometer (distance-counter) of a car shows a reading of 14941 km. This number is called 'palindromic' because it reads the same backwards or forwards.

a) What will be the reading when the next palindromic number appears?

b) How far will the car have travelled by then?

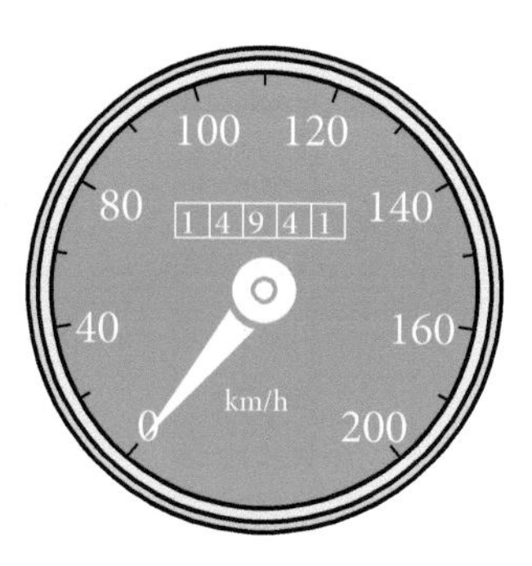

6 Copy and complete the telephone bill shown by finding A, B, C, D and E.

DATE	METER READING	UNITS USED	PRICE PER UNIT	AMOUNT (£)
29/7/2016	18714			
30/4/2016	17956	A	3.80c	B
			Rental Charges	21.50
		Total Charges (excluding tax)		C
		Tax at $17\frac{1}{2}\%$		D
		Total Charges (including tax)		E

7. A salesman is paid a basic salary of \$5400 per year, plus commission of 5% on all his sales. Calculate his total salary if his sales totalled \$40 000.

8. Petrol costs 184.3 cents per litre. How many litres can be bought for \$8? Give your answer to one decimal place.

Exercise 18

1. A calorie guide shows how many calories are contained in various foods:

   Bread 1.2 calories per g

   Cheese 2.5 calories per g

   Meat 1.6 calories per g

   Butter 6 calories per g

   Calculate the number of calories in the following meals:

   a) 50 g bread, 40 g cheese, 100 g meat, 15 g butter

   b) 150 g bread, 85 g cheese, 120 g meat, 20 g butter.

2. Write as a single number.

   a) 8^2 **b)** 1^4

   c) 10^2 **d)** 3×10^3

   e) 2^5 **f)** 3^4

3. A cylinder has a volume of 200 cm³ and a height of 10 cm. Calculate the area of its base, A.

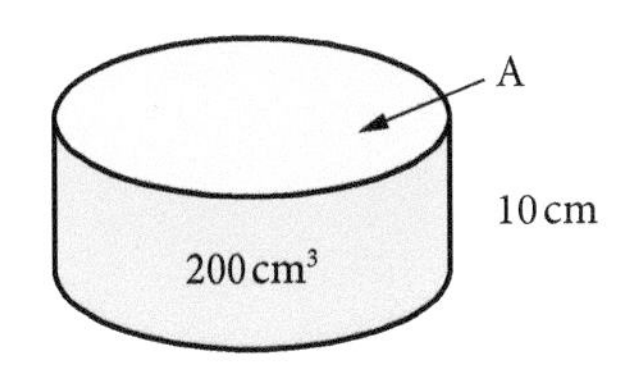

4. The diagram represents a railway siding. Each ● is a junction where a train can turn left or right. A turn to the left has a code 0 and a turn to the right has a code 1.

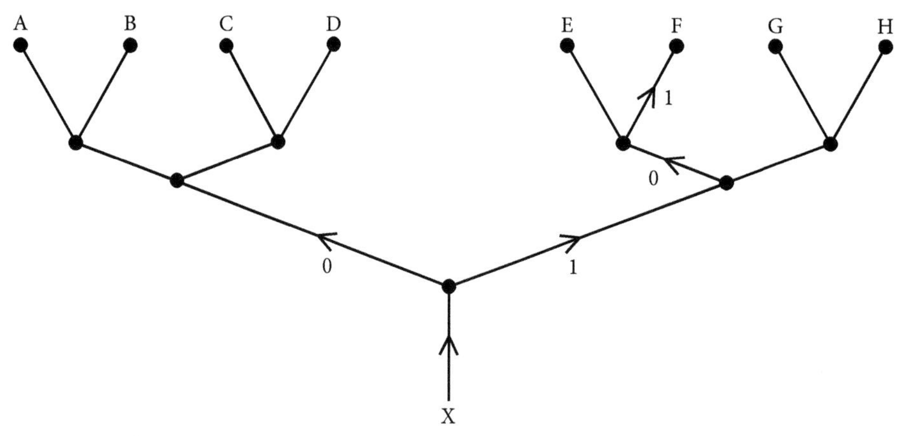

For example, a train starting at X would have code 101 in order to arrive at F.

Copy and complete the table below.

Point	A	B	C	D	E	F	G	H
Code						101		

5. A group of four adults is planning a holiday in France. The ferry costs, for the return journey, are:

Adult	\$25
Car	\$62

Travel around France is estimated at 2000 km and petrol costs \$1.80 per litre. The car travels 10 km on one litre of petrol.

a) Calculate the total cost of the return journey on the ferry.

b) Calculate the number of litres of petrol to be used.

c) Calculate the total cost of the petrol.

6. A journey by boat takes 2 hours 47 minutes. How long will it take at half the speed?

7. Copy the following tables and write down the next *two* lines:

a) $2^2 = 1^2 + 3$

$3^2 = 2^2 + 5$

$4^2 = 3^2 + 7$

$5^2 = 4^2 + 9$

b) $3^2 = 4 + 1^2 + 2^2$

$5^2 = 12 + 2^2 + 3^2$

$7^2 = 24 + 3^2 + 4^2$

$9^2 = 40 + 4^2 + 5^2$

8. The area of an island is 6000 km^2. What volume of rain falls on the island during a day when there is 2 cm of rain? Give the answer in m^3.

9. Ten posts are equally spaced in a straight line. It is 450 m from the first to the tenth post. What is the distance between the pairs of posts?

10. Find the smallest whole number that is exactly divisible by all the numbers 1 to 10 inclusive.

Exercise 19

1. Seven fig rolls together weigh 560 g. A calorie guide shows that 10 g of fig roll contains 52 calories.
   a) How much does one fig roll weigh?
   b) How many calories are there in 1 g of fig roll?
   c) How many calories are there in one fig roll?
2. The number t is greater than 6 and the number x is less than 4. Arrange the numbers 5, t and x in order of size, starting with the smallest.
3. To the nearest whole number 5.84, 16.23 and 7.781 are 6, 16 and 8 respectively.
   a) Use these approximate values to obtain an approximate result for $\frac{5.84 \times 16.23}{7.781}$.
   b) Use the same approach to obtain approximate results for:
   i) $\frac{15.72 \times 9.78}{20.24}$ **ii)** $\frac{23.85 \times 9.892}{4.867}$
4. A king has three coins which look the same, but in fact one of them weighs more than the other two.
   Describe how he could discover the fake coin using an ordinary balance and only *one* weighing operation.

5. An aircraft uses 150 litres of fuel to fly 375 km. How much fuel is needed for a journey of 500 km?

6. A pile of 400 sheets of paper is 2.5 cm thick. What is the thickness in cm of one sheet of paper?

7. A map uses a scale of 1 to 100 000.

   a) Calculate the actual length, in km, of a canal which is 5.4 cm long on the map.

   b) A path is 600 m long. Calculate, in cm, the length this would be on the map.

8. Given the circumference, C, of a circle it is possible to estimate the area A by the following method:

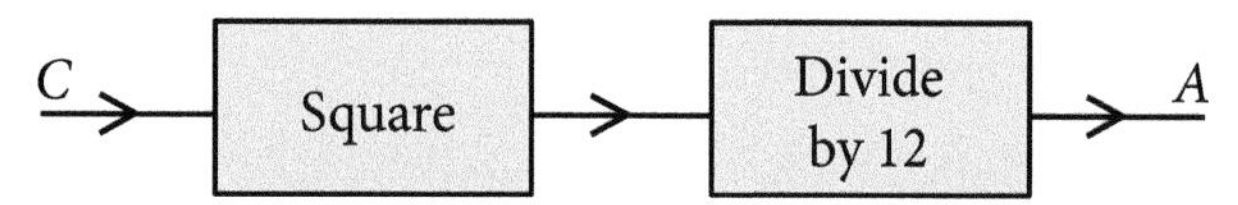

   a) Find A when $C = 6$ cm.

   b) Find A when $C = 18$ cm.

   c) Write down the formula involving A and C.

9. I think of a number. If I subtract 4 and then divide the result by 4 the answer is 3. What number was I thinking of?

10. Try to draw four straight lines which pass through all of the 9 points in the diagram, without taking your pen from the paper and without going over any line twice.

Revision exercise 7A

1. A motorist travelled 800 km during May, when the cost of petrol was \$1.80 per litre. In June the cost of petrol increased by 10% and he travelled 5% less distance.

   a) What was the cost, in cents per litre, of petrol in June?

   b) What distance did he travel in June?

2. Work out on a calculator, correct to 4 s.f.

   a) $3.61 - (1.6 \times 0.951)$

   b) $\dfrac{(4.65 + 1.09)}{(3.6 - 1.714)}$

3. Evaluate the following and give the answers to 3 significant figures:

   a) $\sqrt[3]{(9.61 \times 0.0041)}$ b) $\left(\dfrac{1}{9.5} - \dfrac{1}{11.2}\right)^3$

   c) $\dfrac{15.6 \times 0.714}{0.0143 \times 12}$ d) $\sqrt[4]{\left(\dfrac{1}{5 \times 10^3}\right)}$

4. Estimate the answer correct to one significant figure. Do not use a calculator.

   a) $(612 \times 52) \div 49.2$ b) $(11.7 + 997.1) \times 9.2$

   c) $\sqrt{\left(\dfrac{91.3}{10.1}\right)}$ d) $\pi\sqrt{(5.2^2 + 18.2^2)}$

5. The mass of the planet Jupiter is about 350 times the mass of the Earth. The mass of the Earth is approximately 6.03×10^{21} tonnes. Give an estimate correct to 2 significant figures for the mass of Jupiter.

6. Evaluate the following using a calculator: (answers to 4 s.f.)

   a) $\dfrac{0.74}{0.81 \times 1.631}$ b) $\sqrt{\left(\dfrac{9.61}{8.34-7.41}\right)}$

   c) $\left(\dfrac{0.741}{0.8364}\right)^4$ d) $\dfrac{8.4-7.642}{3.333-1.735}$

7. Copy and complete the table.

	Fraction	Decimal	Percentage
a)	$\frac{3}{5}$		
b)		0.75	
c)			5%
d)	$\frac{1}{8}$		

8. A wedding cake weighing 9.2 kg is shared between 107 guests. About how much cake, in grams, does each person get? [No calculator!]

9. The total weight of 95 000 marbles is 308 kg. Roughly how many grams does each marble weigh?

10. Here are nine calculations and nine answers. Write down each calculation and choose, by estimating, the correct answer from the list given.

    a) 1.8×10.4 b) 9.8×9.1

    c) 7.9×8.1 d) 76.2×1.9

    e) 3.8×8.2 f) 8.15×5.92

    g) $36.96 \div 4$ h) $9.6 \div 5$

    i) $0.11 + 3.97$

    Answers: 63.99, 18.72, 31.16, 4.08, 1.92, 9.24, 144.78, 89.18, 48.248.

11. a) Copy this pattern and write down the next two lines.

    $3 \times 5 = 15$

    $33 \times 5 = 165$

    $333 \times 5 = 1\,665$

    $3333 \times 5 = 16\,665$

    b) Copy and complete $333\,333\,333 \times 5 =$

12. a) Copy this pattern and write down the next line.

    $1 \times 9 = 9$

    $21 \times 9 = 189$

    $321 \times 9 = 2\,889$

    $4\,321 \times 9 = 38\,889$

    $54\,321 \times 9 = 488\,889$

    b) Complete this line $87\,654\,321 \times 9 =$

Examination-style exercise 7B

1. Aminata bought 20 metres of cloth at a cost of \$80.
   She sold 15 metres of the cloth at \$5.40 per metre and 5 metres at \$3 per metre.
   (a) Calculate the profit she made. [2]
   (b) Calculate this profit as a percentage of the original cost. [1]
   Cambridge IGCSE Mathematics 0580
   Paper 11 Q16 June 2007

2. Write, in its simplest form, the ratio 3.5 kilograms : 800 grams. [2]
   Cambridge IGCSE Mathematics 0580
   Paper 1 Q4 June 2005

3. Write the following in order, with the smallest first.

   $\frac{3}{5}$ 0.58 62% [1]

   Cambridge IGCSE Mathematics 0580
   Paper 11 Q2 June 2007

4. 0.072 72% 0.702 $\frac{7}{10}$ $\frac{7}{100}$ 7.2%

   From the values listed above, write down
   (a) the smallest, [1]
   (b) the largest, [1]
   (c) the two which are equal. [1]
   Cambridge IGCSE Mathematics 0580
   Paper 1 Q9 November 2005

5. 0.09 90% $\frac{9}{1000}$ 9% 0.9 $\frac{9}{100}$ 900%
   Write down the three numbers from the list above which have the same value. [1]
   Cambridge IGCSE Mathematics 0580
   Paper 1 Q2 June 2006

6. Hakim and Bashira measure their heights. Hakim's height is 157 cm and Bashira's height is 163 cm, both correct to the nearest centimetre.
   Find the greatest possible difference between their heights. [2]
   Cambridge IGCSE Mathematics 0580
   Paper 11 Q5 June 2009

7. The distance, d kilometres, between Auckland and Tokyo is 8800 km, correct to the nearest 100 kilometres.
   Complete the statement about the value of d.
   $\ldots \le d < \ldots$ [2]
   Cambridge IGCSE Mathematics 0580
   Paper 12 Q7 November 2007

8. **(a)** Scott changed 300 Australian dollars (AUD) into euros (€) when the rate was €1 = 1.56 AUD.
How many euros did Scott receive? [2]

(b) Write the number 2.99893 correct to 3 significant figures. [1]

9. Joseph, Maria and Rebecca each win a prize. Their total prize money is $30.

Joseph wins $\frac{7}{12}$ of the $30.

Maria wins 30% of the $30.

Rebecca wins the rest of the $30.

Calculate the amount each receives. [5]

Cambridge IGCSE Mathematics 0580
Paper 1 Q19 June 2006

10. Insert brackets to make the following statement correct.

$$2 \times 3 - 4 + 5 = 3$$

[1]

Cambridge IGCSE Mathematics 0580
Paper 1 Q2 November 2006

11. **(a)** Work out

$$\frac{12.48 \times 0.063}{\sqrt{8} + 7.52}$$

Write down all the figures on your calculator display. [1]

(b) Write your answer to part **(a)** correct to 2 significant figures. [1]

Cambridge IGCSE Mathematics 0580
Paper 1 Q6 June 2006

12. Aida, Bernado and Cristiano need $30 000 to start a business.

(a) **i)** They borrow $\frac{2}{5}$ of this amount.
Show that they still need $18 000. [1]

ii) They provide the $18 000 themselves in the ratio

Aida : Bernado : Christiano = 5 : 4 : 3

Calculate the amount each of them provides. [3]

(b) **i)** Office equipment costs 35% of the $30 000.
Calculate the cost of the equipment. [2]

ii) Office expenses cost another $6500.
Write this as a fraction of $30 000.
Give your answer in its lowest terms. [2]

iii) How much remains of the $30 000 now? [1]

(c) They invest $12 500.
After one year this has increased to $15 500.
Calculate this percentage increase. [3]

Cambridge IGCSE Mathematics 0580
Paper 3 Q1 November 2008

8 Probability

C8.1 Calculate the probability of a single event as either a fraction, decimal or percentage.
C8.2 Understand and use the probability scale from 0 to 1.
C8.3 Understand that the probability of an event occurring = 1 – the probability of the event not occurring.
C8.4 Understand relative frequency as an estimate of probability. Expected frequency of occurrences.
C8.5 Calculate the probability of simple combined events, using possibility diagrams, tree diagrams and Venn diagrams.

8.1 Probability of an event

In probability we ask questions like . . .

'How likely is it?'
'What are the chances of . . . ?'

Here are some questions where we do not know the answer . . .

'Will my parachute open?'
'Will I live to be over 100 years old?'

'Who will win the Football World Cup?'

Some events are certain. Some events are impossible.

Some events are in between certain and impossible.

The probability of an event is a measure of the chance of it happening.

The probability (or chance) of an event occurring is measured on a scale like this . . .

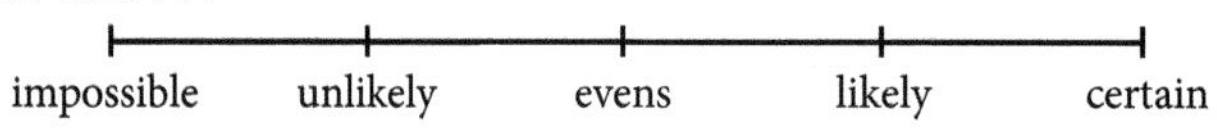

Exercise 1

Draw a probability scale like this . . .

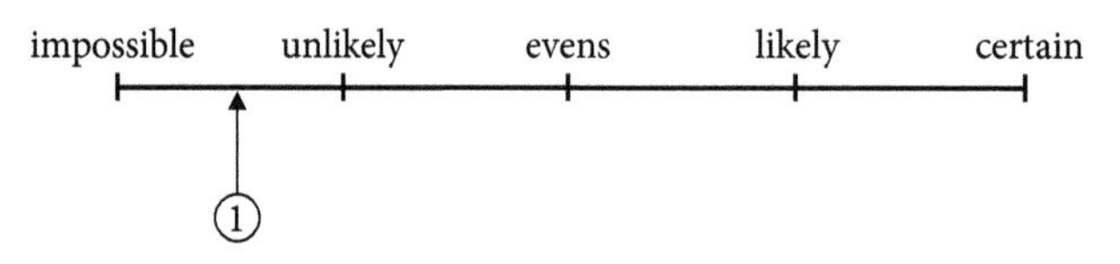

Draw an arrow to show the chance of the events below happening.
[The arrow for Question **1** has been done for you.]

1. When a card is selected from a pack it will be an 'ace'.
2. When a fair coin is tossed it will show a 'head'.
3. The letter 'a' appears somewhere on the next page of this book.
4. When a drawing pin is dropped it will land 'point up'.
5. There will be at least one baby born somewhere in China on the first day of next month.
6. Your local priest will win the lottery next week.
7. The day after Monday will be Tuesday.
8. There will be a burst pipe in the school heating system next week and the school will have to close for 3 days.
9. You will blink your eyes in the next minute.
10. You will be asked to tidy your room this week.
11. When a slice of toast is dropped, it will land on the floor buttered side down.
12. You will get maths homework this week.
13. England will win the next World Cup at football.
14. Your maths teacher has a black belt in Judo.
15. You will be captured by aliens tonight.

Probability as a number

Different countries have different words for saying how likely or unlikely any particular event is.

All over the world people use probability as a way of doing this, using numbers on a scale instead of words.

The scale looks like this . . .

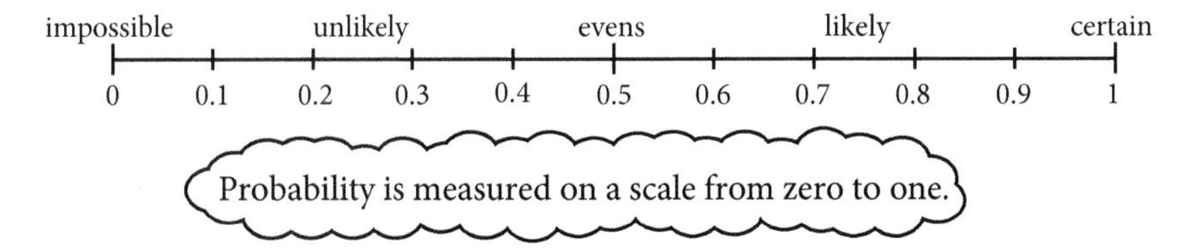

Exercise 2

Look at the events in the last exercise and for each one estimate the probability of it occurring using a probability from 0 to 1.

As an example in Question **1** you might write 'about 0.1'. Copy each question and write your estimate of its probability at the end.

Working out probabilities

The probability of an event occurring can be calculated using symmetry. We argue, for example, that when we toss a coin we have an equal chance of getting a 'head' or a 'tail'. So the probability of spinning a 'head' is a half.

We write 'p (spinning a head) $= \frac{1}{2}$'.

Exercise 3

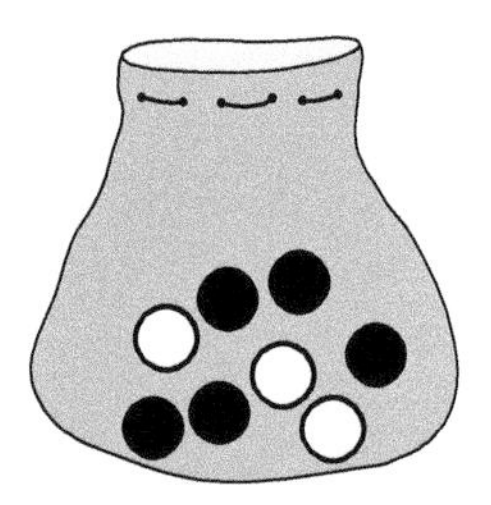

1. A bag contains 3 white discs and 5 black discs.
   One disc is taken out at random.
   What is the probability that it is:

   a) white

   b) black?

2. Nine counters numbered 1, 2, 3, 4, 5, 6, 7, 8, 9 are placed in a bag.
   One is taken out at random. What is the probability that it is:

   a) a '5'   **b)** divisible by 3

   c) less than 5   **d)** divisible by 4?

3. A bag contains 5 green balls, 2 red balls and 4 yellow balls.
   One ball is taken out at random.
   What is the probability that it is:

   a) green

   b) red

   c) yellow?

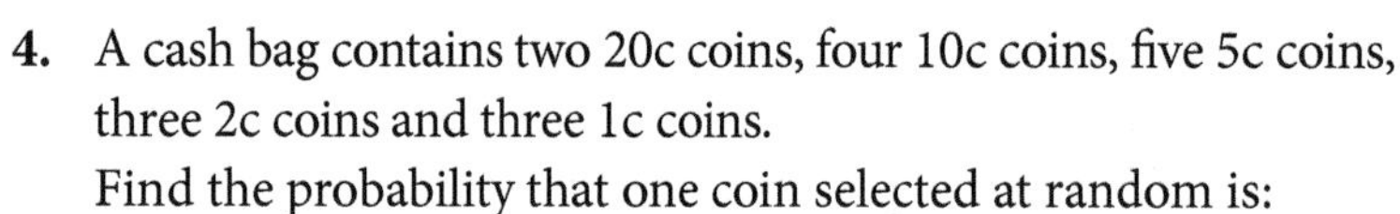

4. A cash bag contains two 20c coins, four 10c coins, five 5c coins, three 2c coins and three 1c coins.
   Find the probability that one coin selected at random is:

   a) a 10c coin   **b)** a 2c coin.

5. A bag contains 8 orange balls, 5 green balls and 4 silver balls.
   Find the probability that a ball picked out at random is:

   a) silver   **b)** orange   **c)** green.

6. The numbers of matches in ten boxes are as follows:
   48, 46, 45, 49, 44, 46, 47, 48, 45, 46.
   One box is selected at random.

Find the probability of the box containing:

a) 49 matches

b) 46 matches

c) more than 47 matches.

7. One ball is selected at random from those in this box. Find the probability of selecting:

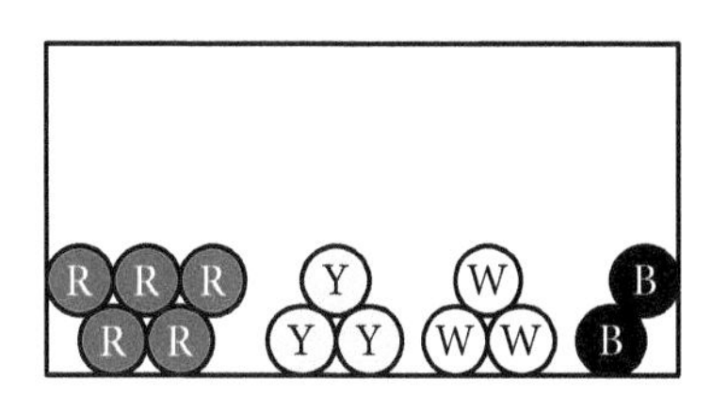

a) a white ball

b) a yellow or a black ball

c) a ball which is not red.

8. a) A bag contains 5 red balls, 6 green balls and 2 black balls. Find the probability of selecting:

i) a red ball **ii)** a green ball.

b) One black ball is removed from the bag. Find the new probability of selecting:

i) a red ball **ii)** a black ball.

9. A bag contains 12 white balls, 12 green balls and 12 purple balls. After 3 white balls, 4 green balls and 9 purple balls have been removed, what is the probability that the next ball to be selected will be white?

10. One person is chosen at random from a large group. What is the probability that person's birthday is on a Monday in that year?

11. The numbering on a set of 28 dominoes is as follows:

6	6	6	6	6	6	6	5	5	5
6	5	4	3	2	1	0	5	4	3

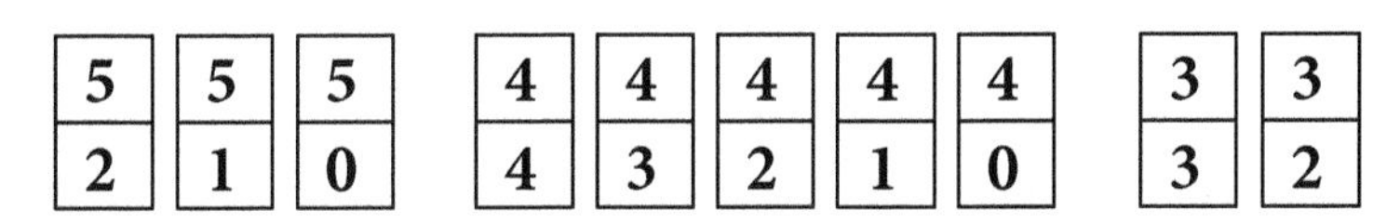

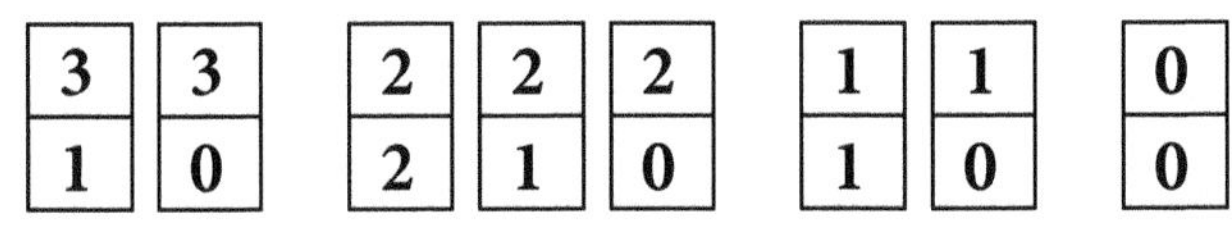

a) What is the probability of drawing a domino from a full set with:

i) at least one six on it

ii) at least one four on it

iii) at least one two on it?

b) What is the probability of drawing a 'double' from a full set?

c) If I draw a double five which I do not return to the set, what is the probability of drawing another domino with a five on it?

Expected frequency

Example

A fair dice is rolled 240 times. How many times would you expect to roll a number greater than 4?

We can roll a 5 or a 6 out of the six equally likely outcomes.

$\therefore p$ (number greater than 4) $= \frac{2}{6} = \frac{1}{3}$

Expected number of successes = (probability of a success) × (number of trials)

Expected number of scores greater than 4 $= \frac{1}{3} \times 240$

$= 80$

Exercise 4

1. A fair dice is rolled 300 times. How many times would you expect to roll a 'six'?
2. The spinner shown has four equal sectors.
   How many 3s would you expect in 100 spins?

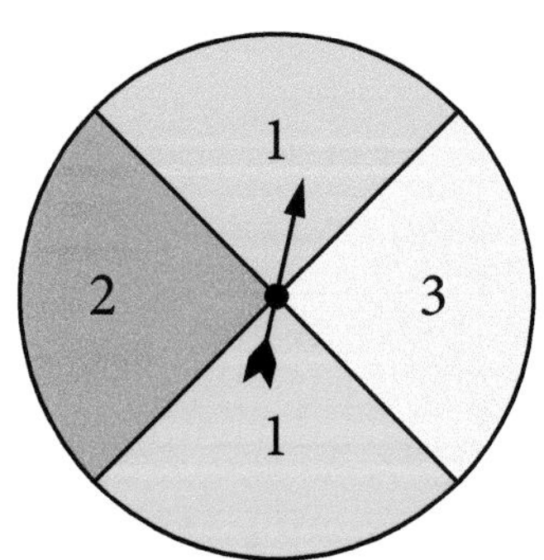

3. About one in eight of the population is left-handed. How many left-handed people would you expect to find in a company employing 400 people?
4. A bag contains a large number of marbles of which one in five is red. If I randomly select one marble on 200 occasions, how many times would I expect to select a red marble?
5. The spinner shown is used for a simple game. A player pays 10c and then spins the pointer, winning the amount indicated.
   a) What is the probability of winning nothing?
   b) If the game is played by 200 people, how many times would you expect the 50c to be won?

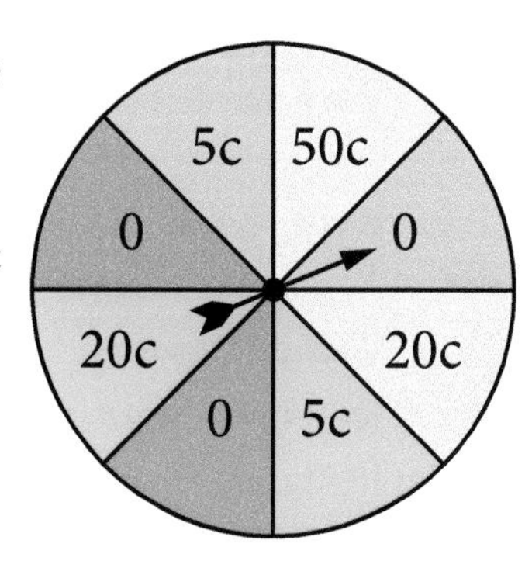

6. The numbered cards are shuffled and put into a pile.

One card is selected at random and not replaced. A second card is then selected.

If the first card was the '11' find the probability of selecting an even number with the second draw.

8.2 Exclusive events

Events are **mutually exclusive** if they cannot occur at the same time.

Examples
- Selecting an ace } from a
  Selecting a ten } pack of cards

- Tossing a 'head'
  Tossing a 'tail'

- Getting a total of 5 on two dice
  Getting a total of 7 on two dice

The total sum of the probabilities of mutually exclusive events is 1.

The probability of something happening is 1 minus the probability of it not happening.

Example

Every day Anna has the choice of going to work by bus, by train or by taxi.
The probability of choosing to go by bus is 0.5 and the probability of choosing to go by train is 0.3.
Find:

a) the probability of choosing not to go by train
b) the probability of choosing to go by taxi.

The three events 'going by bus', 'going by train' and 'going by taxi' are mutually exclusive.

a) p (not going by train) $= 1 - p$ (going by train)
$= 1 - 0.3$
$= 0.7$

b) The sum of the probabilities is 1.
$\therefore$ p (going by taxi) $= 1 - (0.5 + 0.3)$
$= 0.2$

Exercise 5

1. A bag contains a large number of coloured balls.

   The probability of selecting a red ball is $\frac{1}{5}$. What is the probability of selecting a ball which is not red?

2. A bag contains 7 white balls, 4 blue balls and 9 yellow balls. Find the probability of selecting:

   a) a white ball

   b) a ball which is not white.

3. A motorist does a survey at some traffic lights on his way to work every day.
   He finds that the probability that the lights are 'red' when he arrives is 0.24. What is the probability that the lights are not 'red'?

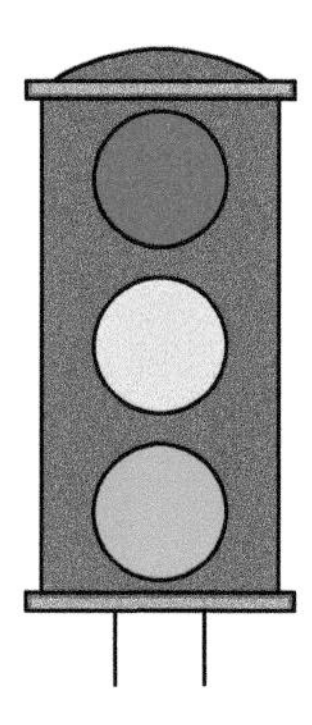

4. Government birth statistics show that the probability of a woman giving birth to a boy is 0.506.

   What is the probability of having a girl?

5. The spinner has 8 equal sectors Find the probability of:

   a) spinning a 5

   b) not spinning a 5

   c) spinning a 2

   d) not spinning a 2

   e) spinning a 7

   f) not spinning a 7.

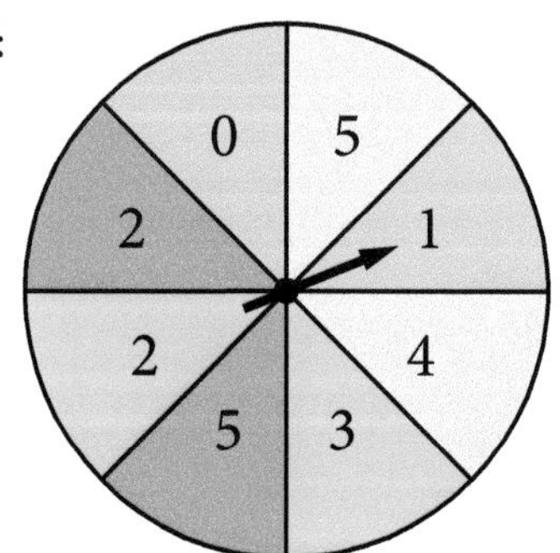

6. A bag contains a large number of balls coloured red, white, black or green. The probabilities of selecting each colour are as follows:

Colour	Red	White	Black	Green
Probability	0.3	0.1		0.3

   Find the probability of selecting a ball:

   a) which is black

   b) which is not white.

7. In a survey the number of people in cars is recorded.

   When a car passes the school gates, the probability of having 1, 2, 3, ... occupants is as follows.

Number of people	1	2	3	4	more than 4
Probability	0.42	0.23		0.09	0.02

   a) Find the probability that the next car past the school gates contains: **i)** three people **ii)** less than 4 people.

   b) One day 2500 cars passed the gates. How many of the cars would you expect to have 2 people inside?

8.3 Relative frequency

To work out the probability of a drawing pin landing point up we can conduct an experiment in which a drawing pin is dropped many times. If the pin lands 'point up' on x occasions out of a total number of N trials, the **relative frequency** of landing 'point up' is $\frac{x}{N}$.

When an experiment is repeated many times we can use the relative frequency as an estimate of the probability of the event occurring.

Here are the results of an experiment in which a dice, suspected of being biased, was rolled 300 times. After each set of 25 rolls the number of sixes obtained was noted and the results were as follows:

5 4 6 6 6 5 3 7 6 5 6 5

After 25 rolls the relative frequency of sixes $= \frac{5}{25} = 0.2$

After 50 rolls the relative frequency of sixes $= \frac{5+4}{50} = 0.18$

After 75 rolls the relative frequency of sixes $= \frac{5+4+6}{75} = 0.2$ and so on.

The results are plotted on this graph.

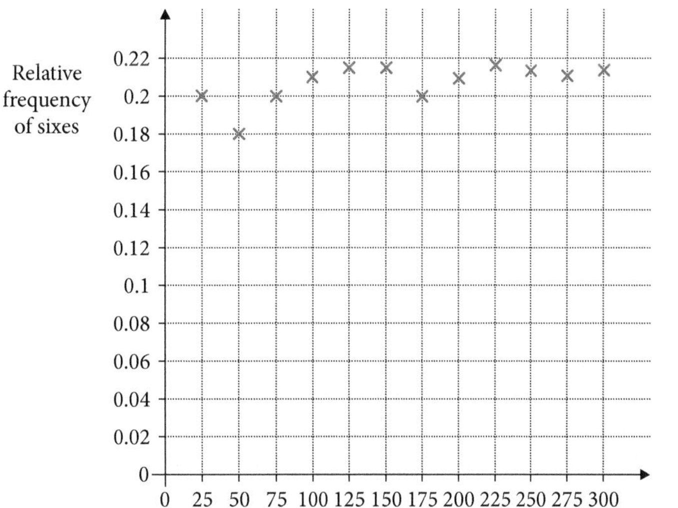

As we include more and more results, the average number of sixes per roll settles down at slightly over 0.21.

For this dice we say the **relative frequency** of sixes was just over 0.21.

If the dice was fair we would expect to get a 6 on $\frac{1}{6}$ of the throws. So the relative frequency would be $0.1\dot{6}$. The dice in the experiment does appear to be biased so that sixes occur more frequently than we would expect for a fair dice.

Exercise 6

1. Conduct an experiment where you cannot predict the result. You could roll a dice with a piece of 'Blu Tack' stuck to it. Or make a spinner where the axis is not quite in the centre. Or drop a drawing pin.

   Conduct the experiment many times and work out the relative frequency of a 'success' after every 10 or 20 trials.

   Plot a relative frequency graph like the one on the previous page to see if the results 'settle down' to a consistent value.

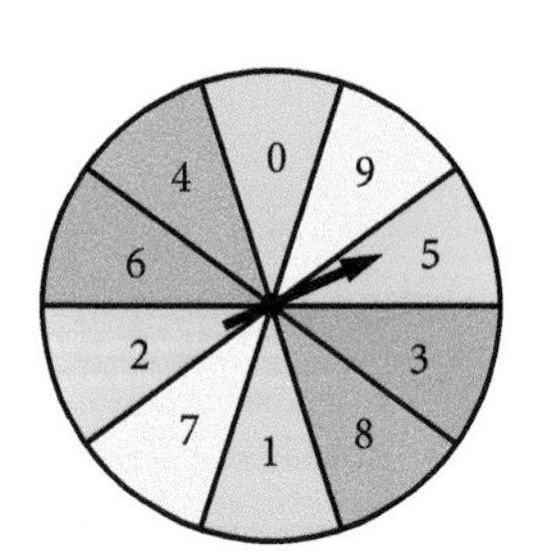

2. The spinner has an equal chance of giving any digit from 0 to 9. Four friends did an experiment when they spun the pointer a different number of times and recorded the number of zeros they got.

   Here are their results.

	Number of spins	Number of zeros	Relative frequency
Steve	10	2	0.2
Nick	150	14	0.093
Mike	200	41	0.205
Jason	1000	104	0.104

   One of the four recorded his results incorrectly. Say who you think this was and explain why.

8.4 Venn diagrams

A *Venn diagram* shows all the possible ways in which something can be included in or excluded from several sets.

In the following diagram, $\mathscr{E}$ represents the *universal set*, which in this example is the set of all the whole numbers from 1 to 10.

P is the set of prime numbers, and E is the set of even numbers.

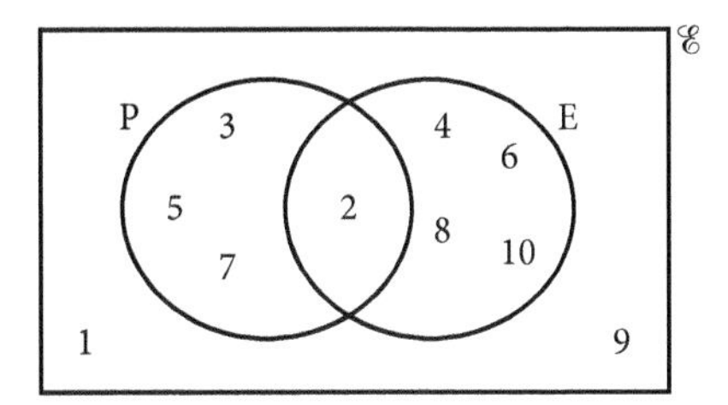

Exercise 7

1. In the Venn diagram,

   $\mathscr{E}$ = {people in a hotel}

   T = {people who like toast}

   E = {people who like eggs}

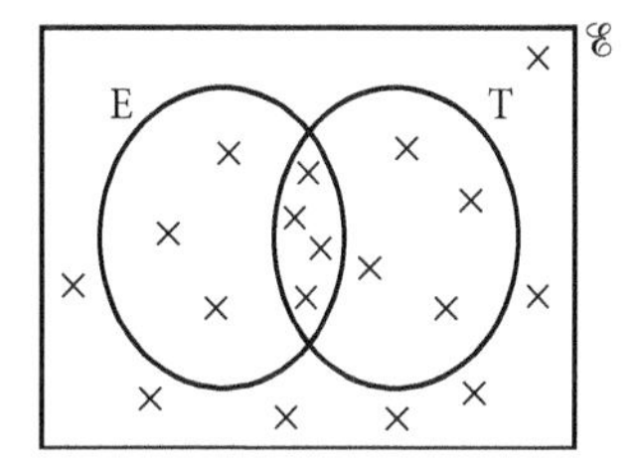

   a) How many people like toast?

   b) How many people like eggs but not toast?

   c) How many people like toast and eggs?

   d) How many people are in the hotel?

   e) How many people like neither toast nor eggs?

2. In the Venn diagram,

   $\mathscr{E}$ = {boys in a Year 10 class}

   R = {members of the rugby team}

   C = {members of the cricket team}

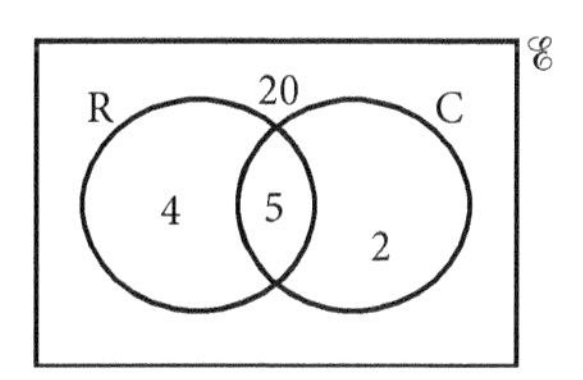

   a) How many are in the rugby team?

   b) How many are in both teams?

   c) How many are in the rugby team but not in the cricket team?

   d) How many are in neither team?

   e) How many are there in Year 10?

3. A class of 30 students travel to school one morning.

   12 students travel by car for part of the way, then walk the rest of the way.

6 students travel all the way by car, and 8 students walk all the way.

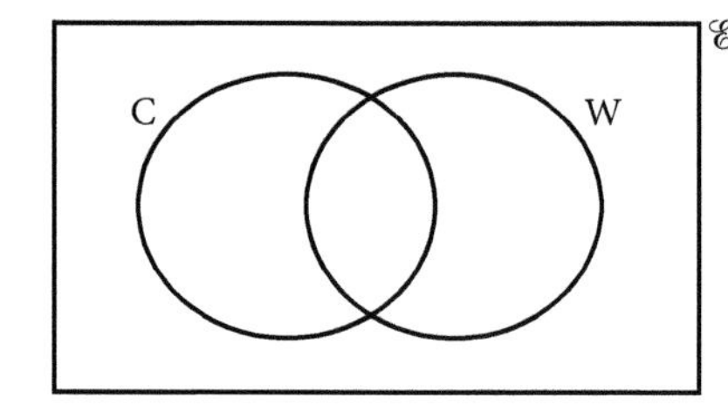

𝓔 = {students in the class}

C = {students who travel to school by car}

W = {students who walk to school}

Copy and complete the Venn diagram to illustrate this information.

4. In a university mathematics class of 50 students, some students study geometry, some study logic, some study both, and some study neither.

   27 study geometry, 19 study logic, and 14 study neither.

   𝓔 = {students in the mathematics class}

   G = {students who study geometry}

   L = {students who study logic}

   Draw a Venn diagram to illustrate this information.

Using Venn diagrams to find probabilities

Example

A group of 30 cats were given two different types of food. 7 cats liked only food A, 5 liked only food B, 16 liked both and 2 liked neither. This information is displayed in the following Venn diagram.

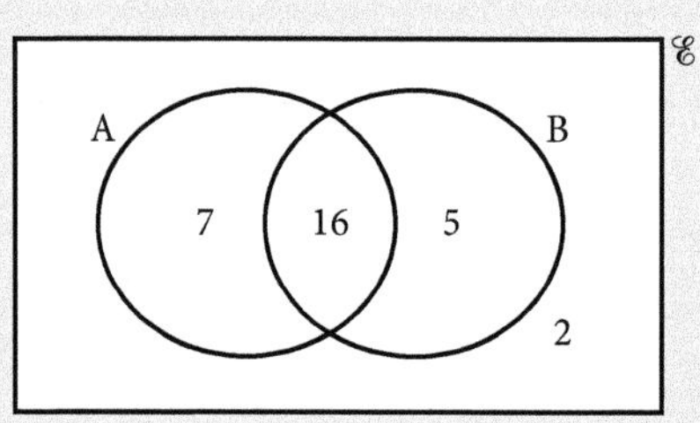

a) What is the probability that a randomly selected cat will like both foods A and B?

p (the cat likes both foods) $= \frac{16}{30} = \frac{8}{15}$

You don't have to simplify your fractions in probability questions if you would rather not.

b) What is the probability that a randomly selected cat will like only food A?

p (the cat likes only food A) $= \frac{7}{30}$

c) What is the probability that a randomly selected cat does not like food B?

p (the cat does not like food B) $= \frac{9}{30}$

Exercise 8

1. In a class of 25 students, some choose to study French, some choose to study German, some choose both, and some choose neither. This information is illustrated in the following Venn diagram.

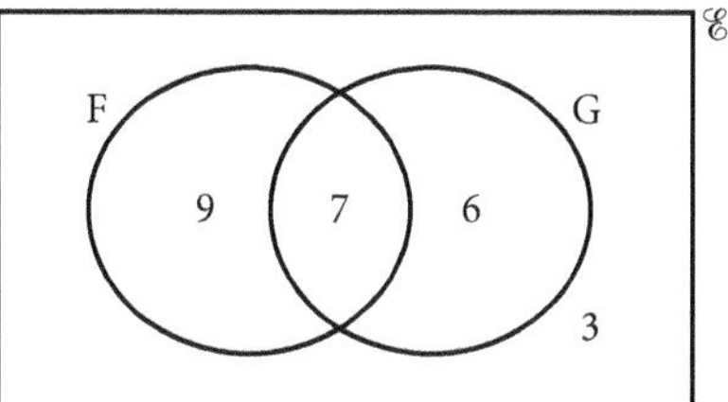

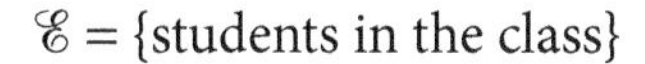

ℰ = {students in the class}

F = {students who study French}

G = {students who study German}

What is the probability that a student, chosen randomly from the class

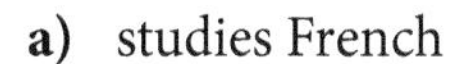

a) studies French

b) studies French and German

c) studies neither French nor German

d) studies German but does not study French?

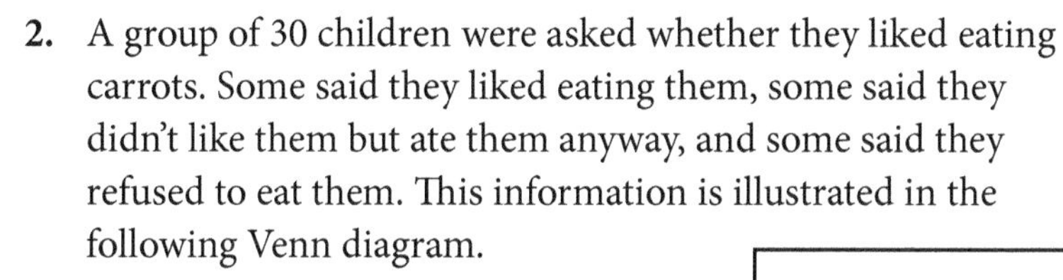

2. A group of 30 children were asked whether they liked eating carrots. Some said they liked eating them, some said they didn't like them but ate them anyway, and some said they refused to eat them. This information is illustrated in the following Venn diagram.

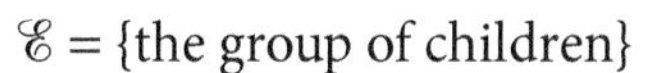

ℰ = {the group of children}

C = {those who eat carrots}

L = {those who like carrots}

ℰ C L 7 10 4 8

a) What is the probability that a randomly selected child

i) likes carrots

ii) does not like carrots but does eat them

iii) does not like carrots and refuses to eat them?

b) What type of person does the number 4 in the diagram represent?

3. A club for paranormal investigators has 50 members. 20 of them believe in ghosts and aliens. 18 of them believe in ghosts but not in aliens. 3 believe in neither.

a) Copy and complete this Venn diagram to illustrate this information.

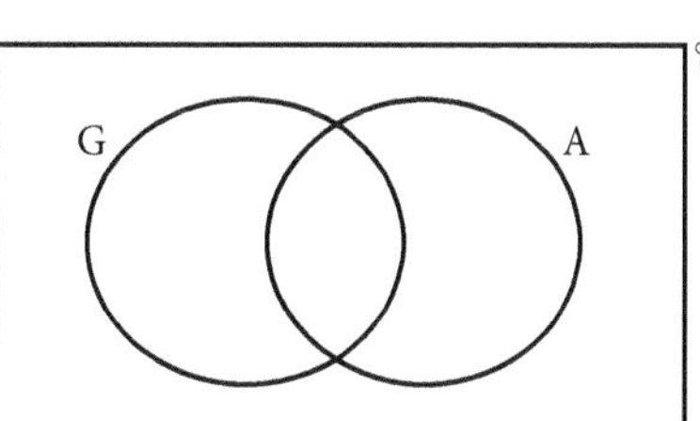

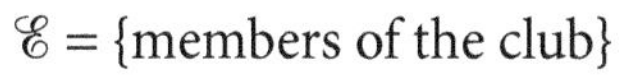

ℰ = {members of the club}

G = {those who believe in ghosts}

L = {those who believe in aliens}

b) What is the probability that a randomly selected member of the club

i) believes in aliens but not in ghosts

ii) believes in ghosts

iii) believes in aliens?

4. A book club has 20 members. 13 of them like detective stories, 10 of them like horror stories, and 4 of them like neither.

a) Illustrate this information in a Venn diagram.

b) What is the probability that a randomly selected member

i) likes both detective stories and horror stories

ii) likes horror stories but not detective stories

iii) does not like detective stories?

5. A group of 12 friends were discussing the various places they had visited. 2 said they had been to America but not Italy. 4 had been to Italy but not America. Twice the number of people who had been to neither had been to both.

a) Illustrate this information in a Venn diagram.

b) What is the probability that a randomly selected member

i) had been to Italy and America

ii) had been to Italy

iii) had not been to Italy?

8.5 Probability diagrams

Other diagrams are sometimes useful for solving probability questions.

Possibility diagrams and *tree diagrams* are used to display all the possible outcomes of an event.

Possibility diagrams

Example 1

A black die and a white die are thrown at the same time. Display all the possible outcomes. Find the probability of obtaining:

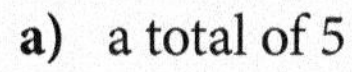

a) a total of 5

b) a total of 11

c) a 'two' on the black die and a 'six' on the white die.

It is convenient to display all the possible outcomes on a grid.

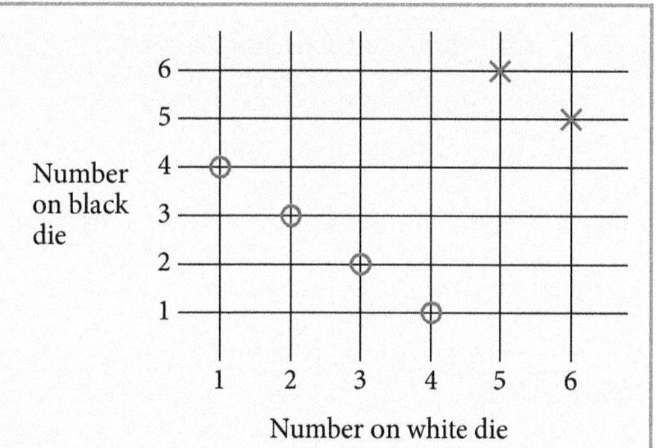

There are 36 possible outcomes, shown where the lines cross.

a) There are four ways of obtaining a total of 5 on the two dice. They are shown circled on the diagram.

$\therefore$ Probability of obtaining a total of 5 $= \frac{4}{36}$

b) There are two ways of obtaining a total of 11. They are shown with a cross on the diagram.

$\therefore$ p (total of 11) $= \frac{2}{36} = \frac{1}{18}$

c) There is only one way of obtaining a 'two' on the black die and a 'six' on the white die.

$\therefore$ p (2 on black and 6 on white) $= \frac{1}{36}$

Exercise 9

1. The two sides of a coin are known as 'head' and 'tail'. A 10c and a 5c coin are tossed at the same time. List all the possible outcomes.

Find the probability of obtaining:

a) two heads **b)** a head and a tail.

2. A red die and a blue die are thrown at the same time. List all the possible outcomes in a systematic way. Find the probability of obtaining:

a) a total of 10 **b)** a total of 12

c) a total less than 6 **d)** the same number on both dice

e) a total more than 9.

What is the most likely total?

3. Two volunteers at a mind-reading magic show are asked to choose a whole number between 3 and 7. Find the probability that:

   a) they choose the same number
   b) the sum of their numbers is 10
   c) the sum of their numbers starts with a 1
   d) they have chosen two consecutive numbers.

Tree diagrams

Example 2

A bag contains 5 red balls and 3 green balls. A ball is drawn at random and then replaced. Another ball is drawn.

What is the probability that both balls are green?

The branch marked * involves the selection of a green ball twice.

The probability of this event is obtained by simply multiplying the fractions on the two branches.

$\therefore p$ (two green balls) $= \frac{3}{8} \times \frac{3}{8} = \frac{9}{64}$

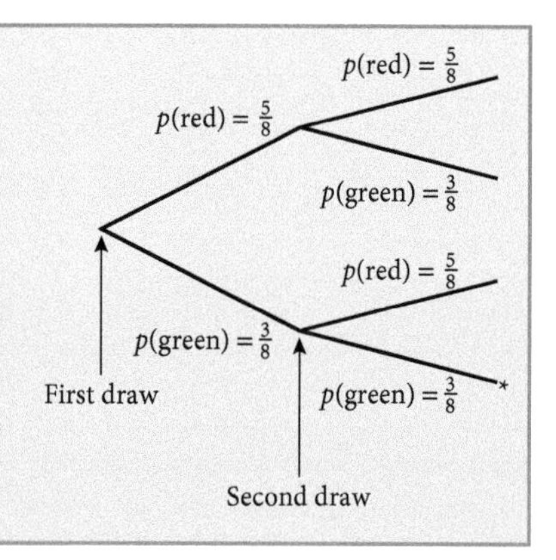

Example 3

A bag contains 5 red balls and 3 green balls. A ball is selected at random and not replaced. A second ball is then selected. Find the probability of selecting:

a) two green balls

b) one red ball and one green ball.

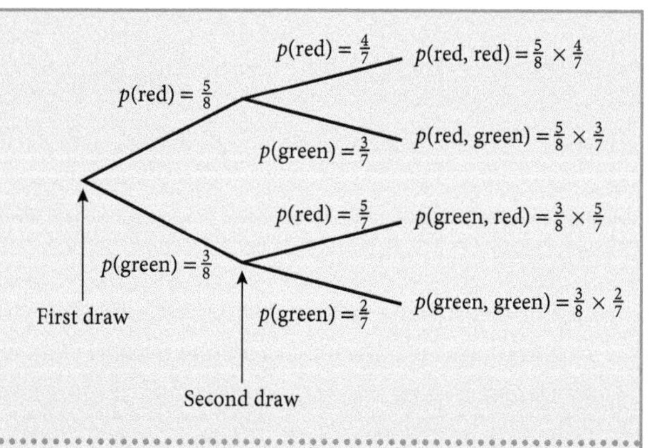

a) p(two green balls) $= \frac{3}{8} \times \frac{2}{7}$

$= \frac{3}{28}$

b) p(one red, one green) $= \left(\frac{5}{8} \times \frac{3}{7}\right) + \left(\frac{3}{8} \times \frac{5}{7}\right)$

$= \frac{15}{28}$

Exercise 10

1. A bag contains 10 discs; 7 are black and 3 white. A disc is selected, and then replaced. A second disc is selected. Copy and complete the tree diagram showing all the probabilities and outcomes. Find the probability of the following:

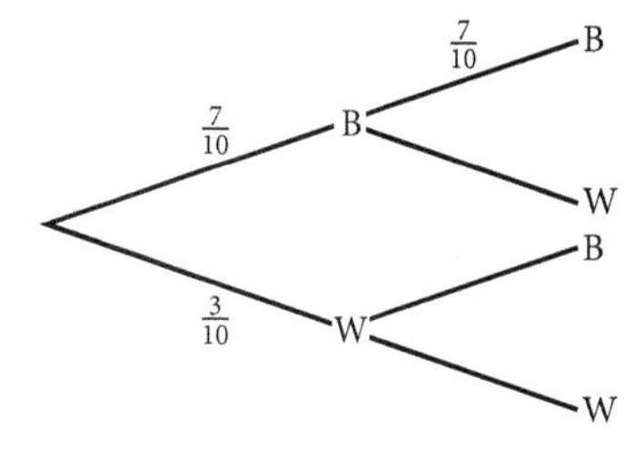

   a) both discs are black **b)** both discs are white.

2. A bag contains 5 red balls and 3 green balls. A ball is drawn and then replaced before a ball is drawn again. Draw a tree diagram to show all the possible outcomes. Find the probability that:

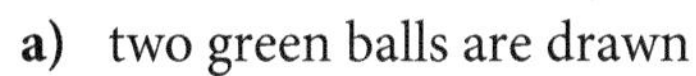

   a) two green balls are drawn

   b) the first ball is red and the second is green.

3. A bag contains 7 green discs and 3 blue discs. A disc is drawn and *not* replaced.

   A second disc is drawn. Copy and complete the tree diagram.

   Find the probability that:

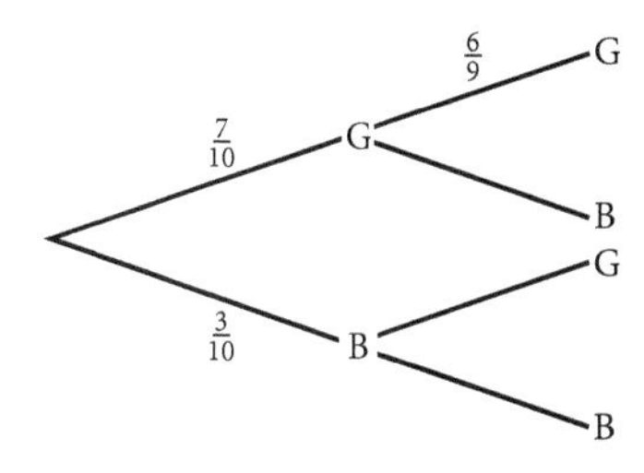

   a) both discs are green **b)** both discs are blue.

4. A six-sided die is thrown three times. Draw a tree diagram, showing at each branch the two events: 'six' and 'not six'. What is the probability of throwing a total of:

   a) three sixes

   b) no sixes

   c) one six

   d) at least one six (use part (**b**)).

5. A bag contains 6 red marbles and 4 blue marbles. A marble is drawn at random and not replaced. Two further draws are made, again without replacement. Find the probability of drawing:

   a) three red marbles **b)** three blue marbles

   c) no red marbles **d)** at least one red marble.

6. When a cutting is taken from a geranium the probability that it grows is $\frac{3}{4}$. Three cuttings are taken. What is the probability that:

   a) all three grow

   b) none of them grow?

Revision exercise 8A

1. A bag contains 3 red balls and 5 white balls. One ball is selected at random. Find the probability of selecting:

a) a red ball **b)** a white ball.

2. A box contains 2 yellow discs, 4 blue discs and 5 green discs. A disc is selected at random. Find the probability of selecting:

a) a yellow disc **b)** a green disc

c) a blue or a green disc.

3. When two fair dice are thrown simultaneously, what is the probability of obtaining the same number on both dice?

4. A fair coin is tossed four times. What is the probability of obtaining at least three 'heads'?

5. Two fair dice are thrown. What is the probability that the *product* of the numbers on top is:

a) 12 **b)** 4 **c)** 11?

6. A bag contains a large number of discs of which one in six is gold. If I randomly select one disc on 300 occasions, how many times would I expect to select a gold disc?

7. a) What is the probability of getting a 6 with this spinner?

b) Draw a spinner like this with 8 equal sectors. Shade some sectors so that the chance of getting a shaded sector is three times the chance of getting a white sector.

c) This spinner has some 1s, 2s and 3s written in the sectors. The chance of getting a 2 is twice the chance of getting a 3. The chance of getting a 1 is three times the chance of getting a 3. Draw the spinner and replace the question marks with the correct number of 1s, 2s and 3s.

8. Cards with numbers 1, 2, 3, 4, 5, 6, 7, 8, 9, 10 are shuffled and then placed face down in a line. The cards are then turned over one at a time from the left. In this example the first card is a '4'.

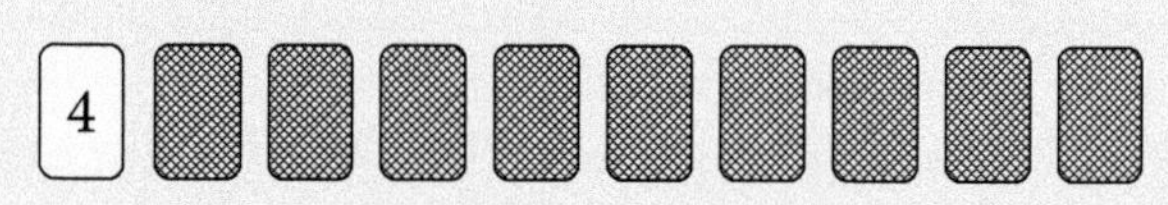

Find the probability that the next card turned over will be:

a) 7 **b)** a number higher than 4.

9. Suppose the second card is a 1.

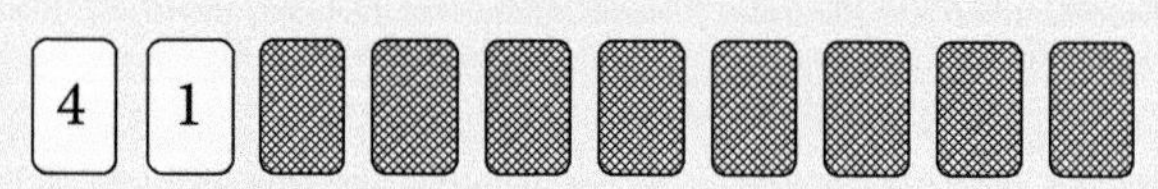

Find the probability that the next card will be:

a) the 6 **b)** an even number

c) higher than 1.

10. A coin is biased so that the probability of a 'head' is $\frac{3}{4}$. Find the probability that, when tossed three times, it shows:

a) three tails

b) two heads and one tail

c) one head and two tails

d) no tails.

Write down the sum of the probabilities in parts (**a**), (**b**), (**c**) and (**d**).

Examination-style exercise 8B

1. A bag of 30 sweets contains 8 chocolates, 13 nougats and 9 toffees.
A sweet is selected at random.
What is the probability that it is a toffee? [1]

Cambridge IGCSE Mathematics 0580
Paper 1 Q2 June 2005

2. **(a)** A bowl of fruit contains 3 apples, 4 bananas, 2 pears and 1 orange.
Aminata chooses one piece of fruit at random.
What is the probability that she chooses

i) a banana, [1]

ii) a mango? [1]

(b) The probability that it will rain in Switzerland on 1st September is $\frac{5}{12}$.

State the probability that it will **not** rain in Switzerland on 1st September. [1]

Cambridge IGCSE Mathematics 0580
Paper 1 Q9 June 2006

3. **(a)** 85% of the seeds in a packet will produce red flowers.
One seed is chosen at random.
What is the probability that it will **not** produce a red flower? [1]

(b) A box of 15 pencils contains 5 red, 4 yellow and 6 blue pencils.
One pencil is chosen at random from the box.
Find the probability that it is

i) yellow, [1]

ii) yellow or blue, [1]

iii) green. [1]

Cambridge IGCSE Mathematics 0580
Paper 11 Q20 November 2008

4. **(a)** There are 12 rabbits and 16 cats in an animal hospital.
The vet chooses one animal at random.
What is the probability that this is a rabbit?
Write your answer as a fraction in its simplest form. [1]

(b) The probability that Fluffy the cat arrives at the hospital before 09 00 is $\frac{13}{18}$.
What is the probability that Fluffy does not arrive before 09 00?
Write your answer as a fraction. [1]

5. The diagram shows a six-sided spinner.

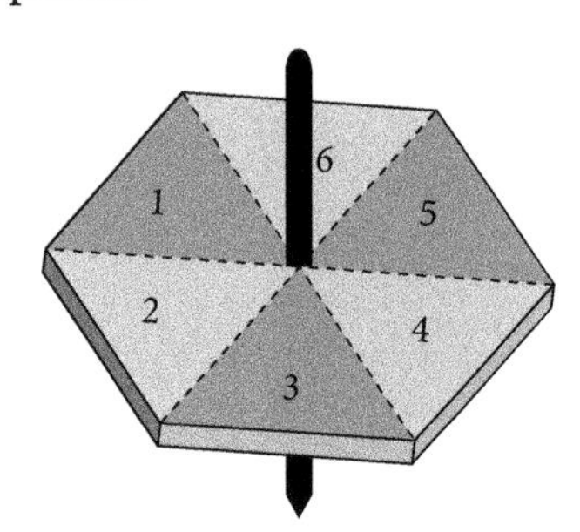

(a) Amy spins a biased spinner and the probability she gets a two is $\frac{5}{36}$.
Find the probability she
i) does not get a two, [1]
ii) gets a seven, [1]
iii) gets a number on the spinner less than 7. [1]

(b) Joel spins his spinner 99 times and gets a two 17 times. Write down the relative frequency of getting a two with Joel's spinner. [1]

(c) The relative frequency of getting a two with Piero's spinner is $\frac{21}{102}$.
Which of the three spinners, Amy's, Joel's or Piero's, is most likely to give a two? [1]

Cambridge IGCSE Mathematics 0580
Paper 1 Q23 November 2006

6. Carlos is in a class of 12 students.
He compares the results of the students in a mathematics test with their results in a history test.
The table shows these results.

Student	A	B	C	D	E	F	G	H	I	J	K	L
Mathematics mark	17	8	11	15	14	19	9	12	19	18	13	15
History mark	10	13	10	8	11	7	14	11	10	11	11	10

(a) A student is chosen at random.
What is the probability that the student scored **more than** 10 marks
i) in mathematics, [1]
ii) in mathematics and in history, [1]
iii) in at least one subject? [1]

(b) The mean mathematics marks is 14.2. Calculate the mean history mark. [2]

(c)

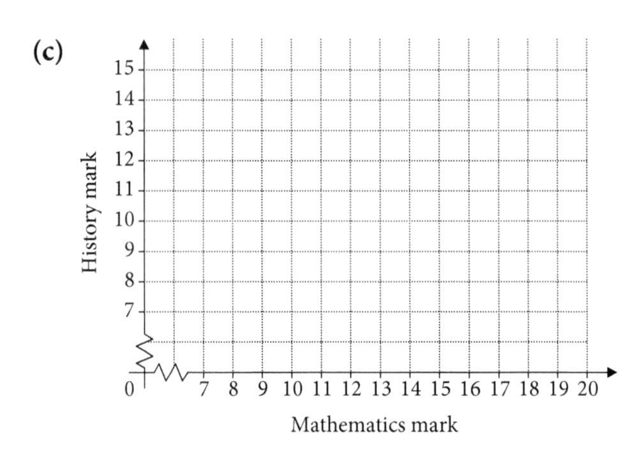

i) On the grid, plot the points to show the results of the 12 students. [3]

ii) Draw a line of best fit. [1]

iii) What type of correlation does this show? [1]

Cambridge IGCSE Mathematics 0580
Paper 3 Q8 November 2007

7. A play is being performed twice; first on a Friday night and again on a Saturday night.

100 people who expressed an interest in seeing the play, were asked which of the two nights they would be able to attend. 58 people said they could attend the Friday performance, 74 said they could attend the Saturday performance, and 4 said they could attend neither.

a) Complete the following Venn diagram to illustrate this information. [3]

$\mathscr{E}$ = {the 100 people questioned}

F = {those who could attend on Friday}

S = {those who could attend on Saturday}

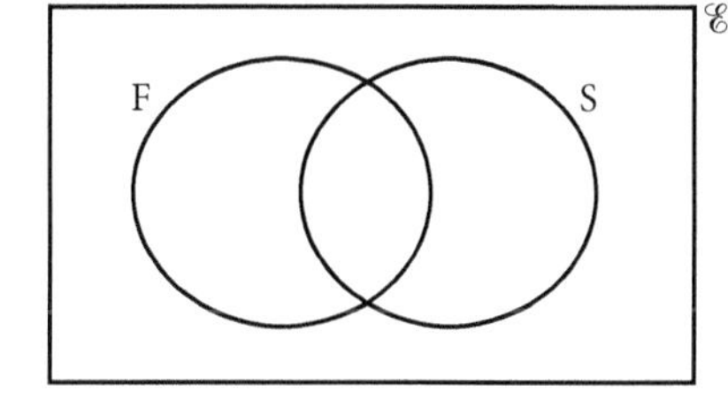

b) What is the probability that a randomly selected person from the 100 questioned

i) could attend either performance [1]

ii) could only attend the Saturday performance [1]

iii) could not attend the Saturday performance? [1]

9 Shape and Space 3

C4.4 Calculate lengths of similar figures.
C4.5 Recognise congruent shapes.
C6.2 Apply Pythagoras' theorem and the sine, cosine and tangent ratios for acute angles to the calculation of a side or of an angle of a right-angled triangle.

9.1 Similar shapes

If one shape is an enlargement of another, the two shapes are mathematically **similar**.

The two triangles A and B are similar if they have the same angles.

For other shapes to be similar, not only must corresponding angles be equal, but also corresponding edges must be in the same proportion.

The two quadrilaterals C and D are similar. All the edges of shape D are twice as long as the edges of shape C.

The two rectangles E and F are not similar even though they have the same angles.

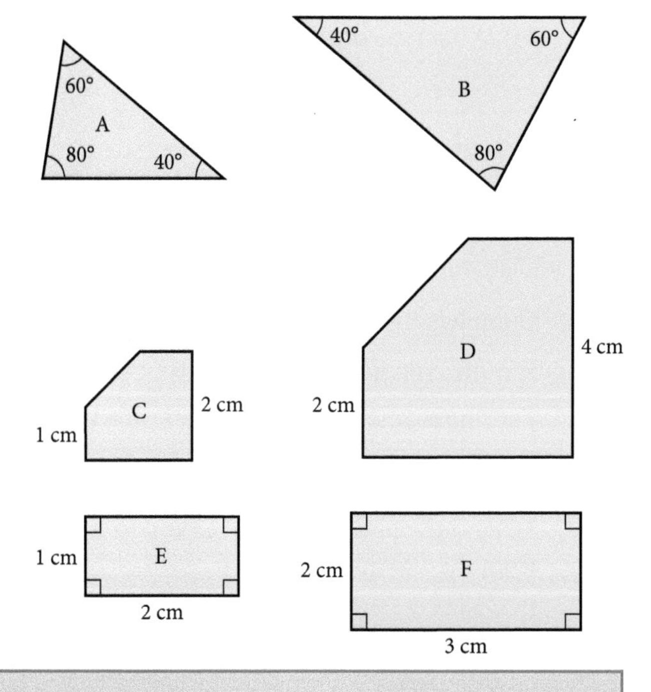

Example

The triangles below are similar.

Find x.

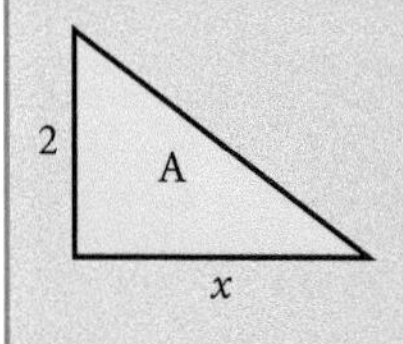

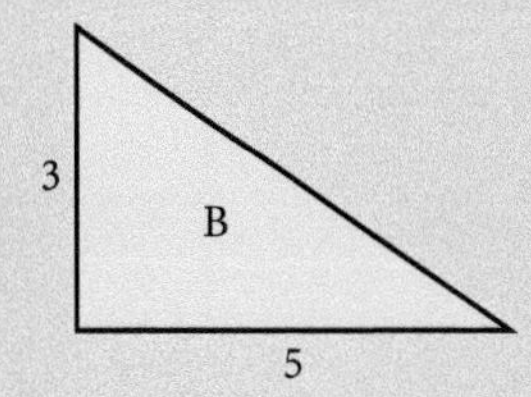

Triangle B is an enlargement of triangle A.

The scale factor of the enlargement is $\frac{3}{2}$.

Corresponding sides are in the same ratio.

$$\therefore \frac{x}{5} = \frac{2}{3}$$

$$x = \frac{2}{3} \times 5$$

$$x = 3\frac{1}{3}$$

Exercise 1

1. Which of the shapes B, C, D is/are similar to shape A?

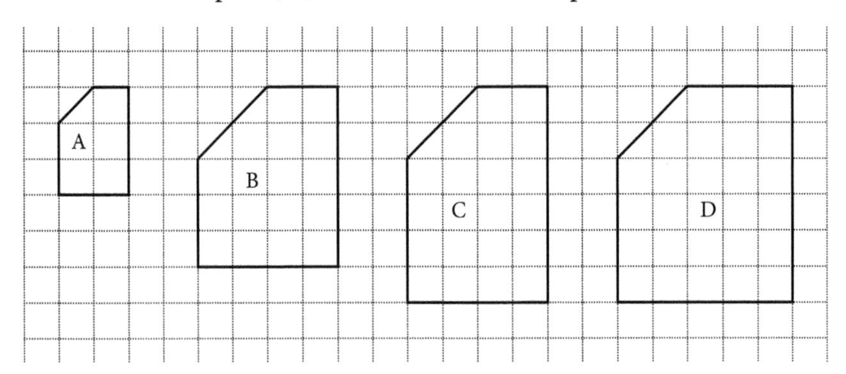

In Questions **2** to **7**, find the sides marked with letters; all lengths are given in cm. The pairs of shapes are similar.

2.

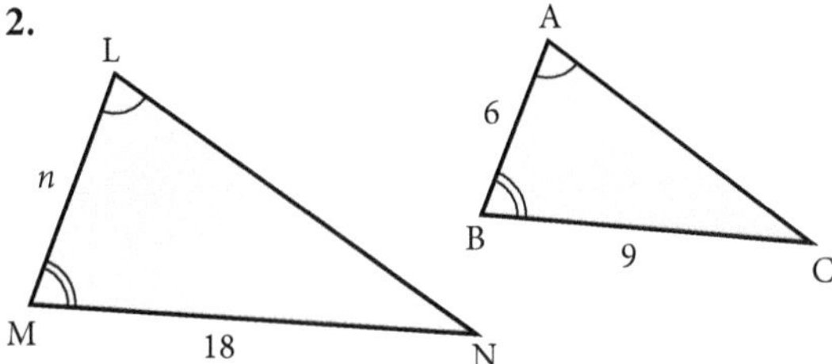

3.

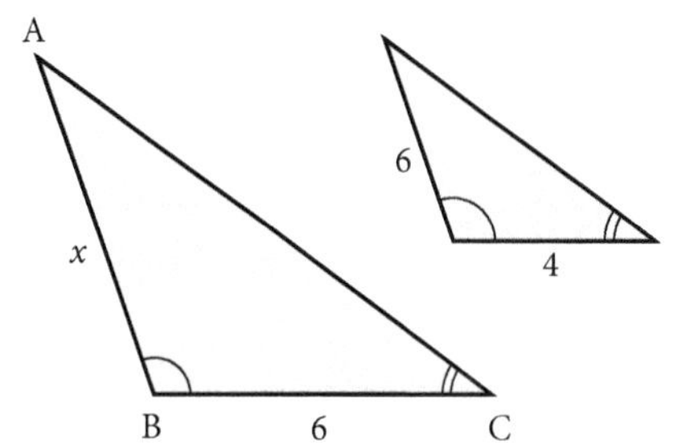

4.

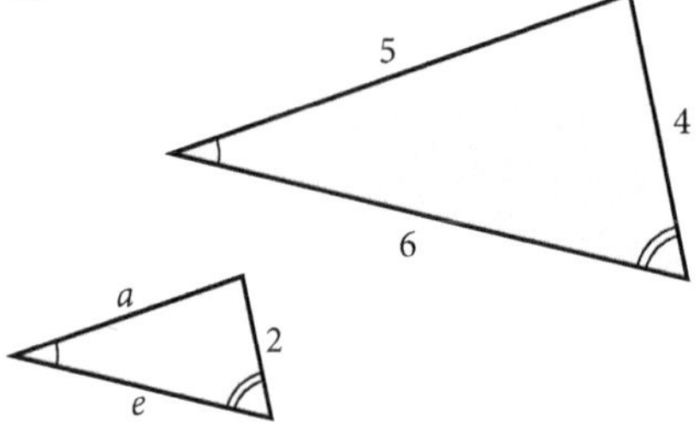

5.

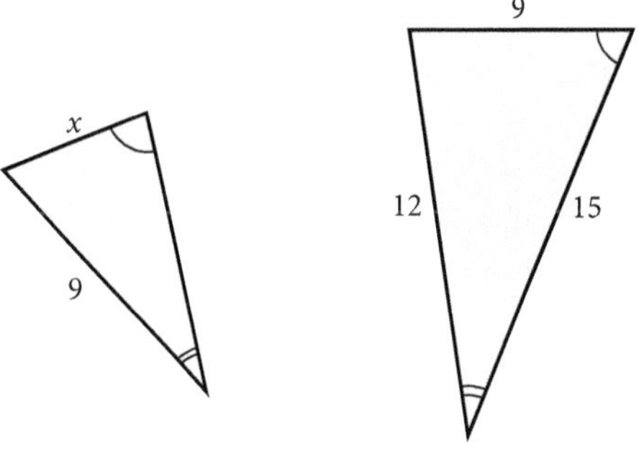

6.

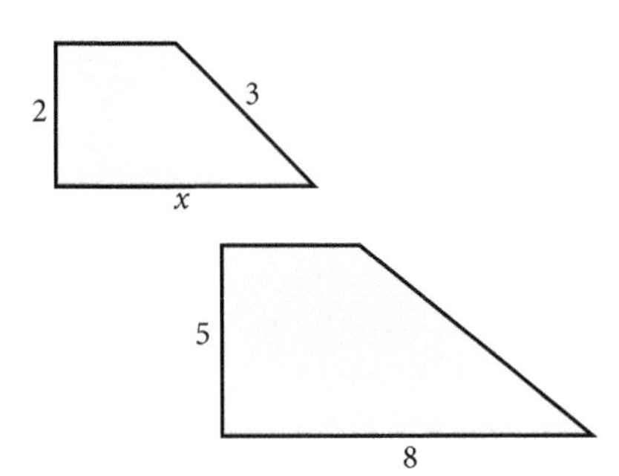

7.

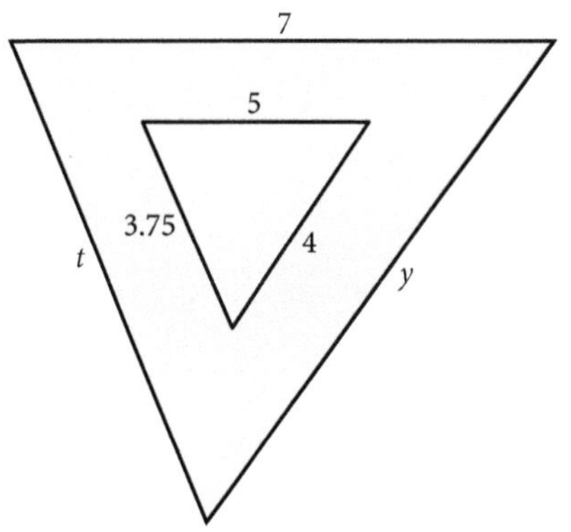

8. Picture B is an enlargement of picture A. Calculate the length x.

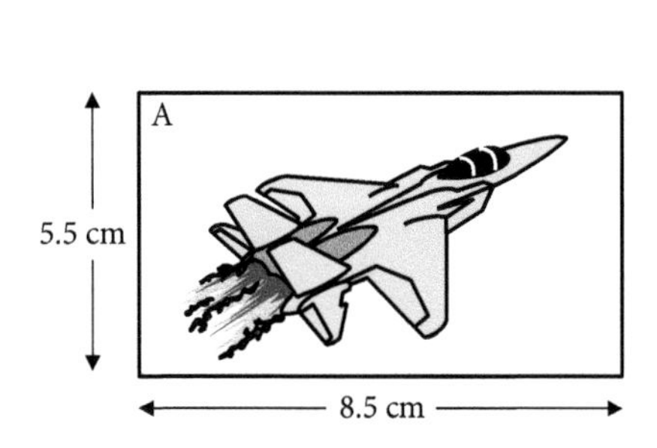

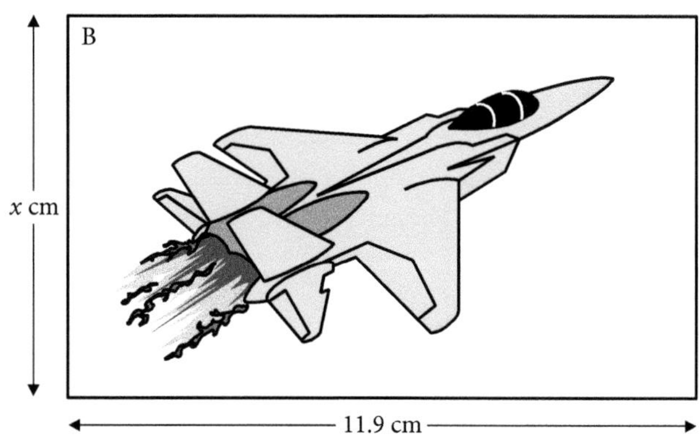

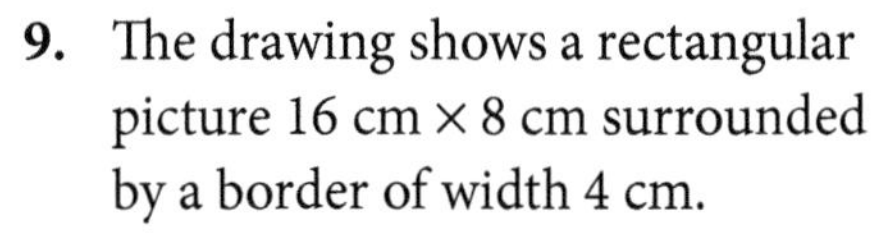

9. The drawing shows a rectangular picture 16 cm × 8 cm surrounded by a border of width 4 cm.

Are the two rectangles similar?

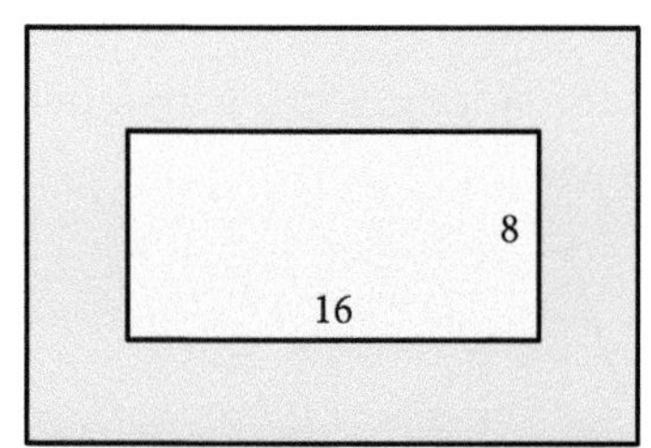

10. Which of the following *must* be similar to each other?

a) Two equilateral triangles. **b)** Two rectangles. **c)** Two isosceles triangles.

d) Two squares. **e)** Two regular pentagons. **f)** Two kites.

g) Two rhombuses. **h)** Two circles.

11.

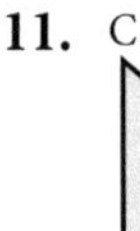

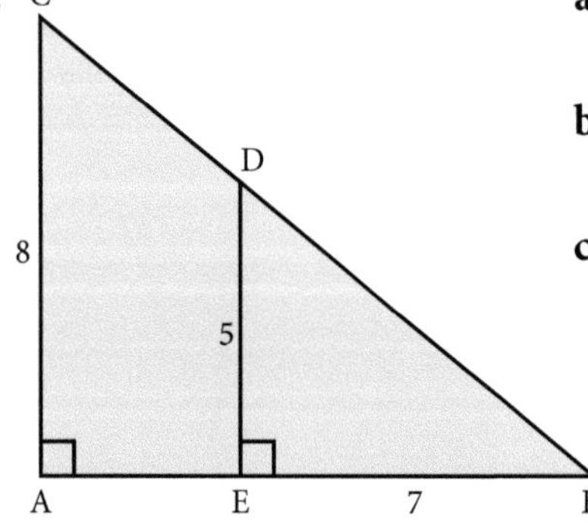

a) Explain why triangles ABC and EBD are similar.

b) Given that EB = 7 cm, calculate the length AB.

c) Write down the length AE.

In Questions **12, 13** and **14** use similar triangles to find the sides marked with letters. All lengths are in cm.

12.

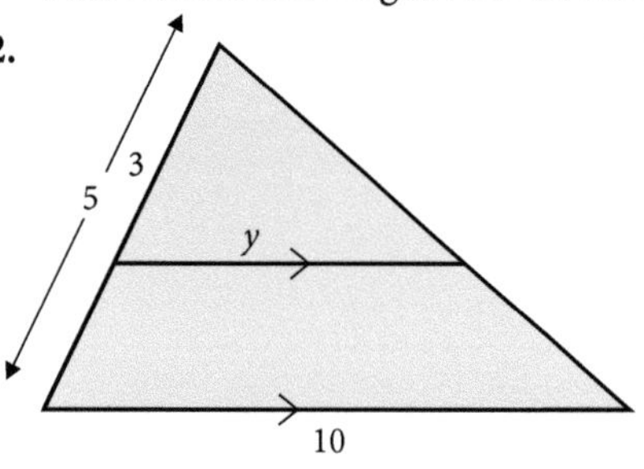

13.

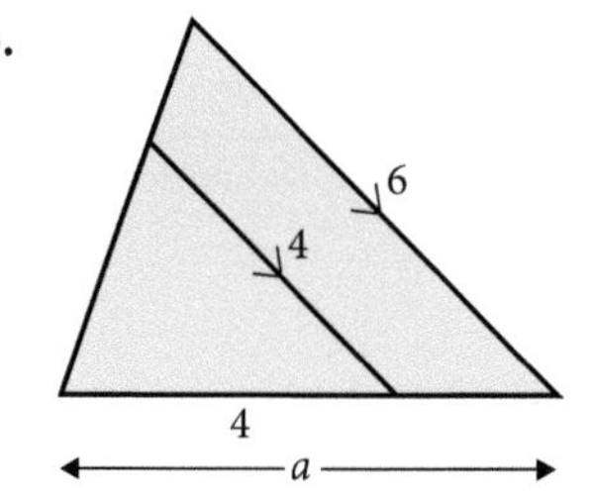

14.

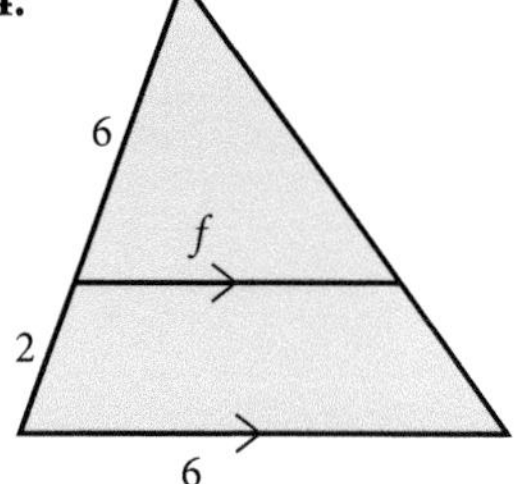

15. A tree of height 4 m casts a shadow of length 6.5 m.
Find the height of a house casting a shadow 26 m long.

16. A small cone is cut from a larger cone.
Find the radius of the smaller cone.

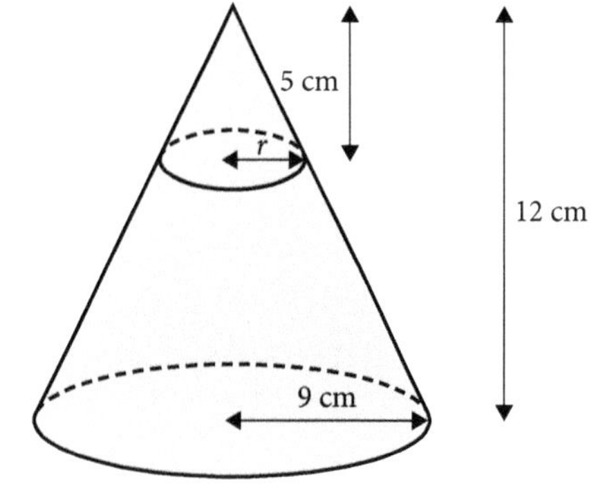

17. The diagram shows the side view of a swimming pool being filled with water.
Calculate the length x.

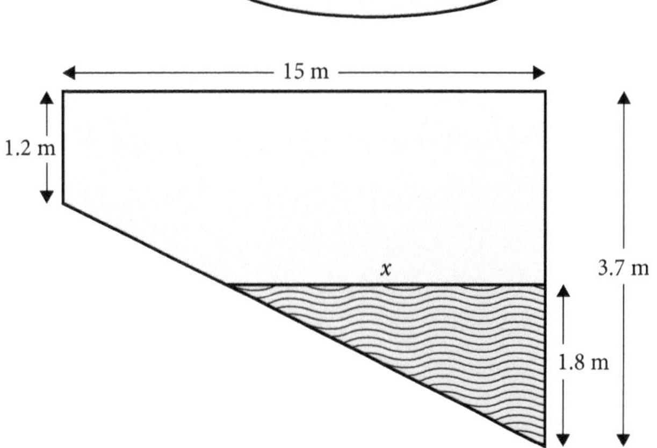

18. The diagonals of a trapezium ABCD intersect at O. AB is parallel to DC, AB = 3 cm and DC = 6 cm. Show that triangles ABO and CDO are similar. If CO = 4 cm and OB = 3 cm, find AO and DO.

9.2 Congruent shapes

Two shapes are congruent if one shape fits exactly on the other.
They must be the same size and the same shape.

Exercise 2

1. Identify the pairs of congruent shapes in this diagram.

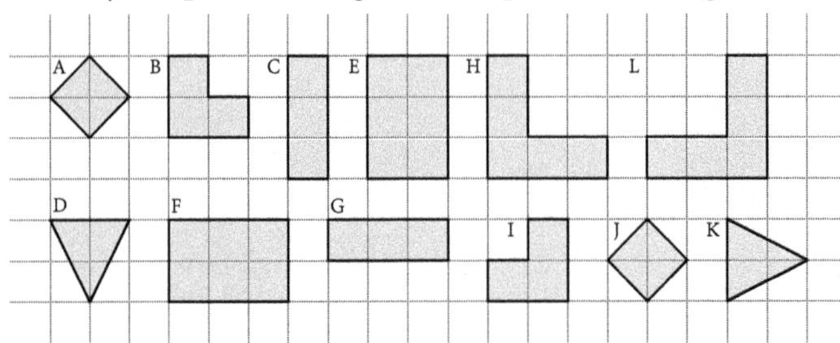

2. Identify the pairs of congruent shapes in this diagram.

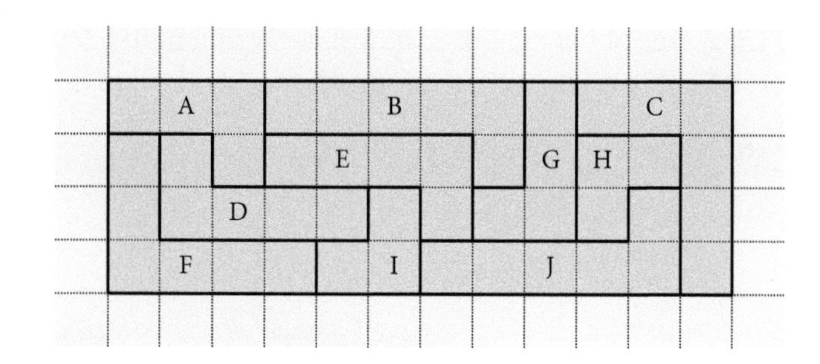

9.3 Trigonometry in right-angled triangles

Trigonometry is used to calculate sides and angles in right-angled triangles.

The side opposite the right angle is called the **hypotenuse** (H).
It is the longest side.

The side opposite the marked angle is called the opposite (O).

The other side is called the adjacent (A).

Consider two triangles, one of which is an enlargement of the other.

It is clear that, for the angle 30°, the

$$\text{ratio} = \frac{\text{opposite}}{\text{hypotenuse}} = \frac{6}{12} = \frac{2}{4} = \frac{1}{2}$$

This is the same for both triangles.

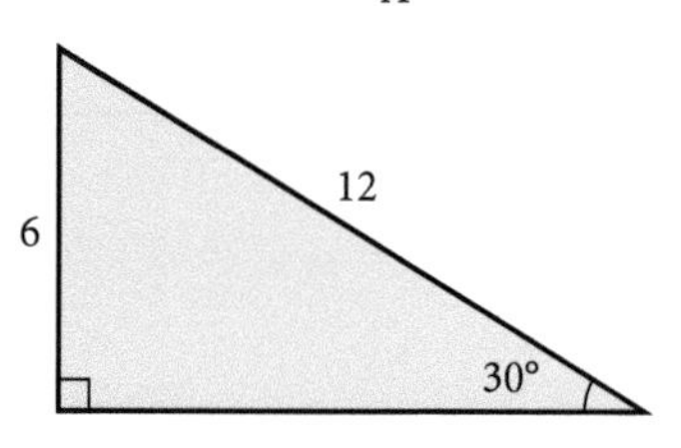

Sine, cosine, tangent

Three important ratios are defined for angle x.

$$\sin x = \frac{\text{O}}{\text{H}} \qquad \cos x = \frac{\text{A}}{\text{H}} \qquad \tan x = \frac{\text{O}}{\text{A}}$$

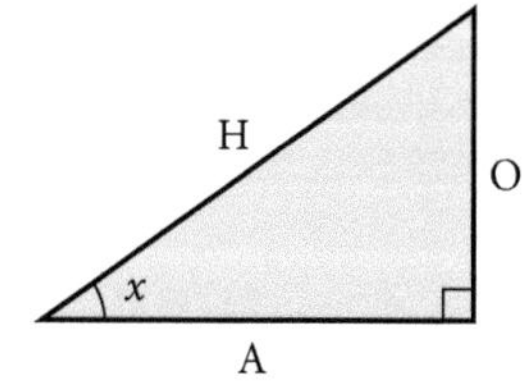

It is important to get the letters in the correct positions.

Some people find a simple sentence helpful where the first letters of each word describe sine, cosine or tangent, Hypotenuse, Opposite or Adjacent. An example is:

Silly Old Harry Caught A Herring Trawling Off Afghanistan

e.g. SOH $\sin = \frac{\text{O}}{\text{H}}$

An alternative way of remembering the order of the letters is to use the mnemonic **SOHCAHTOA**.

Finding the length of a side

Example

Find the length of l.

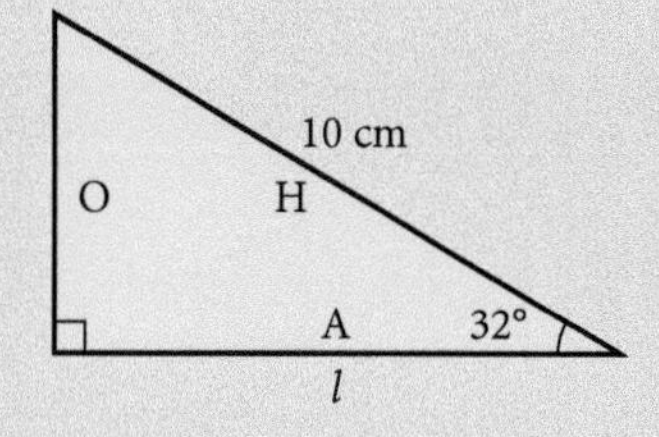

$$\cos 32° = \frac{\text{A}}{\text{H}} = \frac{l}{10}$$

$$\therefore\ l = 10 \times \cos 32°$$

$$l = 8.5 \text{ cm (to 1 d.p)}$$

Exercise 3

Find the lengths marked with letters. All lengths are in cm.

Give answers correct to 1 d.p.

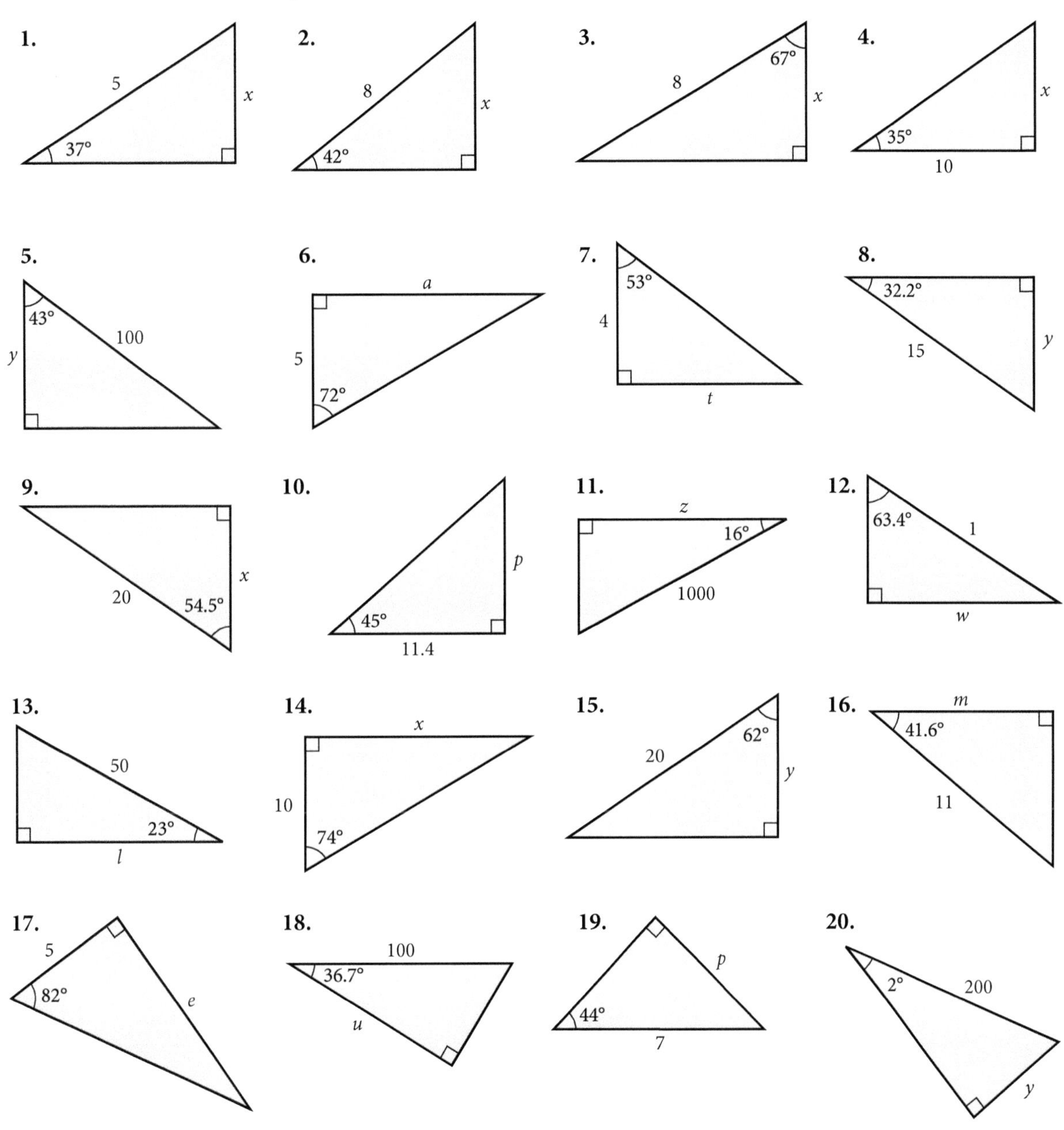

Example

Find the length of x.

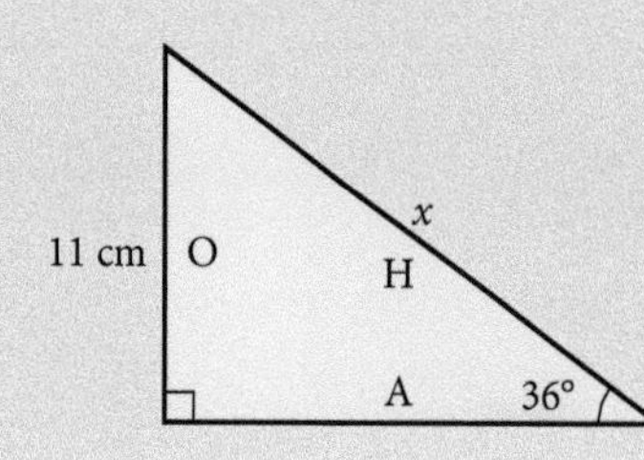

$$\sin 36° = \frac{O}{H} = \frac{11}{x}$$

$\therefore x \sin 36° = 11$ [Multiply by x]

$$x = \frac{11}{\sin 36°} = 18.7 \text{ cm} \quad \text{(to 1 d.p.)}$$

Exercise 4

This exercise is more difficult. Find the lengths marked with letters.

Give answers correct to 1 d.p.

1.

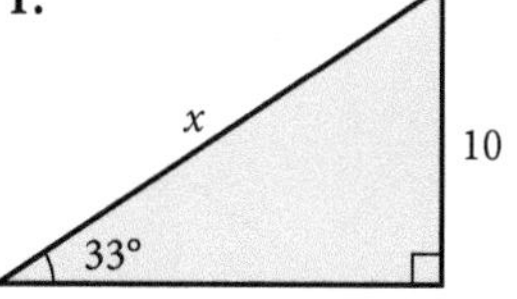

2.

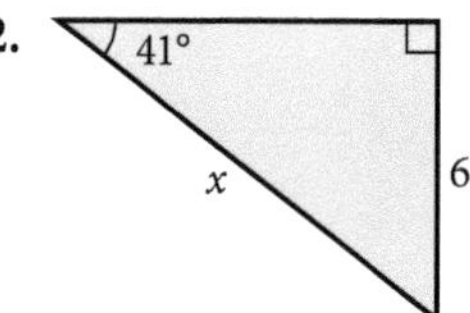

3.

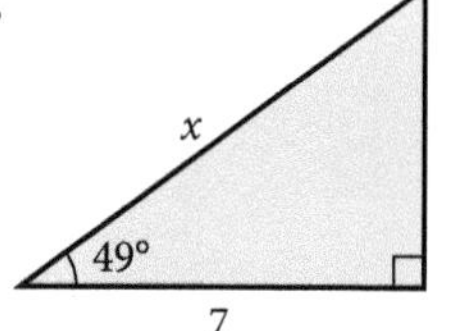

4.

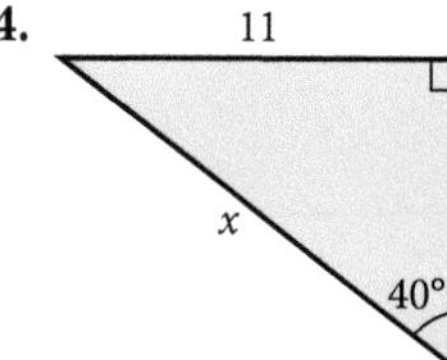

5.

6.

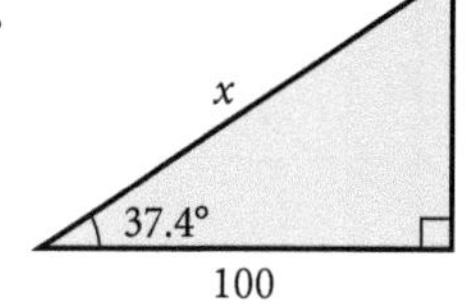

7.

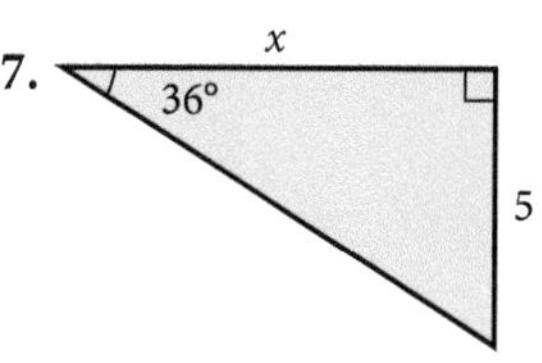

8.

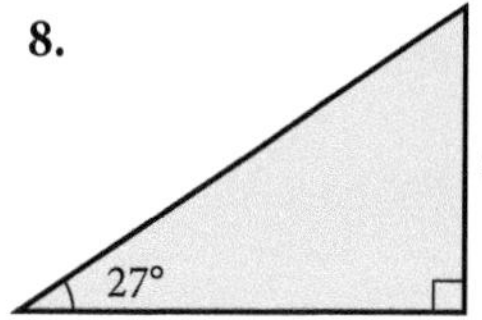

9.

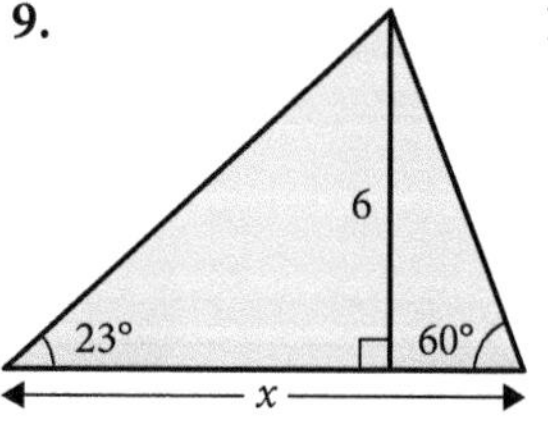

10.

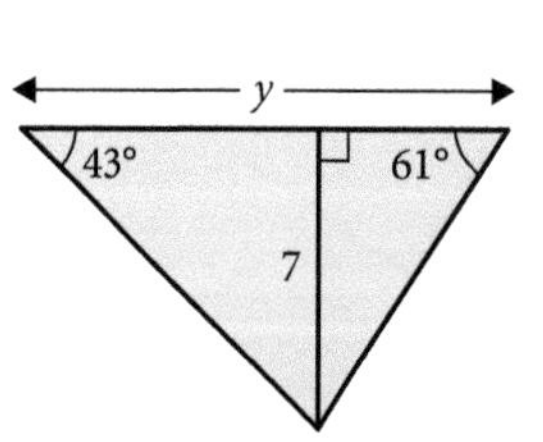

11.

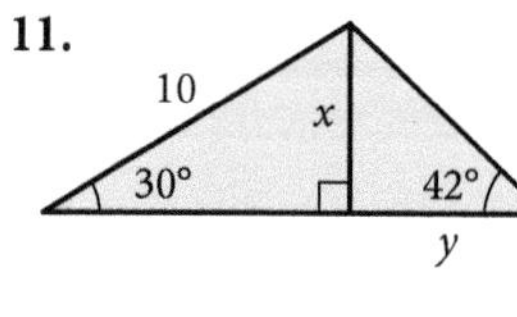

12.

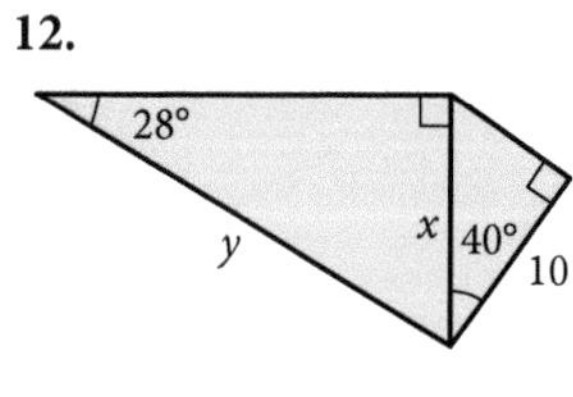

13.

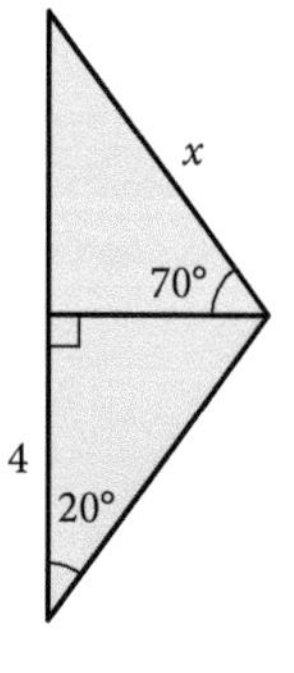

14.

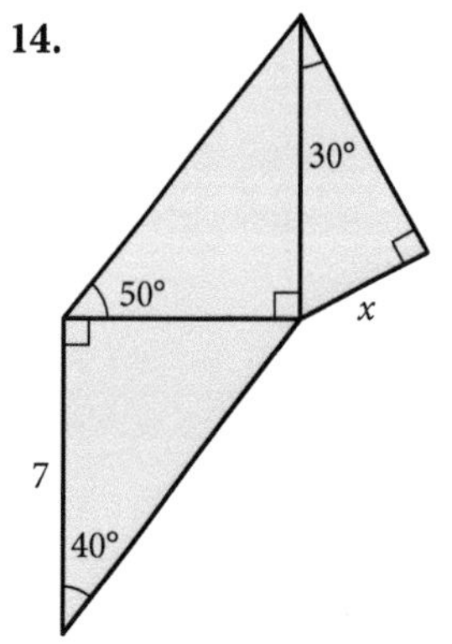

15.

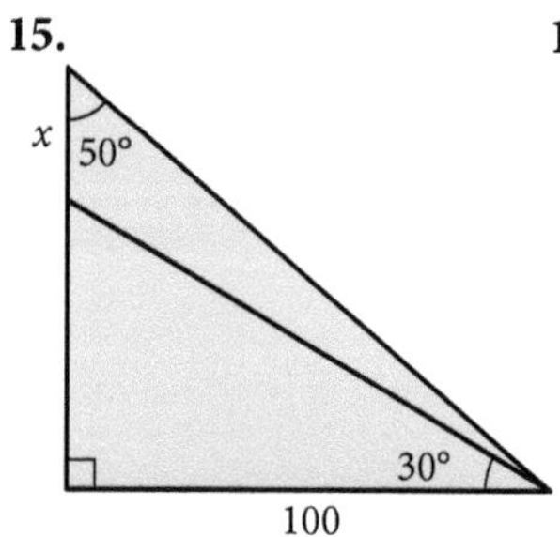

16.

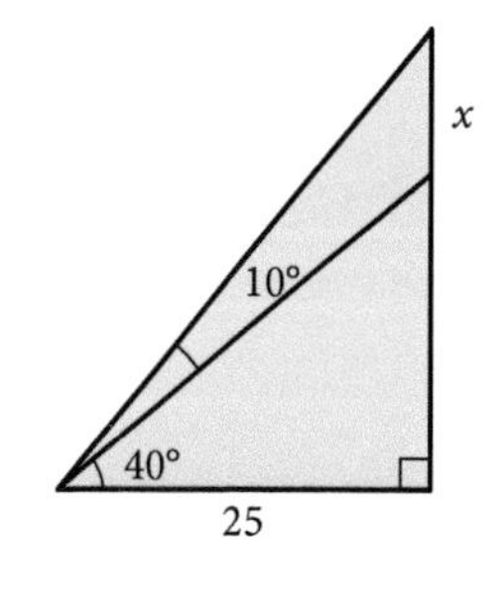

Finding angles

Example

Find the angle x.

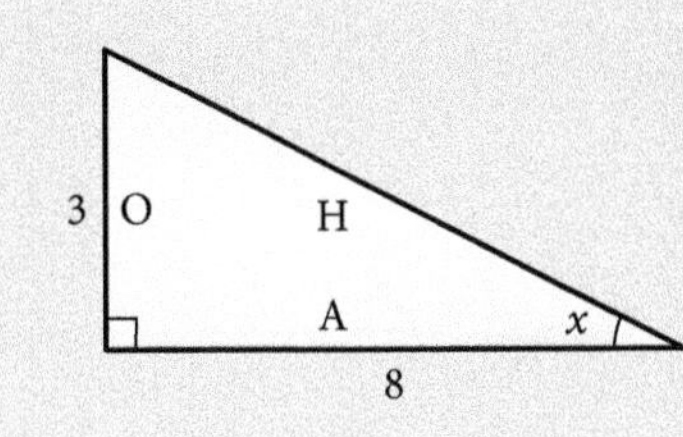

$$\tan x = \frac{\text{O}}{\text{A}} = \frac{3}{8}$$

$\tan x = 0.375$

$x = 20.6°$ (to 1 d.p.)

On a calculator:

3 ÷ 8 = INV tan

Exercise 5

Find the angles marked with letters. Give the answers correct to 1 d.p.

1.

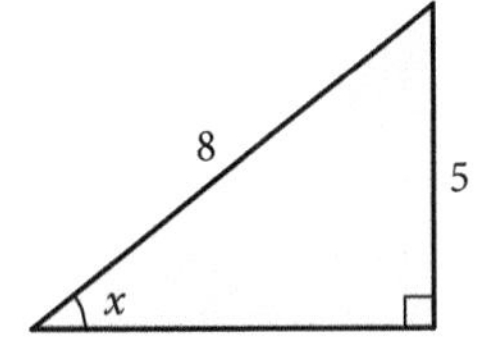

2.

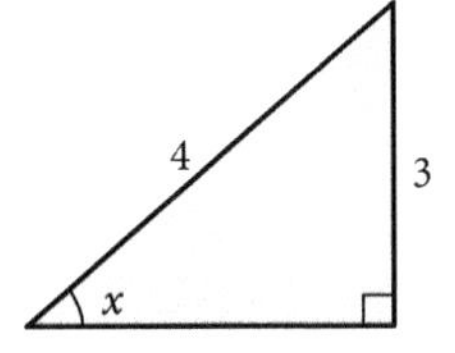

3.

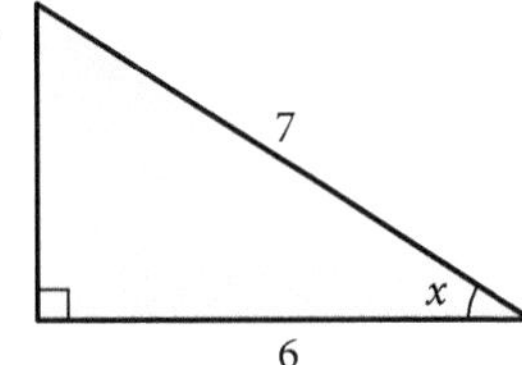

4.

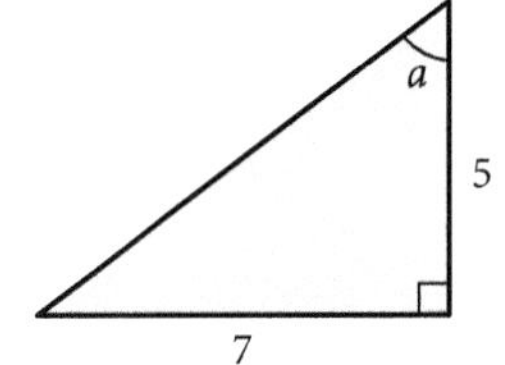

5.

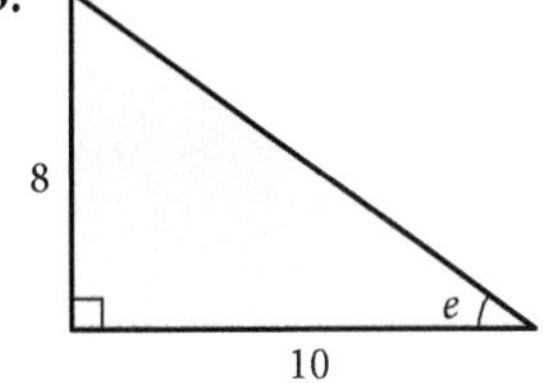

6.

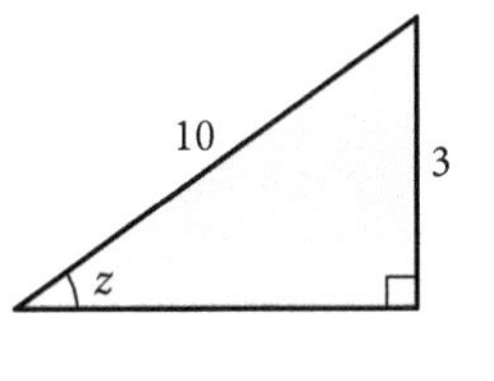

7.

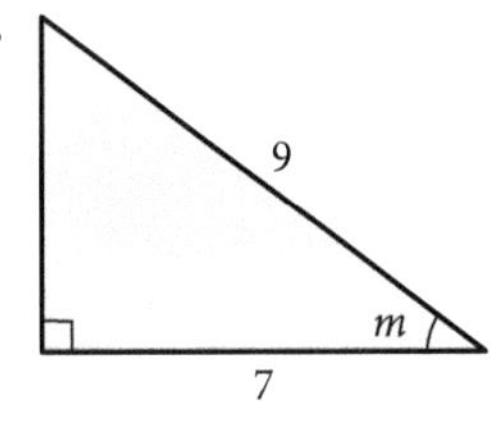

8.

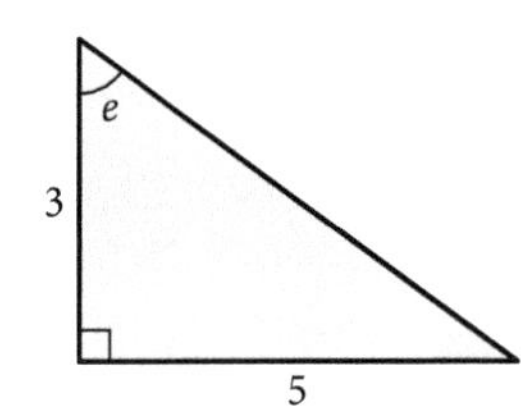

9.

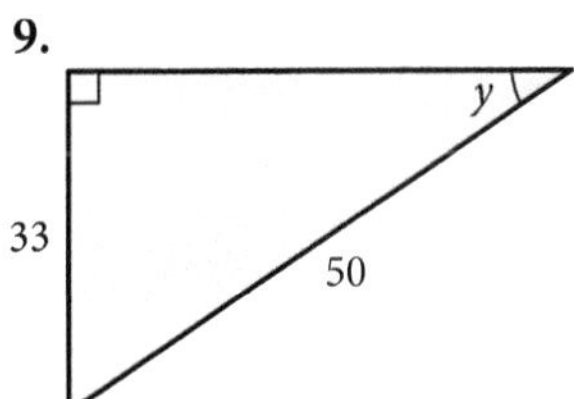

10.

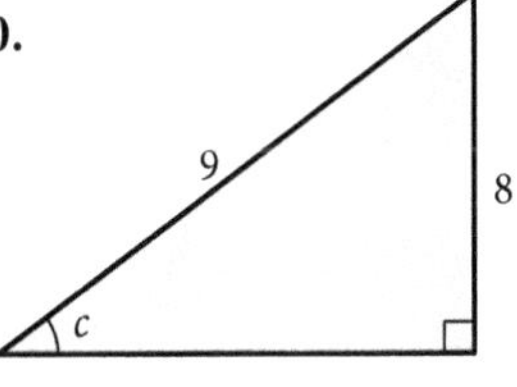

11.

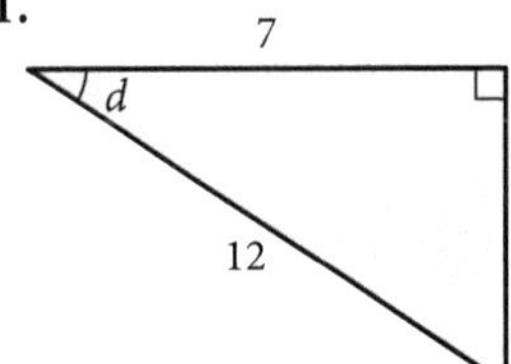

12.

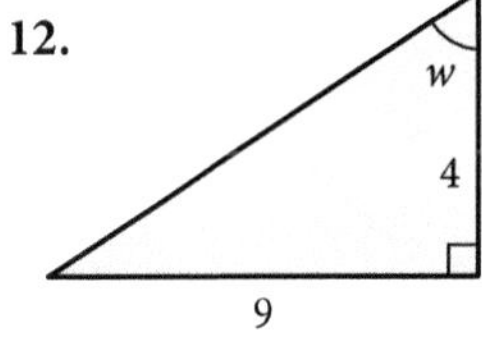

13.

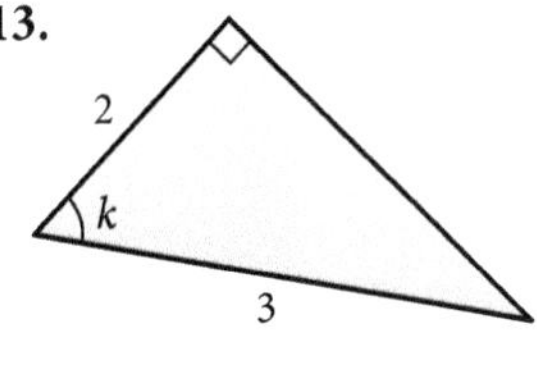

14.

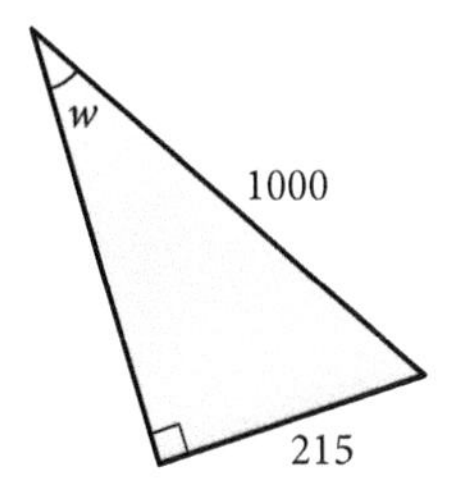

15.

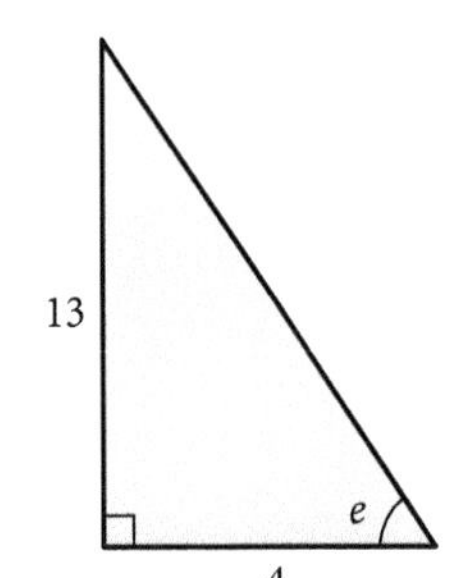

16.

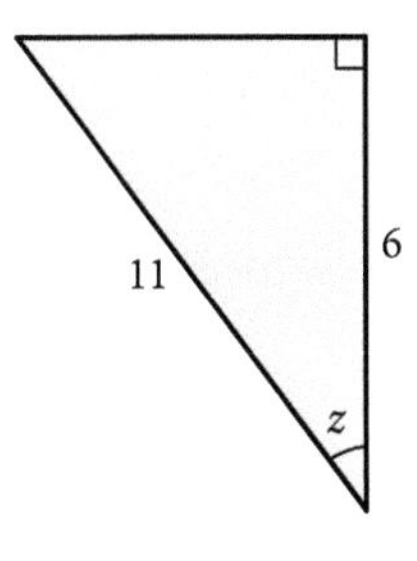

17. **18.** **19.** **20.**

Exercise 6

Begin each question by drawing a large clear diagram.

1. A ladder of length 4 m rests against a vertical wall so that the base of the ladder is 1·5 m from the wall.

   Calculate the angle between the ladder and the ground.

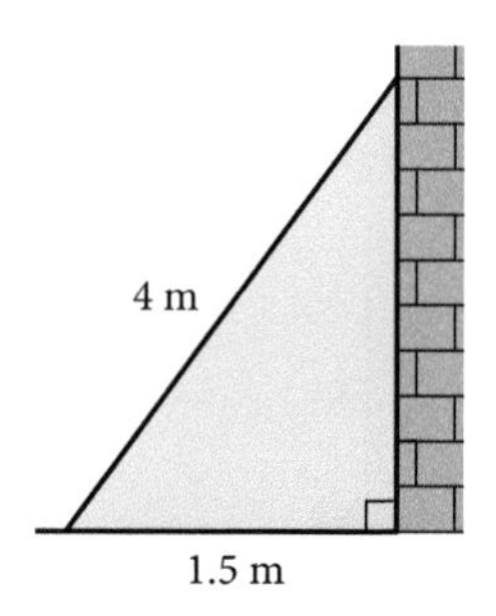

2. A ladder of length 4 m rests against a vertical wall so that the angle between the ladder and the ground is 66°. How far up the wall does the ladder reach?
3. From a distance of 20 m the angle of elevation to the top of a tower is 35°.

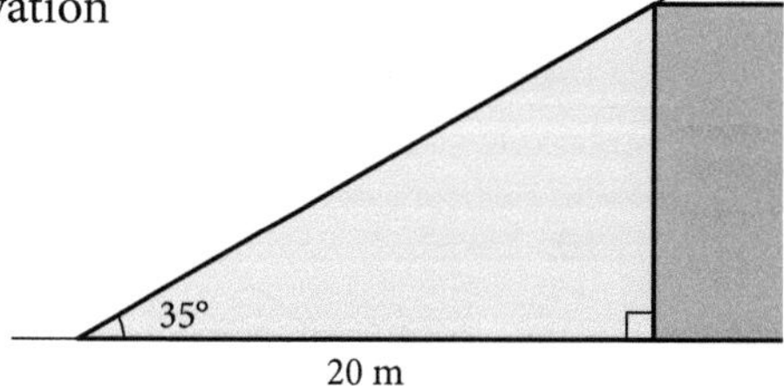

   How high is the tower?

4. A point G is 40 m away from a building, which is 15 m high.

   What is the angle of elevation to the top of the building from G?
5. A boy is flying a kite from a string of length 60 m.

   If the string makes an angle of 71° with the horizontal, what is the height of the kite?

   Ignore the height of the boy.

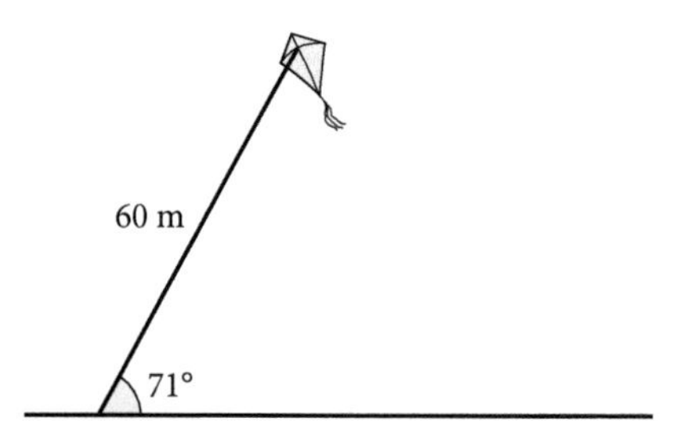

6. A straight tunnel is 80 m long and slopes downwards at an angle of 11° to the horizontal. Find the vertical drop in travelling from the top to the bottom of the tunnel.

7. The frame of a bicycle is shown in the diagram.

Find the length of the crossbar.

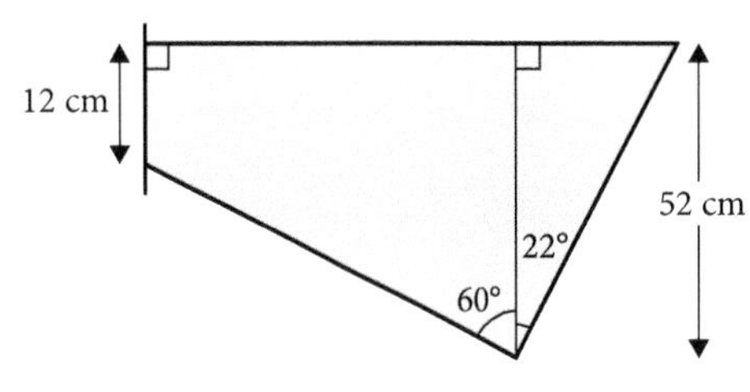

8. Calculate the length x.

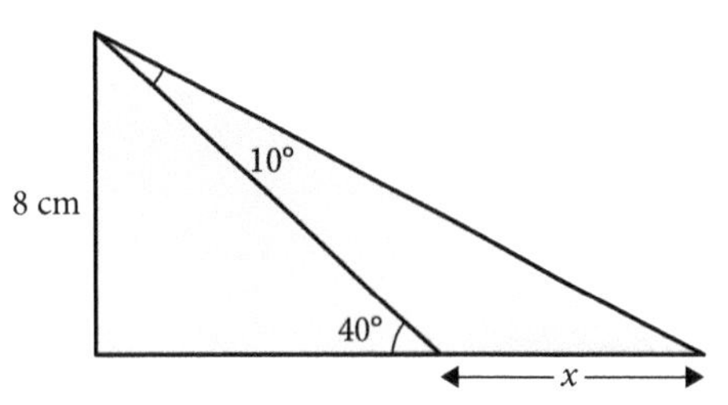

9. AB is a chord of a circle of radius 5 cm and centre O.

The perpendicular bisector of AB passes through O, and also bisects the angle AOB.

If $A\hat{O}B = 100°$, calculate the length of the chord AB.

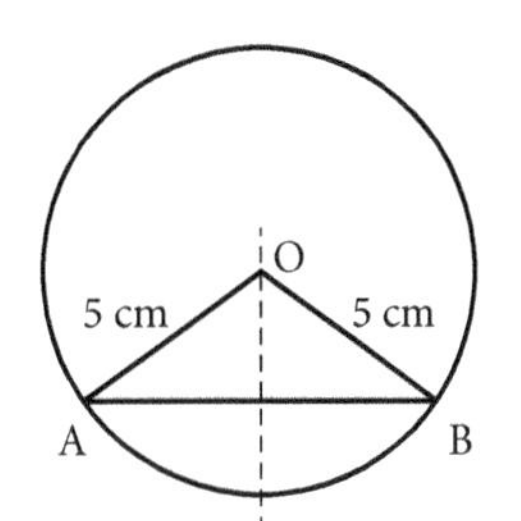

10. A ship is due South of a lighthouse L.

It sails on a bearing of 055° for a distance of 80 km until it is due East of the lighthouse.

How far is it now from the lighthouse?

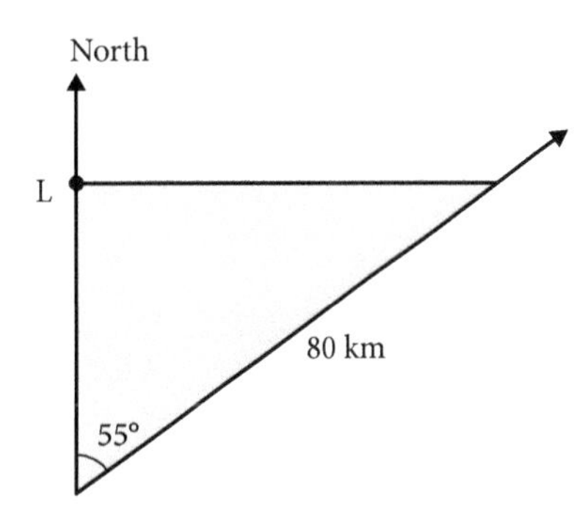

11. A ship is due South of a lighthouse. It sails on a bearing of 071° for a distance of 200 km until it is due East of the lighthouse. How far is it now from the lighthouse?

12. A ship is due North of a lighthouse. It sails on a bearing of 200° at a speed of 15 km/h for five hours until it is due West of the lighthouse. How far is it now from the lighthouse?

13. An isosceles triangle has sides of length 8 cm, 8 cm and 5 cm.

Find the angle between the two equal sides.

14. The angles of an isosceles triangle are 66°, 66° and 48°.

If the shortest side of the triangle is 8.4 cm, find the length of one of the two equal sides.

15. A regular pentagon is inscribed in a circle of radius 7 cm.

Find the angle a and then the length of a side of the pentagon.

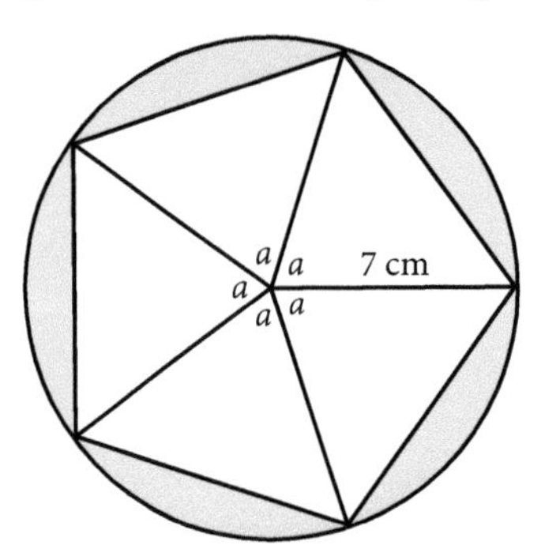

16. Find the acute angle between the diagonals of a rectangle whose sides are 5 cm and 7 cm.

Revision exercise 9A

1. Given BD = 1 m. calculate the length AC.

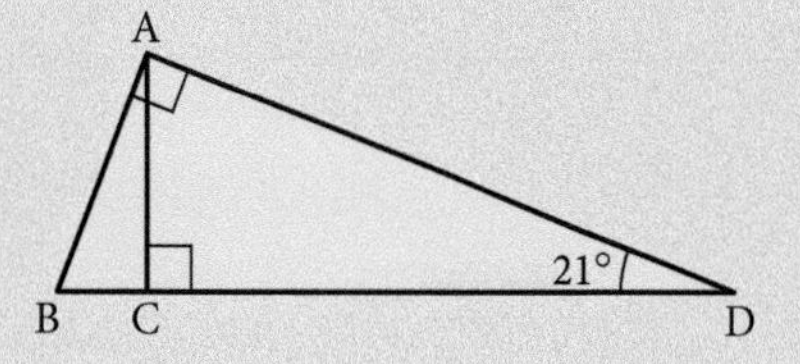

2. Calculate the side or angle marked with a letter.

a)

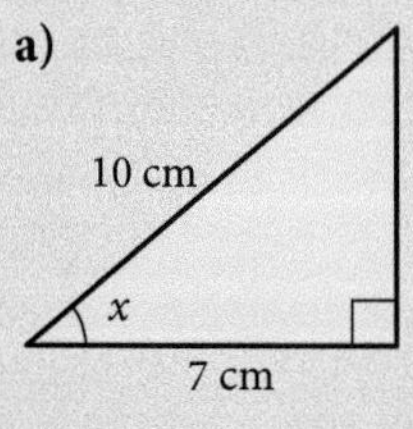

b)

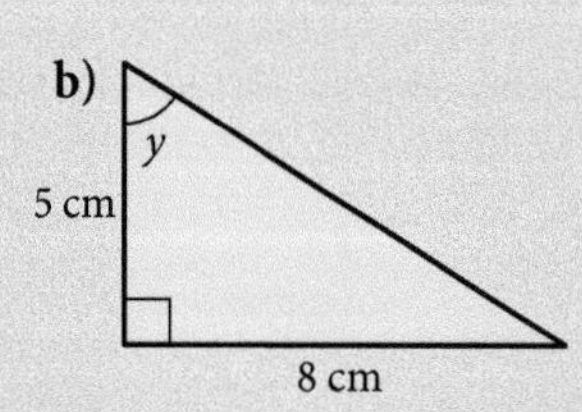

c)

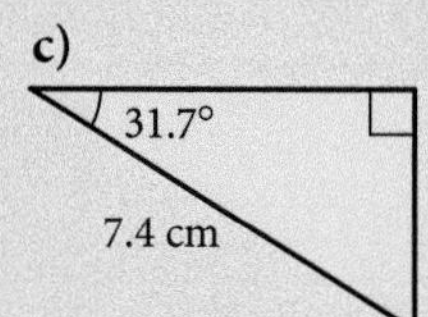

d)

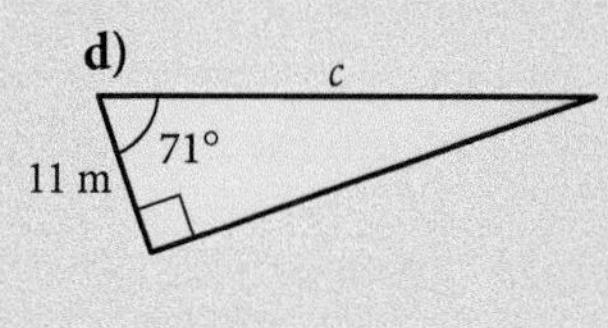

3. Rectangle B is an enlargement of rectangle A. Calculate the length x.

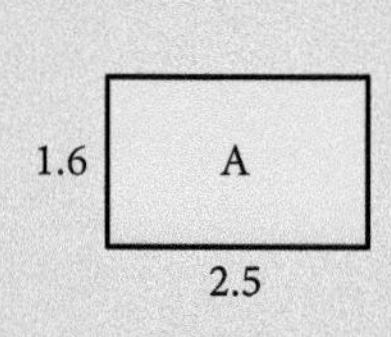

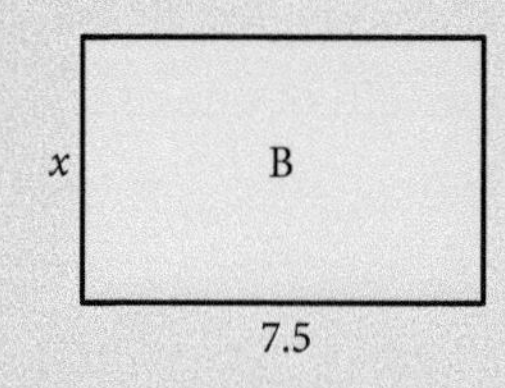

4. The pairs of shapes are similar. Find the sides marked with letters.

a)

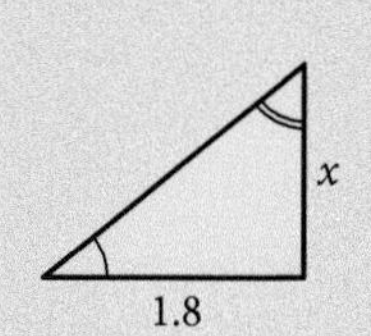

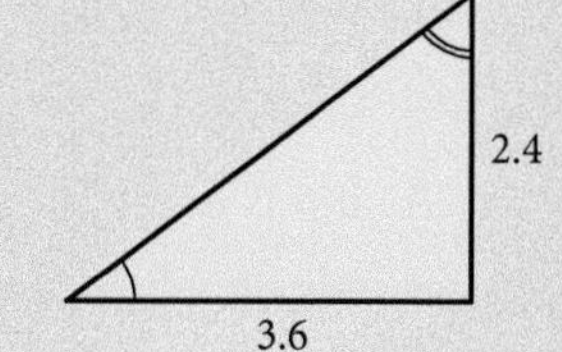

b)

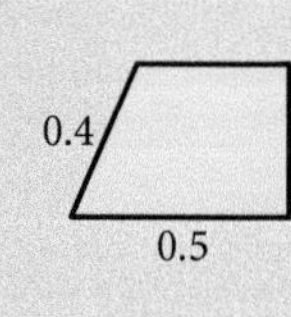

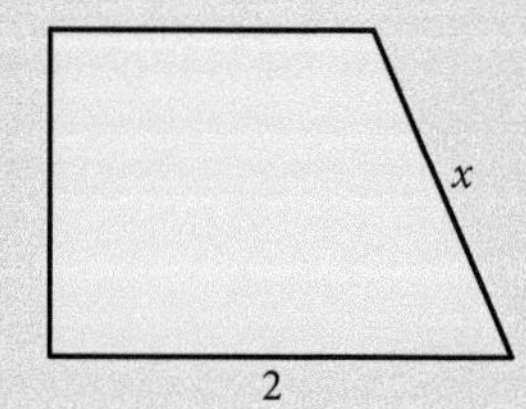

5. The sides of triangle ABC are each increased by 1 cm to form triangle DEF. Are triangles ABC and DEF similar?

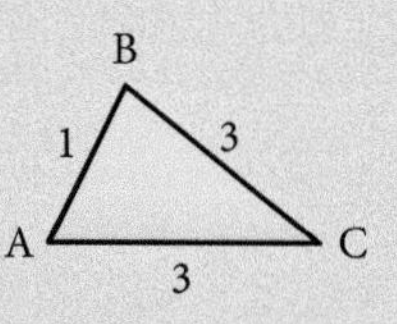

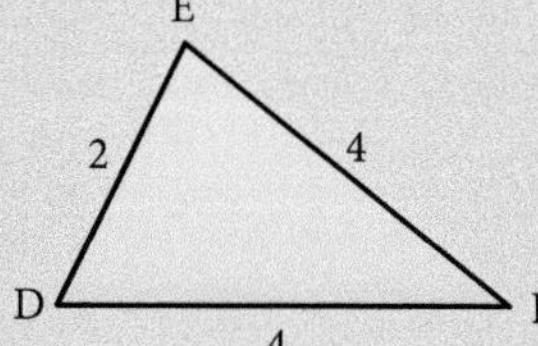

6. Calculate the length x.

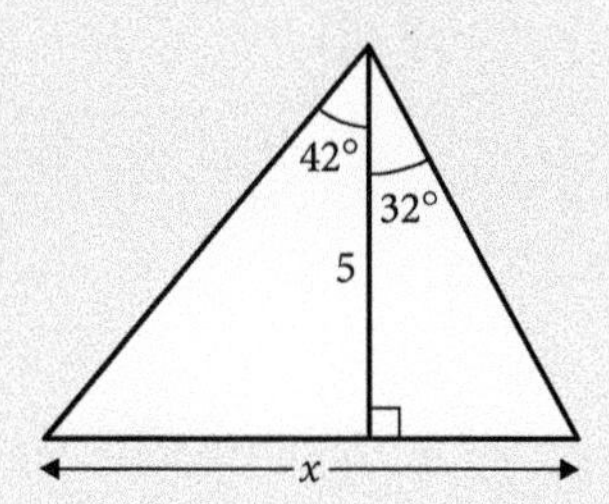

7. a) Explain why triangles PQR and PST are similar.

b) Given that PQ = 8 cm, calculate the length QS.

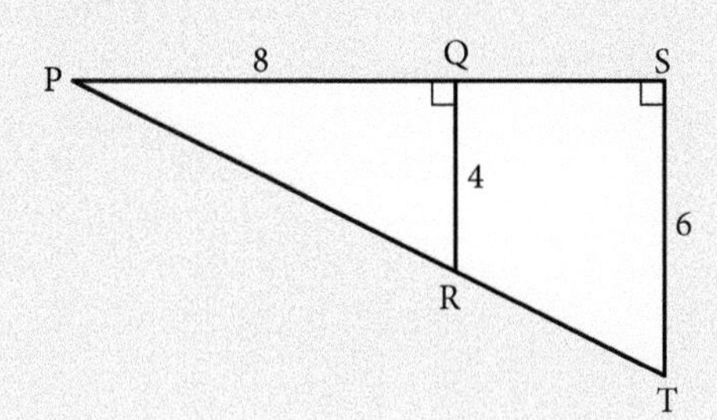

8. a) Identify the sets of congruent shapes in the following diagram.

b) Which shape is not congruent to any of the others?

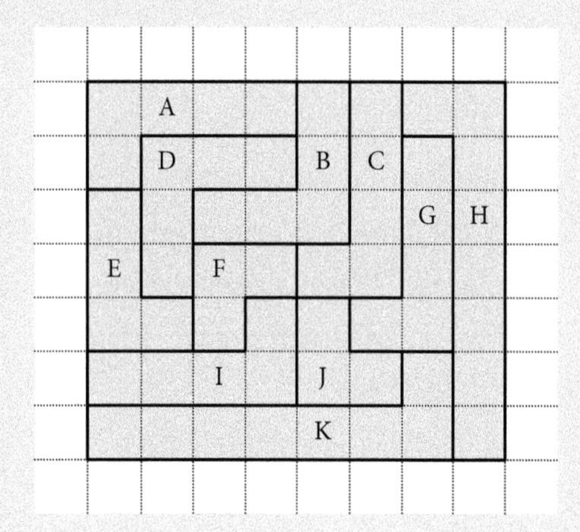

Examination-style exercise 9B

1.

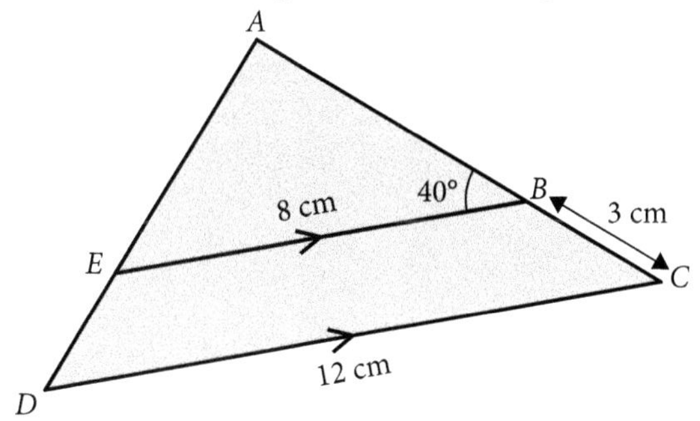

In the diagram BE is parallel to CD.

(a) Copy and complete the following statement.

Triangle ACD is .... to triangle ABE. [1]

(b) $BE = 8$ cm, $CD = 12$ cm and $BC = 3$ cm.

Calculate the length of AB. [2]

(c) Angle $ABE = 40°$.

Calculate the size of the reflex angle at C. [2]

2.

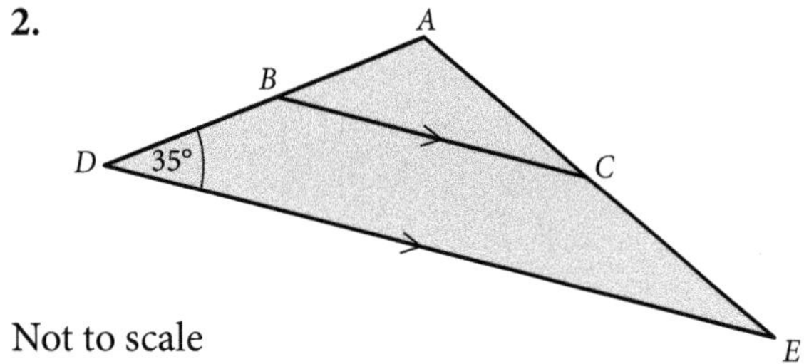

Not to scale

In the diagram BC is parallel to DE. ABD and ACE are straight lines.

(a) Choose one of the following words to complete the statement.

congruent   equilateral   isosceles   similar

Triangle ABC and triangle ADE are .... [1]

(b) Angle $BDE = 35°$. [1]

Calculate the size of angle DBC.

Cambridge IGCSE Mathematics 0580
Paper 1 Q13 June 2005

3.

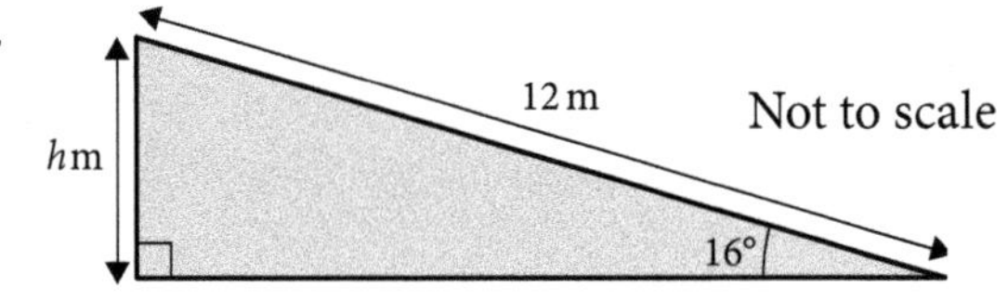

A ramp from a car park to a shopping centre slopes upward at an angle of 16° to the horizontal.

The length of the ramp is 12 metres.

Calculate the difference in height, h metres, between the car park and the shopping centre. [2]

Cambridge IGCSE Mathematics 0580
Paper 1 Q10 June 2005

4.

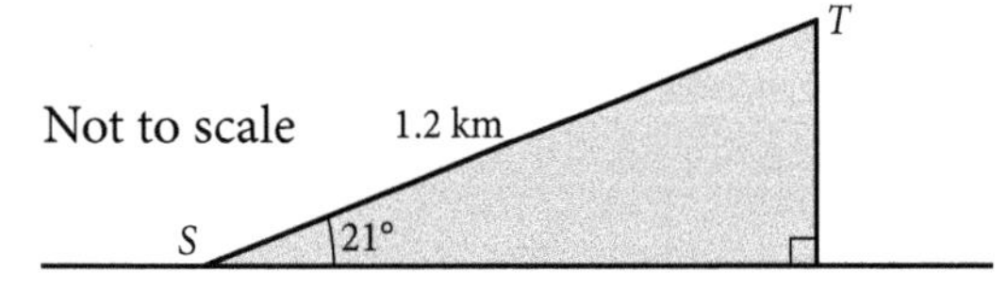

The diagram shows a path, ST, up a hill.

The path is 1.2 kilometres long and slopes at an angle of 21° to the horizontal.

Calculate the height of the hill, showing all your working.

Give your answer in **metres**. [3]

Cambridge IGCSE Mathematics 0580
Paper 1 Q12 November 2005

5. In the diagram below ABD is a straight line.
$AB = 4$ m and $AC = 6$ m. Angle $BAC = 90°$.

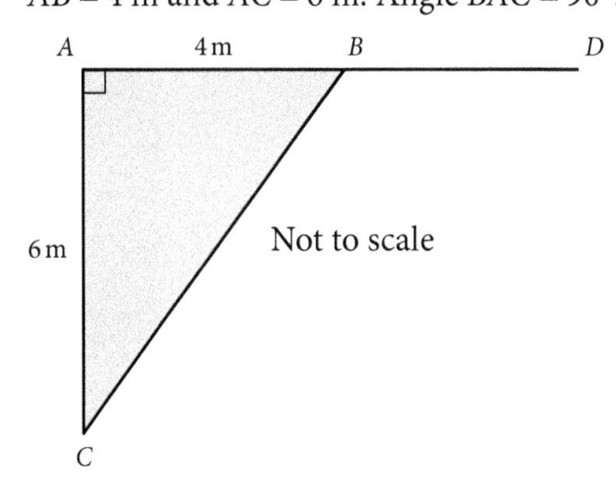

(a) i) **Use trigonometry** to calculate angle ABC. [2]

ii) Find angle CBD. [1]

(b) **Calculate** the length of BC. [2]

(c) Work out the perimeter and area of triangle ABC.
Give the correct units for each. [3]

Cambridge IGCSE Mathematics 0580
Paper 3 Q2 November 2005

6.

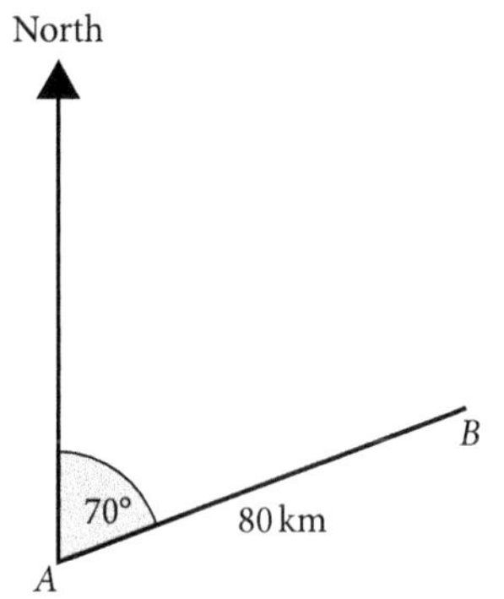

A plane flies 80 km from A to B on a bearing of 070°, as shown in the diagram.

Calculate how far east B is from A. [3]

7.

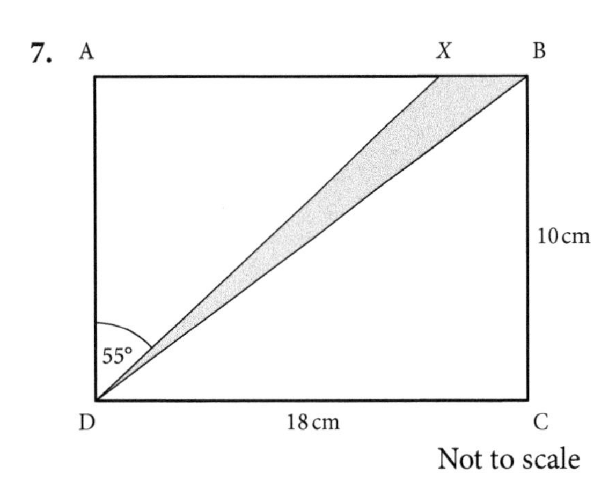

Not to scale

The diagram shows a rectangular tile $ABCD$ which has a shaded triangle DXB.

$DC = 18$ centimetres, $BC = 10$ centimetres and angle $ADX = 55°$.

(a) Calculate the area of triangle BDC. [2]

(b) Calculate the length of AX. [2]

(c) Calculate the shaded area. [3]

(d) Calculate the length of BD. [2]

Cambridge IGCSE Mathematics 0580
Paper 3 Q5 November 2006

8.

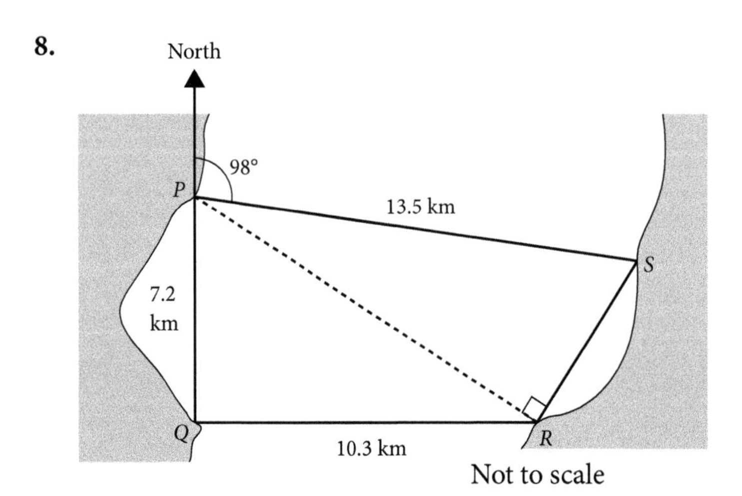

Not to scale

P, Q, R and S are ferry ports on a wide river, as shown in the diagram above.

A ferry sails from P, stopping at Q, R and S before returning to P.

(a) Q is 7.2 kilometres due south of P and R is 10.3 kilometres due east of Q.

i) Show by calculation that angle $QPR = 55°$. [2]

ii) Write down the bearing of R from P. [1]

(b) The bearing of S from P is 098° and $SP = 13.5$ km.

i) Explain why angle $RPS = 27°$. [1]

ii) Angle $PRS = 90°$. Calculate the distance RS. [2]

iii) Find the total distance the ferry sails. [1]

(c) The total sailing time for the ferry is 4 hours 30 minutes.

Calculate the average sailing speed, in kilometres per hour, for the whole journey. [2]

Cambridge IGCSE Mathematics 0580
Paper 3 Q7 June 2008

9.

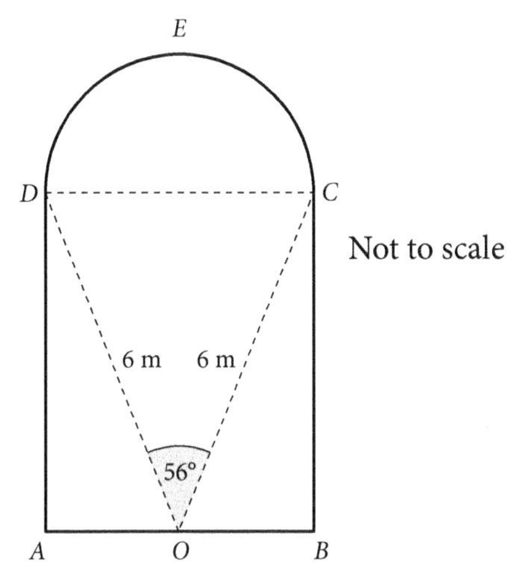

Not to scale

$ABCED$ is the cross-section of a tunnel.

$ABCD$ is a rectangle and DEC is a semi-circle.

O is the mid-point of AB.

$OD = OC = 6$ m and angle $DOC = 56°$.

(a) i) Show that angle $COB = 62°$. [1]

ii) Calculate the length of OB. [2]

iii) Write down the width of the tunnel, AB. [1]

iv) Calculate the length of BC. [2]

(b) Calculate the area of

i) the rectangle $ABCD$, [2]

ii) the semi-circle DEC, [2]

iii) the cross-section of the tunnel. [1]

(c) The tunnel is 500 metres long.

i) Calculate the volume of the tunnel. [2]

ii) A car travels through the tunnel at a constant speed of 60 kilometres per hour.

How many seconds does it take to go through the tunnel? [3]

Cambridge IGCSE Mathematics 0580
Paper 3 Q6 June 2007

10 Number 3

C1.3 Calculate with squares, square roots, cubes and cube roots and other powers and roots of numbers.
C1.4 Use directed numbers in practical situations.
C1.7 Understand the meaning of indices (fractional, negative and zero) and use the rules of indices. Use the standard form $A \times 10^n$ where n is a positive or negative integer, and $1 \leqslant A < 10$.
C1.8 Use the four rules for calculations with whole numbers, decimals and fractions (including mixed numbers and improper fractions), including correct ordering of operations and use of brackets.
C2.1 Substitute numbers for words and letters in formulae.
C2.2 Manipulate directed numbers.
C2.4 Use and interpret positive, negative and zero indices. Use the rules of indices.

10.1 Powers and roots

Indices

- Indices are used as a neat way of writing products.

  $2 \times 2 \times 2 \times 2 = 2^4$ [2 to the power 4]

  $5 \times 5 \times 5 = 5^3$ [5 to the power 3]

  $3 \times 3 \times 3 \times 3 \times 3 \times 10 \times 10 = 3^5 \times 10^2$
- Numbers like 3^2, 5^2, 11^2 are **square numbers**.
- Numbers like 2^3, 6^3, 11^3 are **cube numbers**.
- To work out 3.2^2 on a calculator, press [3.2] [x^2]

  To work out 3^4 on a calculator, press [3] [x^y] [4] [=]

  or [3] [∧] [4] [=]

Exercise 1

Write in a form using indices.

1. $3 \times 3 \times 3 \times 3$
2. 5×5
3. $6 \times 6 \times 6$
4. $10 \times 10 \times 10 \times 10 \times 10$
5. $1 \times 1 \times 1 \times 1 \times 1 \times 1 \times 1$
6. $8 \times 8 \times 8 \times 8$
7. $7 \times 7 \times 7 \times 7 \times 7 \times 7$
8. $2 \times 2 \times 2 \times 5 \times 5$
9. $3 \times 3 \times 7 \times 7 \times 7 \times 7$
10. $3 \times 3 \times 10 \times 10 \times 10$
11. $5 \times 5 \times 5 \times 5 \times 11 \times 11$
12. $2 \times 3 \times 2 \times 3 \times 3$
13. $5 \times 3 \times 3 \times 5 \times 5$
14. $2 \times 2 \times 3 \times 3 \times 3 \times 11 \times 11$

15. Work out without a calculator:

a) 4^2 **b)** 6^2 **c)** 10^2 **d)** 3^3 **e)** 10^3

16. Use the $\boxed{x^2}$ button to work out:

a) 9^2 **b)** 21^2 **c)** 1.2^2 **d)** 0.2^2 **e)** 3.1^2

f) 100^2 **g)** 25^2 **h)** 8.7^2 **i)** 0.9^2 **j)** 81.4^2

17. Find the areas of these squares.

a)

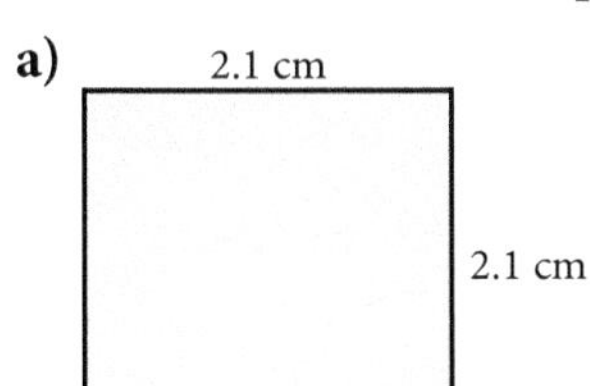

b)

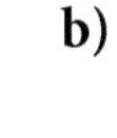

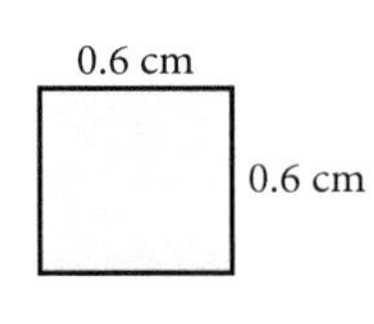

c)

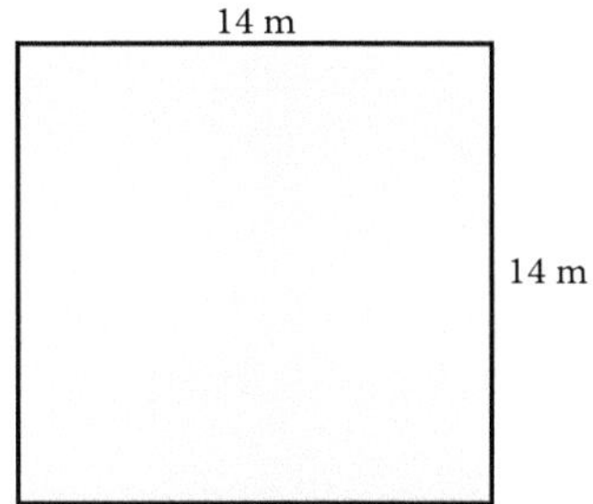

18. Write in index form:

a) $a \times a \times a$ **b)** $n \times n \times n \times n$ **c)** $s \times s \times s \times s \times s$

d) $p \times p \times q \times q \times q$ **e)** $b \times b \times b \times b \times b \times b \times b$

19. Use the $\boxed{x^y}$ button to work out:

a) 6^3 **b)** 2^8 **c)** 3^5 **d)** 10^5 **e)** 4^3

f) 0.1^3 **g)** 1.7^4 **h)** $3^4 \times 7$ **i)** $5^3 \times 10$

20. A scientist has a dish containing 10^9 germs.

One day later there are 10 times as many germs.
How many germs are in the dish now?

21. A field has 2^8 daisies growing on the grass.

A cow eats half of the daisies.
How many daisies are left?

22. A maths teacher decided to set a test to a class of 25 children.
The person coming 25th received 2c, the 24th received 4c, the 23rd received 8c, the 22nd received 16c and so on, doubling the amount each time.

a) Write 2, 4, 8, 16 as powers of 2.

b) How much, in dollars, would be given to the person who came first in the test?

23. Abdul says 'If you work out the product of any four consecutive numbers and then add one, the answer will be square number.'
For example: $1 \times 2 \times 3 \times 4 = 24$

$24 + 1 = 25$, which is a square number.

Is Abdul right? Test his theory on four (or more) sets of four consecutive numbers.

Square roots and cube roots

A square has an area of 529 cm^2.

How long is a side of the square?

In other words, what number *multiplied by itself* makes 529?

The answer is the **square root** of 529.

On a calculator press [√] [529] [=]

[On older calculators you may need to press [529] [√]]

The side of the square is 23 cm.

529 cm^2

?

A cube has a volume of 512 cm^3.

How long is a side of the cube?

The answer is the **cube root** of 512.

On a calculator press [∛] [512] [=]

The side of the cube is 8 cm. [Check $8 \times 8 \times 8 = 512$]

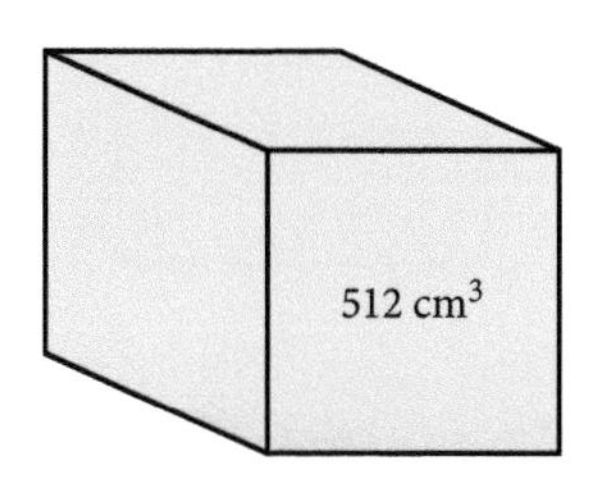

Exercise 2

1. Work out, without a calculator:

   a) $\sqrt{16}$ **b)** $\sqrt{36}$ **c)** $\sqrt{1}$ **d)** $\sqrt{100}$

2. Find the sides of the squares.

   a)

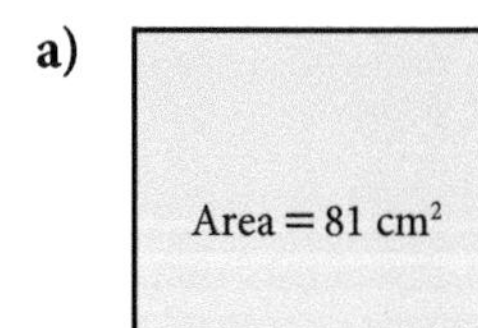

   b) Area = 49 cm^2

   c)

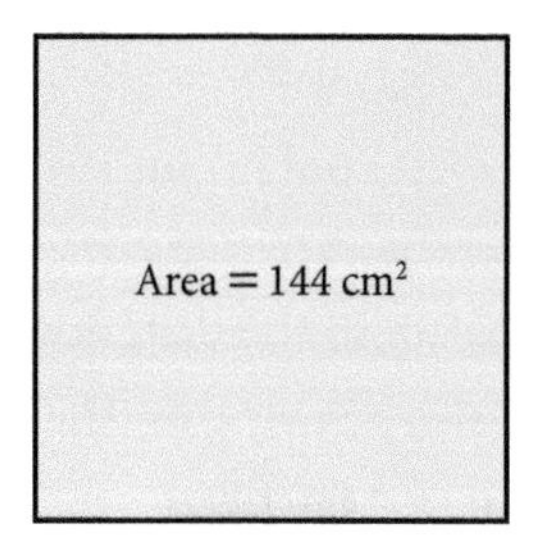

3. Use a calculator to find the following, correct to 1 d.p.

   a) $\sqrt{10}$ **b)** $\sqrt{29}$ **c)** $\sqrt{107}$ **d)** $\sqrt{19.7}$

   e) $\sqrt{2406}$ **f)** $\sqrt{58.6}$ **g)** $\sqrt{0.15}$ **h)** $\sqrt{0.727}$

4. A square photo has an area of 150 cm^2. Find the length of each side of the photo, correct to the nearest mm.

5. A square field has an area of 20 hectares. How long is each side of the field, correct to the nearest metre?
   [1 hectare = 10 000 m^2]

6. The area of square A is equal to the sum of the areas of squares B and C.
   Find the length x, correct to 1 d.p.

   A = B + C

   x 3.5 cm 7 cm

7. Find the following:

   a) $\sqrt[3]{64}$ **b)** $\sqrt[3]{125}$ **c)** $\sqrt[3]{1000}$

8. A cube has a volume of 200 cm³.
Find the length of the side of the cube, correct to 1 d.p.

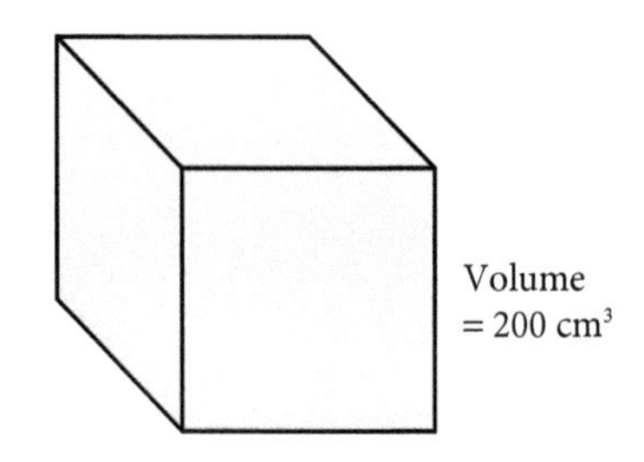

Negative indices and the zero index

- Look at this sequence.

  $2^4 \quad 2^3 \quad 2^2 \quad 2^1 \quad 2^0 \quad 2^{-1}$

  $16 \rightarrow 8 \rightarrow 4 \rightarrow 2 \rightarrow \boxed{1} \rightarrow \boxed{\frac{1}{2}}$

  From left to right the index goes down by one each time.
  Also we divide by two each time.

  we see that $2^0 = 1$ and that $2^{-1} = \frac{1}{2}$
- In general $x^0 = 1$ for any value of x which is not zero.
  In general $x^{-1} = \dfrac{1}{x}$

  Note also that $x^1 = x$ for all x.

  Also $2^{-3} = \dfrac{1}{2^3}$ $\quad 3^{-2} = \dfrac{1}{3^2}$
- The **reciprocal** of 3 is $\frac{1}{3}$. The reciprocal of 10 is $\frac{1}{10}$.
- The reciprocal of n is $\frac{1}{n}$ (which can be written n^{-1}).

Exercise 3

In Questions **1** to **12**, work out the value of the number given.

1. 3^{-1} **2.** 4^{-1} **3.** 10^{-1} **4.** 1^{-4} **5.** 3^{-2} **6.** 4^{-2}
7. 10^{-2} **8.** 8^0 **9.** 7^{-2} **10.** $(-6)^0$ **11.** 9^{-2} **12.** 1^{-7}

In Questions **13** to **32** answer 'true' or 'false'.

13. $2^3 = 8$ **14.** $3^2 = 6$ **15.** $5^3 = 125$ **16.** $2^{-1} = \frac{1}{2}$
17. $10^{-2} = \frac{1}{20}$ **18.** $3^{-3} = \frac{1}{9}$ **19.** $2^2 > 2^3$ **20.** $2^3 < 3^2$
21. $2^{-2} > 2^{-3}$ **22.** $3^{-2} < 3^3$ **23.** $1^9 = 9$ **24.** $(-3)^2 = -9$
25. $5^{-2} = \frac{1}{10}$ **26.** $10^{-3} = \frac{1}{1000}$ **27.** $10^{-2} > 10^{-3}$ **28.** $5^{-1} = 0.2$
29. $10^{-1} = 0.1$ **30.** $2^{-2} = 0.25$ **31.** $5^0 = 1$ **32.** $16^0 = 0$

Multiplying and dividing

Example

To multiply powers of the same number *add* the indices.

$3^2 \times 3^4 = (3 \times 3) \times (3 \times 3 \times 3 \times 3) = 3^6$

$2^3 \times 2^2 = (2 \times 2 \times 2) \times (2 \times 2) = 2^5$

$7^3 \times 7^5 = 7^8$ [add the indices]

To divide powers of the same number *subtract* the indices.

$$2^4 \div 2^2 = \frac{2\times2\times2\times2}{2\times2} = 2^2$$

$$\left.\begin{array}{l} 5^6 \div 5^2 = 5^4 \\ 7^8 \div 7^3 = 7^5 \end{array}\right\} \text{[subtract the indices]}$$

$x^a \times x^b = x^{a+b}$

and

$x^a\ x^b = x^{a-b}$

Exercise 4

Write in a more simple form.

1. $5^2 \times 5^4$ **2.** $6^3 \times 6^2$ **3.** $10^4 \times 10^5$ **4.** $7^5 \times 7^3$

5. $3^6 \times 3^4$ **6.** $8^3 \times 8^3$ **7.** $2^3 \times 2^{10}$ **8.** $3^6 \times 3^{-2}$

9. $5^4 \times 5^{-1}$ **10.** $7^7 \times 7^{-3}$ **11.** $5^{-3} \times 5^5$ **12.** $3^{-2} \times 3^{-2}$

13. $6^{-3} \times 6^8$ **14.** $5^{-2} \times 5^{-8}$ **15.** $7^{-3} \times 7^9$ **16.** $7^4 \div 7^2$

17. $6^7 \div 6^2$ **18.** $8^5 \div 8^4$ **19.** $5^{10} \div 5^2$ **20.** $10^7 \div 10^5$

21. $9^6 \div 9^8$ **22.** $3^8 \div 3^{10}$ **23.** $2^6 \div 2^2$ **24.** $3^3 \div 3^5$

25. $7^2 \div 7^8$ **26.** $3^{-2} \div 3^2$ **27.** $5^{-3} \div 5^2$ **28.** $8^{-1} \div 8^4$

29. $5^{-4} \div 5^1$ **30.** $6^2 \div 6^{-2}$ **31.** $3^4 \div 3^4$ **32.** $5^2 \div 5^2$

33. $\dfrac{3^4 \times 3^5}{3^2}$ **34.** $\dfrac{2^8 \times 2^4}{2^5}$ **35.** $\dfrac{7^3 \times 7^3}{7^4}$ **36.** $\dfrac{5^9 \times 5^{10}}{5^{20}}$

Further rules of indices

To raise a power of a number to a further power, **multiply** the indices.

Example 1

$(x^2)^3 = x^2 \times x^2 \times x^2 = x^6$ $(a^4)^2 = a^4 \times a^4 = a^8$

Example 2

$3x^2 \times 4x^5 = 12x^7$ — (3×4), $(2 + 5)$

$4a^7 \times 5a^2 = 20a^9$ — (4×5), $(7 + 2)$

$12x^5 \div 3x^2 = 4x^3$ — $(12 \div 3)$, $(5 - 2)$

$(3a^2)^3 = 3^3 \times a^6 = 27a^6$

Exercise 5

Write in a more simple form.

1. $(3^3)^2$	**2.** $(5^4)^3$	**3.** $(7^2)^5$	**4.** $(8^2)^{10}$	**5.** $(x^2)^3$	**6.** $(a^5)^3$
7. $(n^7)^2$	**8.** $(y^3)^3$	**9.** $(2^{-1})^2$	**10.** $(3^{-2})^2$	**11.** $(7^{-1})^{-2}$	**12.** $(x^3)^{-1}$
13. $2a^2 \times 3a^3$	**14.** $4n^3 \times 5n^1$	**15.** $7x^4 \times 2x$	**16.** $8y^5 \times 3y^2$	**17.** $5n^3 \times n^4$	**18.** $6y^2 \times 2$
19. $3p^3 \times 3p^2$	**20.** $2p \times 5p^5$	**21.** $(2x^2)^3$	**22.** $(3a^2)^3$	**23.** $(4y^3)^2$	**24.** $(5x^4)^2$

Solve the equations for x.

25. $x^2 = 9$	**26.** $x^5 = 1$	**27.** $x^3 = 27$	**28.** $x^5 = 0$
29. $2^x = 8$	**30.** $3^x = 3$	**31.** $5^x = 25$	**32.** $10^x = 1000$
33. $2^x = \frac{1}{2}$	**34.** $4^x = \frac{1}{4}$	**35.** $7^x = 1$	**36.** $3x^3 = 24$
37. $10x^3 = 640$	**38.** $2x^3 = 0$	**39.** $10^x = 0.1$	**40.** $5^x = 1$

10.2 Standard form

When dealing with either very large or very small numbers, it is not convenient to write them out in full in the normal way. It is better to use standard form.

Most calculators represent large and small numbers in this way.

This calculator shows 2.3×10^8.

2.3 08

The number $a \times 10^n$ is in standard form when $1 \leqslant a < 10$ and n is a positive or negative integer.

Example

Write the following numbers in standard form:

a) $2000 = 2 \times 1000 = 2 \times 10^3$

b) $150 = 1.5 \times 100 = 1.5 \times 10^2$

c) $0.0004 = 4 \times \frac{1}{10\,000} = 4 \times 10^{-4}$

Exercise 6

In Questions **1** to **18** write the numbers in standard form.

1. 4000	**2.** 500	**3.** 70 000
4. 60	**5.** 2400	**6.** 380
7. 46 000	**8.** 46	**9.** 900 000
10. 2560	**11.** 0.007	**12.** 0.0004

13. 0.0035

14. 0.421

15. 0.000055

16. 0.01

17. 564000

18. 19 million

19. The population of China is estimated at 1400000000.
Write this in standard form.

20. A hydrogen atom weighs 0.00000000000000000000000167 grams.
Write this mass in standard form.

21. The area of the surface of the Earth is about 510000000 km^2.
Express this in standard form.

22. A certain virus is 0.00000000025 cm in diameter.
Write this in standard form.

23. Avogadro's number is 602300000000000000000000.
Express this in standard form.

24. The speed of light is 300000 km/s.
Express this speed in cm/s in standard form.

25. A very rich man leaves his fortune of \$$3.6 \times 10^8$ to be divided equally between his 100 relatives.
How much does each person receive? Give the answer in standard form.

Example 1

Work out 1500×8000000.

$$1500 \times 8000000 = (1.5 \times 10^3) \times (8 \times 10^6)$$
$$= 12 \times 10^9$$
$$= 1.2 \times 10^{10}$$

Notice that we multiply the numbers and the powers of 10 separately.

Example 2

Many calculators have an [EXP] or $\times 10^x$ button which is used for standard form.

a) To enter 1.6×10^7 into the calculator:
press [1.6] [EXP] [7]

b) To enter 3.8×10^{-3}
press [3.8] [EXP] [−3]

c) To calculate $(4.9 \times 10^{11}) \div (3.5 \times 10^{-4})$:

[4.9] [EXP] [11] [÷] [3.5] [EXP] [−4] [=]

The answer is 1.4×10^{15}.

Exercise 7

In Questions **1** to **22**, give the answer in standard form.

1. 5000×3000

2. $60\,000 \times 5000$

3. $0.000\,07 \times 400$

4. $0.0007 \times 0.000\,01$

5. $8000 \div 0.004$

6. $(0.002)^2$

7. 150×0.0006

8. $0.000\,033 \div 500$

9. $0.007 \div 20\,000$

10. $(0.0001)^4$

11. $(2000)^3$

12. $0.005\,92 \div 8000$

13. $(1.4 \times 10^7) \times (3.5 \times 10^4)$

14. $(8.8 \times 10^{10}) \div (2 \times 10^{-2})$

15. $(1.2 \times 10^{11}) \div (8 \times 10^7)$

16. $(4 \times 10^5) \times (5 \times 10^{11})$

17. $(2.1 \times 10^{-3}) \times (8 \times 10^{15})$

18. $(8.5 \times 10^{14}) \div 2000$

19. $(3.3 \times 10^{12}) \times (3 \times 10^{-5})$

20. $(2.5 \times 10^{-8})^2$

21. $(1.2 \times 10^5)^2 \div (5 \times 10^{-3})$

22. $(6.2 \times 10^{-4}) \times (1.1 \times 10^{-3})$

23. If $a = 512 \times 10^2$
$b = 0.478 \times 10^6$
$c = 0.0049 \times 10^7$
arrange a, b and c in order of size (smallest first).

24. If the number 2.74×10^{15} is written out in full, how many zeros follow the 4?

25. If the number 7.31×10^{-17} is written out in full, how many zeros would there be between the decimal point and the digit 7?

26. If $x = 2 \times 10^5$ and $y = 3 \times 10^{-3}$, find the values of:

a) xy **b)** $\frac{x}{y}$

27. Oil flows through a pipe at a rate of 40 m³/s. How long will it take to fill a tank of volume 1.2×10^5 m³?

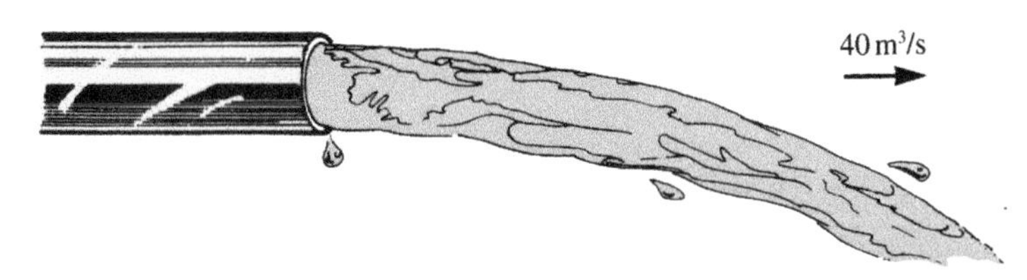

28. Given that $L = 2\sqrt{\frac{a}{k}}$, find the value of L in standard form when $a = 4.5 \times 10^{12}$ and $k = 5 \times 10^7$.

29. A light year is the distance travelled by a beam of light in a year. Light travels at a speed of approximately 3×10^5 km/s.

a) Work out the length of a light year in km.

b) Light takes about 8 minutes to reach the Earth from the Sun. How far is the Earth from the Sun in km?

30. A gardener counts 30 seeds from a packet of seeds and finds their mass is 6×10^{-2} grams.

Use his sample to estimate the total number of seeds in the 50 gram packet.

10.3 Fractions

- Common fractions are added or subtracted from one another directly only when they have a common denominator.
- A **vulgur** fraction is an ordinary fraction like $\frac{3}{4}$ or $\frac{7}{5}$. Where the numerator (top number) is greater than the denominator the fraction is called an **improper** fraction. For example $\frac{9}{4}$ or $\frac{11}{3}$.

  Fractions like $\frac{3}{5}, \frac{2}{11}, \frac{1}{9}$ are called **proper** fractions.

  An improper fraction can be written as a mixed number.
  For example $\frac{5}{3} = 1\frac{2}{3}$; $\frac{13}{3} = 4\frac{1}{3}$

Example

a) $\frac{3}{4}+\frac{2}{5}=\frac{15}{20}+\frac{8}{20}$
$=\frac{23}{20}$
$=1\frac{3}{20}$

b) $2\frac{3}{8}-1\frac{5}{12}=\frac{19}{8}-\frac{17}{12}$
$=\frac{57}{24}-\frac{34}{24}$
$=\frac{23}{24}$

c) $\frac{2}{5}\times\frac{6}{7}=\frac{12}{35}$

d) $2\frac{2}{5}\div 6=\frac{12}{5}\div\frac{6}{1}$
$=\frac{12}{5}\times\frac{1}{6}=\frac{2}{5}$

Exercise 8

Work out and simplify where possible.

1. $\frac{1}{3}+\frac{1}{2}$ **2.** $\frac{1}{3}\times\frac{1}{2}$ **3.** $\frac{1}{3}\div\frac{1}{2}$ **4.** $\frac{3}{4}-\frac{1}{3}$ **5.** $\frac{3}{4}\times\frac{1}{3}$

6. $\frac{3}{4}\div\frac{1}{3}$ **7.** $\frac{2}{5}+\frac{1}{2}$ **8.** $\frac{2}{5}\times\frac{1}{2}$ **9.** $\frac{2}{5}\div\frac{1}{2}$ **10.** $\frac{3}{7}+\frac{1}{2}$

11. $\frac{3}{7}\times\frac{1}{2}$ **12.** $\frac{3}{7}\div\frac{1}{2}$ **13.** $\frac{5}{8}-\frac{1}{4}$ **14.** $\frac{5}{8}\times\frac{1}{4}$ **15.** $\frac{5}{8}\div\frac{1}{4}$

16. $\frac{1}{6}+\frac{4}{5}$ **17.** $\frac{1}{6}\times\frac{4}{5}$ **18.** $\frac{1}{6}\div\frac{4}{5}$ **19.** $\frac{3}{7}+\frac{1}{3}$ **20.** $\frac{3}{7}\times\frac{1}{3}$

21. $\frac{3}{7} \div \frac{1}{3}$

22. $\frac{4}{5} - \frac{1}{4}$

23. $\frac{4}{5} \times \frac{1}{4}$

24. $\frac{4}{5} \div \frac{1}{4}$

25. $\frac{2}{3} - \frac{1}{8}$

26. $\frac{2}{3} \times \frac{1}{8}$

27. $\frac{2}{3} \div \frac{1}{8}$

28. $\frac{5}{9} + \frac{1}{4}$

29. $\frac{5}{9} \times \frac{1}{4}$

30. $\frac{5}{9} \div \frac{1}{4}$

31. $2\frac{1}{2} - \frac{1}{4}$

32. $2\frac{1}{2} \times \frac{1}{4}$

33. $2\frac{1}{2} \div \frac{1}{4}$

34. $3\frac{3}{4} - \frac{2}{3}$

35. $3\frac{3}{4} \times \frac{2}{3}$

36. $3\frac{3}{4} \div \frac{2}{3}$

37. $\dfrac{\frac{1}{2} + \frac{1}{5}}{\frac{1}{2} - \frac{1}{5}}$

38. $\dfrac{\frac{3}{4} - \frac{1}{3}}{\frac{3}{4} + \frac{1}{3}}$

39. $\dfrac{2\frac{1}{4} \times \frac{4}{5}}{\frac{3}{5} - \frac{1}{2}}$

40. $\dfrac{3\frac{1}{2} \times 2\frac{2}{3}}{\frac{1}{2} + 1\frac{1}{18}}$

41. $\frac{3}{2} + \frac{6}{4}$

42. $\frac{5}{3} \times \frac{8}{5}$

43. $\frac{4}{3} + \frac{10}{6}$

44. $\frac{11}{2} - \frac{5}{4}$

45. $\frac{8}{3} \div \frac{9}{4}$

46. $\frac{20}{12} \times \frac{18}{5}$

47. $\frac{11}{4} \div \frac{7}{3}$

48. $\frac{16}{9} \times \frac{15}{10}$

49. $\frac{14}{6} - \frac{15}{8}$

50. $\frac{10}{4} + \frac{14}{6}$

Exercise 9

1. Arrange the fractions in order of size:

a) $\frac{7}{12}, \frac{1}{2}, \frac{2}{3}$

b) $\frac{3}{4}, \frac{2}{3}, \frac{5}{6}$

c) $\frac{1}{3}, \frac{17}{24}, \frac{5}{8}, \frac{3}{4}$

d) $\frac{5}{6}, \frac{8}{9}, \frac{11}{12}$

Write all the fractions with the same denominator, so in part **(a)** write $\frac{7}{12}, \frac{6}{12}, \frac{8}{12}$.

2. Find the fraction which is mid-way between the two fractions given:

a) $\frac{2}{5}, \frac{3}{5}$

b) $\frac{5}{8}, \frac{7}{8}$

c) $\frac{2}{3}, \frac{3}{4}$

d) $\frac{1}{3}, \frac{4}{9}$

e) $\frac{4}{15}, \frac{1}{3}$

f) $\frac{3}{8}, \frac{11}{24}$

3. Vishal earns \$36 for her Saturday job. She got $\frac{1}{3}$ extra as a bonus.

How much did she receive including the bonus?

4. Copy and complete.

a) $2\frac{1}{4} = \frac{\square}{4}$

b) $\frac{15}{7} = \square\frac{\square}{7}$

c) $3\frac{1}{10} = \frac{\square}{10}$

5. Of the cars in a mechanic's workshop:

$\frac{1}{4}$ had broken brakes

$\frac{1}{3}$ had broken steering

$\frac{1}{6}$ had broken lights

the rest had worn tyres.

What fraction of the cars had worn tyres?

6. A rubber ball is dropped from a height of 300 cm. After each bounce, the ball rises to $\frac{4}{5}$ of its previous height.
   a) How high, to the nearest cm, will it rise after the first bounce?
   b) How high, to the nearest cm, will it rise after the fourth bounce?

7. Karol spends his income as follows:
   a) $\frac{2}{5}$ of his income goes in tax,
   b) $\frac{2}{3}$ of what is left goes on food, rent and transport,
   c) he spends the rest on gym membership and computer games.
   What fraction of his income is spent on gym membership and computer games?

8. Here is a list of the number of hours for which a computer was used over 5 days: $6\frac{1}{2}$, $6\frac{1}{4}$, $5\frac{1}{2}$, $5\frac{3}{4}$, $6\frac{1}{2}$.
   a) For how many hours was the computer used altogether?
   b) The computer is rented at \$10 per hour. What is the total rent for the week?

9. A set of drills starts at $\frac{1}{8}$ cm and goes up to $\frac{5}{8}$ cm in steps of $\frac{1}{16}$ cm.
   a) How many drills are there in the full set?
   b) Which size is half-way between $\frac{1}{4}$ cm and $\frac{3}{8}$ cm?

10. A fraction is equivalent to $\frac{2}{3}$ and its denominator (bottom number) is 8 more than its numerator (top number). What is the fraction?

11. In this equation, all the asterisks stand for the same number. What is the number? $\left[\frac{*}{*} - \frac{*}{6} = \frac{*}{30}\right]$

12. Work out one-half of one-third of 65% of \$360.

13. Figures 1 and 2 show an equilateral triangle divided into thirds and quarters. They are combined in Figure 3. Calculate the fraction of Figure 3 that is shaded.

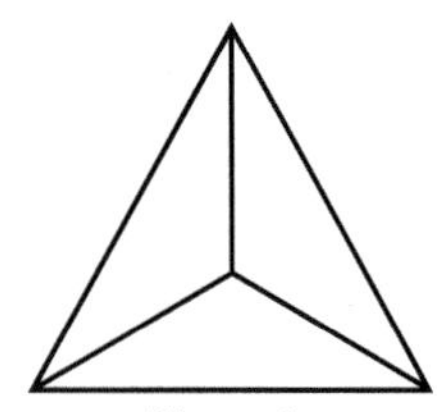
Figure 1

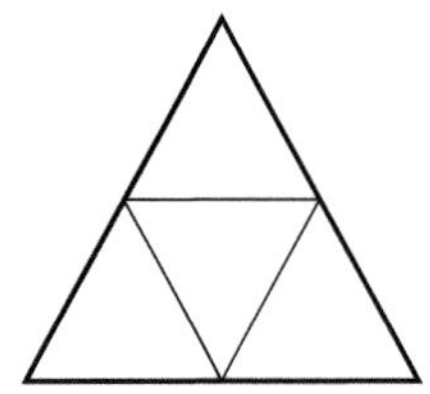
Figure 2

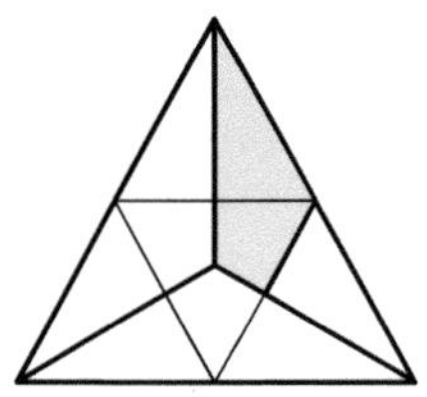
Figure 3

10.4 Negative numbers

- If the weather is very cold and the temperature is 3 degrees below zero, it is written $-3°$.
- If a golfer is 5 under par for his round, the scoreboard will show -5.
- On a bank statement if someone is £55 overdrawn [or 'in the red'] it would appear as –£55.

The above are examples of the use of negative numbers.

An easy way to begin calculations with negative numbers is to think about changes in temperature:

a) Suppose the temperature is $-2°$ and it rises by $7°$.

The new temperature is $5°$.

We can write $-2 + 7 = 5$.

b) Suppose the temperature is $-3°$ and it falls by $6°$.

The new temperature is $-9°$.

We can write $-3 - 6 = -9$.

Exercise 10

In Questions **1** to **12** move up or down the thermometer to find the new temperature.

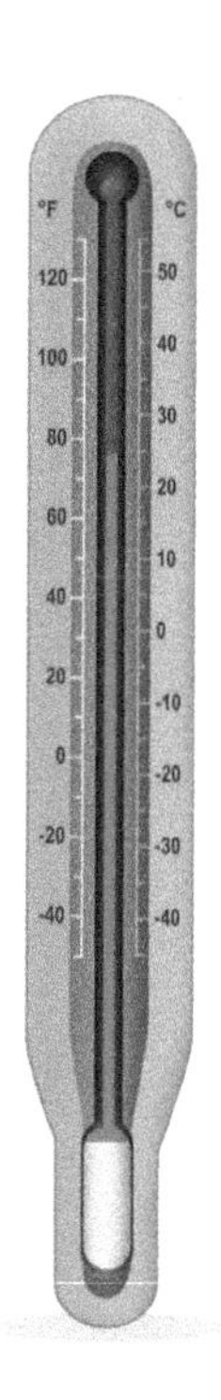

1. The temperature is $+8°$ and it falls by $3°$.

2. The temperature is $+4°$ and it falls by $5°$.

3. The temperature is $+2°$ and it falls by $6°$.

4. The temperature is $-1°$ and it falls by $6°$.

5. The temperature is $-5°$ and it rises by $1°$.

6. The temperature is $-8°$ and it rises by $4°$.

7. The temperature is $-3°$ and it rises by $7°$.

8. The temperature is $+4°$ and it rises by $8°$.

9. The temperature is $+9°$ and it falls by $14°$.

10. The temperature is $-13°$ and it rises by $13°$.

11. The temperature is $-6°$ and it falls by $5°$.

12. The temperature is $-25°$ and it rises by $10°$.

In Questions **13** to **22** state whether the temperature has risen or fallen and by how many degrees.

13. It was $-5°$ and it is now $-8°$.

14. It was $5°$ and it is now $-1°$.

15. It was $9°$ and it is now $-1°$.

16. It was $-2°$ and it is now $-7°$.

17. It was –11° and it is now –4°.

18. It was –8° and it is now 3°.

19. It was –15° and it is now 0°.

20. It was –7° and it is now –2°.

21. It was –3° and it is now –83°.

22. It was 4° and it is now –11°.

23. Copy each sequence and fill in the missing numbers.

a) 9, 6, 3, ☐, ☐

b) ☐, –1, 3, 7, 11

c) ☐, ☐, –10, –5, 0

24. A diver is below the surface of the water at –15 m. He dives down by 6 m, then rises 4 m. Where is he now?

25. Some land in Bangladesh is below sea level.
Here are the heights, above sea level, of five villages.

A 1 m **B** –4 m **C** 21 m **D** –2 m **E** –1.5 m

a) Which village is safest from flooding?

b) Which village is most at risk from serious flooding?

26. Arjun is overdrawn at the bank by \$90 (this means he owes the bank \$90).
If Arjun pays in \$150, how much money will he have in the bank?

- For adding and subtracting use the number line.

Example 1

Find: **a)** $-1 + 4$ **b)** $-2 - 3$ **c)** $4 - 6$

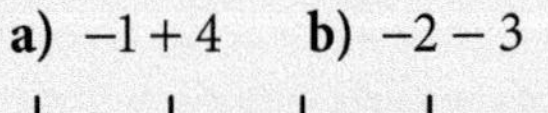

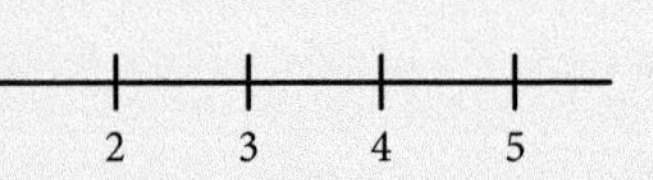

a) – 1 (start here) + (go right) 4 (4 places) $-1 + 4 = 3$

b) – 2 (start here) – (go left) 3 (3 places) $-2 - 3 = -5$

c) 4 (start here) – (go left) 6 (6 places) $4 - 6 = -2$

When you have two (+) or (–) signs together use this rule:

$++ = +$ $+- = -$

$-- = +$ $-+ = -$

Example 2

a) $3 - (-6) = 3 + 6 = 9$

b) $-4 + (-5) = -4 - 5 = -9$

c) $-5 - (+7) = -5 - 7 = -12$

Exercise 11

Work out:

1. $-6 + 2$	**2.** $-7 - 5$	**3.** $-3 - 8$	**4.** $-5 + 2$
5. $-6 + 1$	**6.** $8 - 4$	**7.** $4 - 9$	**8.** $11 - 19$
9. $4 + 15$	**10.** $-7 - 10$	**11.** $16 - 20$	**12.** $-7 + 2$
13. $-6 - 5$	**14.** $10 - 4$	**15.** $-4 + 0$	**16.** $-6 + 12$
17. $-7 + 7$	**18.** $2 - 20$	**19.** $8 - 11$	**20.** $-6 - 5$
21. $-3 + (-5)$	**22.** $-5 - (+2)$	**23.** $4 - (+3)$	**24.** $-3 - (-4)$
25. $6 - (-3)$	**26.** $16 + (-5)$	**27.** $-4 + (-4)$	**28.** $20 - (-22)$
29. $-6 - (-10)$	**30.** $95 + (-80)$	**31.** $-3 - (+4)$	**32.** $-5 - (+4)$
33. $6 + (-7)$	**34.** $-4 + (-3)$	**35.** $-7 - (-7)$	**36.** $3 - (-8)$
37. $-8 + (-6)$	**38.** $7 - (+7)$	**39.** $12 - (-5)$	**40.** $9 - (+6)$

When two directed numbers with the same sign are multiplied together, the answer is positive.

Example 1

a) $+7 \times (+3) = +21$

b) $-6 \times (-4) = +24$

When two directed numbers with different signs are multiplied together, the answer is negative.

Example 2

a) $-8 \times (+4) = -32$

b) $+7 \times (-5) = -35$

c) $-3 \times (+2) \times (+5) = -6 \times (+5) = -30$

When dividing directed numbers, the rules are the same as in multiplication.

Example 3

a) $-70 \div (-2) = +35$

b) $+12 \div (-3) = -4$

c) $-20 \div (+4) = -5$

Exercise 12

Work out:

1. $-3 \times (+2)$
2. $-4 \times (+1)$
3. $+5 \times (-3)$
4. $-3 \times (-3)$
5. $-4 \times (2)$
6. $-5 \times (3)$
7. $6 \times (-4)$
8. $3 \times (2)$
9. $-3 \times (-4)$
10. $6 \times (-3)$
11. $-7 \times (3)$
12. $-5 \times (-5)$
13. $6 \times (-10)$
14. $-3 \times (-7)$
15. $8 \times (6)$
16. $-8 \times (2)$
17. $-7 \times (6)$
18. $-5 \times (-4)$
19. $-6 \times (7)$
20. $11 \times (-6)$
21. $8 \div (-2)$
22. $-9 \div (3)$
23. $-6 \div (-2)$
24. $10 \div (-2)$
25. $-12 \div (-3)$
26. $-16 \div (4)$
27. $4 \div (-1)$
28. $8 \div (-8)$
29. $16 \div (-8)$
30. $-20 \div (-5)$
31. $-16 \div (1)$
32. $18 \div (-9)$
33. $36 \div (-9)$
34. $-45 \div (-9)$
35. $-70 \div (7)$
36. $-11 \div (-1)$
37. $-16 \div (-1)$
38. $1 \div \left(-\frac{1}{2}\right)$
39. $-2 \div \left(\frac{1}{2}\right)$
40. $50 \div (-10)$
41. $-8 \times (-8)$
42. $-9 \times (3)$
43. $10 \times (-60)$
44. $-8 \times (-5)$
45. $-12 \div (-6)$
46. $-18 \times (-2)$
47. $-8 \div (4)$
48. $-80 \div (10)$
49. $-16 \times (-10)$
50. $32 \div (-16)$

Questions on negative numbers are more difficult when the different sorts are mixed together. The remaining questions are given in the form of three short tests.

Test 1

1. $-8 - 8$
2. $-8 \times (-8)$
3. -5×3
4. $-5 + 3$
5. $8 - (-7)$
6. $20 - 2$
7. $-18 \div (-6)$
8. $4 + (-10)$
9. $-2 + 13$
10. $+8 \times (-6)$
11. $-9 + (+2)$
12. $-2 - (-11)$
13. $-6 \times (-1)$
14. $2 - 20$
15. $-14 - (-4)$
16. $-40 \div (-5)$
17. $5 - 11$
18. -3×10
19. $9 + (-5)$
20. $7 \div (-7)$

Test 2

1. $-2 \times (+8)$
2. $-2 + 8$
3. $-7 - 6$
4. $-7 \times (-6)$
5. $+36 \div (-9)$
6. $-8 - (-4)$
7. $-14 + 2$
8. $5 \times (-4)$
9. $11 + (-5)$
10. $11 - 11$
11. $-9 \times (-4)$
12. $-6 + (-4)$
13. $3 - 10$
14. $-20 \div (-2)$
15. $16 + (-10)$
16. $-4 - (+14)$
17. $-45 \div 5$
18. $18 - 3$
19. $-1 \times (-1)$
20. $-3 - (-3)$

Test 3

1. $-10 \times (-10)$
2. $-10 - 10$
3. $-8 \times (+1)$
4. $-8 + 1$
5. $5 + (-9)$
6. $15 - 5$
7. $-72 \div (-8)$
8. $-12 - (-2)$
9. $-1 + 8$
10. $-5 \times (-7)$
11. $-10 + (-10)$
12. $-6 \times (+4)$
13. $6 - 16$
14. $-42 \div (+6)$
15. $-13 + (-6)$
16. $-8 - (-7)$
17. $5 \times (-1)$
18. $2 - 15$
19. $21 + (-21)$
20. $-16 \div (-2)$

10.5 Substituting into formulae

When a calculation is repeated many times it is often helpful to use a formula. When a building society offers a mortgage it may use a formula like '$2\frac{1}{2}$ times the main salary plus the second salary'.

Publishers use a formula to work out the selling price of a book based on the production costs and the expected sales of the book.

Example 1

A formula connecting velocity with acceleration and time is $v = u + at$.
Find the value of v when $u = 3$,
$a = 4$,
$t = 6$.

$v = u + at$
$v = 3 + (4 \times 6)$
$v = 27$

Example 2

A formula for the tension in a spring is $T = \frac{kx}{a}$.
Find the value of T when $k = 13$,
$x = 5$,
$a = 2$.

$T = \frac{kx}{a}$

$T = \frac{13 \times 5}{2}$

$T = 32\frac{1}{2}$

Exercise 13

1. A formula involving force, mass and acceleration is $F = ma$. Find the value of F when $m = 12$ and $a = 3$.
2. The height of a growing tree is given by the formula $h = 2t + 15$. Find the value of h when $t = 7$.
3. The time required to cook a joint of meat is given by the formula

   $T = (\text{mass of joint}) \times 3 + \frac{1}{2}$

   Find the value of T when (mass of joint) $= 2\frac{1}{2}$.
4. An important formula in physics states that $I = mu - mv$.

   Find the value of I when $m = 6$, $u = 8$, $v = 5$.
5. The distance travelled by an accelerating car is given by the formula $s = \left(\frac{u+v}{2}\right)t$. Find the value of s when $u = 17$, $v = 25$ and $t = 4$.
6. Einstein's famous formula states that $E = mc^2$.

   Find the value of E when $m = 0.0001$ and $c = 3 \times 10^8$.
7. The height of a stone thrown upwards is given by $h = ut - 5t^2$.

   Find the value of h when $u = 70$ and $t = 3$.
8. The speed of an accelerating particle is given by the formula $v^2 = u^2 + 2as$. Find the value of v when $u = 11$, $a = 5$ and $s = 6$.
9. The time period T of a simple pendulum is given by the formula $T = 2\pi\sqrt{\left(\frac{\ell}{g}\right)}$, where ℓ is the length of the pendulum and g is the gravitational acceleration. Find T when $\ell = 0.65$, $g = 9.81$ and $\pi = 3.142$.
10. The sum S of the squares of the integers from 1 to n is given by $S = \frac{1}{6}n(n+1)(2n+1)$. Find S when $n = 12$.

Example

If $x = 3$, $y = -4$, work out the following.

a) $2x + y$

$= 6 + -4$

$= 6 - 4$

$= 2$

b) $xy - y$

$= -12 - -4$

$= -12 + 4$

$= -8$

Do some of the working in your head.

Exercise 14

If $a = -4$, $b = 5$, $c = -2$, work out:

1. $2a + 3$
2. $3b - 7$
3. $4a - 1$
4. $2b + c$
5. $5c - 2a$
6. $6a - 3$
7. $2c + b$
8. $3a - 2b$
9. $6c - 2b$
10. $3c + 4a$
11. $3c - 4$
12. $2a - 3c$
13. $7b + 3a$
14. $8a + 6c$
15. $2b - 4a$
16. $4b + 5$
17. $3a + 8$
18. $2c - a$
19. $5a - 2c$
20. $3b + 7$

If $n = 3$, $x = -1$, $y = 6$, work out:

21. $2x - 3$
22. $3y + 4n$
23. $5n + 2x$
24. $4y - x$
25. $7y - 2$
26. $3x + 2n$
27. $10x + 5$
28. $6x - y$
29. $4x - 5y$
30. $2y - 10$
31. $8n - 2y$
32. $7n + 3y$
33. $6y + 4$
34. $4n + 5x$
35. $2n + 3x$
36. $5y - 20$
37. $9y - n$
38. $8x + 2n$
39. $5x + 6$
40. $3n - 2x$

Reminders:

$a^2 = a \times a$

$a^3 = a \times a \times a$

$2a^2 = 2(a^2)$

$(2a)^2 = 2a \times 2a$

$a(b - c)$: Work out the term in brackets first

$\frac{a+b}{c}$: The division line works like a bracket, so work out $a + b$ first.

Example

If $y = -3$, $x = 2$, work out **a)** y^2 **b)** $3x^2$

a) $y^2 = -3 \times -3 = 9$ **b)** $3x^2 = 3 \times 4 = 12$

Exercise 15

If $m = 2$, $t = -2$, $x = -3$, $y = 4$, work out:

1. m^2
2. t^2
3. x^2
4. y^2
5. m^3
6. t^3
7. x^3
8. y^3
9. $2m^2$
10. $(2m)^2$
11. $2t^2$
12. $(2t)^2$
13. $2x^2$
14. $(2x)^2$
15. $3y^2$
16. $4m^2$
17. $5t^2$
18. $6x^2$
19. $(3y)^2$
20. $3m^3$
21. $x^2 + 4$
22. $y^2 - 6$
23. $t^2 - 3$
24. $m^3 + 10$
25. $x^2 + t^2$
26. $2x^2 + 1$
27. $m^2 + xt$
28. my^2
29. $(mt)^2$
30. $(xy)^2$
31. $(xt)^2$
32. yx^2
33. $m - t$
34. $t - x$
35. $y - m$
36. $m - y^2$
37. $t + x$
38. $2m + 3x$
39. $3t - y$
40. $xt + y$

41. $3(m+t)$ **42.** $4(x+y)$ **43.** $5(m+2y)$ **44.** $2(y-m)$ **45.** $m(t+x)$

46. $y(m+x)$ **47.** $x(y-m)$ **48.** $t(2m+y)$ **49.** $m^2(y-x)$ **50.** $t^2(x^2+m)$

Exercise 16

If $w=-2$, $x=3$, $y=0$, $z=2$, work out:

1. $\frac{w}{z}+x$ **2.** $\frac{w+x}{z}$ **3.** $y\left(\frac{x+z}{w}\right)$ **4.** $x^2(z+wy)$

5. $x\sqrt{(-wz-x)}$ **6.** $w^2\sqrt{(z^2+y^2)}$ **7.** $2(w^2+x^2+y^2)$ **8.** $2x(w-z)$

9. $\frac{z}{w}+x$ **10.** $\frac{z+w}{x}$ **11.** $\frac{x+w}{z^2}$ **12.** $\frac{y^2-w^2}{xz}$

13. z^2+4z+5 **14.** $\frac{1}{w}+\frac{1}{z}+\frac{1}{x}$ **15.** $\frac{4}{z}+\frac{10}{w}$ **16.** $\frac{yz-xw}{xz-w}$

17. Find $K=\sqrt{\left(\frac{a^2+b^2+c^2-2c}{a^2+b^2+4c}\right)}$ if $a=3$, $b=-2$, $c=-1$.

18. Find $W=\frac{kmn(k+m+n)}{(k+m)(k+n)}$ if $k=\frac{1}{2}$, $m=-\frac{1}{3}$, $n=\frac{1}{4}$.

10.6 Problems 3

Exercise 17

1. A maths teacher bought 40 calculators at \$8.20 each and a number of other calculators costing \$2.95 each. In all she spent \$387.
   How many of the cheaper calculators did she buy?
2. The total mass of a jar one-quarter full of jam is 250 g. The total mass of the same jar three-quarters full of jam is 350 g.

$\frac{1}{4}$ 250 g

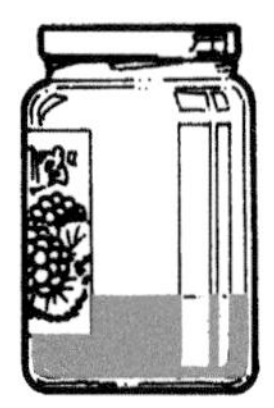

$\frac{3}{4}$ 350 g

   What is the mass of the empty jar?
3. I have lots of 1c, 2c, 3c and 4c stamps. How many different combinations of stamps can I make which total 5c?
4. 8% of 2500 + 37% of $P = 348$. Find the value of P.
5. Express 419 965 in terms of its prime factors.

6. A map is 278 mm wide and 445 mm long. When reduced on a photocopier, the copy is 360 mm long. What is the width of the copy, to the nearest millimetre?

7. How many prime numbers are there between 120 and 130?

8. You are given that $41 \times 271 = 11\,111$. Work out the following *in your head.*

a) 246×271

b) $22\,222 \div 271$

9. Booklets have a mass of 19 g each, and they are posted in an envelope of mass 38 g. Postage charges are shown in the table below.

Mass (in grams) not more than	60	100	150	200	250	300	350	600
Postage (in cents)	24	30	37	44	51	59	67	110

a) A package consists of 15 booklets in an envelope. What is the total mass of the package?

b) The mass of a second package is 475 g. How many booklets does it contain?

c) What is the postage charge on a package of mass 320 g?

d) The postage on a third package was $1.10. What is the largest number of booklets it could contain?

Exercise 18

1. On a baby's first birthday her parents save 1 cent. On her second birthday they save 2 cents. On her third birthday they save 4 cents and so on, doubling the amount each time. How much did they save on her twenty-first birthday?

2. The diagrams show magic squares in which the sum of the numbers in any row, column or diagonal is the same. Find the value of x in each square.

a)

	x	6
3		7
		2

b)

4		5	16
x		10	
	7	11	2
1			13

3. Find a pair of positive whole numbers a and b for which $18a + 65b = 1865$.
4. Work out $100 - 99 + 98 - 97 + 96 - \cdots + 4 - 3 + 2 - 1$.
5. The smallest three-digit product of a one-digit prime and a two-digit prime is

(A)	(B)	(C)	(D)	(E)
102	103	104	105	106

6. Apart from 1, 3 and 5 all odd numbers less than 100 can be written in the form $p + 2^n$ where p is a prime number and n is greater than or equal to 2.

   e.g. $43 = 11 + 2^5$

   $27 = 23 + 2^2$

   For the odd numbers 7, 9, 11, $\cdots$, 39 write as many as you can in the form $p + 2^n$.
7. Evaluate **a)** $\frac{1}{3} \times \frac{2}{4} \times \frac{3}{5} \times \ldots \times \frac{9}{11} \times \frac{10}{12}$ **b)** $\left[(-2)^{-2}\right]^{-2}$
8. What is the smallest number greater than 1000 that is exactly divisible by 13 and 17?
9. Find the smallest value of n for which

   $1^2 + 2^2 + 3^2 + 4^2 + 5^2 + \cdots + n^2 > 800$
10. The reciprocal of 2 is $\frac{1}{2}$. The reciprocal of 7 is $\frac{1}{7}$.

    The reciprocal of x is $\frac{1}{x}$. Find the square root of the reciprocal of the square root of the reciprocal of ten thousand.

Revision exercise 10A

1. $a = \frac{1}{2}, b = \frac{1}{4}$. Which one of the following has the greatest value?

   i) ab **ii)** $a + b$ **iii)** $\frac{a}{b}$

   iv) $\frac{b}{a}$ **v)** $(ab)^2$
2. Given that $x = 4, y = 3, z = -2$, evaluate:

   a) $2x(y + z)$

   b) $(xy)^2 - z^2$

   c) $x^2 + y^2 + z^2$

   d) $(x + y)(x - z)$
3. Work out:

   a) $-6 - 5$ **b)** $-7 + 30$

   c) $-13 + 3$ **d)** -4×5

   e) -3×-2 **f)** $-4 + -10$
4. Given $a = 3$, $b = -2$ and $c = 5$, work out:

   a) $b + c$ **b)** $a - b$

   c) ab **d)** $a + bc$
5. Given $a = 3$, $b = 4$ and $c = -2$, evaluate:

   a) $2a^2 - b$ **b)** $a(b - c)$

   c) $2b^2 - c^2$

6. Throughout his life Lewis's heart has beat at an average rate of 72 beats per minute. Lewis is sixty years old. How many times has his heart beat during his life? Give the answer in standard form correct to two significant figures.

7. a) Given that $x - z = 5y$, express z in terms of x and y.

   b) Given that $mk + 3m = 11$, express k in terms of m.

8. Write in a form using indices:

   a) $4 \times 4 \times 4 \times 4 \times 4$

   b) $1 \times 1 \times 1 \times 1 \times 1 \times 1 \times 1$

   c) $2 \times 2 \times 2 \times 5 \times 5$

9. Write in a more simple form:

   a) $6^2 \times 6^3$ b) $7^4 \times 7^4$

   c) $3^{10} \div 3^3$ d) $10^4 \div 10^1$

   e) $5^{-2} \times 5^6$ f) $2^4 \div 2^5$

10. Solve the equations for x.

   a) $x^3 = 8$ b) $3^x = 9$ c) $2^x = 16$

11. Simplify:

   a) $(x^2)^4$ b) $(n^3)^3$ c) $4a^2 \times 3a$

12. Write in standard form:

   a) 50 000 b) 610 000 c) 0.0003

   d) 0.0015 e) 10 million

13. Use a calculator and give the answer in standard form:

   a) $(2 \times 10^6) \times (1.5 \times 10^4)$

   b) $(8 \times 10^9) \div (2 \times 10^5)$

   c) $(4 \times 10^{-2}) \times (2 \times 10^8)$

   d) $(1.5 \times 10^3) \times (3 \times 10^4)$

14. Work out:

   a) $\frac{3}{5} + \frac{1}{3}$ b) $\frac{3}{8} \times \frac{2}{3}$

   c) $\frac{1}{5} - \frac{1}{10}$ d) $\frac{2}{3} \div \frac{1}{4}$

   e) $1\frac{1}{2} - \frac{2}{5}$ f) $2\frac{1}{4} \times \frac{3}{4}$

15. If $H = \frac{1}{2}\left(\frac{1}{x} + \frac{1}{y}\right)$, find H when $x = 4$ and $y = 6$.

16. How many of the statements below are true?

   $5\% = \frac{1}{20}$, $5^{-1} = 0.5$, $\frac{1}{3} = 0.3$, $\frac{1}{2} \div \frac{1}{2} = \frac{1}{4}$

Examination-style exercise 10B

1. Write down the value of x when

   (a) $2^x = 8$ [1]

   (b) $3^x = \frac{1}{81}$ [1]

Cambridge IGCSE Mathematics 0580
Paper 1 Q16 November 2006

2. (a) $4^p \times 4^5 = 4^{15}$. Find the value of p. [1]

   (b) $2^7 \div 2^q = 2^4$. Find the value of q. [1]

   (c) $5^r = \frac{1}{25}$. Find the value of r. [1]

Cambridge IGCSE Mathematics 0580
Paper 11 Q13 June 2007

3. Simplify

(a) t^0 [1]

(b) $(y^2)^4$ [1]

(c) $\left(\frac{5}{p}\right)^{-2}$ [2]

Cambridge IGCSE Mathematics 0580
Paper 12 Q15 November 2007

4. Simplify

(a) $\left(\frac{1}{p}\right)^{0}$ [1]

(b) $q^4 \times q^7$ [1]

(c) $(r^2)^{-3}$ [1]

Cambridge IGCSE Mathematics 0580
Paper 11 Q16 November 2008

5. $>$ $=$ $<$

Choose one of the symbols above to complete each of the following statements.

(a) $\frac{3}{8}$ .... 38% [1]

(b) $\left(\frac{1}{4}\right)^{-2}$ .... 4 [1]

6. There are 565 sheets of paper in a book.

(a) How many sheets of paper are there in 2000 of these books?
Give your answer in standard form. [2]

(b) A pile of 565 sheets of paper is 25 millimetres high.
Calculate the thickness of 1 sheet of paper.
Give your answer in standard form. [3]

Cambridge IGCSE Mathematics 0580
Paper 1 Q20 June 2006

7. Write 0.003 62 in standard form. [1]

Cambridge IGCSE Mathematics 0580
Paper 12 Q7 June 2008

8. (a) Calculate $\frac{0.0763}{1.85 + 4.7 \times 8}$. [1]

(b) Write 0.0763 in standard form. [1]

Cambridge IGCSE Mathematics 0580
Paper 11 Q2 June 2009

9. **(a)** Write in the missing number: $\frac{3}{4} = \frac{\cdots}{16}$ [1]

(b) Without using your calculator, and writing down all your working,

show that $1\frac{5}{8} - \frac{3}{4} = \frac{7}{8}$ [2]

10. A bottle of lemonade contains $1\frac{1}{2}$ litres.

A glass holds $\frac{1}{8}$ litre.

How many glasses can be filled from one bottle of lemonade? [2]

Cambridge IGCSE Mathematics 0580
Paper 1 Q6 November 2005

11.

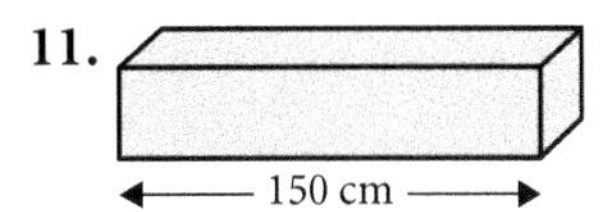

A piece of wood is 150 centimetres long.

It has to be cut into equal lengths of $6\frac{1}{4}$ centimetres.

How many of these lengths can be cut from this piece of wood? [1]

Cambridge IGCSE Mathematics 0580
Paper 11 Q4 June 2007

12. The temperature at noon at an Antarctic weather centre was −15°C.

At midnight it had fallen by 12°C.

What was the temperature at midnight? [1]

Cambridge IGCSE Mathematics 0580
Paper 1 Q1 June 2006

13. $=$ $<$ $>$

Choose one of the symbols given above to complete each of the following statements.

When $x = 6$ and $y = -7$, then

(a) x .... y [1]

(b) x^2 .... y^2 [1]

(c) $y - x$ .... $x - y$ [1]

Cambridge IGCSE Mathematics 0580
Paper 1 Q14 November 2005

11 Using and Applying Mathematics

11.1 Investigation tasks

Investigations in mathematics can be fun and help your understanding of many topics.

There are a large number of possible starting points for investigations here so it may be possible to choose investigations which appeal to you.

Here are a few guidelines:

a) If the set problem is too complicated, try an easier case;

b) Draw your own diagrams;

c) Make tables of your results and be systematic;

d) Look for patterns;

e) Is there a rule or formula to describe the results?

f) Can you *predict* further results?

g) Can you *explain* any rules which you may find?

h) Where possible extend the task further by asking questions like 'what happens if …'

1 Opposite corners

Here the numbers are arranged in 9 columns.

In the 2×2 square …

6	7
15	16

$6 \times 16 = 96$

$7 \times 15 = 105$

… the difference between them is 9.

1	2	3	4	5	6	7	8	9
10	11	12	13	14	15	16	17	18
19	20	21	22	23	24	25	26	27
28	29	30	31	32	33	34	35	36
37	38	39	40	41	42	43	44	45
46	47	48	49	50	51	52	53	54
55	56	57	58	59	60	61	62	63
64	65	66	67	68	69	70	71	72
73	74	75	76	77	78	79	80	81
82	83	84	85	86	87	88	89	90

In the 3×3 square …

22	23	24
31	32	33
40	41	42

$22 \times 42 = 924$

$24 \times 40 = 960$

… the difference between them is 36.

Investigate to see if you can find any rules or patterns connecting the size of square chosen and the difference.

If you find a rule, use it to *predict* the difference for larger squares.

Test your rule by looking at squares like 8×8 or 9×9.

Can you *generalise* the rule?

[What is the difference for a square of size $n \times n$?]

Can you *prove* the rule?

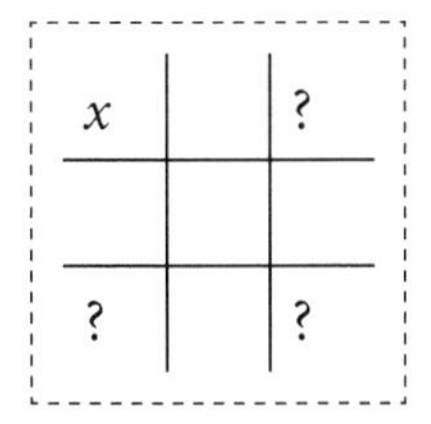

In a 3×3 square …

What happens if the numbers are arranged in six columns or seven columns?

1	2	3	4	5	6
7	8	9	10	11	12
13	14	15	16	17	18
19					

1	2	3	4	5	6	7
8	9	10	11	12	13	14
15	16	17	18	19	20	21
22						

2 Hiring a car

You are going to hire a car for one week (7 days).

Which of the firms below should you choose?

Gibson car hire	**Snowdon rent-a-car**	**Hav-a-car**
\$170 per week unlimited travel	\$10 per day 6.5c per km	\$60 per week 500 km without charge 22c per km over 500 km

Work out as detailed an answer as possible.

3 Half-time score

The final score in a football match was 3–2. How many different scores were possible at half-time?

Investigate for other final scores where the difference between the teams is always one goal [1–0, 5–4, etc.]. Is there a pattern or rule which would tell you the number of possible half-time scores in a game which finished 58-57?

Suppose the game ends in a draw. Find a rule which would tell you the number of possible half-time scores if the final score was 63–63.

Investigate for other final scores [3–0, 5–1, 4–2, etc.].

Find a rule which gives the number of different half-time scores for *any* final score (say $a - b$).

4 An expanding diagram

Look at the series of diagrams below.

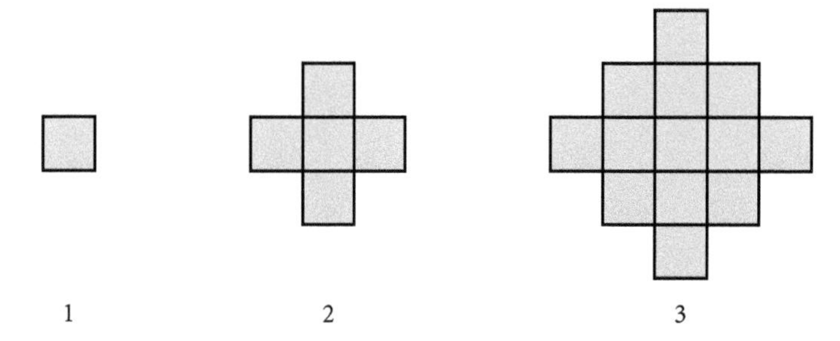

Continue the series by drawing the fourth, fifth and sixth diagrams in the sequence. Each new diagram is obtained by drawing squares all around the outside of the previous diagram. For each diagram count the number of squares it contains.

Using the results of the first six diagrams, can you predict the number of squares in the seventh diagram? See if you were right by drawing the diagram.

Can you predict the number of squares in the eighth diagram? Again draw the diagram to see if you were right.

Can you predict the number of squares in:

a) the 12th diagram, **b)** the 20th diagram?

Try to find a rule which will enable you to predict the number of squares for any member of the sequence of diagrams.

5 Maximum box

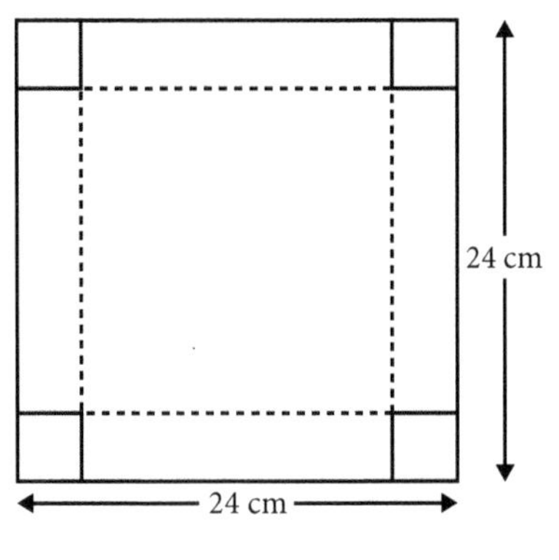

a) You have a square sheet of card 24 cm by 24 cm.

You can make a box (without a lid) by cutting squares from the corners and folding up the sides.

What size corners should you cut out so that the volume of the box is as large as possible?

Try different sizes for the corners and record the results in a table.

Length of the side of the corner square (cm)	Dimensions of the open box (cm)	Volume of the box (cm^3)
1	$22 \times 22 \times 1$	484
2		
–		
–		

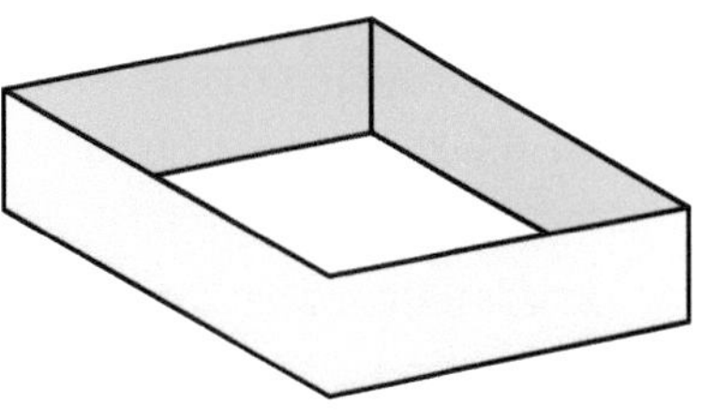

Now consider boxes made from different-sized cards:

15 cm × 15 cm and 20 cm by 20 cm.

What size corners should you cut out this time so that the volume of the box is as large as possible?

Is there a connection between the size of the corners cut out and the size of the square card?

b) Investigate the situation when the card is not square.

Take rectangular cards where the length is twice the width (20×10, 12×6, 18×9 etc.).

Again, for the maximum volume is there a connection between the size of the corners cut out and the size of the original card?

6 Timetabling

a) Every year a new timetable has to be written for the school.

We will look at the problem of writing the timetable for one department (mathematics). The department allocates the teaching periods as follows:

U6	2 sets (at the same times); 8 periods in 4 doubles.
L6	2 sets (at the same times); 8 periods in 4 doubles.
Year 5	6 sets (at the same times); 5 single periods.
Year 4	6 sets (at the same times); 5 single periods.
Year 3	6 sets (at the same times); 5 single periods.

Year 2 6 sets (at the same times); 5 single periods.

Year 1 5 mixed ability forms; 5 single periods not necessarily at the same times.

Here are the teachers and the maximum number of maths periods which they can teach.

A	33	F	15	(Must be Years 5, 4, 3)
B	33	G	10	(Must be Years 2, 1)
C	33	H	10	(Must be Years 2, 1)
D	20	I	5	(Must be Year 3)
E	20			

Furthermore, to ensure some continuity of teaching, teachers B and C must teach the U6 and teachers A, B, C, D, E, F must teach Year 5.

Here is a timetable form which has been started

M	5				U6 B, C	U6 B, C		
Tu		5	U6 B, C	U6 B, C				
W					5			
Th						5	U6 B, C	U6 B, C
F	U6 B, C	U6 B, C		5				

Your task is to write a complete timetable for the mathematics department subject to the restrictions already stated.

b) If that was too easy, here are some changes.

U6 and L6 have 4 sets each (still 8 periods).

Two new teachers:

J 20 periods maximum

K 15 periods maximum but cannot teach on Mondays.

Because of games lessons: A cannot teach Wednesday afternoon

B cannot teach Tuesday afternoon

C cannot teach Friday afternoon.

Also: A, B, C and E must teach U6

A, B, C, D, E, F must teach Year 5.

For the students, games afternoons are as follows:

Monday Year 2; Tuesday Year 3; Wednesday Year 5 L6, U6; Thursday Year 4; Friday Year 1.

7 Diagonals

In a 4×7 rectangle, the diagonal passes through 10 squares.

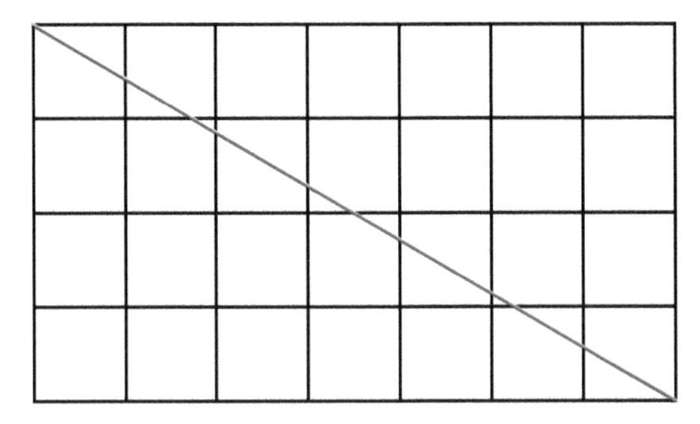

Draw rectangles of your own choice and count the number of squares through which the diagonal passes.

A rectangle is 640×250. How many squares will the diagonal pass through?

8 Painting cubes

The large cube on the right consists of 27 unit cubes.

All six faces of the large cube are painted green.

- How many unit cubes have 3 green faces?
- How many unit cubes have 2 green faces?
- How many unit cubes have 1 green face?
- How many unit cubes have 0 green faces?

Answer the four questions for the cube which is $n \times n \times n$.

11.2 Puzzles and games

1 Crossnumbers

Draw a copy of the crossnumber pattern below and work out the answers using the clues. You can check your working by doing *all* the across and *all* the down clues.

1		2		3			4
		5					
6						7	
		8	9				
	10				11		
12			13	14			
		15		16		17	18
19						20	

Part A

Across

1. $327 + 198$

2. $245 \div 7$

5. $3146 - 729$

6. $248 - 76$

7. 2^6

8. $850 \div 5$

10. $10^2 + 1^2$

11. $3843 \div 7$

12. $1000 - 913$

13. $37 \times 5 \times 3$

16. $152\,300 \div 50$

19. 3^6

20 $100 - \left(\dfrac{17 \times 10}{5}\right)$

Down

1. $3280 + 1938$

2. $65\,720 - 13\,510$

3. 3.1×1000

4. $1284 \div 6$

7. $811 - 127$

9. 65×11

10. $(12^2 - 8) \div 8$

11. $(7^2 + 1^2) \times 11$

12. $7 + 29 + 234 + 607$

14. $800 - 265$

15. $1 + 2 + 3 + 4 + 5 + 6 + 7 + 8 + 13$

17. $(69 \times 6) \div 9$

18. $3^2 + 4^2 + 5^2 + 2^4$

Part B Draw decimal points on the lines between squares where necessary.

Across

1. $4.2 + 1.64$
3. 7×0.5
5. $20.562 \div 6$
6. $(2^3 \times 5) \times 10 - 1$
7. 0.034×1000
8. 61×0.3
10. $8 - 0.36$
11. 19×50
12. $95.7 \div 11$
13. 8.1×0.7
16. $(11 \times 5) \div 8$
19. $(44 - 2.8) \div 5$
20. $2^2 \times 3^2$

Down

1. $62.6 - 4.24$
2. $48.73 - 4.814$
3. $25 + 7.2 + 0.63$
4. $2548 \div 7$
7. 0.315×100
9. 169×0.05
10. $770 \div 100$
11. $14.2 + 0.7 - 5.12$
12. $11.4 - 2.64 - 0.18$
14. 0.0667×10^3
15. $0.6 + 0.7 + 0.8 + 7.3$
17. 0.73 m written in cm
18. 0.028×200

Part C

Across

1. Eleven squared take away six
3. Next in the sequence 21, 24, 28, 33
5. Number of minutes in a day
6. $2 \times 13 \times 5 \times 5$
7. Next in the sequence 92, 83, 74
8. 5% of 11 400
10. $98 + 11^2$
11. $(120 - 9) \times 6$
12. $1\frac{2}{5}$ as a decimal
13. $2387 \div 7$
16. 9.05×1000
19. 8 m – 95 cm (in cm)
20. 3^4

Down

1. Write 18.6 m in cm
2. Fifty-one thousand and fifty-one
3. Write 3.47 km in m
4. $1\frac{1}{4}$ as a decimal
7. 7 m – 54 cm (in cm)
9. 0.0793×1000
10. 2% of 1200
11. $\frac{1}{5}$ of 3050
12. $127 \div 100$
14. Number of minutes between 12:00 and 20:10
15. 4% of 1125
17. $7^2 + 3^2$
18. Last two digits of (67×3)

Part D

Across

1. $1\frac{3}{4}$ as a decimal
3. Two dozen
5. Forty less than ten thousand
6. $10^3 - 10^0$
7. 5% of 740
8. $10 - 0.95$
10. 1.6 m written in cm
11. $5649 \div 7$
12. One-third of 108
13. $6 - 0.28$
16. A quarter to midnight on the 24 h clock
19. $5^3 \times 2^2 + 1^5$
20. $3300 \div 150$

Down

1. $5 \times 7 \times 0.37$
2. Four less than sixty thousand
3. 245×11
4. James Bond
7. Number of minutes between 09:10 and 15:30
9. $\frac{1}{20}$ as a decimal
10. 2^4
11. 8.227 to two decimal places
12. 4 m – 95 cm (in cm)
14. Three to the power 6
15. 20.64 to the nearest whole number
17. $\left(6\frac{1}{2}\right)^2$ to the nearest whole number
18. Number of minutes between 14:22 and 15:14

2 Crossnumbers without clues

Here we have five crossnumber puzzles with a difference. There are no clues, only answers, and it is your task to find where the answers go.

a) Copy out the crossnumber pattern.

b) Fit all the given numbers into the correct spaces.

Tick off the numbers from the lists as you write them in the square.

1.

4	2	1	4	■				
	■						■	
■				■				
		■				■		
			■	■	■			
		■				■		
				■				■
	■						■	
				■				

2 digits	*3 digits*	*4 digits*	*5 digits*	*6 digits*
26	215	5841	21 862	134 953
41	427	9217	83 642	727 542
19	106	9131	21 362	
71	872	1624	57 320	
63	725	1506		
76	385	4214		
	156	5216		
	263	4734		
	234	2007		
	180	2637		

2.

6								
5								
3								

2 digits	*3 digits*	*4 digits*	*5 digits*	*6 digits*
99	571	9603	24715	387566
25	918	8072	72180	338472
52	131	4210	54073	414725
26	328	3824	71436	198264
42	906	8916	82125	
57	249			
30	653			*7 digits*
53	609			8592070
14	111			
61	127			
	276			

The next three are more difficult but they are possible! Don't give up.

3.

7									
		9							

2 digits	*3 digits*	*4 digits*	*5 digits*	*6 digits*
26	306	3654	38975	582778
28	457	3735	49561	585778
32	504	3751	56073	728468
47	827	3755	56315	
49	917	3819	56435	*7 digits*
52	951	6426	57435	8677056
70		7214	58535	
74		7315	58835	
		7618	66430	
		7643	77435	
		9847	77543	

4.

6

2 digits	*3 digits*	*4 digits*	*5 digits*	*6 digits*
11	121	2104	14700	216841
17	147	2356	24567	588369
18	170	2456	25921	846789
19	174	3714	26759	861277
23	204	4711	30388	876452
31	247	5548	50968	
37	287	5678	51789	
58	324	6231	78967	
61	431	6789	98438	
62	450	7630		*7 digits*
62	612	9012		6645678
70	678	9921		
74	772			
81	774			
85	789			
94	870			
99				

5.

2

2 digits		*3 digits*	*4 digits*	*5 digits*	*6 digits*
12	47	129	2096	12641	324029
14	48	143	3966	23449	559641
16	54	298	5019	33111	956782
18	56	325	5665	33210	
20	63	331	6462	34509	
21	67	341	7809	40551	
23	81	443	8019	41503	*7 digits*
26	90	831	8652	44333	1788932
27	91	923		69786	5749306
32	93			88058	
38	98			88961	
39	99			90963	
46				94461	
				99654	

3 Number messages

a) Start at the box containing the letter 'Q'.

b) Work out the answer to the question in the box.

c) Look for the answer in the corner of another box.

d) Write down the letter in the box and then work out the answer to the problem in the box.

e) Look for the answer as before and continue until you arrive back at box 'Q'.

f) Read the message.

1.

27 **Q** $99 - 27$	99 **S** $2212 \div 7$	125 **W** $211 - 99$	444 **N** 110×9
766 **I** $(18 - 13)^2$	112 **O** $(21 - 18)^3$	615 **N** 18×20	25 **S** $108 + 209$
317 **T** $625 \div 5$	990 **E** $840 \div 3$	72 **O** $123 + 321$	118 **U** $3^2 \times 11$
166 **L** $19 + 99$	360 **E** $1000 - 234$	316 **O** $5 + 55 + 555$	280 **P** $200 - 34$

2.

0.42 **Q** $8.1 + 5$	3.3 **R** $6.1 \div 5$	4.1 **B** $19 - 13.7$	10.5 **R** $14.5 - 3$
5.3 **I** $3.24 \div 9$	11.5 **S** $0.84 \div 4$	1.22 **E** $11 - 8.95$	0.01 **H** 4.2×0.1
2.05 **R** 0.313×100	31.3 **U** $8.8 + 9.9$	13.1 **S** $8 - 3.7$	0.21 **A** 0.33×10
4.3 **P** $2.4 + 7$	0.36 **S** $10 - 9.99$	18.7 **B** 8.2×0.5	9.4 **U** 2.1×5

3.

6 **Q** $10 + 3 \times 2$	13 **S** $22 + 20 \div 10$	33 **R** $19 - 12 \div 6$	71 **N** $7 \times 4 - 15 \div 5$
7 **E** $8 + 9 \div 3$	53 **O** $39 - 17 \times 2$	25 **D** $(25 + 23) \div 8$	19 **E** $13 - 3 \times 2$
55 **H** $2 \times 3 + 4 \times 2$	5 **U** $8 \times 7 + 3 \times 5$	16 **T** $12 - 4 \times 2$	17 **T** $(4 + 7) \times 5$
4 **H** $6 \times 3 + 1$	24 **R** $3 \times 14 + 11$	14 **I** $3 \times 5 - 1 \times 2$	11 **A** $5 \times 7 - 2$

4.

50 **Q** $2.5 \times 4 + 3$	8.1 **O** $5 \times 9 - 2 \times 9$	2.13 **N** $7 - 0.04 \times 10$	2 **N** $0.5 \times 2 + 17$
7.2 **L** $0.3 \times 100 - 7$	3.5 **O** $8 \times 5 + 6 \times 7$	84 **G** $11 \times 9 - 7 \times 7$	52.2 **G** $10 \times (3.4 + 5)$
6 **A** $1.7 + 3 \div 10$	23 **A** $13 \div 100 + 2$	13 **C** $8 - 0.2 \times 10$	7.24 **B** $8 + 1 \div 10$
82 **U** $6.2 \div 5 + 6$	27 **I** $8 - 0.4 \times 2$	6.6 **E** $3.2 + 7 \times 7$	18 **Y** $12.5 - 3 \times 3$

5.

−13 **Q** $-6 + 2$	−7 **C** $(-3)^2 + 4^2$	12 **Y** $12 \div (-2)$	0 **A** $12 \times (-10)$	−14 **A** $-8 + 17$
−120 **R** $16 \div (-16)$	−8 **H** $-3 - 15$	−18 **E** $(-2)^2$	8 **E** $(-8) \div (-8)$	4 **R** $-3 + 7 - 9$
−6 **T** $-8 - 9$	13 **E** $-2 + 1 - 1$	−4 **M** $(-3) \times (-4)$	25 **L** $-7 + 20$	1 **R** $-3 - 2 - 8$
9 **C** $(-8) \div 1$	−5 **S** $0 \times (-17)$	−2 **V** $6 - (-2)$	−1 **E** $-2 + 6 - 11$	−17 **E** -2×7

6.

3.62 **Q** $12 - 8.99$	8 **O** $45 \div 9 - 5$	25 **U** $90 \times 2 - 5$	300 **S** $-8 - 6$	1.3 **L** $6 + 9 \div 3$
−9 **A** 2.6×0.5	6 **Y** $0.7 \div 100$	0.27 **R** $(-1)^2 + (-2)^2$	21 **N** $200 - 41$	159 **G** $25.34 \div 7$
0 **R** $1.4 + 19$	1.24 **A** $9 \times 5 - 3 \times 7$	3.01 **M** $18 - 3 \times 4$	5 **O** $6 \times (11 - 7.5)$	175 **L** $6.2 \div 5$
9 **C** $(-2)^2 + 21$	− 14 **W** 2.7×0.1	20-4 **I** 0.3×1000	24 **T** $-7 + 15$	0.007 **C** $-36 \div 4$

4 Calculator words

On a calculator the number 4915 looks like the word 'SIGH' when the calculator is held upside down.

Find the words given by the clues below.

1. $221 \times 7 \times 5$ (Sounds like 'cell')

2. $5 \times 601 \times 5 \times 3$ (Wet blow)

3. $88^2 - 6$ (Ringer)

4. $0.9 \times 5900 - 1$ (Leaves)

5. $62^2 - (4 \times 7 \times 5)$ (Nothing to it)

6. $0.88^2 - \frac{1}{1000}$ (O Hell)

7. $(5 \times 7 \times 10^3) + (3 \times 113)$ (Gaggle)

8. 44^4 + Half of 67 682 (Readable)

9. $5 \times 3 \times 37 \times 1000 - 1420$ (Stick in mind)

10. $3200 - 1320 \div 11$ (Woodwind)

11. $48^4 + 8929$ (Deceitful dame)

12. $31^2 \times 32^2 - 276^2 + 30$ (Not a twig)

13. $(130 \times 135) + (23 \times 3 \times 11 \times 23)$ (Wobbly)

14. $164 \times 166^2 + 734$ (Almost big)

15. $8794^2 + 25 \times 342.28 + 120 \times 25$ (Thin skin)

16. $0.08 - (3^2 \div 10^4)$ (Ice house)

17. $235^2 - (4 \times 36.5)$ (Shiny surface)

18. $(80^2 + 60^2) \times 3 + 81^2 + 12^2 + 3013$ (Ship gunge)

19. $3 \times 17 \times (329^2 + 2 \times 173)$ (Unlimbed)

20. $230 \times 230\frac{1}{2} + 30$ (Fit feet)

21. $33 \times 34 \times 35 + 15 \times 3$ (Beleaguer)

22. $0.32^2 + \frac{1}{1000}$ (Did he or didn't he?)

23. $(23 \times 24 \times 25 \times 26) + (3 \times 11 \times 10^3) - 20$ (Help)

24. $(16^2 + 16)^2 - (13^2 - 2)$ (Slander)

25. $(3 \times 661)^2 - (3^6 + 22)$ (Pester)

26. $(22^2 + 29.4) \times 10$; $(3.03^2 - 0.02^2) \times 100^2$ (Four words) (Goliath)

27. $1.25 \times 0.2^6 + 0.2^2$ (Tissue time)

28. $(710 + (1823 \times 4)) \times 4$ (Liquor)

29. $(3^3)^2 + 2^2$ (Wriggler)

30. $14 + (5 \times (83^2 + 110))$ (Bigger than a duck)

31. $2 \times 3 \times 53 \times 10^4 + 9$ (Opposite to hello, almost!)

32. $(177 \times 179 \times 182) + (85 \times 86) - 82$ (Good salesman)

5 The milk crate problem

You have 18 bottles to put into the crate below which has space for 24 bottles.

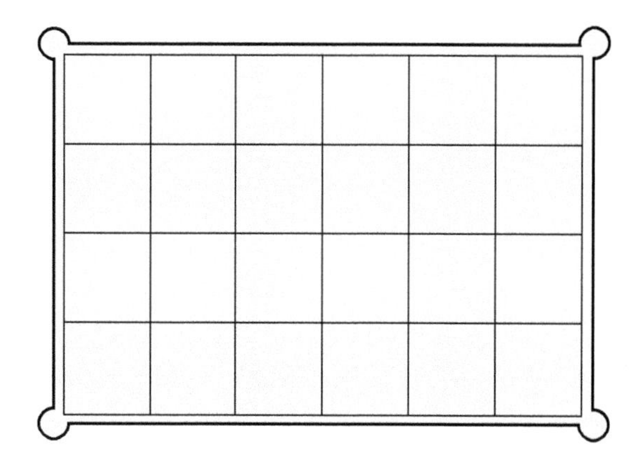

The only condition is that you have to put an *even* number of bottles into every row and every column. Good luck.

6 Estimating game

This is a game for two players. On squared paper draw an answer grid with the numbers shown.

Answer grid

891	7047	546	2262	8526	429
2548	231	1479	357	850	7938
663	1078	2058	1014	1666	3822
1300	1950	819	187	1050	3393
4350	286	3159	442	2106	550
1701	4050	1377	4900	1827	957

The players now take turns to choose two numbers from the question grid below and multiply them on a calculator.

Question grid

11	26	81
17	39	87
21	50	98

The number obtained is crossed out on the answer grid using the player's own colour.

The game continues until all the numbers in the answer grid have been crossed out. The object is to get four answers in a line (horizontally, vertically or diagonally). The winner is the player with most lines of four.

A line of *five* counts as *two* lines of four.

A line of *six* counts as *three* lines of four.

7 Creating numbers

Using only the numbers 1, 2, 3 and 4 once each and the operations +, −, ×, ÷, ! create every number from 1 to 100.

You can use the numbers as powers and you must use all of the numbers 1, 2, 3 and 4.

[4! is pronounced 'four factorial' and means $4 \times 3 \times 2 \times 1$ (i.e. 24)

similarly $3! = 3 \times 2 \times 1 = 6$

$5! = 5 \times 4 \times 3 \times 2 \times 1 = 120$]

Examples: $1 = (4 - 3) \div (2 - 1)$

$20 = 4^2 + 3 + 1$

$68 = 34 \times 2 \times 1$

$100 = (4! + 1)(3! - 2!)$

8 Pentominoes

You probably know of the game of dominoes. A domino is just two squares joined together; there is only one possible shape because the two shapes here count as the same.

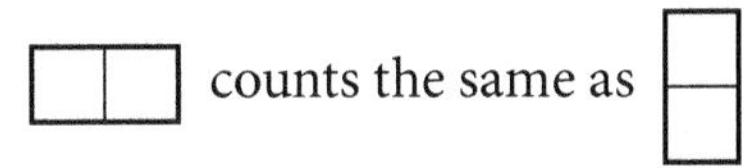

A pentomino is a set of five squares joined along their edges.

1. See how many different pentominoes you can design on squared paper. Here are a few.

a) 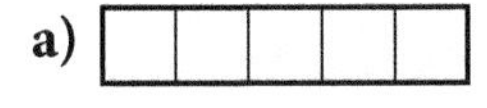

b) 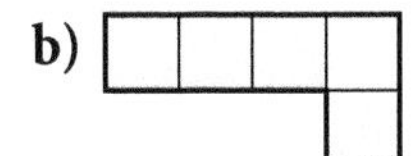

c) 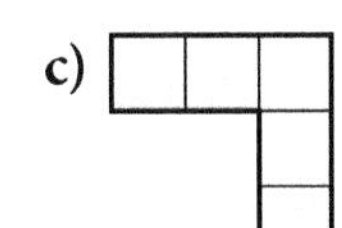

You may find that some of your designs are really the same, for example

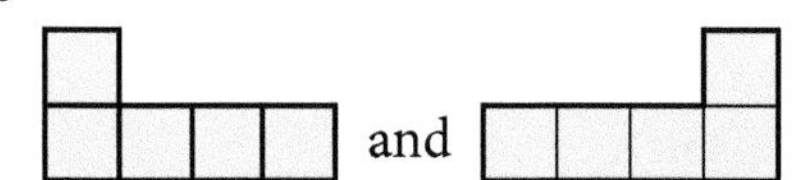

You can use a piece of tracing paper to check if some of your designs are really the same or different.

After about fifteen minutes, compare your designs with those of other people in your class. There are in fact twelve different pentomino shapes. Make a neat copy of these.

2. Fit these five pentominoes together to form a square.

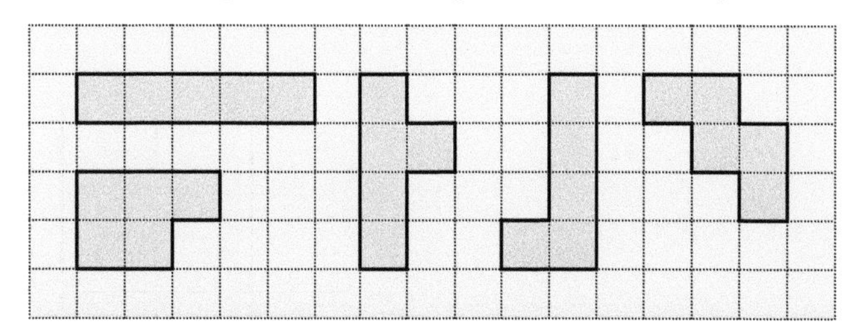

3. On squared paper, draw a square having eight units on each side. Somewhere inside the square draw a small square having two units on each side and shade it.

   Now fill up the rest of the square with as many different pentominoes as you can. There should be no 'holes' left by the time you have finished.

   A start has been made in the diagram on the right.

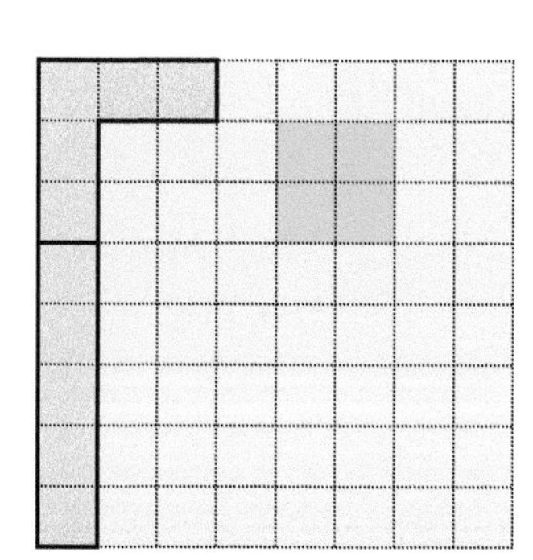

4. Take some more squared paper and draw a rectangle measuring 10 by 6. Fill up the rectangle with as many different pentominoes as you can. This problem is more difficult than the 8 by 8 square.

9 'I can read your mind'

Here is a trick where you can demonstrate your ability to read a friend's mind.

Start by writing any number between 1 and 50 on a card but do not let your friend see it.

Example

I will choose 31

Now ask your friend to do the following:

1. Write any number between 50 and 100. — 74 (say)
2. Add ________ to your number. — Add 68
   $74 + 68 = 142$

[The number to add is 99 minus the number on *your* card]

i.e. $99 - 31 = 68$

3. Cross out the left-hand digit. 142
4. Add this digit to the number remaining. $42 + 1 = 43$
5. Subtract this number from the number you chose at the start. $74 - 43 = 31$
(i.e. in line 1 above)

Now, with a flourish, show your friend your card with the correct number written on it.

10 The chessboard problem

On the 4×4 square below we have placed four objects subject to the restriction that nowhere are there two objects on the same row, column or diagonal.

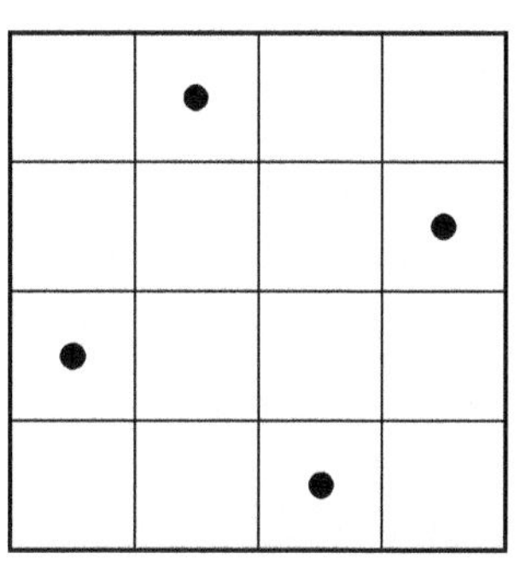

Subject to the same restrictions:

i) find a solution for a 5×5 square, using five objects,

ii) find a solution for a 6×6 square, using six objects,

iii) find a solution for a 7×7 square, using seven objects,

iv) find a solution for a 8×8 square, using eight objects.

It is called the chessboard problem because the objects could be 'Queens' which can move any number of squares in any direction.

11 Miscellaneous puzzles

1. This shape can be divided into equal pieces in several ways. Each piece must be exactly the same size and shape.

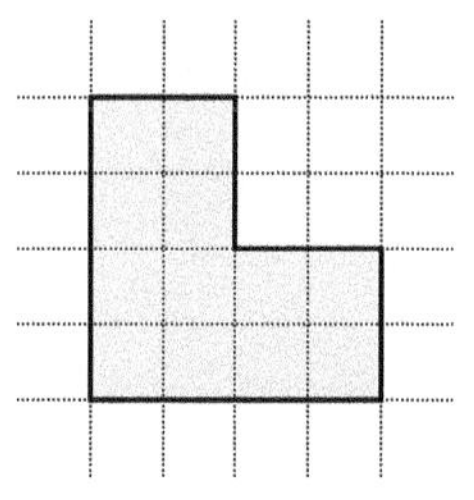

We can easily divide the shape into two equal pieces.

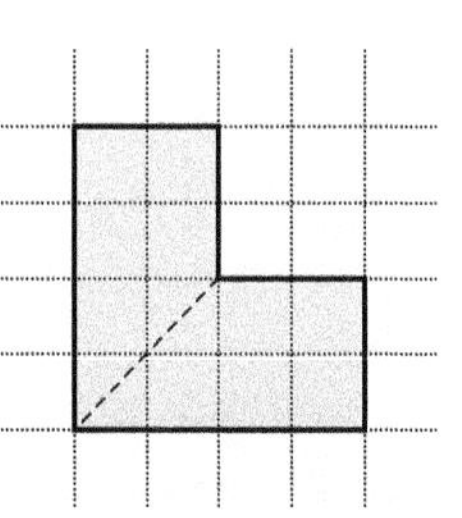

Draw the shape three times and show how it can be divided into:

a) 3 pieces

b) 6 pieces

c) (harder) 4 pieces.

Draw this shape three times and show how it can be divided into:

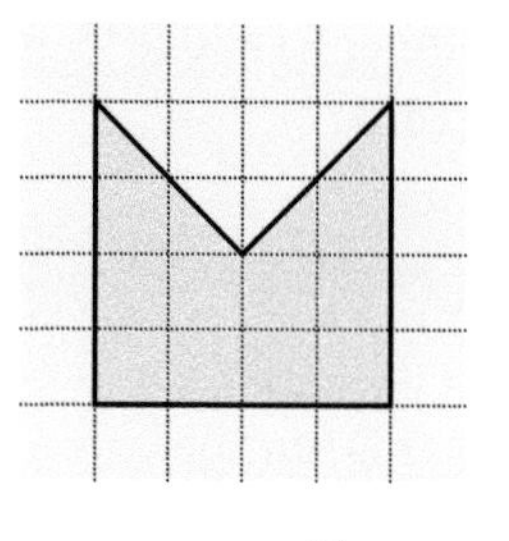

a) 3 pieces

b) 6 pieces

c) (harder) 8 pieces.

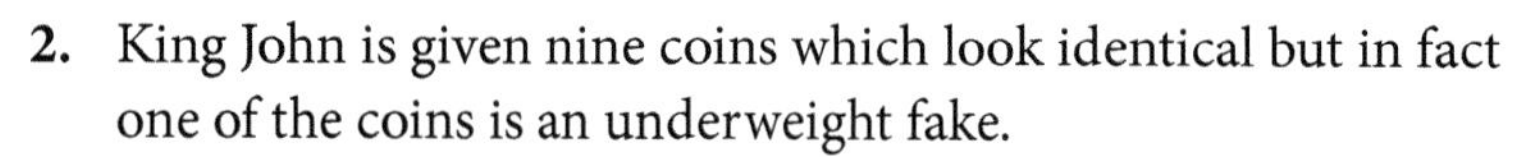

2. King John is given nine coins which look identical but in fact one of the coins is an underweight fake.

Describe how you can use a balance to find the fake in just two weighings.

3. Here we have used 12 matches to enclose an area of 9 squares.

Draw four diagrams to show how 12 matches can be used to enclose areas of 8, 7, 6 and 5 squares.

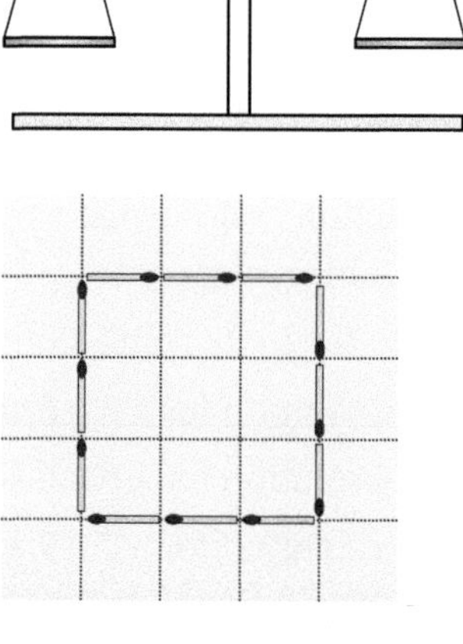

4. There is a fire in the kitchens of Gibson College and the principal, Mr Gibson, is stranded on the roof of the burning building.

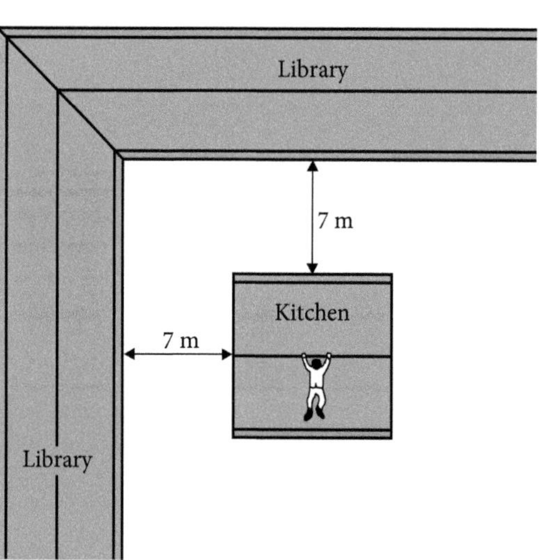

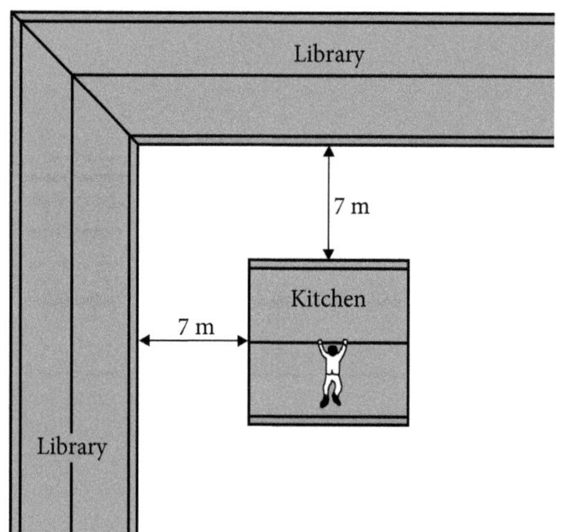

Firemen are on the roof of the library and they have two ladders each 6 m long.

The shortest distance from the library to the kitchen roof is 7 m. How can the firemen rescue Mr Gibson?

5. Two coins have a total value of 60c. One of them is *not* a 50c coin. What are the two coins?

6. In a 24-hour day, from midnight to midnight, how many times are the hands of a clock at right angles to each other?

12 Multiple choice tests

Test 1

1. How many mm are there in 1 m 1 cm?

A 1001
B 1110
C 1010
D 1100

2. The circumference of a circle is 16π cm. The radius, in cm, of the circle is:

A 2
B 4
C $\frac{4}{\pi}$
D 8

3. In the triangle below the value of $\cos x$ is:

A 0.8
B 1.333
C 0.75
D 0.6

4. The line $y = 2x - 1$ cuts the x-axis at P. The coordinates of P are:

A $(0, -1)$
B $\left(\frac{1}{2}, 0\right)$
C $\left(-\frac{1}{2}, 0\right)$
D $(-1, 0)$

5. The mean weight of a group of 11 men is 70 kg. What is the mean weight of the remaining group when a man of weight 90 kg leaves?

A 80 kg
B 72 kg
C 68 kg
D 62 kg

6. A, B, C and D are points on the sides of a rectangle. Find the area in cm^2 of quadrilateral ABCD.

A $27\frac{1}{2}$
B 28
C $28\frac{1}{2}$
D cannot be found

7. The formula $\frac{x}{a} + b = c$ is rearranged to make x the subject. What is x?

A $a(c - b)$
B $ac - b$
C $\frac{c-b}{a}$
D $ac + ab$

8. In standard form the value of $2000 \times 80\,000$ is:

A 16×10^6
B 1.6×10^9
C 1.6×10^7
D 1.6×10^8

9. The sum of the lengths of the edges of a cube is 36 cm. The volume, in cm^3, of the cube is:

A 36
B 27
C 64
D 48

10. In the triangle the size of angle x is:

A 35°
B 70°
C 110°
D 40°

11. A man paid tax on \$9000 at 30%. He paid the tax in 12 equal payments. Each payment was:

A \$2.25
B \$22.50
C \$225
D \$250

12. The approximate value of $\frac{3.96\times(0.5)^2}{97.1}$ is:

A 0.01
B 0.02
C 0.04
D 0.1

13. Given that $\frac{3}{n} = 5$, then $n = ?$

A 2
B -2
C $1\frac{2}{3}$
D 0.6

14. Cube A has side 2 cm.
Cube B has side 4 cm.
$\left(\frac{\text{Volume of B}}{\text{Volume of A}}\right) =$

A 2
B 4
C 8
D 16

15. How many square tiles of side 50 cm will be needed to cover the floor shown?

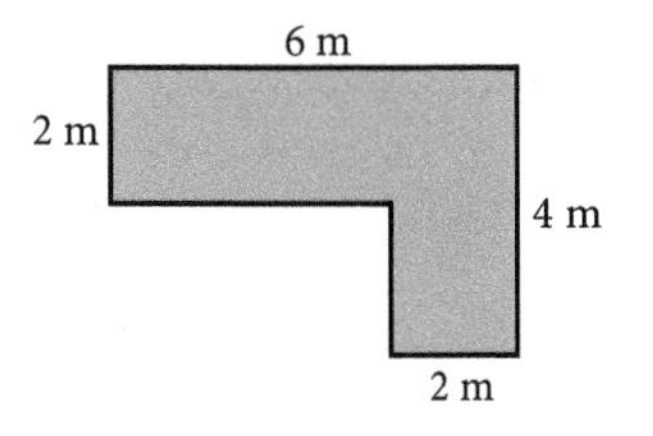

A 16
B 32
C 64
D 84

16. The equation $ax^2 + x - 6 = 0$ has a solution $x = -2$
What is a?

A 1
B -2
C $\sqrt{2}$
D 2

17. Which of the following is/are correct?

1. $\sqrt{0.16} = 0.4$
2. $0.2 \div 0.1 = 0.2$
3. $\frac{4}{7} > \frac{3}{5}$

A **1** only
B **2** only
C **3** only
D **1** and **2**

18. How many prime numbers are there between 30 and 40?

A 0
B 1
C 2
D 3

19. A man is paid \$180 per week *after* a pay rise of 20%. What was he paid before?

A \$144
B \$150
C \$160
D \$164

20. A car travels for 20 minutes at 45 km/h and then for 40 minutes at 60 km/h. The average speed for the whole journey is:

A 52 km/h
B 50 km/h
C 54 km/h
D 55 km/h

21. The point $(3, -1)$ is reflected in the line $y = 2$. The new coordinates are:

A $(3, 5)$
B $(1, -1)$
C $(3, 4)$
D $(0, -1)$

22. Given the equation $5^x = 120$, the best approximate solution is $x =$

A 2
B 3
C 4
D 25

23. The rectangle ABCD is cut out of paper and the edges AB and DC are joined to make a cylinder. The radius of the cylinder in cm is:

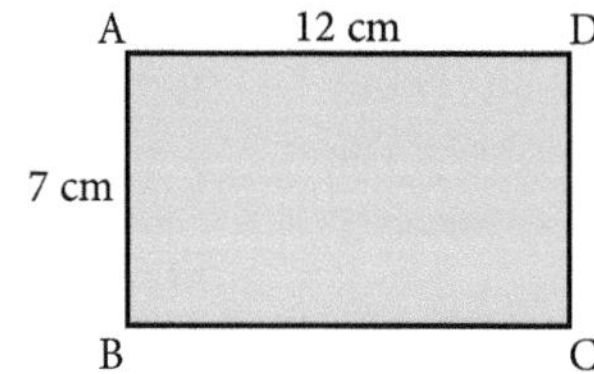

A 6
B 7
C $\frac{6}{\pi}$
d $\frac{12}{\pi}$

24. The shaded area in cm^2 is:

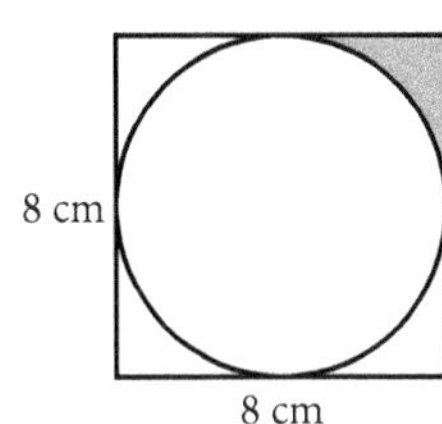

A $16 - 2\pi$

B $16 - 4\pi$

C $\frac{4}{\pi}$

D $64 - 8\pi$

25. What is the sine of 45°?

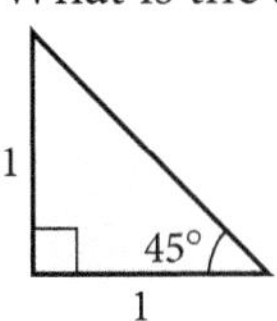

A 1

B $\frac{1}{2}$

C $\frac{1}{\sqrt{2}}$

D $\sqrt{2}$

Test 2

1. What is the value of the expression $(x - 2)(x + 4)$ when $x = -1$?

A 9

B −9

C 5

D −5

2. The perimeter of a square is 36 cm.

What is its area?

A 36 cm^2

B 324 cm^2

C 81 cm^2

D 9 cm^2

3. The total surface area, in cm^2, of this cone is:

10 cm

8 cm

A $80\pi^2$

B 144π

C 720π

D 80π

4. The shape consists of four semi-circles placed round a square of side 2 m. The area of the shape in m^2 is:

A $2\pi + 4$

B $2\pi + 2$

C $4\pi + 4$

D $\pi + 4$

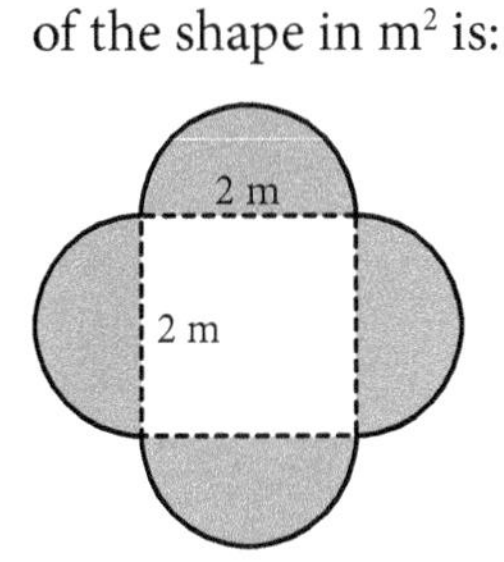

5. A firm employs 1200 people, of whom 240 are men. The percentage of employees who are men is:

A 40%

B 10%

C 15%

D 20%

6. A car is travelling at a constant speed of 30 km/h. How far will the car travel in 10 minutes?

A $\frac{1}{3}$ km

B 3 km

C 5 km

D 6 km

7. What are the coordinates of the point $(1, -1)$ after reflection in the line $y = x$?

A $(-1, 1)$

B $(1, 1)$

C $(-1, -1)$

D $(1, -1)$

8. $\frac{1}{3} + \frac{2}{5} = ?$

A $\frac{2}{8}$

B $\frac{3}{8}$

C $\frac{3}{15}$

D $\frac{11}{15}$

9. In the triangle the size of the largest angle is:

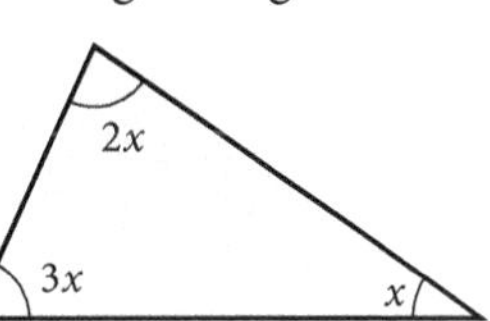

A 30°

B 90°

C 120°

D 80°

10. 800 decreased by 5% is:

A 795

B 640

C 760

D 400

11. Which of the statements is/are true?

1. $\tan 60° = 2$

2. $\sin 60° = \cos 30°$

3. $\sin 30° > \cos 30°$

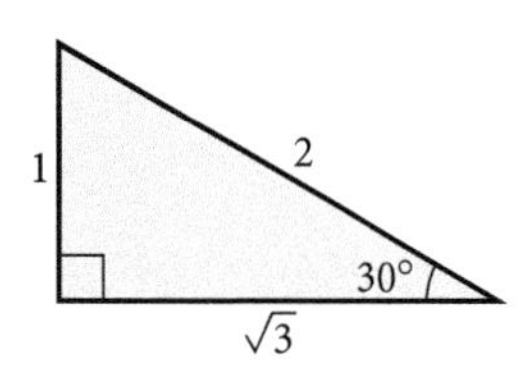

A 1 only
B 2 only
C 3 only
D 2 and **3**

12. Given $a = \frac{3}{5}$, $b = \frac{1}{3}$, $c = \frac{1}{2}$ then:

A $a < b < c$
B $a < c < b$
C $a > b > c$
D $a > c > b$

13. The *larger* angle between South-West and East is:

A 225°
B 240°
C 135°
D 315°

14. In a triangle PQR, PQR= 50° and point X lies on PQ such that QX = XR. Calculate QXR.

A 100°
B 50°
C 80°
D 65°

15. What is the value of $1 - 0.05$ as a fraction?

A $\frac{1}{20}$
B $\frac{9}{10}$
C $\frac{19}{20}$
D $\frac{5}{100}$

16. Find the length x.

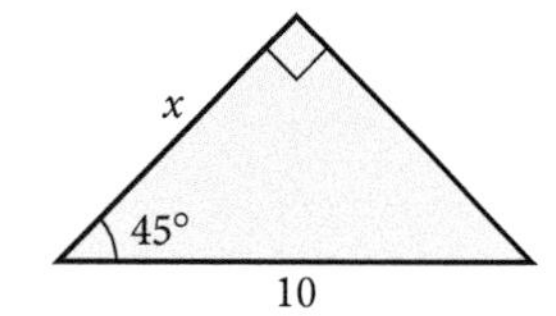

A 5
B 6
C 8
D $\sqrt{50}$

17. Given that $m = 2$ and $n = -3$, what is mn^2?

A −18
B 18
C −36
D 36

18. The graph of $y = (x - 3)(x - 2)$ cuts the y-axis at P. The coordinates of P are:

A (0, 6)
B (6, 0)
C (2, 0)
D (3, 0)

19. $240 is shared in the ratio 2:3:7. The largest share is:

A $130
B $140
C $150
D $160

20. Adjacent angles in a parallelogram are $x°$ and $3x°$. The smallest angles in the parallelogram are each:

A 30°
B 45°
C 60°
D 120°

21. When the sides of the square are increased by 10% the area is increased by:

A 10%
B 20%
C 21%
D 15%

22. The volume, in cm³, of the cylinder is:

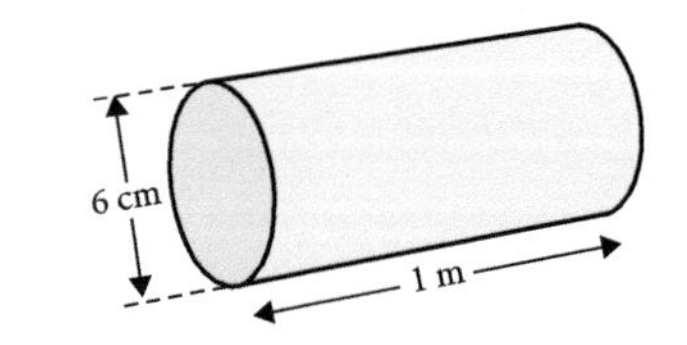

A 9π
B 12π
C 600π
D 900π

23. A car travels for 10 minutes at 30 km/h and then for 20 minutes at 45 km/h. The average speed for the whole journey is:

A 40 km/h
B $37\frac{1}{2}$ km/h
C 20 km/h
D 35 km/h

24. Four people each toss a coin. What is the probability that the fourth person will toss a 'tail'?

A $\frac{1}{2}$

B $\frac{1}{4}$

C $\frac{1}{8}$

D $\frac{1}{16}$

25. What is the area in cm^2, of a circle of diameter 10 cm?

A 10π

B 25π

C 49π

D 100π

Test 3

1. The price of a TV changed from \$240 to \$300. What is the percentage increase?

A 15%

B 20%

C 60%

D 25%

2. Find the length x.

A 6

B 5

C $\sqrt{44}$

D $\sqrt{18}$

3. The bearing of A from B is 120°. What is the bearing of B from A?

A 060°

B 120°

C 240°

D 300°

4. Numbers m, x and y satisfy the equation $y = mx^2$. When $m = \frac{1}{2}$ and $x = 4$ the value of y is:

A 4

B 8

C 1

D 2

5. A school has 400 students, of whom 250 are boys. The ratio of boys to girls is:

A 5 : 3

B 3 : 2

C 3 : 5

D 8 : 5

6. A train is travelling at a speed of 30 km per hour. How long will it take to travel 500 m?

A 2 minutes

B $\frac{3}{50}$ hour

C 1 minute

D $\frac{1}{2}$ hour

7. The approximate value of $\frac{9.65 \times 0.203}{0.0198}$ is:

A 99

B 9.9

C 0.99

D 180

8. Which point does *not* lie on the curve $y = \frac{12}{x}$?

A (6, 2)

B $(\frac{1}{2}, 24)$

C (−3, −4)

D (3, −4)

9. If $t = \frac{c^3}{y}$, $y = ?$

A $\frac{t}{c^3}$

B $c^3 t$

C $c^3 - t$

D $\frac{c^3}{t}$

10. The largest number of 1 cm cubes which will fit inside a cubical box of side 1 m is:

A 10^3

B 10^6

C 10^8

D 10^{12}

11. I start with x, then square it, multiply by 2 and finally subtract 3. The final result is:

A $(2x)^2 - 3$

B $(2x - 3)^2$

C $2x^2 - 3$

D $2(x - 3)^2$

12. Which of the following has the largest value?

A $\sqrt{100}$

B $\sqrt{\frac{1}{0.1}}$

C $\sqrt{1000}$

D $\frac{1}{0.01}$

13. Two dice numbered 1 to 6 are thrown together and their scores are added. The probability that the sum will be 12 is:

A $\frac{1}{6}$

B $\frac{1}{12}$

C $\frac{1}{18}$

D $\frac{1}{36}$

14. The length, in cm, of the minor arc is:

60°

9 cm

A 2π

B 3π

C 6π

D $13\frac{1}{2}\pi$

15. Metal of mass 84 kg is made into 40 000 pins. What is the mass, in kg, of one pin?

A 0.0021

B 0.0036

C 0.021

D 0.21

16. What is the value of x which satisfies both equations?

$3x + y = 1$

$x - 2y = 5$

A -1

B 1

C -2

D 2

17. What is the new fare when the old fare of $250 is increased by 8%?

A $258

B $260

C $270

D $281.25

18. What is the area of this triangle?

$5x$ $5x$

$8x$

A $12x^2$

B $15x^2$

C $16x^2$

D $30x^2$

19. What values of x satisfy the inequality $2 - 3x > 1$?

A $x < -\frac{1}{3}$

B $x > -\frac{1}{3}$

C $x > \frac{1}{3}$

D $x < \frac{1}{3}$

20. A right-angled triangle has sides in the ratio $5:12:13$. The tangent of the smallest angle is:

A $\frac{12}{5}$

B $\frac{12}{13}$

C $\frac{5}{13}$

D $\frac{5}{12}$

21. To one significant figure, $\sqrt{0.1}$ is:

A 0.01

B 0.1

C 0.3

D 0.5

22. The number of letters in the word SNAIL that have line symmetry is:

A 0

B 1

C 2

D 3

23. The probability of an event occurring is 0.35. The probability of the event *not* occurring is:

A $\frac{1}{0.35}$

B 0.65

C 0.35

D 0

24. What fraction of the area of the rectangle is the area of the triangle?

A $\frac{1}{4}$

B $\frac{1}{8}$

C $\frac{1}{16}$

D $\frac{1}{32}$

25. On a map a distance of 40 km is represented by a line of 2 cm. What is the scale of the map?

A 1:2000
B 1:20 000
C 1:200 000
D 1:2 000 000

Test 4

1. What is the value of x satisfying the simultaneous equations
$3x + 2y = 13$
$x - 2y = -1$?

A 7
B 3
C $3\frac{1}{2}$
D 2

2. A straight line is 4.5 cm long. $\frac{2}{5}$ of the line is:

A 0.4 cm
B 1.8 cm
C 2 cm
D 0.18 cm

3. The mean of four numbers is 12. The mean of three of the numbers is 13. What is the fourth number?

A 9
B 12.5
C 7
D 1

4. How many cubes of edge 3 cm are needed to fill a box with internal dimensions 12 cm by 6 cm by 6 cm?

A 8
B 18
C 16
D 24

5. The value of 4865.355 correct to 2 significant figures is:

A 4865.36
B 4865.35
C 4900
D 49

6. The value of 5^0 is:

A 0
B 1
C 5
D 50

For Questions **7** to **9** use the diagram below.

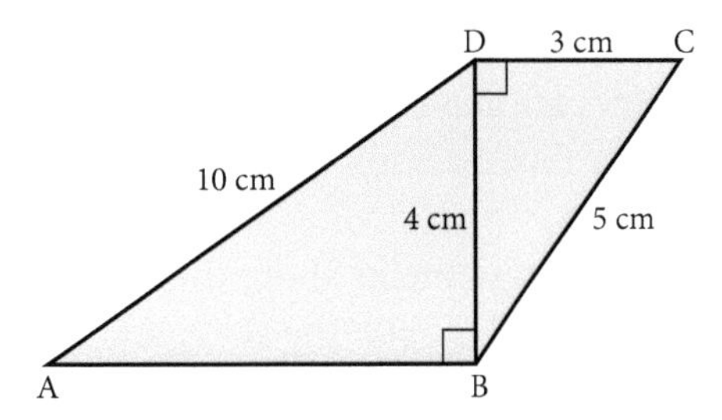

7. The length of AB, in cm, is:

A 6
B $\sqrt{116}$
C 8
D $\sqrt{84}$

8. The sine of angle DCB is:

A 0.8
B 1.25
C 0.6
D 0.75

9. The tangent of angle CBD is:

A 0.6
B 0.75
C 1.333
D 1.6

10. The area of a circle is 100π cm². The radius, in cm, of the circle is:

A 50
B 10
C $\sqrt{50}$
D 5

11. $4(x + 3) - 2(x - 5) = ?$

A $2x + 2$
B $2x - 2$
C $6x + 22$
D $2x + 22$

12. The area, in cm², of this sector is:

5 cm
60°

A 1500π
B $\frac{25}{6}\pi$
C 300
D $\frac{5}{3}\pi$

13. The cube root of 64 is:

A 2
B 4
C 8
D 16

14. Here are four statements about the diagonals of a rectangle. The statement which is not *always* true is

A They are equal in length
B They divide the rectangle into four triangles of equal area
C They cross at right angles
D They bisect each other

15. Given $16^x = 4^4$, what is x?

A -2
B $-\frac{1}{2}$
C $\frac{1}{2}$
D 2

16. What is the area, in m^2, of a square with each side 0.02 m long?

A 0.0004
B 0.004
C 0.04
D 0.4

17. I start with x, then square it, multiply by 3 and finally subtract 4.
The final result is:

A $(3x)^2 - 4$
B $(3x - 4)^2$
C $3x^2 - 4$
D $3(x - 4)^2$

18. The surface area, in cm^2, of this sphere is:

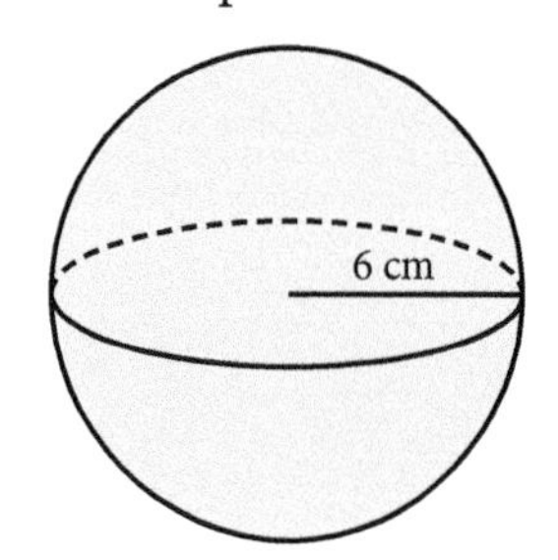

A 288π
B 144π
C 864π
D 48π

19. What are the coordinates of the point $(2, -2)$ after reflection in the line $y = -x$?

A $(-2, 2)$
B $(2, -2)$
C $(-2, -2)$
D $(2, 2)$

20. The area of a circle is 36π cm^2. The circumference, in cm, is:

A 6π
B 18π
C $12\sqrt{\pi}$
D 12π

21. Here are some numbers:
7, 3, 1, 4, 6
The median is:

A 1
B 4
C 4.2
D 3.5

22. When all three sides of a triangle are trebled in length, the area is increased by a factor of:

A 3
B 6
C 9
D 27

23. Solve the equation:
$2(x - 3) + 5 = 7$

A $x = 1$
B $x = 2$
C $x = 4$
D $x = 8$

24. A fair coin is tossed three times. The probability of getting three 'heads' is:

A $\frac{1}{3}$
B $\frac{1}{6}$
C $\frac{1}{8}$
D $\frac{1}{16}$

25. A triangle has sides of length 5 cm, 5 cm and 6 cm. What is the area, in cm^2?

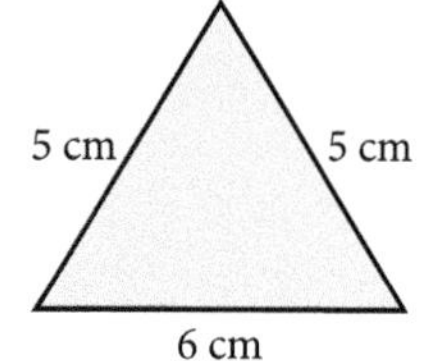

A 12
B 15
C 18
D 20

Examination-style Paper 1

[Short-answer questions; Core level]

1. Work out 4^5. [1]
2. Which of these is **not** a prime number?
   31, 41, 51, 61 [1]
3. Find the median of these five numbers:
   5, 2, 11, 2, 8 [1]
4. Write down the next term in this sequence: 2, 5, 10, 17, ... [1]
5. Writing down your full calculator display, work out $\sqrt{\dfrac{2000}{\pi}}$. [1]
6. In a 100 metre race, the time of the winner was 10.57 seconds, and the time of the athlete who came third was 10.64 seconds. Write down a possible time for the athlete who came second. [1]
7. Find the volume of a cube with all its edges 2.7 cm long. [2]
8. Showing your working, simplify:
   a) $\dfrac{2}{9} \times \dfrac{3}{5}$ **b)** $\dfrac{2}{9} \div \dfrac{3}{5}$ [2]
9. Write 90 as a product of its prime factors. [2]
10. **a)** Simplify: $5x - (2x - 7)$. [1]
    b) Factorise fully: $5pq + 10p$. [2]
11. The populations of three Ethiopian villages are 2000, 2400 and 3600. During a food shortage, a charity sends 200 tonnes of grain. It is shared out in proportion to the population. How much grain should each village receive? [3]
12. Q is a point due North of a point P. A third point, R, is on a bearing of 045° from P. Angle PQR = 60°.
    a) Sketch the triangle PQR, marking the given angles. [1]
    b) Find the bearing of **i)** R from Q **ii)** P from R. [2]
13. The statement $10 - 5 - 2 = 7$ is incorrect. If we put in brackets, the statement $10 - (5 - 2) = 7$ is correct.
    The following statements are all incorrect. Put in brackets to make them correct.
    a) $6 \times 5 + 3 = 48$ [1]
    b) $28 - 12 \div 4 = 4$ [1]
    c) $9 - 3^2 = 36$ [1]
14. Write down, in its simplest form, an expression for the perimeter of this rectangle. [3]

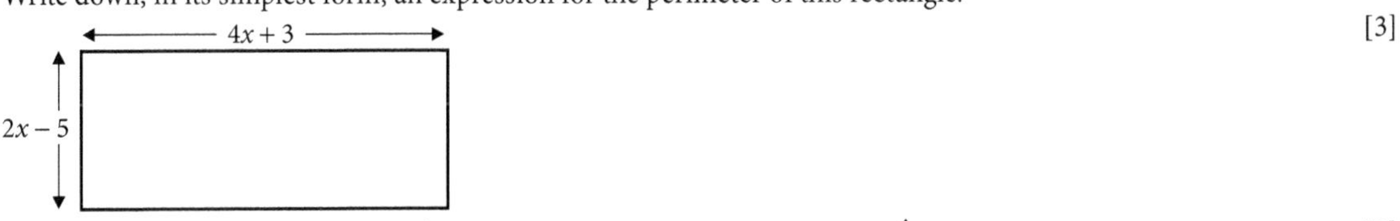

15. Divide this equilateral triangle into four congruent parts. [2]

16.

Dishcloths	$0.75	Buckets	$1.99
Plastic bowls	$1.29	Waste bins	$2.60

a) What is the cost of two dishcloths and a bucket? [1]
b) How much *more* would you pay for a waste bin than for a plastic bowl? [1]
c) Waste bins are offered in the sales at a 30% discount.
What will the price be then? [2]

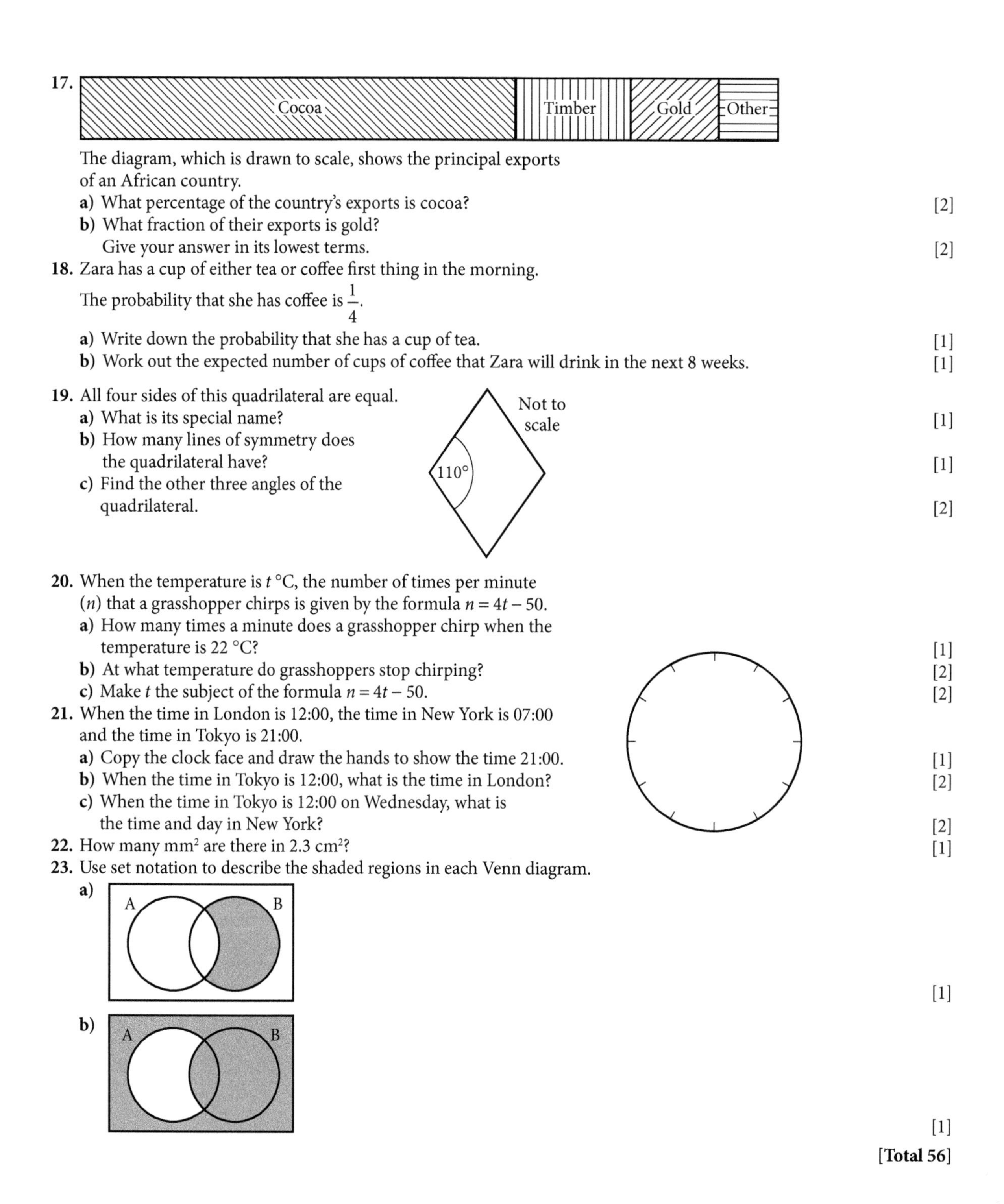

17. The diagram, which is drawn to scale, shows the principal exports of an African country.

a) What percentage of the country's exports is cocoa? [2]

b) What fraction of their exports is gold?
Give your answer in its lowest terms. [2]

18. Zara has a cup of either tea or coffee first thing in the morning.

The probability that she has coffee is $\frac{1}{4}$.

a) Write down the probability that she has a cup of tea. [1]

b) Work out the expected number of cups of coffee that Zara will drink in the next 8 weeks. [1]

19. All four sides of this quadrilateral are equal.

a) What is its special name? [1]

b) How many lines of symmetry does the quadrilateral have? [1]

c) Find the other three angles of the quadrilateral. [2]

20. When the temperature is t °C, the number of times per minute (n) that a grasshopper chirps is given by the formula $n = 4t - 50$.

a) How many times a minute does a grasshopper chirp when the temperature is 22 °C? [1]

b) At what temperature do grasshoppers stop chirping? [2]

c) Make t the subject of the formula $n = 4t - 50$. [2]

21. When the time in London is 12:00, the time in New York is 07:00 and the time in Tokyo is 21:00.

a) Copy the clock face and draw the hands to show the time 21:00. [1]

b) When the time in Tokyo is 12:00, what is the time in London? [2]

c) When the time in Tokyo is 12:00 on Wednesday, what is the time and day in New York? [2]

22. How many mm^2 are there in 2.3 cm^2? [1]

23. Use set notation to describe the shaded regions in each Venn diagram.

a) [1]

b) [1]

[Total 56]

Examination-style Paper 3

[Structured questions; Core level]

1. a) The diagram represents a set square AB = 5 cm and angle CAB = 45°.

Find: **i)** angle ACB [1]

ii) the length of BC [1]

iii) the length of AC. [2]

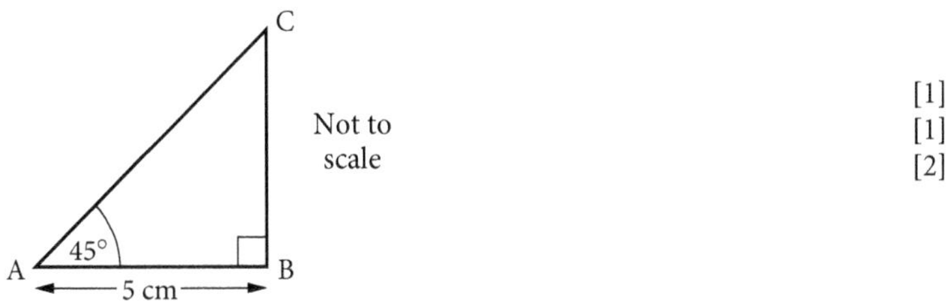

b) The diagram represents another set square DE = 4 cm and angle EDF = 60°.

Find: **i)** angle DFE [1]

ii) the length of EF [2]

iii) the length of DF. [2]

c) Which of the two triangles, ACB and DFE, has the larger area, and by how much? [3]

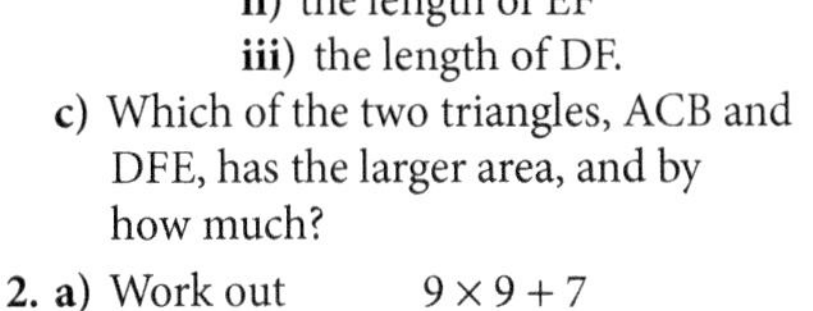

2. a) Work out

$9 \times 9 + 7$

$98 \times 9 + 6$

$987 \times 9 + 5$

$9876 \times 9 + 4$ [2]

b) Write down the next three lines in the sequence above and, in each case, work out and write down the answer. [2]

c) Copy and complete: $987\ 654\ 321 \times 9 =$ .... [1]

3. The table shows the mid-day temperature on the first day of each month during one year at a settlement within the Arctic Circle.

Month	Jan	Feb	Mar	April	May	June	July	Aug	Sept	Oct	Nov	Dec
Temperature (°C)	−20	−17	−12	−3	3	12	14	13	8	−1	−12	−15

a) i) Find the difference between the temperatures listed for October and November. [1]

ii) Find the difference between the highest and lowest listed temperatures. [2]

b) A month is selected at random. What is the probability that the temperature listed for it is greater than 0 °C? [2]

c) For the list of temperatures find:

i) the mode [1]

ii) the median [2]

iii) the mean. [3]

4. The diagram shows a staircase. It has 11 'treads' and 12 'risers'. Each tread is 24 cm long, and each riser is 18 cm high.

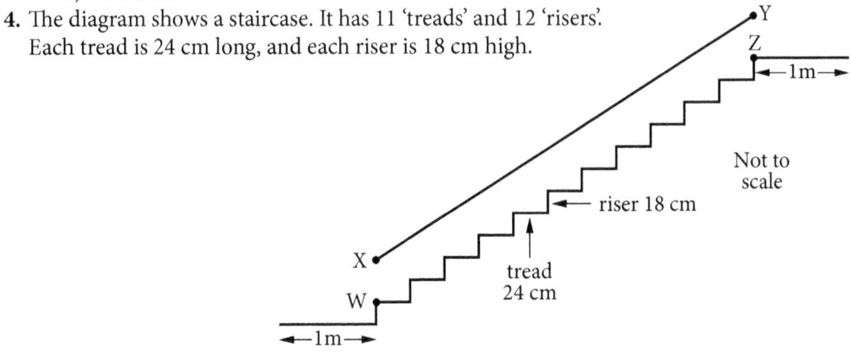

a) A carpet is to be laid, to cover all the stairs and to extend a distance of 1 m at the bottom and 1 m at the top.
The carpet costs \$8.40 per metre length.
Calculate: **i)** the length of the carpet, in metres, [3]
ii) the cost of the carpet, to the nearest dollar. [3]

b) A handrail XY runs parallel to the stairs, such that the lines XW and YZ are vertical and equal in length. Calculate:
i) the angle that the handrail makes with the horizontal [2]
ii) the length of the handrail in metres (to the nearest cm). [3]

5. a) Copy and complete this table of values for the function $y = \frac{6}{x}$, where $x \neq 0$.

x	−6	−5	−4	−3	−2	$-1\frac{1}{2}$	−1		1	$1\frac{1}{2}$	2	3	4	5	6
y		−1.2				−4	−6		6						

[3]

b) Draw x- and y-axes from −6 to +6, using a scale of 1 cm to 1 unit in both directions. Plot the points in the table on your graph grid, and hence draw the two separate branches of the graph $y = \frac{6}{x}$. [4]

c) i) The graph has two lines of symmetry. Mark them clearly on your graph with broken lines,
like this -. [1]
ii) Does the curve have rotational symmetry? If so, describe it. [2]

d) i) Copy and complete the table of values below for the function $y = 3x - 1$. [2]

x	−1	0	1	2
y				

ii) Draw the graph of $y = 3x - 1$ on the same graph grid used in parts (b) and (c). [2]

e) Read off the coordinates of the points of intersection of the two graphs. [2]

6. A set of saucepans are *similar* to each other. That is, the measurements of all the saucepans are in proportion.

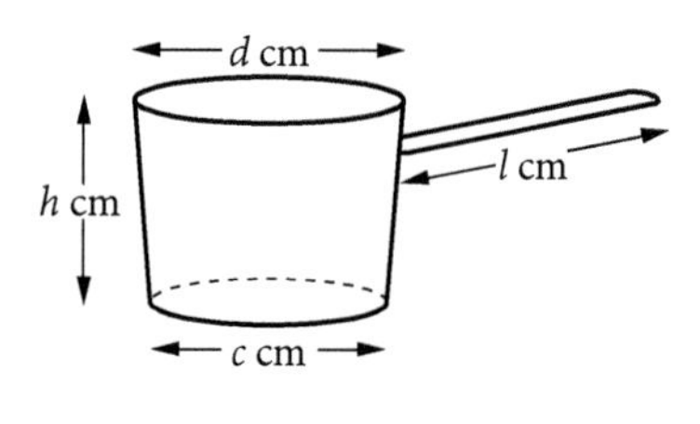

a) Copy and complete the table below.

Saucepan	Diameter of top (d)	Diameter of base (c)	Height (h)	Length of handle (l)
W	10	8	6	9
X	15	12		
Y	$17\frac{1}{2}$		6.9	

[4]

b) A formula for the volume of each saucepan is $V = \frac{\pi h(d^3 - c^3)}{12(d - c)}$.
Work out the volume of the smallest saucepan. [3]

7. a) i) The diagram shows a regular polygon.
What is its special name? [1]
ii) Show by calculation that each interior angle of the regular polygon is 135°. [2]

b) i) Construct an isosceles triangle ABC with AB = AC = 6 cm and angle BAC = 135°. [2]

ii) Measure the length of BC. [1]

iii) Construct the bisector of angle ABC. [2]

iv) The bisector of angle ABC cuts AC at D. Measure angle ABD. [1]

8. Alice Adams grows fruit in her garden. This year she kept a record of how she used what she collected. The results are shown in the table.

Sold	45 kg
Made into jam	15 kg
Made into fruit pies	10 kg
Put into freezer	20 kg

Showing clearly how you calculated the angles, draw a pie chart to represent this data. Use a circle of radius 6 cm. [3]

9. a) Work out the circumference of a circle with a radius of 25 cm. [2]

b) The circumference of a circular tree trunk is 286 cm. Work out the diameter of the trunk. [3]

c) Another tree trunk is cylindrical in shape, with a radius of 50 cm and a height of 12 m.

i) Calculate the volume of the tree trunk, in cubic metres. [3]
[The volume of a cylinder of radius r and height h is $\pi r^2 h$.]

ii) The weight of the wood from this tree is 0.75 tonnes per cubic metre. Calculate the weight of the tree trunk in tonnes. [2]

10. The ages, in years, of 12 people at a party were

15 23 28 34 43 12 34 19 21 36 25 39

a) Complete this stem-and-leaf diagram to display this data.

Stem	Leaf
1	
2	
3	
4	

Key
1 | 9 means 19

[2]

b) Use the diagram to find:

i) the median [1]

ii) the mode [1]

iii) the inter-quartile range. [1]

11. A water trough is in the shape of a cuboid and measures 1.2 m by 1.5 m by 0.8 m.

a) Work out the volume of the trough in m^3. [2]

b) How long, in hours and minutes, will it take to fill the trough if water flows in at a rate of 10 litres per minute? [3]

12. Calculate the volume and surface area of a pyramid with a square base of side length 10 m and a height of 8 m. Give your answers to the nearest whole number.

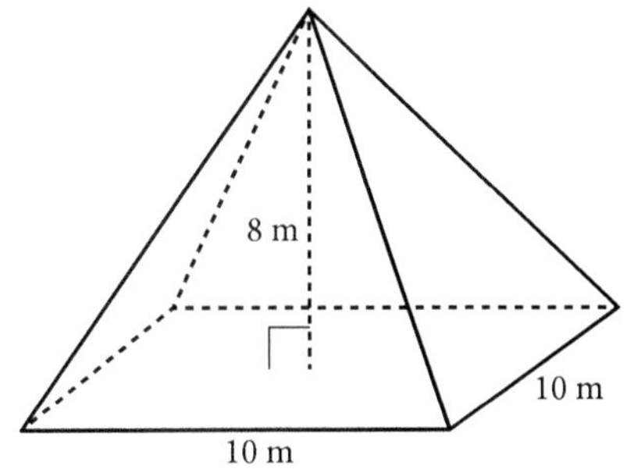

[5]

[Total 99]

Answers

Shape and Space 1

Exercise 1 *page 2*

1. 7.3 cm **2.** 7.9 cm **3.** 8.0 cm **4.** 10.3 cm **5.** 6.4 cm **6.** 6.8 cm
7. 9.0 cm **8.** 9.6 cm **9.** 7.6 cm **10.** 8.7 cm **11.** 8.2 cm **12.** 5.3 cm

Exercise 2 *page 3*

1. 63° **2.** 35° **3.** 62° **4.** 30° **5.** 37° **6.** 94°

Exercise 3 *page 4*

1. a), b), d) **4. d)** pyramid

Exercise 4 *page 5*

1. 70° **2.** 100° **3.** 70° **4.** 100°
5. 44° **6.** 80° **7.** 40° **8.** 48°
9. 40° **10.** 35° **11.** $a = 40°, b = 140°$ **12.** $x = 108°, y = 72°$

Exercise 5 *page 6*

1. 50° **2.** 70° **3.** 29° **4.** 30°
5. 70° **6.** 42° **7.** 40° **8.** $a = 55°, b = 70°$
9. 60° **10.** $x = 122°, y = 116°$ **11.** 135° **12.** 30°
13. 154° **14.** 75° **15.** $x = 30°$ **16.** 28°

Exercise 6 *page 7*

1. 72° **2.** 98° **3.** 80°
4. 74° **5.** 86° **6.** 88°
7. $x = 95°, y = 50°$ **8.** $a = 87°, b = 74°$ **9.** $a = 65°, c = 103°$
10. $a = 68°, b = 42°$ **11.** $y = 65°, z = 50°$ **12.** $a = 55°, b = 75°, c = 50°$

Exercise 7 *page 8*

1. 108° **2.** 50° **3.** 76° **4.** 270°
5. $a = 119°, b = 25°$ **6.** $c = 70°, d = 60°$ **7.** $a = 45°, b = 67\frac{1}{2}°$

Exercise 8 *page 9*

1. 42° **2.** 68° **3.** 100°
4. 73° **5.** 120° **6.** 52°
7. 100° **8.** $a = 70°, b = 60°$ **9.** $x = 58°, y = 109°$
10. 66° **11.** 65° **12.** $e = 70°, f = 30°$
13. $x = 72°, y = 36°$ **14.** $a = 68°, b = 72°, c = 68°$ **15.** 4°
16. $28\frac{1}{2}°$ **17.** 20° **18.** $x = 62°, y = 28°$
19. 34° **20.** 58° **21.** $x = 60°, y = 48°$
22. $a = 65°, b = 40°$ **23.** $x = 49°, y = 61°$ **24.** $a = 60°, b = 40°$
25. 136° **26.** 80° **27.** $x = 65°, y = 35°, z = 55°$
28. 26°

Exercise 9 *page 12*

1. a) $a = 80°, b = 70°, c = 65°, d = 86°, e = 59°$ **2. a)** $a = 36°$ **b)** 144°
3. a) i) 40° **ii)** 20° **iii)** 8° **iv)** 6° **b) i)** 140° **ii)** 160° **iii)** 172° **iv)** 174°
4. $p = 101°, q = 79°, x = 70°, m = 70°, n = 130°$ **5.** 24 **6.** 9 **7.** 20 **8.** 20

Exercise 10 *page 13*

2. 90° **3.** 65° **4.** 45° **5.** 90°
6. $e = 40°, f = 50°$ **7.** $g = 30°$ **8.** $h = 90°, i = 60°$ **9.** $j = 49°$
10. 45° **11.** $l = 60°, m = 50°$ **12.** $n = 40°$ **13.** 50°

Exercise 11 *page 15*

1. a) 1 **b)** 1 **2. a)** 1 **b)** 1 **3. a)** 4 **b)** 4
4. a) 2 **b)** 2 **5. a)** 0 **b)** 6 **6. a)** 0 **b)** 2
7. a) 0 **b)** 2 **8. a)** 4 **b)** 4 **9. a)** 0 **b)** 4
10. a) 4 **b)** 4 **11. a)** 6 **b)** 6 **12. a)** infinite **b)** infinite

Exercise 13 *page 17*

1. 34.6 cm **2.** 25.1 cm **3.** 37.7 cm **4.** 15.7 cm **5.** 28.3 cm
6. 53.4 m **7.** 44.6 m **8.** 72.3 m **9.** 8.48 m **10.** 212
11. 400 m **12.** 226 cm **13.** 823 m **14.** 643 m

Exercise 14 *page 18*

1. 95.0 cm^2 **2.** 78.5 cm^2 **3.** 28.3 m^2 **4.** 38.5 m^2 **5.** 113 cm^2 **6.** 201 cm^2
7. 19.6 m^2 **8.** 380 cm^2 **9.** 29.5 cm^2 **10.** 125 m^2 **11.** 21.5 cm^2 **12.** 4580 g
13. a) 30 **b)** 1508 cm^2 **c)** 508 cm^2 **14.** 40.8 m^2 **15.** 118 m^2

Exercise 15 *page 20*

1. 23.1 cm **2.** 38.6 cm **3.** 20.6 m **4.** 8.23 cm **5.** 28.6 cm **6.** 39.4 m
7. 17.9 cm **8.** 28.1 m **9.** 24.8 cm **10.** 46.3 m **11.** 28.8 cm

Exercise 16 *page 21*

1. 35.9 cm^2 **2.** 84.1 cm^2 **3.** 37.7 cm^2 **4.** 74.6 cm^2 **5.** 13.7 cm^2 **6.** 25.1 cm^2
7. a) 12.5 cm^2 **b)** 50 cm^2 **c)** 78.5 cm^2 **d)** 28.5 cm^2

Exercise 17 *page 22*

1. 2.39 cm **2.** 4.46 cm **3.** 1.11 m **4.** 4.15 cm **5.** 3.48 cm **6.** 3.95 m
7. 2.55 m **8.** 4.37 cm **9.** 4.62 cm **10.** 5.75 cm **11.** 15.9 cm **12.** 5.09 cm
13. 9.2 m **14.** 58.6 cm **15.** 5.39 cm **16.** 17.8 cm **17.** 195 km **18.** 395 cm
19. 215 m^2 **20.** 3.88 m **21.** 575 m^2 **22.** 5.41 cm **23.** 4.5 m

Exercise 18 *page 25*

1. a) 2.62 cm **b)** 6.54 cm^2 **c)** 12.62 cm **2. a)** 11.34 cm **b)** 56.72 cm^2 **c)** 31.34 cm
3. a) 12.57 cm **b)** 50.27 cm^2 **c)** 28.57 cm **4. a)** 17.28 cm **b)** 77.75 cm^2 **c)** 35.28 cm
5. a) 28.27 cm **b)** 84.82 cm^2 **c)** 40.27 cm **6. a)** 43.20 cm **b)** 161.99 cm^2 **c)** 58.20 cm
7. 31.9 cm^2 **8.** 31.2 cm^2 **9. a)** 7.07 cm^2 **b)** 19.5 cm^2 **10. a)** 8.50 cm **b)** 8.90 cm
11. a) 85.9° **b)** 57.3° **c)** 6.25 cm **12. a)** 6.14 cm **b)** 27.6 m **c)** 28.6 cm^2
13. a) 12 cm **b)** 30° **14. a)** 3.98 cm **b)** 74.9° **15. a)** 30° **b)** 10.5 cm

Exercise 19 *page 27*

1. 24 cm^2 **2.** 14 cm^2 **3.** 36 cm^2 **4.** 77 cm^2 **5.** 54 cm^2 **6.** 25 cm^2
7. 36 cm^2 **8.** 48 cm^2 **9.** 51 cm^2 **10.** 36 cm^2 **11.** 24 cm^2 **12.** 24 cm^2
13. 57 cm^2 **14.** 48 cm^2 **15.** 36 cm^2 **16.** 41 cm^2

Exercise 20 *page 27*

Questions **1** to **7** answers in square units.

1. b) 10, 6, 3 **c)** 36 **d)** 17
2. b) 5, 14, 6 **c)** 42 **d)** 17
3. $13\frac{1}{2}$ **4.** $14\frac{1}{2}$ **5.** 24 **6.** 22 **7.** 21
8. a) 248 cm^2 **b)** 120

Exercise 21 *page 29*

1. 42 cm^2 **2.** 22 cm^2 **3.** 103 cm^2 **4.** 60.5 cm^2
5. 143 cm^2 **6. a)** 4 000 000 m^2; 400 hectares **b)** 3 140 000 m^2; 314 hectares
7. $252

Exercise 23 *page 31*

1. 150 cm^3 **2.** 60 m^3 **3.** 480 cm^3 **4.** Volume = 300 cm^3 Surface area = 320 cm^2
5. Volume = 56 m^3 Surface area = 142 m^2 **6.** Volume = 280 cm^3 Surface area = 336 cm^2
7. 145 cm^3 **8.** 448 cm^3 **9.** 108 cm^3

Exercise 24 *page 32*

1. 62.8 cm³ **2.** 113 cm³ **3.** 198 cm³ **4.** 763 cm³
5. 157 cm³ **6.** 385 cm³ **7.** 770 cm³ **8.** 176 m³
9. 228 m³ **10.** 486 cm³ **11.** 113 litres **12.** 141 cm³, 25.1 cm³

Exercise 25 *page 34*

1. 20.9 cm³ **2.** 524 cm³ **3.** 4189 cm³ **4.** 101 cm³ **5.** 268 cm³ **6.** $4.19x^3$ cm³
7. 0.00419 m³ **8.** 3 cm³ **9.** 93.3 cm³ **10.** 48 cm³ **11.** 92.4 cm³ **12.** 5 m
13. 2.43 cm **14.** 23.9 cm **15. a)** 0.36 m **b)** 0.427 cm

Exercise 26 *page 35*

1. 2400 cm³ **2. a)** 200 m² **b)** 2400 m³ **3.** 770 cm³
4. a) 2.25 cm² **b)** 0.451 cm³ **c)** 4510 cm³ **5. a)** 62 800 cm³ **b)** 500 cm³ **c)** 125
6. 8 cm³ **7. a)** 76 cm² **b)** 30 400 cm³ **c)** 237 kg **d)** 33
8. No **9.** 53 times **10.** 98 min

Exercise 27 *page 37*

1. AB = 5 cm **5.** 12 km **6.** Yes (they are 3.6 km apart) **8.** 6.5 m
10. a) i) 14 m **ii)** 6 m **iii)** 4 m **b)** 8 m **c)** 14 m **d)** 2 cm **e)** 12 m **f)** 42 m²

Revision exercise 1A *page 40*

1. a) and c) **2. a)** 91.5 cm² **b)** 119 cm² **3.** 17.7 cm
4. a) 198 cm³ **b)** 1357 mm³ **c)** 145 **5.** Both arrive at the same time.
6. 3.43 cm², 4.57 cm² **7.** 9.95 cm **8.** 25 **9.** 5.14 cm² **10.** 30 cm

Examination-style exercise 1B *page 41*

1. 30° **2. a)** 22° **b)** 90° **c)** 68° **d)** 68°
3. $x = 108°$, $y = 192°$ **4.** 2 **5. a)** 128.6796351 cm² **b)** 129 cm² **6.** 21.45 to 21.6 cm²
7. 16.8 cm **8. a)** 160 m **b)** 50.9 or 51 m **9.** 2.71
10. a) 1 084 000 cm³ **b)** 1.084 **11. a)** 70 cm **b)** 184 cm² **12.** 13.5
13. a) 51.4° **b) i)** isosceles **ii)** $p = 50, q = 80, r = 50, s = 50, t = 80$ **c)** 25
14. a) 141 cm³ **b)** 2 h 56 or 2 h 57 **c)** 36 **d) i)** \$8.60 **ii)** 34.4% or 34%
15. a) 141.37 cm² **b)** 13.42 cm **16.** $\frac{2}{3}$

Algebra 1

Exercise 1 *page 47*

1. a) 17 **b)** 27 **c)** 48 **d)** 30 **e)** 12.5 **f)** 121
2. a) 11 **b)** 16 **c)** −1 **d)** 2.4 **e)** 11 **f)** 0
3. a) 7, 11, 18, 29, 47, 76, 123 **b)** 12, 19, 31, 50
4. a) $6 \times 7 = 6 + 6^2$, $7 \times 8 = 7 + 7^2$ **b)** $10 \times 11 = 10 + 10^2$, $30 \times 31 = 30 + 30^2$
5. $5 + 9 \times 1234 = 11\,111$
$6 + 9 \times 12\,345 = 111\,111$
$7 + 9 \times 123\,456 = 1\,111\,111$
6. 63, 3968 **7.** 3, 5, 5 **8.** Yes
9. b) $(1 + 2 + 3 + \cdots + 10)^2 = 5\,5^2 = 3025$
10. a) 16 **b)** 15 **c)** 26 **d)** 25 **e)** 113 **f) i)** 90 **ii)** 105 **iii)** 199 **iv)** 437
11. a) i) 24 **ii)** 36 **iii)** 75 **b) i)** 23 **ii)** 35 **iii)** 59
c) i) 28 **ii)** 39 **iii)** 50 **iv)** 88 **d) i)** 40 **ii)** 21 **iii)** 31 **iv)** 50

Exercise 2 *page 50*

1. 4 kg **2.** 3 kg **3.** 3 kg **4.** 2 kg **5.** 4 kg **6.** 3 kg

Exercise 3 *page 50*

1. 12 **2.** 9 **3.** 18 **4.** 4 **5.** 17 **6.** −5 **7.** 6 **8.** −7 **9.** 4 **10.** 8
11. 17 **12.** −5 **13.** 5 **14.** 6 **15.** 2 **16.** $\frac{4}{5}$ **17.** $2\frac{1}{3}$ **18.** $7\frac{1}{2}$ **19.** $1\frac{5}{6}$ **20.** 0

21. $\frac{5}{9}$ 22. 1 23. $\frac{1}{5}$ 24. $\frac{2}{7}$ 25. $\frac{3}{4}$ 26. $\frac{2}{3}$ 27. $1\frac{1}{4}$ 28. $1\frac{1}{5}$ 29. $1\frac{5}{9}$ 30. $\frac{1}{3}$

31. $\frac{1}{2}$ 32. $\frac{1}{10}$ 33. $-\frac{3}{8}$ 34. $\frac{9}{50}$ 35. $\frac{1}{2}$ 36. $\frac{3}{5}$ 37. $-\frac{4}{9}$ 38. 0 39. $4\frac{5}{8}$ 40. $-1\frac{3}{7}$

41. $2\frac{1}{3}$ 42. $\frac{3}{4}$ 43. 1 44. $3\frac{3}{5}$ 45. $\frac{1}{3}$ 46. $2\frac{1}{14}$ 47. -1 48. $-\frac{5}{6}$ 49. $8\frac{1}{4}$ 50. -55

Exercise 4 page 51

1. $2\frac{3}{4}$ 2. $1\frac{2}{3}$ 3. 2 4. $\frac{1}{5}$ 5. $\frac{1}{2}$ 6. 2 7. $5\frac{1}{3}$ 8. $1\frac{1}{5}$ 9. 0 10. $\frac{2}{9}$

11. $1\frac{1}{2}$ 12. $\frac{1}{6}$ 13. $1\frac{1}{3}$ 14. $\frac{6}{7}$ 15. $\frac{4}{7}$ 16. 7 17. $\frac{5}{8}$ 18. 5 19. $\frac{2}{3}$ 20. $\frac{1}{3}$

21. 4 22. -1 23. 1 24. $\frac{6}{7}$ 25. $1\frac{1}{4}$ 26. 1 27. $\frac{7}{9}$ 28. $-1\frac{1}{2}$ 29. $\frac{2}{9}$ 30. $-1\frac{1}{2}$

Exercise 5 page 52

1. 3 2. 5 3. $10\frac{1}{2}$ 4. -8 5. $\frac{1}{3}$ 6. $-4\frac{1}{2}$ 7. $3\frac{1}{3}$ 8. $3\frac{1}{2}$ 9. $3\frac{2}{3}$ 10. -2

11. $-5\frac{1}{2}$ 12. $4\frac{1}{5}$ 13. $\frac{3}{7}$ 14. $\frac{7}{11}$ 15. $4\frac{4}{5}$ 16. 5 17. 9 18. $-2\frac{1}{3}$ 19. $\frac{2}{5}$ 20. $\frac{3}{5}$

Exercise 6 page 53

1. $\frac{3}{5}$ 2. $\frac{4}{7}$ 3. $\frac{11}{12}$ 4. $\frac{6}{11}$ 5. $\frac{2}{3}$ 6. $\frac{5}{9}$ 7. $\frac{7}{9}$ 8. $1\frac{1}{3}$ 9. $\frac{1}{2}$ 10. $\frac{2}{3}$

11. 3 12. $1\frac{1}{2}$ 13. 24 14. 15 15. -10 16. 21 17. 21 18. $2\frac{2}{3}$ 19. $4\frac{3}{8}$ 20. $1\frac{1}{2}$

21. $3\frac{3}{4}$ 22. $1\frac{1}{3}$ 23. $3\frac{3}{5}$ 24. 2 25. $\frac{5}{8}$ 26. $\frac{7}{19}$ 27. $-\frac{3}{5}$ 28. -24 29. -70 30. $8\frac{1}{4}$

31. 220 32. -500 33. $-\frac{98}{99}$ 34. 6 35. 30

Exercise 7 page 53

1. 2 2. 3 3. 2 4. 2 5. 2 6. 3 7. 6 8. 1

Exercise 8 page 54

1. 3 2. $\frac{3}{4}$ 3. $4\frac{1}{2}$ 4. $-\frac{3}{10}$ 5. $-\frac{1}{2}$ 6. $17\frac{2}{3}$

7. $\frac{1}{6}$ 8. 5 9. 12 10. $3\frac{1}{3}$ 11. $4\frac{2}{3}$ 12. -9

Exercise 9 page 55

1. $\frac{3}{4}$ 2. $\frac{1}{4}$ 3. $1\frac{3}{8}$ 4. $1\frac{1}{4}$ 5. 7 6. a) $3\frac{3}{5}$ b) $\frac{3}{4}$

7. a) 41 b) 31 8. 29 9. a) 53 b) 65 10. 55, 56, 57

11. 41, 42, 43, 44 12. a) i) $x-3$ ii) $2(x-3)$ b) $x = 12\frac{1}{2}$ 13. $x = 8$, perimeter = 60 cm

14. 11 15. $6 16. $x = 3$

Exercise 11 page 59

17. c) 10.7 cm^2 d) 5.3×1.7 e) 12.25 cm^2 f) 3.5×3.5

Exercise 12 page 61

1. a) 3 b) 2 c) $\frac{1}{2}$ d) $\frac{1}{3}$ e) -1 f) -2 g) -2 h) $-\frac{2}{3}$ i) 6 j) $-\frac{9}{4}$

2. a) $\frac{5}{2}$ b) $-\frac{3}{5}$ c) $\frac{5}{2}$ d) $-\frac{3}{5}$

Exercise 13 page 62

7. (gradient first) A: 2, −2; B: $\frac{1}{3}$, 1; C: −1, −4; D: $-\frac{5}{2}$, 5; E: 0, −5

Exercise 14 page 63

In questions **1** to **16** gradient is first number and y-intercept is second.

1. 2, −3 **2.** 3, 2 **3.** −1, −4 **4.** $\frac{1}{2}$, 3 **5.** $-\frac{2}{3}$, −4

6. −3, 2 **7.** −7, 4 **8.** 2, −1 **9.** $-\frac{1}{2}$, 3 **10.** −2, 7

11. −2, 6 **12.** 3, −7 **13.** 2, 8 **14.** $-\frac{1}{2}$, $1\frac{2}{3}$ **15.** $\frac{2}{5}$, $2\frac{2}{5}$

16. 3, $-\frac{2}{3}$

Exercise 15 page 64

1. $y = 3x$ **2.** $y = 5$ **3.** $y = 3 - x$ **4.** $y = 2x + 3$ **5.** $y = 2x - 1$

6. $y = -x - 4$ **7.** A: $y = 3x - 4$ B: $y = x + 2$ **8.** C: $y = \frac{2}{3}x - 2$ D: $y = -2x + 4$

9. a) $y = 2x + 5$ **b)** $y = -x + 3$ **10. a)** $y = 3x + 1$ **b)** $y = x - 2$

Exercise 16 page 66

1. a) 3.6/3.7 and −1.6/−1.7 **b)** 2.4, −0.4 **c)** −1, 3

2. a) 2.4, −0.4 **b)** 0, 2 **3. a)** 0, 3 **b)** 3.8, −0.8

4. a) −1.6, 3.6 **b)** 2.4, −0.4 **5. a)** 6.5, 0.5 **b)** No intersection

Revision exercise 2A page 67

1. a) 30, 37 **b)** 12, 10 **c)** 7, 10 **d)** 8, 4 **e)** 26, 33

2. a) 9 **b)** 11 **c)** 3 **d)** 7

3. a) 7 **b)** $\frac{1}{4}$ **c)** $\frac{4}{5}$

4. a) 9 **b)** 50 **c)** $7 \times 11 - 6 = 72 - 1$ **5. a)** 4 **b)** 19

6. a) $1 + 2 + 3 + 4 + 5 + 4 + 3 + 2 + 1 = 5^2$ **b)** $\cdots + 4 + \cdots + 9 + \cdots + 1 = 9^2$
$1 + \cdots + 6 + \cdots + 1 = 6^2$

7. A $y = 6$, B $y = \frac{1}{2}x - 3$, C $y = 10 - x$, D $y = 3x$ **8.** $4\frac{1}{6}$ sq. units **9.** (0, 7), (0, −2), $\left(4\frac{1}{2}, 2\frac{1}{2}\right)$

10. a) $6x + 15 < 200$ **b)** 29

Examination-style exercise 2B page 68

1. 3 **2.** −2 **3. a)** m **b)** $y = 2x + 5$ **c)** missing numbers 8, 12, 3 **e)** (−3.8, −2.7) (1.8, 8.7)

4. a) i) 5, −3, 12 **iii)** −0.8 to −0.7, 2.6 to 2.8 **b) i)** 8, 2 **iii)** 3.1 to 3.3

5. $y = 2x - 3$ **6. a)** $-\frac{1}{2}$ **b)** $y = -\frac{1}{2}x + 3$

7. a) i) $x + 3$ **ii)** $x(x + 3)$ **b) i)** −3, −9, −3 **c) i)** 1.5 to 1.6, −4.5 to −4.6 **ii)** 4.5 to 4.6
d) ii) $y = 2x - 3$

8. a) $4p - 3q$ **b)** 7 **c) i)** $2j + 2k$ **ii)** $2j + 2k = 72$ **iii)** 24 **d) i)** $\frac{1}{3}$ **ii)** $s = wr + t$

Number 1

Exercise 1 page 73

1. 20 **2.** 400 **3.** 80 **4.** 6 **5.** 6000 **6.** 20 000

7. 5 000 000 **8.** 800 000 **9.** 200 **10.** 70 **11.** 10 **12.** 800

13. 6000 **14.** 60 **15.** 400 **16.** 70 000, 70

17. a) 720 **b)** 5206 **c)** 16 430 **d)** 500 000 **e)** 300 090 **f)** 8500

18. a) 8753 **b)** 3578

19. a) four thousand, six hundred and twenty **b)** six hundred and seven
c) twenty-five thousand, four hundred **d)** six million, eight hundred thousand
e) twenty-one thousand, four hundred and twenty-five

20. a) 75 423 **b)** 23 574 **21. a)** 257 **b)** 3221 **c)** 704
22. a) 1392 **b)** 26 611 **c)** 257 900 **23. a)** [5][ ][0] **b)** 52 000
24. a) 2058, 2136, 2142, 2290 **b)** 5029, 5299, 5329, 5330 **c)** 25 000, 25 117, 25 171, 25 200, 25 500
25. 100 **26.** 10 **27.** $a = 100, b = 7$ **28.** $p = 1000, q = 10$

Exercise 2 *page 74*

1. 3497 **2.** 2435 **3.** 785 **4.** 68 521 **5.** 212 **6.** 41 **7.** 859
8. 208 **9.** 270 **10.** 5000 **11.** 365 **12.** 856 **13.** 2528 **14.** 64 568
15. 85 **16.** 324 **17.** 639 **18.** 325 **19.** 52 **20.** 52 **21.** 2018
22. 4569 **23.** 7 **24.** 1080 **25.** 1492 **26.** 524 **27.** 5800 **28.** 188
29. 1641 **30.** 365 **31.** 254 **32.** 21 200

page 75

	Test 1	Test 2	Test 3	Test 4
1.	22	22	40	35
2.	45	27	40	18
3.	8	54	10	83
4.	58	45	81	8
5.	77	143	98	32
6.	48	9	90	89
7.	36	5	6	29
8.	9	1300	35	12
9.	110	198	52	100
10.	42	50	190	154
11.	48	57	5	55
12.	7	21	8	11
13.	116	49	110	5000
14.	21	37	195	225
15.	900	12	32	63

Exercise 3 *page 76*

1. a) $\begin{array}{r} 285 \\ +514 \\ \hline 799 \end{array}$ **b)** $\begin{array}{r} 637 \\ +252 \\ \hline 889 \end{array}$ **c)** $\begin{array}{r} 635 \\ +344 \\ \hline 979 \end{array}$

2. a) $\begin{array}{r} 356 \\ +526 \\ \hline 882 \end{array}$ **b)** $\begin{array}{r} 224 \\ +537 \\ \hline 761 \end{array}$ **c)** $\begin{array}{r} 388 \\ +425 \\ \hline 813 \end{array}$

3. a) $\begin{array}{r} 48 \\ \times\ 3 \\ \hline 144 \end{array}$ **b)** $\begin{array}{r} 33 \\ \times\ 7 \\ \hline 231 \end{array}$ **c)** $\begin{array}{r} 321 \\ \times\ 5 \\ \hline 1605 \end{array}$

4. a) 150 **b)** 15 **c)** 9 **d)** 552

5. a) $\begin{array}{r} 445 \\ +285 \\ \hline 730 \end{array}$ **b)** $\begin{array}{r} 427 \\ +177 \\ \hline 604 \end{array}$ **c)** $\begin{array}{r} 535 \\ +264 \\ \hline 799 \end{array}$

6. a) $35 \times 7 = 245$ **b)** 58 **c)** 4 **d)** 950

7. a) 72 **b)** 108 **c)** $\begin{array}{r} 889 \\ -346 \\ \hline 543 \end{array}$ **d)** $\begin{array}{r} 335 \\ -218 \\ \hline 117 \end{array}$

9. a) $4 \times 4 - 4$ **b)** $8 \div 8 + 8$ **c)** $8 \times 8 + 8$
10. a) $-$ **b)** $\div$ **c)** $\times$ **d)** $\div$ **e)** $+$
11. a) $+$ **b)** $-, -$ **c)** $+$

Exercise 4 *page 78*

1. T **2.** F **3.** T **4.** T **5.** T **6.** F **7.** T **8.** T

9. $50 + 7 + \frac{2}{10}$ **10. a)** 235.1 **b)** 67.23 **c)** 98.32 **d)** 3.167

11. 0.2, 0.31, 0.41 **12.** 0.58, 0.702, 0.75 **13.** 0.41, 0.43, 0.432

14. 0.6, 0.609, 0.61 **15.** 0.04, 0.15, 0.2, 0.35 **16.** 0.18, 0.81, 1.18, 1.8

17. 0.061, 0.07, 0.1, 0.7 **18.** 0.009, 0.025, 0.03, 0.2 **19.** CARWASH

20. a) 32.51 **b)** 0.853 **c)** 1.16

21. a) 5.69 **b)** 0.552 **c)** 1.30

22. a) \$3.50 **b)** \$0.15 **c)** \$0.03 **d)** \$0.10 **e)** \$12.60 **f)** \$0.08

23. a) T **b)** F **c)** T **d)** T

Exercise 5 *page 79*

1. 4.3 **2.** 0.7 **3.** 9.4 **4.** 1.2 **5.** 16 **6.** 10.7

7. 17.4 **8.** 128 **9.** 375 **10.** 0.24 **11.** 1.92 **12.** 5.2

13. 0.06 **14.** 1.76 **15.** 3.16 **16.** 105 **17.** 50 **18.** 125

Exercise 6 *page 80*

1. 6.34 **2.** 8.38 **3.** 81.5 **4.** 7.4 **5.** 7245 **6.** 32

7. 6.3 **8.** 142 **9.** 4.1 **10.** 30 **11.** 710 **12.** 39.5

13. 0.624 **14.** 0.897 **15.** 0.175 **16.** 0.236 **17.** 0.127 **18.** 0.705

19. 1.3 **20.** 0.08 **21.** 0.007 **22.** 21.8 **23.** 0.035 **24.** 0.0086

25. 95 **26.** 111.1 **27.** 0.32 **28.** 70 **29.** 5.76 **30.** 9.99

31. 660 **32.** 1 **33.** 0.042 **34.** 6200 **35.** 0.009 **36.** 0.0555

37. a) 0 **b) i)** 5, 2 **ii)** 5, 2, 0 **iii)** 0, 5, 2 and ·

Exercise 7 *page 81*

1. 10.14 **2.** 20.94 **3.** 26.71 **4.** 216.95 **5.** 9.6 **6.** 23.1

7. 9.14 **8.** 17.32 **9.** 0.062 **10.** 1.11 **11.** 4.36 **12.** 2.41

13. 1.36 **14.** 6.23 **15.** 2.46 **16.** 8.4 **17.** 2.8 **18.** 10.3

19. 0.18 **20.** 4.01 **21.** 6.66 **22.** 41.11 **23.** 3.6 **24.** 6.44

Exercise 8 *page 81*

1. 0.06 **2.** 0.15 **3.** 0.12 **4.** 0.006 **5.** 1.8 **6.** 3.5

7. 1.8 **8.** 0.8 **9.** 0.36 **10.** 0.014 **11.** 1.26 **12.** 2.35

13. 8.52 **14.** 3.12 **15.** 0.126 **16.** 127.2 **17.** 0.17 **18.** 0.327

19. 0.126 **20.** 0.34 **21.** 0.055 **22.** 0.52 **23.** 1.3 **24.** 0.001

Exercise 9 *page 82*

1. 2.1 **2.** 3.1 **3.** 4.36 **4.** 4 **5.** 4 **6.** 2.5

7. 16 **8.** 200 **9.** 70 **10.** 0.92 **11.** 30.5 **12.** 6.2

13. 12.5 **14.** 122 **15.** 212 **16.** 56 **17.** 60 **18.** 1500

19. 0.3 **20.** 0.7 **21.** 0.5 **22.** 3.04 **23.** 5.62 **24.** 0.78

25. 0.14 **26.** 3.75 **27.** 0.075 **28.** 0.15 **29.** 1.22 **30.** 163.8

31. 1.75 **32.** 18.8 **33.** 12 **34.** 88 **35.** 580

Crossnumbers *page 83*

A

[1] 9	1		[2] 2	1	[3] 4	0
4		[4] 1	7		5	
	[5] 6	4		[6] 8		[7] 9
[8] 7	0		[9] 3	1	[10] 8	
4			5		[11] 3	6
[12] 4	3	[13] 7		[14] 8	1	
0		[15] 2	3		[16] 6	3

B

[1] 9	6		[2] 1	5	[3] 7	3
3		[4] 5	6		1	
	[5] 8	3		[6] 3		[7] 8
[8] 6	6		[9] 5	9	[10] 4	
3			6		[11] 7	0
[12] 1	7	[13] 4		[14] 8	9	
8		[15] 7	0		[16] 9	3

C

2	6		6	3	1	4
0		3	7		8	
	2	5		2		6
8	0		3	1	5	
4			2		7	7
6	0	2		1	0	
6		5	7		6	4

Exercise 10 *page 85*

1. \$684 **2.** \$642 **3.** \$1652 **4.** \$834 **5.** \$2810 **6.** \$840 **7.** \$5580 **8.** \$2284

Exercise 11 *page 85*

1. a) 11, 22, 11, 33 **b)** 12, 24, 13, 39 **c)** 7, 14, 28, 17, 51
d) 9, 16, 32, 21, 63 **e)** 11, 18, 36, 25, 75 **f)** 13, 20, 40, 29, 87

2. a) 6, 12, 27, 20, 5 **b)** 3, 6, 21, 14, $3\frac{1}{2}$ **c)** 8, 16, 31, 24, 6
d) 10, 20, 35, 28, 7 **e)** 1, 2, 17, 10, $2\frac{1}{2}$ **f)** 12, 24, 39, 32, 8

3. a) 7, 22, 44, 22, $5\frac{1}{2}$ **b)** 10, 25, 50, 28, 7 **c)** 16, 31, 62, 40, 10
d) $\frac{1}{2}$, $15\frac{1}{2}$, 31, 9, $2\frac{1}{4}$ **e)** 100, 115, 230, 208, 52 **f)** 24, 39, 78, 56, 14

4. a) 4, 16, 48, 38, 19 **b)** 5, 25, 75, 65, $32\frac{1}{2}$ **c)** 6, 36, 108, 98, 49
d) 8, 64, 48, 38, 19 **e)** 1, 1, 3, −7, $-3\frac{1}{2}$ **f)** 10, 100, 300, 290, 145

5. ×4, square root, −10, × −2 **6.** reciprocal, +1, square, ÷3 **7.** +3, cube, ÷ −2, +100

Exercise 12 *page 88*

1. 19 **2.** 3 **3.** 36 **4.** 34 **5.** 10 **6.** 58 **7.** 26 **8.** 51
9. 16 **10.** 2 **11.** 10 **12.** 6 **13.** 16 **14.** 99 **15.** 3 **16.** 33
17. 52 **18.** 3

Exercise 13 *page 88*

1. 49 **2.** 9 **3.** 34 **4.** 12 **5.** 5 **6.** 4 **7.** 10 **8.** 2 **9.** 30

Exercise 14 *page 89*

1. a) 1, 2, 3, 6 **b)** 1, 3, 5, 15 **c)** 1, 2, 3, 6, 9, 18
d) 1, 3, 7, 21 **e)** 1, 2, 4, 5, 8, 10, 20, 40
2. 2, 3, 5, 7, 11, 13, 17, 19 **3.** $2+5=7$ $2+11=13$ etc.
4. 101, 151, 293 are prime
5. a) $36=2\times2\times3\times3$ **b)** $60=2\times2\times3\times5$ **c)** $216=2\times2\times2\times3\times3\times3$
d) $200=2\times2\times2\times5\times5$ **e)** $1500=2\times2\times3\times5\times5\times5$
6. $1200=2\times2\times2\times3\times5\times5$
7. a) 3, 6, 9, 12 **b)** 4, 8, 12, 16 **c)** 10, 20, 30, 40 **d)** 11, 22, 33, 44 **e)** 20, 40, 60, 80
8. a) 32 **b)** 56 **9.** 12, 24, etc. **10. a)** even **b)** odd **c)** even
11.

	Prime number	Multiple of 3	Factor of 16
Number > 5	7	9	8
Odd number	5	3	1
Even number	2	6	4

12. a) 7 **b)** 50 **c)** 1 **d)** 5
13. a) 2, 4, 6, 8, 10, 12 **b)** 5, 10, 15, 20, 25, 30 **c)** 10
14. a) 4, 8, 12, 16 **b)** 12, 24, 36, 48 **c)** 12
15. a) 18 **b)** 24 **c)** 70 **d)** 12 **e)** 30 **f)** 252
16. 12 **17.** 6
18. a) 6 **b)** 11 **c)** 9 **d)** 6 **e)** 12 **f)** 10
19. a) 6 **b)** 40 **c)** 11, 22 (or others) **d)** 2, 5 (or others)
20. 15 **21.** 21

Exercise 15 *page 91*

1. Rational: $\left(\sqrt{17}\right)^2$; 3.14; $\frac{\sqrt{12}}{\sqrt{3}}$; $3^{-1} + 3^{-2}$; $\frac{22}{7}$; $\sqrt{2.25}$
3. a) both irrational **b)** both rational
4. a) 6π cm, irrational **b)** 6 cm, rational **c)** 36 cm², rational
d) 9π cm², irrational **e)** $36 - 9\pi$ cm², irrational
7. a) No **b)** Yes e.g. $\sqrt{8} \times \sqrt{2} = 4$

Exercise 16 *page 93*

1. a) $<$ **b)** $>$ **c)** $>$ **d)** $>$ **e)** $>$ **f)** $>$
2. a) $x > 2$ **b)** $x \leqslant 5$ **c)** $x < 100$ **d)** $-2 \leqslant x \leqslant 2$ **e)** $x \geqslant -6$ **f)** $3 < x \leqslant 8$
3. a) 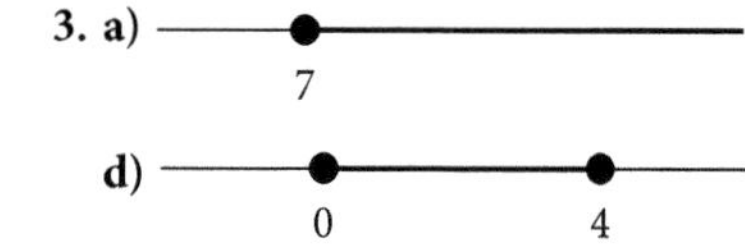

b) 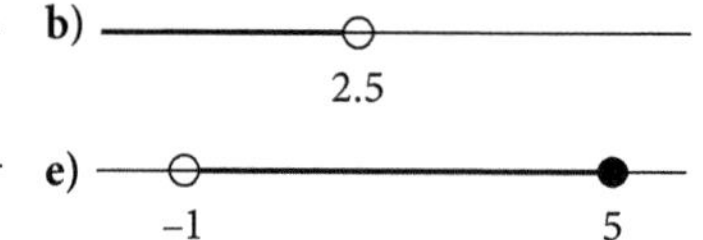

c) 1 7
d) 0 4
e) −1 5

4. a) $A \geqslant 16$ **b)** $3 < A \leqslant 70$ **c)** $150 < T < 175$ **d)** $h \geqslant 1.5$ **5 a)** True **b)** True **c)** True
6. a) $=$ **b)** $<$ **c)** $=$ **d)** $<$ **e)** $=$ **f)** $=$
7. 1, 2, 3, 4, 5, 6 **8.** 7, 11, 13, 17, 19 **9.** 4, 9, 16, 25, 36, 49
10. a) 16 **b)** −16 **c)** 20 **d)** −5

Exercise 17 *page 95*

1. 08:00 **2.** 21:30 **3.** 18:00 **4.** 05:30 **5.** 19:40 **6.** 22:00
7. 19:15 **8.** 22:45 **9.** 08:30 **10.** 04:15 **11.** 02:25 **12.** 13:30
13. 19:20 **14.** 06:50 **15.** 07:10 **16.** 23:58 **17.** 21:30 **18.** 11:55
19. 15:30 **20.** 01:00 **21.** 10:30 **22.** 00:20 **23.** 19:00 **24.** 12:06
25. 00:50 **26.** 7.00 a.m. **27.** 7.30 p.m. **28.** 11.20 a.m. **29.** 4.45 a.m. **30.** 8.30 p.m.
31. 9.15 p.m. **32.** 9.10 a.m. **33.** 11.45 a.m. **34.** 11.10 p.m. **35.** 8.00 p.m. **36.** noon
37. 1.40 a.m. **38.** 4.00 a.m. **39.** 7.07 a.m. **40.** 1.13 p.m. **41.** 12.15 p.m. **42.** 12.30 p.m.
43. 3.45 p.m. **44.** 4.20 p.m. **45.** 5.16 a.m.

Exercise 18 *page 95*

1. 1 h 10 mins **2.** 2 h 10 mins **3.** 55 mins **4.** 35 mins **5.** 3 h 20 mins **6.** 1 h 45 mins
7. 2 h 20 mins **8.** 1 h 53 mins **9.** 53 mins **10.** 5 h 25 mins **11.** 1 h 50 mins **12.** 3 h 14 mins
13. 1 h 15 mins **14.** 4 h 35 mins **15.** 2 h 20 mins **16.** 12 h **17.** 14 h **18.** 7 h 20 mins
19. 3 h 15 mins **20.** 7 h 05 mins **21.** 5 h **22.** 4 h 40 mins **23.** 8 h 30 mins **24.** 2 h 25 mins
25. 8 h 10 mins **26.** 19 h **27.** 19 h **28.** 17 h 30 mins **29.** 9 h 25 mins **30.** 34 h

Exercise 19 *page 96*

1. a) 25 mins **b)** 45 mins **c)** 1 h 6 mins **2.** 7 **3.** 09:54
4. 11:35 **5.** 15 mins **6.** 12:52
7. a) 1 h 42 mins **b)** 2 h 32 mins **c)** 3 h 43 mins
8. 2 **9.** 14:07 **10.** 09:21 **11.** 27 mins **12.** 12:01

Exercise 20 *page 97*

1. 805 **2.** 459 **3.** 650 **4.** 1333 **5.** 2745
6. 1248 **7.** 4522 **8.** 30 368 **9.** 28 224 **10.** 8568
11. 46 800 **12.** 66 281 **13.** 57 602 **14.** 89 516 **15.** 97 525

Exercise 21 *page 98*

1. 32 **2.** 25 **3.** 18 **4.** 13 **5.** 35
6. 22 r 2 **7.** 23 r 24 **8.** 18 r 10 **9.** 27 r 18 **10.** 13 r 31
11. 35 r 6 **12.** 23 r 24 **13.** 64 r 37 **14.** 151 r 17 **15.** 2961 r 15

Exercise 22 *page 98*

1. \$47.04 **2.** 46 **3.** 7592 **4.** 21, 17c change **5.** 8
6. \$80.64 **7.** \$14 million **8.** \$85 **9.** \$21 600

Exercise 23 *page 99*

1.

5	×	12	→	60
×		÷		
20	+	24	→	44
↓		↓		
100	×	$\frac{1}{2}$	→	50

2.

7	×	6	→	42
÷		÷		
14	−	3	→	11
↓		↓		
$\frac{1}{2}$	×	2	→	1

3.

19	×	2	→	38
−		÷		
12	×	4	→	48
↓		↓		
7	−	$\frac{1}{2}$	→	$6\frac{1}{2}$

4.

17	×	10	→	170
−		÷		
9	÷	100	→	0.09
↓		↓		
8	−	0.1	→	7.9

5.

0.3	×	20	→	6
+		−		
11	÷	11	→	1
↓		↓		
11.3	−	9	→	2.3

6.

$\frac{1}{2}$	×	50	→	25
−		÷		
0.1	+	$\frac{1}{2}$	→	0.6
↓		↓		
0.4	×	100	→	40

7.

7	×	0.1	→	0.7
÷		×		
4	÷	0.2	→	20
↓		↓		
1.75	+	0.02	→	1.77

8.

1.4	+	8	→	9.4
−		×		
0.1	×	0.1	→	0.01
↓		↓		
1.3	+	0.8	→	2.1

9.

100	×	0.3	→	30
−		×		
2.5	÷	10	→	0.25
↓		↓		
97.5	+	3	→	100.5

10.

3	÷	2	→	1.5
÷		÷		
8	÷	16	→	$\frac{1}{2}$
↓		↓		
$\frac{3}{8}$	+	$\frac{1}{8}$	→	$\frac{1}{2}$

11.

$\frac{1}{4}$	−	$\frac{1}{16}$	→	$\frac{3}{16}$
×		×		
$\frac{1}{2}$	÷	4	→	$\frac{1}{8}$
↓		↓		
$\frac{1}{8}$	+	$\frac{1}{4}$	→	$\frac{3}{8}$

12.

0.5	−	0.01	→	0.49
+		×		
3.5	×	10	→	35
↓		↓		
4	÷	0.1	→	40

13.

5.2	−	1.8	→	3.4
−		÷		
4.56	×	5	→	22.8
↓		↓		
0.64	+	0.36	→	1

14.

0.7	×	30	→	21
×		−		
16	−	−19	→	35
↓		↓		
11.2	−	49	→	−37.8

15.

−12	×	−6	→	72
÷		+		
4	+	7	→	11
↓		↓		
−3	+	1	→	−2

Exercise 24 *page 101*

1. \$12 **2.** \$8 **3.** \$10 **4.** \$3 **5.** \$2.40 **6.** \$24
7. \$45 **8.** \$72 **9.** \$244 **10.** \$9.60 **11.** \$42 **12.** \$88
13. 8 kg **14.** 12 kg **15.** 272 g **16.** 45 m **17.** 40 km **18.** \$710
19. 4.94 kg **20.** 60 g **21.** \$204

Exercise 25 *page 101*

1. \$0.28 **2.** \$1.16 **3.** \$1.22 **4.** \$2.90 **5.** \$3.57 **6.** \$0.45
7. \$0.93 **8.** \$37.03 **9.** \$16.97 **10.** \$0.38 **11.** \$0.79 **12.** \$1.60
13. \$13.40 **14.** \$50 **15.** \$2.94 **16.** \$11.06 **17.** \$1.23 **18.** \$4.40
19. \$11.25 **20.** \$22.71 **21.** \$9.19

Exercise 26 *page 102*

1. \$63 **2.** \$736 **3.** \$77.55 **4.** \$104 **5.** \$1960 **6.** \$792
7. \$132 **8.** \$45.75 **9.** \$110.30 **10.** \$42 **11.** \$12.03 **12.** \$9.49
13. \$7.35 **14.** \$7.01 **15.** \$12.34 **16.** \$16.92 **17.** \$31.87 **18.** \$9.02
19. \$8.88 **20.** \$14.14

Exercise 27 *page 102*

1. \$35.20 **2.** \$5724 **3.** \$171.50 **4.** \$8.84 **5.** 2.828 kg **6.** \$58.50
7. 59 400 **8.** \$9.52 **9.** 3.348 kg **10.** \$2762.50

Exercise 28 *page 103*

1. \$17.51 **2.** \$40.66 **3.** \$77.96 **4.** \$185.34
5. a) \$28 **b)** 21 **6. a)** \$480 **b) i)** \$16.20 **ii)** \$1053

Exercise 29 *page 104*

1. a) \$216 **b)** \$115.50 **c)** 2 years **d)** 5 years **2.** \$2295 interest; \$9045
3. 7.5% annual rate

Exercise 30 *page 105*

1. a) \$2180 **b)** \$2376.20 **c)** \$2590.06 **2. a)** \$5550 **b)** \$6838.16 **c)** \$8425.29
3. \$13 107.96 **4. a)** \$36 465.19 **b)** \$40 202.87
5. a) \$9540 **b)** \$107 19 **c)** \$161 18 **6. a)** \$140 33 **b)** \$734 **c)** \$107 946
7. \$9211.88

Exercise 31 *page 106*

1. \$7200 **2.** \$8800 **3.** \$18 800 **4.** \$3640

Exercise 32 *page 107*

1. 200 m **2.** 500 m **3. b)** 200 m **c)** 1 km **d)** 0.6 km **4.** 63 m
5. 24 km **6.** 120 m **7. a)** 2.8 km **b)** 3.25 km **c)** 2.7 km

Exercise 33 *page 108*

1. 150 cm **2.** 125 cm **3.** 28 cm **4.** 5.9 cm
5. a) 60 cm **b)** 84 cm **c)** 56 cm **d)** 140 cm **e)** 100 cm **6.** 2.5 cm

Exercise 34 *page 109*

1. \$10, \$20 **2.** \$45, \$15 **3.** 330 g, 550 g **4.** \$480, \$600 **5.** 36, 90
6. \$10, \$20, \$30 **7.** \$70 **8.** \$50 **9.** 3250

Exercise 35 *page 110*

1. 8 **2.** 5 **3.** 9 **4.** 30 g zinc, 40 g tin
5. 24 **6.** 2.4 kg **7.** 6 **8.** 18 cm
9. 22.5 cm **10.** 7.2 cm **11.** 300 g **12.** 5 : 3
13. \$200 **14.** 42c **15.** \$175 000 **16.** $\frac{1}{4}$m^3

Exercise 36 *page 112*

1. £28 **2.** \$6 **3.** \$3 **4.** 400 **5.** 10 min **6.** \$4.80
7. \$8.40 **8.** 12 days **9.** 12 hours **10.** 1 day **11.** 9 hours **12.** 24 men
13. 20 hours **14. a)** 800 **b)** 2400 **c)** $1\frac{1}{2}$ hours **d)** 100

Exercise 37 *page 113*

1. \$3.66 **2.** \$19.04 **3.** 12 litres **4.** 10 hours **5.** 10 days
6. 28 min **7.** 6 hours **8.** 3655 g **9.** 400 bottles **10.** 165 min
11. 11 grapefruit **12.** £24.35 **13.** 5 men **14.** 55 litres
15. a) 180 hens **b)** 9 days **c)** 10 hens **d)** 6 days
16. 7500 batteries **17.** 1 h 15 min **18.** $2n$ hours

Exercise 38 *page 114*

1. a) €18.60 **b)** £44.10 **c)** 758 pesos **d)** 69.75 rupees **e)** 209.76 yen **f)** 0.27 dinars
2. a) \$537.63 **b)** \$3968.25 **c)** \$0.16 **d)** \$3000 **e)** \$33.04 **f)** \$663.72
3. £3.39 **4.** Cheaper in U.K. by \$9.23 **5.** \$494.67
6. Kuwait £325.86, France £495, Japan £706.14 **7.** €433.63

Exercise 39 *page 116*

1. a) $2\frac{1}{2}$ hours **b)** 3 h $7\frac{1}{2}$ min **c)** 75 seconds **d)** 4 hours
2. a) 20 m/s **b)** 30 m/s **c)** $83\frac{1}{2}$ m/s **d)** 108 km/h **e)** 79.2 km/h
f) 1.2 cm/s **g)** 90 m/s **h)** 25 mph
3. a) 75 km/h **b)** 4.52 km/h **c)** 7.6 m/s **d)** 400 m/s **e)** 1×10^5 m/s
f) 200 km/h **g)** 3 km/h
4. a) 110 000 m **b)** 10 000 m **c)** 56 400 m **d)** 4500 m **e)** 80 m
f) 1.6×10^6 m **g)** 96 000 m
5. a) 3 h $7\frac{1}{2}$ min **b)** 76.8 km/h
6. a) 4 hours 27 minutes **b)** 23.6 km/h **7.** 46 km/h

Exercise 40 *page 117*

1. a) 0.8 **b)** 16 **c)** 390 **d)** 4800 **e)** 1460
2. a) 1.5 **b)** 2.5 **c)** 90 **d)** 36
3. 13.3 litres per minute **4.** 12.6 kwh/day **5.** 5.79 days
6. a) 2500 **b)** 66.7

Exercise 41 *page 119*

1. 2.35 **2.** 0.814 **3.** 26.2 **4.** 35.6 **5.** 113 **6.** 211 **7.** 0.825
8. 0.0312 **9.** 5.9 **10.** 1.2 **11.** 0.55 **12.** 0.72 **13.** 0.14 **14.** 1.8
15. 25 **16.** 31 **17.** 486.7 **18.** 500.4 **19.** 2.889 **20.** 3.113 **21.** 0.07 154
22. 3.041 **23.** 2464 **24.** 488 900 **25.** 0.513 **26.** 5.8 **27.** 66 **28.** 587.6
29. 0.6 **30.** 0.07 **31.** 5.84 **32.** 88 **33.** 2500 **34.** 52 700 **35.** 0.006
36. 7000

Exercise 42 *page 120*

1. 5.38 **2.** 11.05 **3.** 0.41 **4.** 0.37 **5.** 8.02 **6.** 87.04 **7.** 9.01
8. 0.07 **9.** 8.4 **10.** 0.7 **11.** 0.4 **12.** 0.1 **13.** 6.1 **14.** 19.5
15. 8.1 **16.** 7.1 **17.** 8.16 **18.** 3.0 **19.** 0.545 **20.** 0.0056 **21.** 0.71
22. 6.83 **23.** 0.8 **24.** 19.65 **25.** 0.0714 **26.** 60.1 **27.** −7.3 **28.** −5.42
29. a) i) 5.9 cm by 3.3 cm **ii)** 5.1 cm by 2.9 cm **b) i)** 19.5 cm^2 **ii)** 14.8 cm^2

Exercise 43 *page 120*

1. 0.57 **2.** 3.45 **3.** 431 **4.** 19.3 **5.** 0.22 **6.** 3942.7 **7.** 53
8. 18.4 **9.** 0.059 **10.** 1.1 **11.** 6140 **12.** 127.89 **13.** 20.3 **14.** 47.6
15. 599.1 **16.** 0.16

Exercise 44 *page 121*

1. 0.85 m **2.** 2400 m **3.** 63 m **4.** 0.25 m **5.** 0.7 cm
6. 20 mm **7.** 1200 m **8.** 700 cm **9.** 580 m **10.** 0.815 m
11. 0.65 km **12.** 2.5 cm **13.** 5000 g **14.** 4200 g **15.** 6400 g
16. 3000 g **17.** 800 g **18.** 0.4 kg **19.** 2000 kg **20.** 0.25 kg
21. 500 kg **22.** 620 kg **23.** 0.007 *t* **24.** 1.5 kg **25.** 0.8 litres
26. 2000 ml **27.** 1 litre **28.** 4500 ml **29.** 6000 ml **30.** 3000 cm^3
31. 2000 litres **32.** 5500 litres **33.** 900 cm^3 **34.** 0.6 litres **35.** 15 000 litres
36. 0.24 litres **37.** 0.28 m **38.** 550 cm **39.** 0.305 kg **40.** 46 m
41. 0.016 litres **42.** 0.208 m **43.** 2.8 cm **44.** 0.27 m **45.** 0.788 km
46. 14 000 kg **47.** 1300 g **48.** 0.09 m^3 **49.** 2900 kg **50.** 0.019 litres
51. (For discussion)

Exercise 45 *page 122*

1. 200 mm^2 **2.** 4500 mm^2 **3.** 16 cm^2 **4.** 0.48 cm^2 **5.** 30 000 cm^2
6. 260 000 cm^2 **7.** 0.86 m^2 **8.** 0.076 m^2 **9.** 5 000 000 m^2 **10.** 4.5 km^2
11. 8000 mm^3 **12.** 21 000 mm^3 **13.** 48 cm^3 **14.** 6 000 000 cm^3 **15.** 28 m^3

Exercise 46 *page 122*

(For discussion)
1. a) Nelson's Column 56 m **b)** Empire State Building 450 m **c)** Mount Everest 8700 m
2. a) No **b)** No **3. a)** No **b)** Probably
4. a) Yes **b)** about 54 times

Exercise 47 *page 124*

1. 4c **2.** 11c **3.** 9c **4.** \$0.10 **5.** 4c **6.** \$0.18 **7.** 6c
8. 13c **9.** \$1.75 **10.** 36c **11.** 2.5c **12.** \$7.25 **13.** 15c **14.** \$5
15. 16c **16.** \$0.89 **17.** 14c **18.** 2c **19.** \$3.60 **20.** 15c

Exercise 48 *page 124*

1. 582 **2.** \$5.12 **3.** 130 years **4.** \$28.50 **5.** 1455
6. 15 h 5 min **7.** \$10.35 **8.** \$21.10 **9.** 3854 **10.** \$1792
11. a) i) 350 **ii)** 340 **iii)** 280 **b)** Kyoto **c)** Kyoto **d)** 100 **e)** 140 **f)** 1920

Exercise 49 *page 126*

1. \$3.25, \$1.80, 7, \$17.10 **2.** 6c **3. a)** double 18 **b)** \$11 111
4. 140 **5.** 4, 15 **6.** *m*, 9, *z* **7.** 24 **8.** Both same (!) **9.** 1.50 m
10. a) WHAT TIME DO WE FINISH **b)** SPURS ARE RUBBISH **c)** WE ARE UNDER ATTACK

Exercise 50 *page 127*

1. 9 **2. a)** 5 m **b)** 50 m **c)** 6 km **3.** 51.4°
4. a) 40 hectares **b)** 15 hectares **c) i)** 10% **ii)** 30% **iii)** 37.5% **iv)** 22.5%
5. 78 **6.** \$184.50 **7.** \$251.85 **8.** \$5.85
9. a) $99+\frac{9}{9}$ **b)** $6+\frac{6}{6}$ **c)** $55+5$ **d)** $55+5+\frac{5}{5}$ **e)** $\frac{7+7}{7+7}$ **f)** $\frac{88}{8}$
10. From left to right **a)** 7, 3 **b)** 4, 3 **c)** 7, 8, 6 **d)** 3, 7, 0 **e)** 3, 6 **f)** 6, 8, 0
11. a) i) \$92 **ii)** \$8 **iii)** \$36 **b)** \$106 **c)** \$156 **d)** \$612

Exercise 51 *page 129*

1. \$3.26 **2.** \$1.70 **3. a)** 108 m^2 **b)** 3
5. 100 m **6. a)** \$3200 **b)** 8% **7.** 10 h 30 min
8. a) 0.54 **b)** 40 **c)** 0.004 **d)** 2.2 **e)** \$9 **f)** \$40 **9.** 315 million
10. a) 4, 3 **b)** 7, 6 **c)** 8, 4 **d)** 24, 2

Exercise 52 *page 131*

1. a) 69 b) 65 2. 120 3. 360 000 kg
4. 0.012, 0.021, 0.03, 0.12, 0.21 5. 16 7. 64 km/h
8. a) Yes b) No c) Yes d) Yes e) Yes f) Yes g) Yes

Revision exercise 3A *page 132*

1. 95c for 1 lb 2. a) 0.005 m s b) 1.6 s c) 173 km
3. 20.75 litres 4. a) 1:50 000 b) 1:4 000 000
5. a) $143 000 b) 198 c) $715 d) $141 570 e) $1430 less
6. a) i) 13, 49, 109 ii) 4, 49 iii) 13, 109
b) i) 27 ii) 33 c) 148, 193 d) 94, 127
7. a) 2 cm b) 8 m 8. 12 km 9. a) $720 b) 144 c) $1630 profit
10. $80 11. $184 12. a) 1810 s b) 72.4 s 13. 0.8 cm
14. $25.60, $6.70, 4, total $55.30 15. 17 kg
16. $33\frac{1}{3}$ km/h 17. a) $13 b) $148 c) $170

Examination-style exercise 3B *page 134*

1. 9 2. 1 393 000 3. B and D 4. a) 12 b) 3 5. 28
6. a) 36 b) 27 c) 31 d) 34 7. a) 36% b) 35
8. $131 9. 3 h 29 min 10. a) 40 b) 9 11. a) $48.40 b) $49.44
12. a) $1332 b) $1350.26 13. $1.80 14. 11.5 km
15. a) i) 1 ii) 8 or −8 iii) 4 iv) 6 b) i) 3 ii) multiple of 60
c) i) 9 ii) 3 and 223
16. a) i) 2 000 000 ii) 4 iii) 100 b) 16.8 minutes or 16 minutes 48 seconds

Handling Data 1

Exercise 1 *page 138*

1. a) Sharon b) $11 c) Half of a $ symbol
2. a) 2 b)

Make	Number of cars	
Ford	4	
Renault	6	
Toyota	6	
Audi	3	

Exercise 2 *page 140*

1. a)

Stem	Leaf
2	1 6 9
3	3 6 7
4	2 5 5 8 8
5	2 3 3 6
6	0 2 2 2 4 6 8
7	1 4 6

Key
2 | 6 means 26

b) 53 c) 55
2. a) 12 b) 14.35 seconds c) 2.8 seconds d) 15.2 seconds

3. a)

Girls		Boys
7 5 1	16	
4	17	5 7
8 5	18	2 8
4 3	19	3
8	20	
0	21	0 9
	22	2 7
	23	1

Key (Girls)
4 | 17 means 17.4 cm

Key (Boys)
19 | 3 means 19.3 cm

b) Girls 18.65 cm, Boys 20.15 cm
c) Girls 4.9 cm, Boys 5.6 cm

4. a)

Horror		Action
9 8 5	8	8
9 5 4 2 0	9	0 3 9
5 0	10	0 6
	11	0 0 9
	12	1

Key (Horror)
2 | 9 means 92 mins

Key (Action)
10 | 6 means 106 mins

b) Horror 94.5 minutes, Action 103 minutes
c) On average, the action films are longer.

Exercise 3 *page 142*

1. a) \$425 **b)** \$150 **c)** \$250 **d)** \$75
2. a) \$13 333.30 **b)** \$15 000 **c)** \$6666.70 **d)** \$10 000 **e)** \$12 000
3. a) \$21 600 000 **b)** \$8 000 000 **c)** \$1 000 000
4. a) i) 8 min **ii)** 34 min **iii)** 10 min **b)** 18°
5. a) Lucy **b)** 20 minutes **c)** 22 minutes

Exercise 4 *page 143*

1. a) i) 45° **ii)** 200° **iii)** 110° **iv)** 5° **2. a)** $\frac{3}{10}, \frac{4}{10}, \frac{1}{5}, \frac{1}{10}$
3. $x = 60°$, $y = 210°$ **4.** Barley 60°, Oats 90°, Rye 165°, Wheat 45°
5. a) 180° **b)** 36° **c)** 90° **d)** 54°

Exercise 5 *page 145*

1. a) 5 **b)** 19 **c)** 23 **d)** 55 **e)** $\frac{6}{23}$
3. a) £3000 approx. **b)** Profits increase in months before Christmas. Very few sales after Christmas.

Exercise 6 *page 147*

1. a) 5 **b)** 24 **c)** 35
2. a) D **b)** A **c)** A **d)** C **e)** B
4. No significant change.

Exercise 7 *page 150*

1. a) i) \$2.50 **ii)** \$2 **iii)** \$3 **b) i)** £0.80 **ii)** £2.80 **iii)** £2
2. a) i) 2.5 kg **ii)** 3.6 kg **iii)** 0.9 kg **b) i)** 4.4 lb **ii)** 6.6 lb **iii)** 3.3 lb **c)** 2.2 lb **d)** 3.2 kg
3. DM 0.6 less **4. a)** 10 °C **b)** 68 °F **c)** −18 °C

Exercise 8 *page 153*

2. a) strong positive correlation b) no correlation c) weak negative correlation
3. a) no correlation b) strong positive correlation
 c) no correlation d) strong negative correlation

Exercise 9 *page 155*

1. $p \approx 11$ 2. $p \approx 9$ 3. not possible
4. c) About 26 d) About 43
5. b) About 34 m.p.g. c) About 64 m.p.h. 6. b) About 20

Exercise 11 *page 166*

1. a) mean = 6, median = 5, mode = 4 b) mean = 9, median = 7, mode = 7
 c) mean = 6.5, median = 8, mode = 9 d) mean = 3.5, median = 3.5, mode = 4
2. 2 °C 3. a) 3 b) 3 5. 70.4, 73.25, No 6. 6
7. a) 1.6 m b) 1.634 m 8. a) 51 kg b) 50 kg
9. a) 7.2 b) 5 c) 6
10. a) mean = \$47 920, median = \$22 500, mode = \$22 500
 b) The mean is skewed by one large number.
11. a) mean = 157.1 kg, median = 91 kg
 b) mean. No: over three quarters of the cattle are below the mean weight.
12. a) mean = 74.5 cm, median = 91 cm b) Yes

Exercise 12 *page 171*

2. a) 25 b) 90
4. a) 62 b) Sport B has more heavy people. Sport A has a much smaller range of weights compared to sport B.
5. a) Plants with fertilizer are significantly taller b) No significant effect

Revision exercise 4A *page 173*

1. a) 5.89 b) 6 c) 7 2. 1.55 m
3. a) i) 560 kg ii) 57 kg b) 50 kg 4. a) 84 b) 19.2
5. a) 25 b) 75 c) 20
6. Spain 108°, France 45°, Greece 90°, Portugal 136°, USA 81°
7. a) 29 b) 23 c) wrong 8. a) F b) possible c) possible
9. a)

Stem	Leaf
0	7 9 9
1	2 2 2 3 4 4 7
2	0 3

 b) i) 12.5°C ii) 12°C iii) 16°C

Examination-style exercise 4B *page 174*

1. a) 45°, 5, 75° 2. a) i) 35 ii) 7 iii) 8 iv) 7.71 b) i) 72
3. negative 4. positive 5. a) 117 b) i) 756 ii) 759 iii) 29
6. a) i) 163.4 or 163 ii) 24 b) iv) positive v) larger hand span greater height
7. a) i) 3, 6, 8, 7, 6, 11, 2 ii) 5.71 iii) 7 iv) 5 v) 5.5 vi) 17.6 vii) 54 or 53
 b) i) 12, 25, 19, 2 ii) 5 and 6
8. a) i) 2012 Median = 44.65 seconds, 2016 Median = 44.15 seconds
 ii) 2012 Range = 1.2 seconds, 2016 Range = 1.6 seconds
 b) The median was lower in 2016 so, on average, the 2016 athletes were faster. The range, however, was lower in 2012, so the 2016 athletes were not more consistent.

Shape and Space 2

Exercise 2 *page 181*

2. d) (7, −7), (−5, 5), (5, 7) 3. d) (7, 5), (−5, 7), (5, −7) 4. g) (−3, 6), (−6, 6), (−6, 4)
5. g) (3, 1), (7, 1), (7, 3) 6. a) $y = 0$ (x-axis) b) $x = 1$ c) $y = 1$ d) $y = -x$

Exercise 3 *page 183*

7. Shape 1: C, 90° CW; Shape 2: B, 180°; Shape 3: A, 90° ACW; Shape 4: B, 90° CW; Shape 5: F, 180°

Exercise 4 *page 184*

2. e) (−2, 1), (2, 1), (1, −2)
3. e) (−2, 2), (0, 0), (−2, −2)

Exercise 6 *page 187*

1. a) Yes **b)** No **c)** Yes **d)** Yes
2. 78 mm
3. $y = 24$ mm, $z = 67.5$ mm
7. $OA' = 2 \times OA$, $OB' = 2 \times OB$
9. b) Scale factor $= 1\frac{1}{2}$

Exercise 7 *page 190*

7. e) (3, 0), (−5, −1), (3, −1)
8. e) (3, 3), (−6, −1), (3, −3)
9. e) (3, −1), (2, −1), (5, −7)

Exercise 9 *page 194*

1. a) $\begin{pmatrix}4\\6\end{pmatrix}$ **b)** $\begin{pmatrix}6\\4\end{pmatrix}$ **c)** $\begin{pmatrix}6\\0\end{pmatrix}$ **d)** $\begin{pmatrix}6\\0\end{pmatrix}$ **e)** $\begin{pmatrix}5\\-2\end{pmatrix}$
f) $\begin{pmatrix}1\\2\end{pmatrix}$ **g)** $\begin{pmatrix}-2\\5\end{pmatrix}$ **h)** $\begin{pmatrix}2\\-2\end{pmatrix}$ **i)** $\begin{pmatrix}-4\\-3\end{pmatrix}$ **j)** $\begin{pmatrix}2\\-6\end{pmatrix}$
k) $\begin{pmatrix}1\\-8\end{pmatrix}$ **l)** $\begin{pmatrix}-6\\-1\end{pmatrix}$ **m)** $\begin{pmatrix}0\\-4\end{pmatrix}$ **n)** $\begin{pmatrix}6\\1\end{pmatrix}$

Exercise 10 *page 195*

1. $\begin{pmatrix}7\\2\end{pmatrix}$ **2.** $\begin{pmatrix}16\\5\end{pmatrix}$ **3.** $\begin{pmatrix}4\\1\end{pmatrix}$ **4.** $\begin{pmatrix}6\\1\end{pmatrix}$ **5.** $\begin{pmatrix}0\\-3\end{pmatrix}$
6. $\begin{pmatrix}6\\4\end{pmatrix}$ **7.** $\begin{pmatrix}12\\6\end{pmatrix}$ **8.** $\begin{pmatrix}16\\-8\end{pmatrix}$ **9.** $\begin{pmatrix}100\\55\end{pmatrix}$ **10.** $\begin{pmatrix}16\\2\end{pmatrix}$

Exercise 11 *page 195*

1. c) Rotation 180° about 0
2. c) Rotation 180° about (0, 0)
3. d) 5 units right, 2 units up
4. a) Rotation 90° clockwise, centre (3, 1)
b) Reflection in $y=3\frac{1}{2}$
c) Rotation 90° anticlockwise, centre (3, 6)
5. a) Rotation 90° anticlockwise, centre (0, 0)
b) Reflection in $y = 0$
c) Reflection in $y = x$
d) Translation, 9 units right
e), f) Various answers
6. a) Reflection in $y = x$
b) Rotation 180°, centre (0, −2)
c) Reflection in $y = -2$
d) Rotation 90° anticlockwise, centre $\left(-4\frac{1}{2}, 4\frac{1}{2}\right)$
7. a) Reflection in $y = x$
b) Rotation 180°, centre (5, 0)
c) Rotation 90° clockwise, centre (−2, 2)
d) Rotation 180°, centre $\left(\frac{1}{2}, 1\frac{1}{2}\right)$
e) Reflection in $y=-3\frac{1}{2}$
8. a) Reflection in $y = 0$, Translation $\begin{pmatrix}-7\\0\end{pmatrix}$
b) Yes
9. Enlargement scale factor 2. Reflection in $y = -x$

Exercise 12 *page 199*

1. a) Trapezium **b)** Square **c)** Parallelogram
2. a) (6, 6) **b)** (6, 4) **c)** (0, 6), (1, 6), (3, 6)

3.

	How many lines of symmetry?	How many pairs of opposite sides are parallel?	Diagonals always equal?	Diagonals are perpendicular?
Square	4	2	Y	Y
Rectangle	2	2	Y	N
Kite	1	0	N	Y
Rhombus	2	2	N	Y
Parallelogram	0	2	N	N
Arrowhead	1	0	N	Y (outside)

4. a) 50° **b)** 100° **c)** 90° **d)** 130° **e)** 80° **f)** 95°
7. Kite **8.** Kite, parallelogram
9. a) yes, yes, no **b)** can make *any* kind of triangle

Exercise 13 *page 201*

1. C(−3, −3), D(−4, 2) **2. a)** 34° **b)** 56°
3. a) 35° **b)** 35° **4. a)** 72° **b)** 108° **c)** 80°
5. a) 40° **b)** 30° **c)** 110° **6. a)** 116° **b)** 32° **c)** 58°
7. a) 55° **b)** 55° **8. a)** 26° **b)** 26° **c)** 77°
9. a) 52° **b)** 64° **c)** 116° **10.** 110°
11. a) 54° **b)** 72° **c)** 36° **12. a)** 60° **b)** 15° **c)** 75°

Exercise 14 *page 202*

1. 5 **3.** 5 **4.** 6 **5. a)** square **b)** equilateral triangle **7.** No

Exercise 15 *page 203*

1. A 035°, B 070°, C 155°, D 220°, E 290°, L 340°
2. A 040°, B 065°, C 130°, D 160°, E 230°, F 330°

Exercise 16 *page 205*

1. a) $147\frac{1}{2}°$ **b)** 122° **c)** 090° **2. a)** 286° **b)** 225° **c)** 153°
3. a) 061° **b)** $327\frac{1}{2}°$ **4. a)** 302° **b)** 344° **c)** 045°

Exercise 19 *page 207*

1. 11.5 km **2.** 14.1 km **3. a)** 12.5 km **b)** 032°
4. 6.9 km **5. a)** 8.5 km **b)** 074°
6. a) 8.4 km **b)** 029° **7. b)** 5.2 h **8.** No

Exercise 20 *page 209*

1. 10 cm **2.** 4.12 cm **3.** 10.6 cm **4.** 5.66 cm **5.** 4.24 cm **6.** 990
7. 4.58 cm **8.** 5.20 cm **9.** 9.85 cm **10.** 7.07 cm **11.** 3.46 m **12.** 40.3 km
13. 9.49 cm **14.** 32.6 cm **15.** 5.39 units **16.** Yes **17.** 6.63 cm **18.** 5.57
19. 8.72 **20.** 5.66 **21.** 6.63 cm **22.** 2.24 **23. a) i)** 13 **ii)** 25 **iii)** 9
24. a) 5 cm **b)** 7.81 cm **25.** Philip

Exercise 21 *page 212*

1. 113 litres **2.** 17.3 litres **3. a)** $\frac{1}{3}$ **b)** $\frac{4}{9}$ **c)** 25 cm^2
4. 2500 **5.** 1100 m **6. a)** 24 cm^2 **b)** 35 cm^2
7. 740 cm^3 **8.** 2.4 cm **9. a)** 2.5 cm **b)** 3.25 cm
10. 40 **11.** 100 **12.** 900
13. a) 384 cm^2 **b)** 80 cm **14. a)** 6 **b)** 12 **c)** 8 **d)** 1

Revision exercise 5A *page 214*

1. 4.1 cm **2. a)** $40°$ **b)** $100°$

3. a) 14.1 cm, 48.3 cm square **b)** 1930 cm^2

4. a) $1\frac{2}{3}$ **b)** 20 cm

5. a) reflection in the x-axis **b)** reflection in $x = -1$ **c)** reflection in $y = x$
d) rotation, centre (0, 0), 90° clockwise **e)** reflection in $y = -1$
f) rotation, centre (0, –1), 180°

6. a) enlargement; scale factor $1\frac{1}{2}$, (1, –4)
b) rotation 90° clockwise, (0, –4) **c)** reflection in $y = -x$ **d)** translation $\begin{pmatrix} 11 \\ 10 \end{pmatrix}$
e) enlargement; scale factor $\frac{1}{2}$, (–3, 8)
f) rotation 90° anticlockwise, $\left(\frac{1}{2}, 6\frac{1}{2}\right)$ **g)** enlargement; scale factor 3, (–2, 5)

7. c) $\triangle 2$ (6, 0); $\triangle 3$ (2, –8); $\triangle 4$ (–8, 2); $\triangle 6$ (1, –5); $\triangle 7$ (–1, 3)

8. b) 85.5 km (±1.5 km)

9. a) 7.2 cm **b)** 9.2 cm **c)** 7.3 cm

10. a) 220° **b)** 295°

Examination-style exercise 5B *page 216*

1. a) i) translation $\begin{pmatrix} -7 \\ -4 \end{pmatrix}$ **ii)** enlargement s.f. 3, centre (0, 0)

2. a) translation $\begin{pmatrix} 2 \\ -4 \end{pmatrix}$ **b)** reflection in y-axis **c)** rotation 90° anticlockwise about (0, 0)

3. a) $\begin{pmatrix} -1 \\ 3 \end{pmatrix}$ **b)** (–2, –1) **4. a)** D (5, 2) **b)** $\begin{pmatrix} -2 \\ 4 \end{pmatrix}$ **c)** $\begin{pmatrix} 3 \\ 3 \end{pmatrix}$

5. 325° **6. b)** 282.5°

7. a) i) $\begin{pmatrix} 0 \\ 4 \end{pmatrix}$ **ii)** $\begin{pmatrix} -4 \\ 4 \end{pmatrix}$ **b)** line from **P** to (–1, 6)

8. 1.2 m

9. a) i) (–3, –2) **ii)** $\begin{pmatrix} 4 \\ 2 \end{pmatrix}, \begin{pmatrix} -3 \\ 2 \end{pmatrix}$ **b)** (1, –5) (5, –3) (2, –1)
c) i) P(5, 2) Q(–1, 6) **ii)** enlargement s.f. 2 centre A **d)** image of C(0, –4)

10. a) i) 2.60 **ii)** 3.90 **iii)** 31.2 **b) i)** 18 **iii)** 502 cm^2 **iv)** $32.40

Algebra 2

Exercise 1 *page 221*

1. $3n + 2$ **2. a)** $4n + 1$ **b)** $6n - 4$ **3.** $5n + 1$ **4.** $4n + 2$

5. a) $2n + 3$ **b)** $4n - 1$ **c)** $6n - 4$

6. a) $8n - 6$ **b)** $3n + 4$ **c)** $9n + 12$

7. $5n - 2$ **8.** $3n$ **9.** $6n + 1$ **10.** $2n + 4$ **11.** $n + 5$

12. $3n - 2$ **13.** $8n - 3$ **14.** $5n + 2$ **15.** $3n - 4$ **16.** $10n + 3$

17. $3n + 3$ **18.** $5n + 1$

Exercise 2 *page 224*

1. $w = b + 4$ **2.** $w = 2b + 6$ **3.** $w = 2b - 12$

4. $m = 2t + 1$ **5.** $m = 3t + 2$ **6.** $s = t + 2$

7. a) $p = 5n - 2$ **b)** $k = 7n + 3$ **c)** $w = 2n + 11$

8. a) $y = 3n + 1$ **b)** $h = 4n - 3$ **c)** $k = 3n + 5$

9. $m = 8c + 4$

Exercise 3 page 226

1. $n^2 + 3$ 2. $2n^2$ 3. $n^2 - 1$ 4. $\frac{1}{2}n^2$ 5. $n^2 - 7$
6. $-n^2$ 7. $-n^2 + 1$ 8. $n^3 + 1$ 9. $2n^3$ 10. $n^3 - 2$

Exercise 4 page 227

1. a) (3, 7) b) (1, 3) c) (11, –1) 2. (2, 4) 3. (2, 3)
4. (3, 1) 5. (1, 5) 6. (5, 3)
7. a) (4, 0) b) (1, 6) c) (–2, –3) d) (8, –1) e) (–0.6, 1.2)

Exercise 5 page 229

1. $x = 2, y = 1$ 2. $x = 4, y = 2$ 3. $x = 3, y = 1$ 4. $x = -2, y = 1$
5. $x = 3, y = 2$ 6. $x = 5, y = -2$ 7. $x = 2, y = 1$ 8. $x = 5, y = 3$
9. $x = 3, y = -1$ 10. $a = 2, b = -3$ 11. $a = 5, b = \frac{1}{4}$ 12. $a = 1, b = 3$
13. $m = \frac{1}{2}, n = 4$ 14. $w = 2, x = 3$ 15. $x = 6, y = 3$ 16. $x = \frac{1}{2}, z = -3$
17. $m = 1\frac{15}{17}, n = \frac{11}{17}$ 18. $c = 1\frac{16}{23}, d = -2\frac{12}{23}$

Exercise 6 page 230

1. $x = 2, y = 4$ 2. $x = 1, y = 4$ 3. $x = 2, y = 5$ 4. $x = 3, y = 7$
5. $x = 5, y = 2$ 6. $a = 3, b = 1$ 7. $x = 1, y = 3$ 8. $x = 1, y = 3$
9. $x = -2, y = 3$ 10. $x = 4, y = 1$ 11. $x = 1, y = 5$ 12. $x = 0, y = 2$
13. $x = \frac{5}{7}, y = 4\frac{3}{7}$ 14. $x = 1, y = 2$ 15. $x = 2, y = 3$ 16. $x = 4, y = -1$
17. $x = 3, y = 1$ 18. $x = 1, y = 2$ 19. $x = 2, y = 1$ 20. $x = -2, y = 1$

Exercise 7 page 231

1. $5\frac{1}{2}, 9\frac{1}{2}$ 2. 6, 3 or $2\frac{2}{5}, 5\frac{2}{5}$ 3. 4, 10
4. 10.5, 7.5 5. $a = 2, c = 7$ 6. $m = 4, c = -3$
7. $a = 30, b = 5$ 8. TV \$200, DVD player \$450 9. w 2 g, b $3\frac{1}{2}$ g
10. $2c \times 15, 5c \times 25$ 11. $10c \times 14, 50c \times 7$

Exercise 8 page 232

1. a) 40 km b) 60 km c) Gap, Sisteron d) 15 min
e) i) 11:00 ii) 13:45 f) i) 40 km/h ii) 60 km/h iii) 100 km/h
2. a) 25 km b) 15 km c) 09:45 d) 1 h
e) i) 26.7 km/h ii) 5 km/h iii) 30 km/h iv) 40 km/h
3. a) i) 14:00 ii) 13:45 b) i) 15:45 ii) owards Aston
c) i) 15 mph ii) 40 mph iii) 40 mph iv) 20 mph d) $16{:}07\frac{1}{2}$
4. a) 45 min b) 09:15 c) 60 km/h d) 47 km e) 57.1 km/h
5. a) 09:15 b) 64 km/h c) 37.6 km/h d) 47 km e) 80 km/h
6. 11:05 7. 12:42 8. 12:35

Exercise 9 page 235

1. a) 740c b) \$280 c) \$14 000 d) \$11 000
4. a) 2 b) i) 40 km ii) 24 km iii) 72 km iv) 8 km c) i) 40 miles ii) 35 miles iii) 10 miles
iv) 20 miles 5. a) i) €28 ii) €112 iii) €70 b) i) \$40 ii) \$60 iii) \$100 c) \$110
6. a) 30 litres b) i) 8 km/l ii) 6 km/l c) 6.7 km/l d) 30 litres
7. 180 km 8. 2.5 h

Exercise 10 page 239

1. B 2. D 3. a) C b) A c) D d) B
4. a) i) B ii) A b) 8 s to 18 s c) about 15 s
d) about 9 s e) B f) A
6. a) runners slow down for takeover b) baton dropped at third takeover

Exercise 11 page 241

1. $3x+9$
2. $4x-8$
3. $10x+5$
4. $4a+28$
5. $12x+6$
6. $50-10x$
7. $12x+15$
8. $27+9x$
9. $5y-10$
10. $7a-14$
11. $22x-11y$
12. $24x+16y$
13. $4x+2x^2$
14. $3x^2-2x$
15. $4y^2+7y$
16. $2a^2-6a$
17. $12x-18x^2$
18. $12y^2+20y$
19. $15a^2-20a$
20. $42p-49p^2$
21. $12x^2+3x^3$
22. $4x^3-12x^2$
23. x^2+3x+2
24. $x^2+10x+24$
25. x^2+x-6
26. $x^2+4x-12$
27. $x^2-2x-35$
28. $x^2-5x-24$
29. x^2-3x+2
30. $x^2-8x+15$
31. $x^2-17x+72$
32. $2x^2+5x+2$
33. $3x^2-x-2$
34. $2x^2+5x-12$
35. $4x^2+8x+3$

Exercise 12 page 242

1. $2(3x+2y)$
2. $3(3x+4y)$
3. $2(5a+2b)$
4. $4(x+3y)$
5. $5(2a+3b)$
6. $6(3x-4y)$
7. $4(2u-7v)$
8. $5(3s+5t)$
9. $8(3m+5n)$
10. $9(3c-8d)$
11. $4(5a+2b)$
12. $6(5x-4y)$
13. $3(9c-11d)$
14. $7(5u+7v)$
15. $4(3s-8t)$
16. $8(5x-2t)$
17. $12(2x+7y)$
18. $4(3x+2y+4z)$
19. $3(4a-2b+3c)$
20. $5(2x-4y+5z)$
21. $4(5a-3b-7c)$
22. $8(6m+n-3x)$
23. $7(6x+7y-3z)$
24. $3(2x^2+5y^2)$
25. $5(4x^2-3y^2)$
26. $7(a^2+4b^2)$
27. $9(3a+7b-4c)$
28. $6(2x^2+4xy+3y^2)$
29. $8(8p-9q-5r)$
30. $12(3x-5y+8z)$
31. $a(a+4)$
32. $x(3+4x)$
33. $x(4x-1)$
34. $x(7-3x)$
35. $2x(x+2)$
36. $3x(2-x)$
37. $4x(3+4x^2)$
38. $5x^2(5-3x)$
39. $10x^2(3x+1)$
40. $10y^2(8y-3)$
41. $3x(-3x+4)(2x+1)$
42. $2a(2a^2-3+4a)$

Exercise 13 page 243

1. $e-b$
2. $m+t$
3. $a+b+f$
4. $A+B-h$
5. y
6. $b-a$
7. $m-k$
8. $w+y-v$
9. $\frac{b}{a}$
10. $\frac{m}{h}$
11. $\frac{a+b}{m}$
12. $\frac{c-d}{k}$
13. $\frac{e+n}{v}$
14. $\frac{y+z}{3}$
15. $\frac{r}{p}$
16. $\frac{h-m}{m}$
17. $\frac{a-t}{a}$
18. $\frac{k+e}{m}$
19. $\frac{m+h}{u}$
20. $\frac{t-q}{e}$
21. $\frac{v^2+u^2}{k}$
22. $\frac{s^2-t^2}{g}$
23. $\frac{m^2-k}{a}$
24. $\frac{m+v}{m}$
25. $\frac{c-a}{b}$
26. $\frac{y-t}{s}$
27. $\frac{z-y}{c}$
28. $\frac{a}{h}$
29. $\frac{2b}{m}$
30. $\frac{cd-ab}{k}$
31. $\frac{c+ab}{a}$
32. $\frac{e+cd}{c}$
33. $\frac{n^2-m^2}{m}$
34. $\frac{t+ka}{k}$
35. $\frac{k+h^2}{h}$
36. $\frac{n-mb}{m}$
37. $2a$
38. $\frac{d-ac}{c}$
39. $\frac{e-mb}{m}$

Exercise 14 page 244

1. mt
2. en
3. ap
4. amt
5. abc
6. ey^2
7. $a(b+c)$
8. $t(c-d)$
9. $m(s+t)$
10. $k(h+i)$
11. $\frac{ab}{c}$
12. $\frac{mz}{y}$
13. $\frac{ch}{d}$
14. $\frac{em}{k}$
15. $\frac{hb}{e}$
16. $c(a+b)$
17. $m(h+k)$
18. $\frac{mu}{y}$
19. $t(h-k)$
20. $(z+t)(a+b)$
21. $\frac{e}{7}$
22. $\frac{e}{a}$
23. $\frac{h}{m}$
24. $\frac{bc}{a}$
25. $\frac{ud}{c}$
26. $\frac{m}{t^2}$
27. $\frac{b^2c^2}{a^2}$

Exercise 15 page 244

1. $\frac{h+d}{a}$ 2. $\frac{m-k}{z}$ 3. $\frac{f-ed}{d}$ 4. $\frac{d-ma}{m}$ 5. $\frac{c-a}{b}$ 6. $b-a$
7. $\frac{z}{y}$ 8. $e+c$ 9. $\frac{b+n}{m}$ 10. $\frac{b-a^2}{a}$ 11. $\frac{a}{d}$ 12. mt
13. mn 14. $\frac{y}{d}$ 15. $\frac{a}{t}$ 16. $\frac{d}{n}$ 17. $k(a+b)$ 18. $\frac{v}{y}$
19. $\frac{m}{c}$ 20. mb 21. $\frac{b-ag}{g}$ 22. x^2-h^2 23. $y-z$ 24. $\frac{c}{2m}$
25. $\frac{t-ay}{a}$ 26. $\frac{y^2+t^2}{u}$ 27. $\frac{c-t}{3}$ 28. $k-m$ 29. $\frac{c-b}{a}$ 30. $\frac{c-am}{m}$
31. $pq-ab$ 32. a^2-t 33. $\frac{w}{v^2}$ 34. $c-t$ 35. $\frac{t}{x}$ 36. $k-n$

Revision exercise 6A page 245

1. a) $l=2d-4$ b) 149
3. A, swimmer; B, car ferry from Calais; C, hovercraft; D, train from Dover; E, marker buoy; F, car ferry from Dover
4. a) $s=t(r+3)$ b) $r=\frac{s-3t}{t}$
5. b) 1, 4, 9, 16 c) square numbers d) 49
6. a) $c=5, d=-2$ b) $x=2, y=-1$
7. a) i) Consett ii) Durham iii) Consett b) i) 55 km ii) 40 km
c) i) 80 km/h ii) 55 km/h iii) 70 km/h iv) 80 km/h d) $1\frac{3}{4}$h
8. b) $3 \rightarrow 14, 4 \rightarrow 18, 5 \rightarrow 22, 6 \rightarrow 26$ c) i) 42 ii) 62 d) $n=4x+2$

Examination-style exercise 6B page 247

1. $x(3y-2)$
2. $5x^2-3xy$
3. a) $7c-20d$ b) $q(p-q)$
4. a) 23 b) 43 c) $4n+3$
5. b) 22, 29, 36 c) i) 71 ii) $7n+1$ d) 16
6. a) 12 mins b) 20 km/h c) 28 km
7. a) i) $x-4$ ii) $2x+5$ iii) $2x+5=3(x-4)$ iv) 17 b) $x=2, y=1.5$
8. a) 12 b) i) 0.833… ii) 49.8 to 50 c) 46 km
9. a) i) 30 ii) line from (1100, 20) to (1145, 80)
10. b) 70.7 cm² b) 5.05 cm c) $r=\sqrt{\frac{2A}{5\pi}}$
11. a) i) 6 ii) 9 iii) 1.5 b) i) $p+q=12$ ii) $25p+40q=375$ iii) $p=7, q=5$
12. a) i) 360 ii) 7.5 iii) $m=\frac{2E}{v^2}$ b) $xy(y-x)$ c) 2 d) (3, 1)
13. a) i) 6 ii) 72 b) i) 1.5 ii) $4z+2=10z-1$ iii) 0.5 c) i) $a-b=3, 4a+b=17$ ii) $a=4, b=1$
14. a) 35 b) 120 c) $(n+1)^2-1$ (or equivalent)

Number 2

Exercise 1 page 254

1. 8% 2. 10% 3. 25% 4. 2% 5. 4%
6. $2\frac{1}{2}$% 7. 20% 8. 50% 9. 15% 10. 80%
11. 25% 12. 20% 13. $12\frac{1}{2}$% 14. $33\frac{1}{3}$% 15. 80%
16. 5% 17. 6% 18. 20% 19. 5% 20. $2\frac{1}{2}$%

Exercise 2 page 254

1. 36.4% 2. 19.0% 3. 19.4% 4. 22.0% 5. 12.2%
6. 9.4% 7. 14.0% 8. 17.4% 9. 32.7% 10. 10.2%
11. 7.7% 12. 35.3% 13. 30.8% 14. 5.2% 15. 14.1%
16. 14.5% 17. 19.1% 18. 3.6% 19. 31.1% 20. 6.5%

Exercise 3 page 255

1. 12% 2. 29% 3. 16% 4. 0.25% 5. 15%
6. 61.1% 7. 15% 8. 13.7% 9. 1.5% 10. 23.8%

Exercise 4 page 256

1. a) 25c b) $12.80 c) $2.80 d) 28%
2. a) $10 b) i) $4.20 ii) 42%
3. a) i) 120 cm ii) 75 cm iii) 10 000 cm^2 iv) 9000 cm^2 b) 10%
4. a) $57 500 b) i) $61 900 ii) 7.7%
5. 250 m^2

Exercise 5 page 257

1. a) 0.25 b) 0.4 c) 0.375 d) $0.41\dot{6}$ e) $0.1\dot{6}$ f) $0.\dot{2}8571\dot{4}$
2. a) $\frac{1}{5}$ b) $\frac{9}{20}$ c) $\frac{9}{25}$ d) $\frac{1}{8}$ e) $1\frac{1}{20}$ f) $\frac{7}{1000}$
3. a) 25% b) 10% c) 72% d) 7.5% e) 2% f) $33\frac{1}{3}$%
4. '$\frac{1}{3}$ off' 5. $\frac{1}{6}$ of $5000 6. 25% 7. 20%
8. a) $\frac{1}{4}$, 0.25, 25% b) $\frac{1}{5}$, 0.2, 20% c) $\frac{4}{5}$, 0.8, 80% d) $\frac{1}{100}$, 0.01, 1%
   e) $\frac{3}{10}$, 0.3, 30% f) $\frac{1}{3}$, $0.\dot{3}$, $33\frac{1}{3}$% 9. a) 0.14625 b) $15.84
10. a) 45%, $\frac{1}{2}$, 0.6 b) 4%, $\frac{6}{16}$, 0.38 c) 11%, 0.111; $\frac{1}{9}$
11. 0.58 12. 1.42 13. 0.65 14. 1.61 15. 0.07
16. 0.16 17. 3.64 18. 0.60 19. 62.5%

Exercise 6 page 259

1. B 2. C 3. B 4. A 5. B 6. C 7. B
8. B 9. A 10. B 11. A 12. A 13. C (or B) 14. C
15. $5800 16. about 20
17. a) True b) True c) True d) False e) False f) True g) True
   h) False i) True

Exercise 7 page 261

1. B 2. A 3. C 4. B 5. C 6. A 7. B
8. B 9. A 10. C 11. B 12. A 13. A 14. C
15. C 16. B 17. C 18. A 19. B 20. B 21. C
22. B 23. B 24. A 25. B 26. B 27. A
28. No – it will be approximately $450 29. He got it wrong. Correct answer is $10.45 each
30. a) (Say) 200 g per paper: 3250 papers per tree b) about 5×10^{11} c) For discussion

Exercise 8 page 264

1. b) $7.5 \leqslant V < 8.5$ c) $71.5 \leqslant m < 72.5$ d) $3.15 \leqslant t < 3.25$ e) $5.75 \leqslant r < 5.85$
2. 83.5 cm 3. 5.25 kg 4. a) 8.45 cm b) 4.25 cm
5. 173.5 cm 6. 3.65 kg 7. 92.5 million miles (= 92 500 000 miles)
8. 20.625 seconds 9. 17.85 g

10.

	Lower bound	Upper bound
a)	5.55 cm	5.65 cm
b)	36.5 cm	37.5 m
c)	0.265 mg	0.275 mg
d)	225 °C	235 °C
e)	314.5 km	315.5 km

Test 1 *page 265*

1. \$3.50 **2.** \$4.95 **3.** 48 **4.** 10c, 10c, 20c **5.** $6\frac{1}{2}$ **6.** $\frac{1}{100}$
7. 56 **8.** 75% **9.** 15 **10.** \$5.60 **11.** 50 min **12.** 6.5
13. 130 m **14.** 770 **15.** 11 **16.** 25 **17.** $1\frac{1}{4}$ **18.** \$10
19. 10 **20.** 60.5 **21.** 55 **22.** 16 **23.** 1h **24.** $4\frac{1}{2}$
25. 75 or 105 **26.** 20 **27.** \$2.40 **28.** 82% **29.** \$4000 **30.** 48 c

Test 2 *page 266*

1. 96 **2.** 19 **3.** 06:30 **4.** \$2.75 **5.** \$1.90 **6.** 95°
7. 5 018 001 **8.** 15 **9.** \$6 **10.** 3.5c **11.** 53 **12.** 800 g
13. 74 **14.** 28 km **15.** 40 **16.** 4 **17.** 62 **18.** 5
19. 5 **20.** 480 **21.** 158 **22.** 95 **23.** 0.2 **24.** 0.7
25. \$84 **26.** \$2455 **27.** 64 **28.** 90 c **29.** 55 km/h **30.** 28

Test 3 *page 267*

1. 70 **2.** 240 **3.** 900 **4.** 10 705 **5.** 10:45 **6.** 245
7. 20 **8.** \$3.05 **9.** \$1.76 **10.** 20, 20, 20, 1 or 50, 5, 5, 1 **11.** 0.75
12. 5 **13.** Tuesday **14.** 1.5 kg **15.** \$150.50 **16.** 640 m **17.** \$722
18. \$25 000 **19.** 4 **20.** \$1.10 **21.** 12 000 **22.** 9 **23.** 91
24. \$6 **25.** 98c **26.** \$4.46 **27.** \$3.30 **28.** \$42 **29.** 960
30. False

Test 4 *page 269*

1. \$8.05 **2.** 75 **3.** 25 **4.** 0.1 cm **5.** 24 c **6.** 104
7. \$0.40 **8.** \$88 **9.** 5:50 **10.** \$8.20 **11.** 4 km **12.** 45 km
13. \$4.25 **14.** 998 **15.** 20 **16.** 200 **17.** 22.5 cm **18.** \$75
19. 10 **20.** 16 **21.** 20 **22.** \$9.82 **23.** 22 min **24.** 1540
25. \$7.94 **26.** \$0.70 **27.** 200 **28.** 35% **29.** 100 **30.** \$2500

Test 5 *page 270*

1. 25 km **2.** \$4.40 **3.** \$210 **4.** \$26 **5.** 8 min **6.** 25
7. 500 (±50) **8.** $\frac{1}{1000}$ **9.** 2.65 **10.** — **11.** \$15 000 **12.** \$3.85
13. \$27.50 **14.** 8 **15.** 84 **16.** 1200 **17.** 30 litres **18.** 7 cm
19. 153 **20.** 4 **21.** 7 **22.** 105 m^2 **23.** 2 000 000 **24.** 51
25. 6 **26.** \$6 **27.** 2300 g **28.** 150 **29.** 133 **30.** Wednesday

Test 6 *page 271*

1. 60° **2.** 0.05 **3.** 80% **4.** 8000 **5.** \$16.90 **6.** 0.7
7. 5 h 20 min **8.** $12\frac{1}{2}$% **9.** 6 cm **10.** 0.001 **11.** 7, 8 **12.** \$2
13. 1.8 **14.** 49.2 **15.** \$12.50 **16.** 165 **17.** 72° **18.** 240
19. 34 c **20.** \$9 **21.** 60 km/h **22.** 302 **23.** 500 **24.** 37
25. £1.11 **26.** \$15 **27.** 12 **28.** 8, 9 **29.** \$16 **30.** \$13.80

Test 7 *page 272*

1. 82°
2. 72 cents
3. 0.25
4. 90 nautical miles
5. 8
6. 11
7. 325
8. $\frac{1}{12}$
9. $25 000
10. 49 000
11. 6.3
12. $8.70
13. $2.40
14. 5
15. $37.50
16. 13.55 cm
17. 10 cm
18. $9
19. 200
20. $1.20
21. 250
22. 500 m²
23. $8.70
24. 0.025
25. 2550 g
26. $40 000
27. 150°
28. $150
29. 11
30. 9

Exercise 9 *page 275*

1. 19
2. 4
3. 3
4. 0
5. 35
6. 60
7. 16
8. 6
9. 13
10. 14
11. 23
12. 71
13. 20
14. 36
15. 9
16. 8
17. 32
18. 30
19. 4
20. 0
21. 6
22. 5
23. 1
24. 47
25. 6
26. 3
27. 16
28. 12
29. 52
30. 15
31. 87
32. 17
33. 23
34. 8
35. 2
36. 26

Exercise 10 *page 276*

1. $7 + 5 \times 4$
2. $3 \times 5 + 10$
3. $4 \div 2 + 3$
4. $11 + 3 \times 3$
5. $31 - 10 \times 2$
6. $10 + 6 \times 5$
7. $4 \times 8 - 7$
8. $12 + 9 \times 2$
9. $18 - 4 \times 4$
10. $28 - 10 \times 2$
11. $21 \div 3 - 5$
12. $7 + 3 \times 3$
13. $10 \div 2 + 3$
14. $10 \times 3 + 12$
15. $18 \div 3 + 7$
16. $31 + 40 \div 5$
17. $15 - 16 \div 4$
18. $15 + 8 \times 9$
19. $37 + 35 \div 5$
20. $11 \times 5 + 9$
21. $8 + 3 \times 2 - 4$
22. $12 - 3 \times 3 + 1$
23. $11 + 4 - 1 \times 6$
24. $15 \div 5 + 2 \times 4$
25. $7 \times 2 - 3 \times 3$
26. $12 - 2 + 3 \times 4$
27. $8 \times 9 - 6 \times 11$
28. $20 \div 20 + 9 \times 0$
29. $20 - 30 \div 10 + 8$
30. $30 + 6 \times 11 - 11$

Exercise 11 *page 276*

1. 1851
2. 6.889
3. 1.214
4. 0.4189
5. 7.889
6. 19.35
7. 0.049 47
8. 221.5
9. 24.37
10. 6.619
11. 3.306
12. 2.303
13. 41.73
14. 8.163
15. 0.1090
16. 0.5001
17. 20.63
18. 10.09
19. 6.191
20. 10.27
21. 8.627
22. 22.02
23. 1.093
24. 44.72
25. 45.66
26. 52.86
27. 22.51
28. 5.479
29. 5.272
30. 0.2116

Exercise 12 *page 278*

1. 14.52
2. 1.666
3. 1.858
4. 0.8264
5. 2.717
6. 4.840
7. 10.87
8. 7.425
9. 13.49
10. 0.7392
11. 1135
12. 13.33
13. 5.836
14. 86.39
15. 10.23
16. 5540
17. 14.76
18. 8.502
19. 57.19
20. 19.90
21. 6.578
22. 9.097
23. 0.082 80
24. 1855
25. 2.367
26. 1.416
27. 7.261
28. 3.151
29. 149.9
30. 74 020
31. 8.482
32. 75.21
33. 1.226
34. 6767
35. 5.964
36. 15.45
37. 25.42
38. 2.724
39. 4.366
40. 0.2194
41. 0.000 465 9
42. 0.3934
43. −0.7526
44. 2.454
45. 40 000
46. 3.003
47. 0.006 562
48. 0.1330

Exercise 13 *page 279*

1. −21
2. 10
3. −2
4. −40
5. 4
6. −4
7. 20
8. −19
9. −5
10. 21
11. −5
12. −31
13. 8.5
14. −3.4
15. 15
16. 1.2
17. 32
18. −68
19. 6
20. −2
21. −2
22. −9.7
23. −1.4
24. 8.3
25. 2.8
26. 4.3
27. −1.8
28. 15.7
29. 8.3
30. −34.4

Exercise 14 *page 280*

1. a) 1850, 1850, 92.5 b) 4592, 4592, 14 c) 50.4, 50.4, 63 d) 31.6, 31.6, 221.2
   e) 42.3, 42.3, 384.93 f) 39.51, 39.51, 13.71 g) 21.2, 21.2, 95.4 h) 42.4, 42.4
   i) 6.2449..., 6.2449... j) 29.63, 29.63
2. A–T, B–P, C–S, D–R, E–Q
3. a) 281 b) 36 c) 101.16
4. $1000
5. 6 times
6. a) 5 b) 100
   c) $3000 d) 1 e) 0.2 f) 2
   g) 100 h) $2000 i) 400

Exercise 15 *page 281*

1. SOIL **2.** ISLES **3.** HE LIES **4.** SOS
5. HO HO HO **6.** ESSO OIL **7.** SOLID **8.** SOLO
9. BOILED EGGS **10.** HE IS BOSS **11.** LODGE **12.** SIGH
13. HEDGEHOG **14.** GOSH **15.** GOBBLE **16.** BEG
17. BIG SLOB **18.** SID **19.** HILL **20.** LESLIE
21. HOBBIES **22.** GIGGLE **23.** BIGGLES **24.** BOBBLE
25. HEIDI **26.** BOBBIE **27.** HIGH **28.** HELLS BELLS
29. GOD BLESS **30.** SHE DIES **31.** SOLEIL

Exercise 16 *page 282*

1. 42 kg **2.** $120
3. a) 7.2 **b)** 11.28 **c)** 0.1 **d)** 0.026 **e)** 28.2 **f)** 0.01
4. a) 3.32 **b)** 1.61 **c)** 1.46 **d)** 4.4 **e)** 6.2 **f)** 2.74
5. a) 8 hectares **b)** 24 tonnes
6. $345 **7. a)** $6400 **b)** $83 200
8. $13.50 **9. a)** 600 **b)** $204

Exercise 17 *page 284*

1. a) 15 **b) i)** 20% **ii)** 16% **iii)** 70% **iv)** 2%
2. a) 177 147 **b)** 1 594 323
3. a) 36 **b)** 24 **c)** 240 **d)** 240
4. $7\frac{1}{2}$ cm² **5. a)** 15051 **b)** 110 km **6.** Total charges = $59.11
7. $7400 **8.** 4.3

Exercise 18 *page 285*

1. a) 410 **b)** 704.5 **2. a)** 64 **b)** 1 **c)** 100 **d)** 3000 **e)** 32 **f)** 81
3. 20 cm² **4.** 000, 001, 010, 011, 100, 101, 110, 111
5. a) $162 **b)** 200 **c)** $360 **6.** 5 h 34 min
7. a) $6^2 = 5^2 + 11$, $7^2 = 6^2 + 13$ **b)** $11^2 = 60 + 5^2 + 6^2$, $13^2 = 84 + 6^2 + 7^2$
8. 120 000 000 m³ **9.** 50 m **10.** 2520

Exercise 19 *page 287*

1. a) 80 g **b)** 5.2 **c)** 416 **2.** x, 5, t
3. a) 12 **b) i)** 8 **ii)** 48 **5.** 200 litres
6. 0.006 25 cm **7. a)** 5.4 km **b)** 0.6 cm
8. a) 3 cm² **b)** 27 cm² **c)** $A = \frac{C^2}{12}$ **9.** 16

Revision exercise 7A *page 288*

1. a) $1.98 **b)** 760 **2. a)** 2.088 **b)** 3.043
3. a) 0.340 **b)** 4.08×10^{-6} **c)** 64.9 **d)** 0.119
4. a) 600 **b)** 9000 or 10 000 **c)** 3 **d)** 60
5. 2.1×10^{24} tonnes
6. a) 0.5601 **b)** 3.215 **c)** 0.6161 **d)** 0.4743
7. a) $\frac{3}{5}$, 0.6, 60% **b)** $\frac{3}{4}$, 0.75, 75% **c)** $\frac{1}{20}$, 0.05, 5% **d)** $\frac{1}{8}$, 0.125, $12\frac{1}{2}$%
8. a) €192 **b)** 3.00 **9.** about 3 g
10. a) 18.72 **b)** 89.18 **c)** 63.99 **d)** 144.78 **e)** 31.16
f) 48.248 **g)** 9.24 **h)** 1.92 **i)** 4.08
11. a) $33\,333 \times 5 = 166\,665$
$333\,333 \times 5 = 1\,666\,665$
b) $333\,333\,333 \times 5 = 1\,666\,666\,665$
12. a) $654\,321 \times 9 = 5\,888\,889$ **b)** $87\,654\,321 \times 9 = 788\,888\,889$

Examination-style exercise 7B page 290

1. a) \$16 **b)** 20% **2.** 35 : 8

3. 0.58, $\frac{3}{5}$, 62% **4. a)** $\frac{7}{100}$ **b)** 72% **c)** 0.072, 7.2%

5. 0.09, 9%, $\frac{9}{100}$ **6.** 7 cm **7.** $8750 \leqslant d < 8850$

8. a) 225 to 226.891 **b)** 1.20 **9.** Joseph \$17.50, Maria \$9, Rebecca \$3.50

10. $2 \times (3 - 4) + 5 = 3$ **11. a)** 0.075 976 763(...) **b)** 0.0 76

12. a) ii) Aida \$7500, Bernado \$6000, Christiano \$4500 **b) i)** \$10 500 **ii)** $\frac{13}{60}$ **iii)** \$13 000 **c)** 24%

Probability

Exercise 3 page 294

1. a) $\frac{3}{8}$ **b)** $\frac{5}{8}$ **2. a)** $\frac{1}{9}$ **b)** $\frac{1}{3}$ **c)** $\frac{4}{9}$ **d)** $\frac{2}{9}$

3. a) $\frac{5}{11}$ **b)** $\frac{2}{11}$ **c)** $\frac{4}{11}$ **4. a)** $\frac{4}{17}$ **b)** $\frac{3}{17}$

5. a) $\frac{4}{17}$ **b)** $\frac{8}{17}$ **c)** $\frac{5}{17}$ **6. a)** $\frac{1}{10}$ **b)** $\frac{3}{10}$ **c)** $\frac{3}{10}$

7. a) $\frac{3}{13}$ **b)** $\frac{5}{13}$ **c)** $\frac{8}{13}$ **8. a) i)** $\frac{5}{13}$ **ii)** $\frac{6}{13}$ **b) i)** $\frac{5}{12}$ **ii)** $\frac{1}{12}$

9. $\frac{9}{20}$ **10.** $\frac{1}{7}$ **11. a) i)** $\frac{1}{4}$ **ii)** $\frac{1}{4}$ **iii)** $\frac{1}{4}$ **b)** $\frac{1}{4}$ **c)** $\frac{6}{27} = \frac{2}{9}$

Exercise 4 page 296

1. 50 **2.** 25 **3.** 50

4. 40 **5. a)** $\frac{3}{8}$ **b)** 25 **6.** $\frac{1}{2}$

Exercise 5 page 298

1. $\frac{4}{5}$ **2. a)** $\frac{7}{20}$ **b)** $\frac{13}{20}$ **3.** 0.76

4. 0494 **5. a)** $\frac{1}{4}$ **b)** $\frac{3}{4}$ **c)** $\frac{1}{4}$ **d)** $\frac{3}{4}$ **e)** 0 **f)** 1

6. a) 0.3 **b)** 0.9 **7. a) i)** 0.24 **ii)** 0.89 **b)** 575

Exercise 6 page 300

2. Mike. With large number of spins he should get zero with a probability of about $\frac{1}{10}$.

Exercise 7 page 301

1. a) 8 **b)** 3 **c)** 4 **d)** 18 **e)** 7

2. a) 9 **b)** 5 **c)** 4 **d)** 20 **e)** 31

3.

ℰ
C
W
6
12
8
4

4.

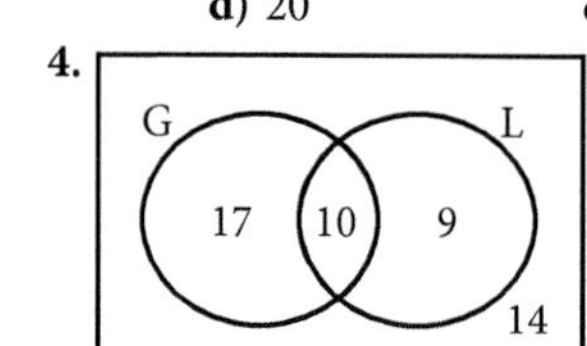

Exercise 8 page 303

1. a) $\frac{16}{25}$ **b)** $\frac{7}{25}$ **c)** $\frac{3}{25}$ **d)** $\frac{6}{25}$

2. a) i) $\frac{14}{30}$ **ii)** $\frac{7}{30}$ **iii)** $\frac{8}{30}$

b) Children who like carrots but do not eat them

3. a)

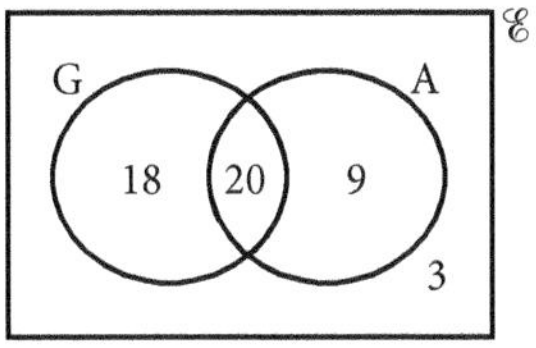

b) i) $\frac{9}{50}$ **ii)** $\frac{38}{50}$ **iii)** $\frac{29}{50}$

4. a)

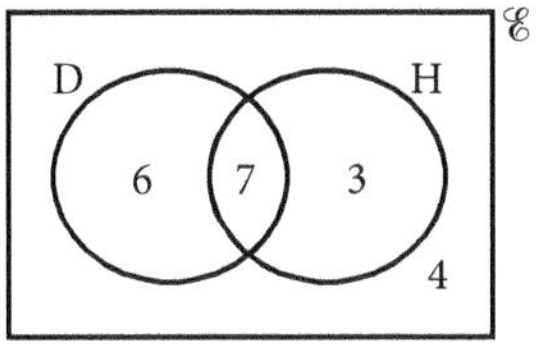

b) i) $\frac{7}{20}$ **ii)** $\frac{3}{20}$ **iii)** $\frac{7}{20}$

5. a)

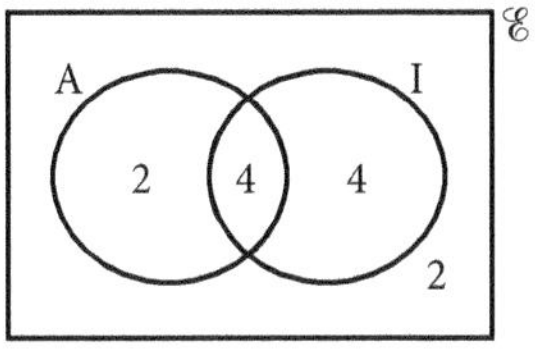

b) i) $\frac{4}{12}$ **ii)** $\frac{8}{12}$ **iii)** $\frac{4}{12}$

Exercise 9 *page 305*

1. a) $\frac{1}{4}$ **b)** $\frac{1}{2}$

2. a) $\frac{1}{12}$ **b)** $\frac{1}{36}$ **c)** $\frac{5}{18}$ **d)** $\frac{1}{6}$ **e)** $\frac{1}{6}$

The most likely total is 7.

3. a) $\frac{5}{25}$ **b)** $\frac{5}{25}$ **c)** $\frac{15}{25}$ **d)** $\frac{8}{25}$

Exercise 10 *page 307*

1. a) $\frac{49}{100}$ **b)** $\frac{9}{100}$ **2. a)** $\frac{9}{64}$ **b)** $\frac{15}{64}$ **3. a)** $\frac{7}{15}$ **b)** $\frac{1}{15}$

4. a) $\frac{1}{216}$ **b)** $\frac{125}{216}$ **c)** $\frac{25}{72}$ **d)** $\frac{91}{216}$

5. a) $\frac{1}{6}$ **b)** $\frac{1}{30}$ **c)** $\frac{1}{30}$ **d)** $\frac{29}{30}$ **6. a)** $\frac{27}{64}$ **b)** $\frac{1}{64}$

Revision exercise 8A *page 308*

1. a) $\frac{3}{8}$ **b)** $\frac{5}{8}$ **2. a)** $\frac{2}{11}$ **b)** $\frac{5}{11}$ **c)** $\frac{9}{11}$ **3.** $\frac{1}{6}$

4. $\frac{5}{16}$ **5. a)** $\frac{1}{9}$ **b)** $\frac{1}{12}$ **c)** 0 **6.** 50

7. a) $\frac{1}{2}$ **b)** Spinner has 6 sectors shaded **c)** Spinner has six 1s, four 2s, and two 3s

8. a) $\frac{1}{9}$ **b)** $\frac{6}{9}$ **9. a)** $\frac{1}{8}$ **b)** $\frac{4}{8}$ **c)** 1

10. a) $\frac{1}{64}$ **b)** $\frac{27}{64}$ **c)** $\frac{9}{64}$ **d)** $\frac{27}{64}$ The sum is 1.

Examination-style exercise 8B *page 309*

1. $\frac{9}{30} = \frac{3}{10}$ **2. a) i)** $\frac{4}{10}$ **ii)** 0 **b)** $\frac{7}{12}$ **3. a)** 15% **b) i)** $\frac{4}{15}$ **ii)** $\frac{2}{3}$ **iii)** 0

4. a) $\frac{3}{7}$ **b)** $\frac{5}{18}$ **5. a) i)** $\frac{31}{36}$ **ii)** 0 **iii)** 1 **b)** $\frac{77}{99}$ **c)** Piero

6. a) i) $\frac{10}{12}$ **ii)** $\frac{4}{12}$ **iii)** 1 **b)** 10.5 **c) iii)** negative

7. a)

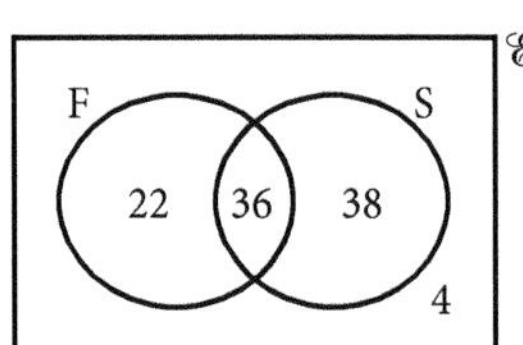

b) i) $\frac{36}{100}$ **ii)** $\frac{38}{100}$ **iii)** $\frac{26}{100}$

Shape and Space 3

Exercise 1 *page 313*

1. C only **2.** $n = 12$ **3.** $x = 9$ **4.** $a = 2\frac{1}{2}, e = 3$ **5.** $x = 6.75$
6. $x = 3.2$ **7.** $t = 5.25, y = 5.6$ **8.** 7.7 cm **9.** No
10. a) Yes **b)** No **c)** No **d)** Yes **e)** Yes **f)** No **g)** No **h)** Yes
11. b) 11.2 **c)** 4.2 **12.** $y = 6$ **13.** $a = 6$ **14.** $f = 4.5$
15. 16 m **16.** 3.75 cm **17.** 10.8 m **18.** AO = 2 cm, DO = 6 cm

Exercise 2 *page 315*

1. A and J, B and I, C and G, D and K, E and F, H and L **2.** A and G, B and J, C and F, D and E, H and I

Exercise 3 *page 317*

1. 3.0 cm **2.** 5.4 cm **3.** 3.1 cm **4.** 7.0 cm **5.** 73.1 cm
6. 15.4 cm **7.** 5.3 cm **8.** 8.0 cm **9.** 11.6 cm **10.** 11.4 cm
11. 961.3 cm **12.** 0.9 cm **13.** 46.0 cm **14.** 34.9 cm **15.** 9.4 cm
16. 8.2 cm **17.** 35.6 cm **18.** 80.2 cm **19.** 4.9 cm **20.** 7.0 cm

Exercise 4 *page 318*

1. 18.4 **2.** 9.1 **3.** 10.7 **4.** 17.1 **5.** 13.7 **6.** 125.8
7. 6.9 **8.** 11.8 **9.** 17.6 **10.** 11.4 **11.** 5, 5.6 **12.** 13.1, 27.8
13. 4.3 **14.** 3.5 **15.** 26.2 **16.** 8.8

Exercise 5 *page 319*

1. 38.7° **2.** 48.6° **3.** 31.0° **4.** 54.5° **5.** 38.7°
6. 17.5° **7.** 38.9° **8.** 59.0° **9.** 41.3° **10.** 62.7°
11. 54.3° **12.** 66.0° **13.** 48.2° **14.** 12.4° **15.** 72.9°
16. 56.9° **17.** 36.9° **18.** 41.8° **19.** 78.0° **20.** 89.4°

Exercise 6 *page 320*

1. 68.0° **2.** 3.65 m **3.** 14.0 m **4.** 20.6° **5.** 56.7 m
6. 15.3 m **7.** 90.3 cm **8.** 4.32 cm **9.** 7.66 cm **10.** 65.5 km
11. 189 km **12.** 25.7 km **13.** 36.4° **14.** 10.3 cm **15.** $a = 72°$, 8.23 cm
16. 71.1°

Revision exercise 9A *page 322*

1. 0.335 m **2. a)** 45.6° **b)** 58.0° **c)** 3.89 cm **d)** 33.8 m **3.** 4.8
4. a) 1.2 **b)** 1.6 **5.** No **6.** 7.6 **7. b)** 4
8. a) A, C, G and I, B and D, F and J, H and K **b)** E

Examination-style exercise 9B *page 323*

1. a) similar **b)** 6 cm **c)** 320°
2. a) similar **b)** 145° **3.** 3.31 m **4.** 430 m
5. a) i) 56.3° **ii)** 123.7° **b)** 7.21 m **c)** 17.2 m, 12 m^2
6. 75.2 km **7. a)** 90 cm^2 **b)** 14.3 cm **c)** 18.5 to 18.6 cm^2 **d)** 20.6 cm
8. a) ii) 125° **b) ii)** 6.13 km **iii)** 37.1 km **c)** 8.24 to 8.25 km/h
9. a) ii) 2.82 m **iii)** 5.63 to 5.64 m **iv)** 5.3 m
b) i) 29.8 to 29.9 m^2 **ii)** 12.5m^2 **iii)** 42.3 to 42.4 m^2
c) i) 21 100 to 21 200 m^3 **ii)** 30

Number 3

Exercise 1 *page 328*

1. 3^4 **2.** 5^2 **3.** 6^3 **4.** 10^5 **5.** 1^7
6. 8^4 **7.** 7^6 **8.** $2^3 \times 5^2$ **9.** $3^2 \times 7^4$ **10.** $3^2 \times 10^3$
11. $5^4 \times 11^2$ **12.** $2^2 \times 3^3$ **13.** $3^2 \times 5^3$ **14.** $2^2 \times 3^3 \times 11^2$
15. a) 16 **b)** 36 **c)** 100 **d)** 27 **e)** 1000
16. a) 81 **b)** 4.41 **c)** 1.44 **d)** 0.04 **e)** 9.61
f) 10 000 **g)** 625 **h)** 75.69 **i)** 0.81 **j)** 6625.96
17. a) 4.41 cm^2 **b)** 0.36 cm^2 **c)** 196 m^2
18. a) a^3 **b)** n^4 **c)** s^5 **d)** $p^2 \times q^3$ **e)** b^7
19. a) 216 **b)** 256 **c)** 243 **d)** 100 000 **e)** 64
f) 0.001 **g)** 8.3521 **h)** 567 **i)** 1250
20. 10^{10} **21.** 2^7
22. a) $2^1, 2^2, 2^3, 2^4$ **b)** 2^{25} cents = $335 544.32 **23.** Yes

Exercise 2 *page 330*

1. a) 4 **b)** 6 **c)** 1 **d)** 10
2. a) 9 cm **b)** 7 cm **c)** 12 cm
3. a) 3.2 **b)** 5.4 **c)** 10.3 **d)** 4.4
e) 49.1 **f)** 7.7 **g)** 0.4 **h)** 0.9
4. 12.2 cm **5.** 447 m **6.** 7.8 cm
7. a) 4 **b)** 5 **c)** 10 **8.** 5.8 cm

Exercise 3 *page 331*

1. $\frac{1}{3}$ **2.** $\frac{1}{4}$ **3.** $\frac{1}{10}$ **4.** 1 **5.** $\frac{1}{9}$ **6.** $\frac{1}{16}$ **7.** $\frac{1}{100}$
8. 1 **9.** $\frac{1}{49}$ **10.** 1 **11.** $\frac{1}{81}$ **12.** 1 **13.** T **14.** F
15. T **16.** T **17.** F **18.** F **19.** F **20.** T **21.** T
22. T **23.** F **24.** F **25.** F **26.** T **27.** T **28.** T
29. T **30.** T **31.** T **32.** F

Exercise 4 *page 332*

1. 5^6 **2.** 6^5 **3.** 10^9 **4.** 7^8 **5.** 3^{10} **6.** 8^6
7. 2^{13} **8.** 3^4 **9.** 5^3 **10.** 7^4 **11.** 5^2 **12.** 3^{-4}
13. 6^5 **14.** 5^{-10} **15.** 7^6 **16.** 7^2 **17.** 6^5 **18.** 8^1
19. 5^8 **20.** 10^2 **21.** 9^{-2} **22.** 3^{-2} **23.** 2^4 **24.** 3^{-2}
25. 7^{-6} **26.** 3^{-4} **27.** 5^{-5} **28.** 8^{-5} **29.** 5^{-5} **30.** 6^4
31. 3^0 **32.** 5^0 **33.** 3^7 **34.** 2^7 **35.** 7^2 **36.** 5^{-1}

Exercise 5 page 333

1. 3^6 **2.** 5^{12} **3.** 7^{10} **4.** 8^{20} **5.** x^6 **6.** a^{15}
7. n^{14} **8.** y^9 **9.** 2^{-2} **10.** 3^{-4} **11.** 7^2 **12.** x^{-3}
13. $6a^5$ **14.** $20n^4$ **15.** $14x^5$ **16.** $24y^7$ **17.** $5n^7$ **18.** $12y^2$
19. $9p^5$ **20.** $10p^6$ **21.** $8x^6$ **22.** $27a^6$ **23.** $16y^6$ **24.** $25x^8$
25. 3 **26.** 1 **27.** 3 **28.** 0 **29.** 3 **30.** 1
31. 2 **32.** 3 **33.** −1 **34.** −1 **35.** 0 **36.** 2
37. 4 **38.** 0 **39.** −1 **40.** 0

Exercise 6 page 333

1. 4×10^3 **2.** 5×10^2 **3.** 7×10^4 **4.** 6×10 **5.** 2.4×10^3
6. 3.8×10^2 **7.** 4.6×10^4 **8.** 4.6×10 **9.** 9×10^5 **10.** 2.56×10^3
11. 7×10^{-3} **12.** 4×10^{-4} **13.** 3.5×10^{-3} **14.** 4.21×10^{-1} **15.** 5.5×10^{-5}
16. 1×10^{-2} **17.** 5.64×10^5 **18.** 1.9×10^7 **19.** 1.4×10^9 **20.** 1.67×10^{-24}
21. 5.1×10^8 **22.** 2.5×10^{-10} **23.** 6.023×10^{23} **24.** 3×10^{10} **25.** $\$3.6 \times 10^6$

Exercise 7 page 335

1. 1.5×10^7 **2.** 3×10^8 **3.** 2.8×10^{-2} **4.** 7×10^{-9}
5. 2×10^6 **6.** 4×10^{-6} **7.** 9×10^{-2} **8.** 6.6×10^{-8}
9. 3.5×10^{-7} **10.** 10^{-16} **11.** 8×10^9 **12.** 7.4×10^{-7}
13. 4.9×10^{11} **14.** 4.4×10^{12} **15.** 1.5×10^3 **16.** 2×10^{17}
17. 1.68×10^{13} **18.** 4.25×10^{11} **19.** 9.9×10^7 **20.** 6.25×10^{-16}
21. 2.88×10^{12} **22.** 6.82×10^{-7} **23.** c, a, b **24.** 13
25. 16 **26. a)** 6×10^2 **b)** 6.67×10^7 **27.** 50 min
28. 6×10^2 **29. a)** 9.46×10^{12} km **b)** 144 million km **30.** 25 000

Exercise 8 page 336

1. $\frac{5}{6}$ **2.** $\frac{1}{6}$ **3.** $\frac{2}{3}$ **4.** $\frac{5}{12}$ **5.** $\frac{1}{4}$ **6.** $2\frac{1}{4}$ **7.** $\frac{9}{10}$ **8.** $\frac{1}{5}$
9. $\frac{4}{5}$ **10.** $\frac{13}{14}$ **11.** $\frac{3}{14}$ **12.** $\frac{6}{7}$ **13.** $\frac{3}{8}$ **14.** $\frac{5}{32}$ **15.** $2\frac{1}{2}$ **16.** $\frac{29}{30}$
17. $\frac{2}{15}$ **18.** $\frac{5}{24}$ **19.** $\frac{16}{21}$ **20.** $\frac{1}{7}$ **21.** $1\frac{2}{7}$ **22.** $\frac{11}{20}$ **23.** $\frac{1}{5}$ **24.** $3\frac{1}{5}$
25. $\frac{13}{24}$ **26.** $\frac{1}{12}$ **27.** $5\frac{1}{3}$ **28.** $\frac{29}{36}$ **29.** $\frac{5}{36}$ **30.** $2\frac{2}{9}$ **31.** $2\frac{1}{4}$ **32.** $\frac{5}{8}$
33. 10 **34.** $3\frac{1}{12}$ **35.** $2\frac{1}{12}$ **36.** $5\frac{5}{8}$ **37.** $2\frac{1}{3}$ **38.** $\frac{5}{13}$ **39.** 18 **40.** 6
41. 3 **42.** $2\frac{2}{3}$ **43.** 3 **44.** $4\frac{1}{4}$ **45.** $1\frac{5}{27}$ **46.** 6 **47.** $1\frac{5}{28}$ **48.** $2\frac{2}{3}$
49. $\frac{11}{24}$ **50.** $4\frac{5}{6}$

Exercise 9 page 337

1. a) $\frac{1}{2}, \frac{7}{12}, \frac{2}{3}$ **b)** $\frac{2}{3}, \frac{3}{4}, \frac{5}{6}$ **c)** $\frac{1}{3}, \frac{5}{8}, \frac{17}{24}, \frac{3}{4}$ **d)** $\frac{5}{6}, \frac{8}{9}, \frac{11}{12}$
2. a) $\frac{1}{2}$ **b)** $\frac{3}{4}$ **c)** $\frac{17}{24}$ **d)** $\frac{7}{18}$ **e)** $\frac{3}{10}$ **f)** $\frac{5}{12}$
3. \$48 **4. a)** $\frac{9}{4}$ **b)** $2\frac{1}{7}$ **c)** $\frac{31}{10}$ **5.** $\frac{1}{4}$
6. a) 240 cm **b)** 123 cm **7.** $\frac{1}{5}$ **8. a)** 30.5 **b)** \$305
9. a) 9 **b)** $\frac{5}{16}$ **10.** $\frac{16}{24}$ **11.** 5 **12.** \$39 **13.** $\frac{5}{24}$

Exercise 10 page 339

1. 5°	**2.** −1°	**3.** −4°	**4.** −7°	**5.** −4°
6. −4°	**7.** 4°	**8.** 12°	**9.** −5°	**10.** 0°
11. −11°	**12.** −15°	**13.** fallen 3°	**14.** fallen 6°	**15.** fallen 10°
16. fallen 5°	**17.** risen 7°	**18.** risen 11°	**19.** risen 15°	**20.** risen 5°
21. fallen 80°	**22.** fallen 15°	**23. a)** 0, −3	**b)** −5	**c)** −20, −15
24. −17 m	**25. a)** C	**b)** B	**26.** $60	

Exercise 11 page 341

1. −4	**2.** −12	**3.** −11	**4.** −3	**5.** −5	**6.** 4	**7.** −5	**8.** −8
9. 19	**10.** −17	**11.** −4	**12.** −5	**13.** −11	**14.** 6	**15.** −4	**16.** 6
17. 0	**18.** −18	**19.** −3	**20.** −11	**21.** −8	**22.** −7	**23.** 1	**24.** 1
25. 9	**26.** 11	**27.** −8	**28.** 42	**29.** 4	**30.** 15	**31.** −7	**32.** −9
33. −1	**34.** −7	**35.** 0	**36.** 11	**37.** −14	**38.** 0	**39.** 17	**40.** 3

Exercise 12 page 342

1. −6	**2.** −4	**3.** −15	**4.** 9	**5.** −8	**6.** −15	**7.** −24	**8.** 6
9. 12	**10.** −18	**11.** −21	**12.** 25	**13.** −60	**14.** 21	**15.** 48	**16.** −16
17. −42	**18.** 20	**19.** −42	**20.** −66	**21.** −4	**22.** −3	**23.** 3	**24.** −5
25. 4	**26.** −4	**27.** −4	**28.** −1	**29.** −2	**30.** 4	**31.** −16	**32.** −2
33. −4	**34.** 5	**35.** −10	**36.** 11	**37.** 16	**38.** −2	**39.** −4	**40.** −5
41. 64	**42.** −27	**43.** −600	**44.** 40	**45.** 2	**46.** 36	**47.** −2	**48.** −8
49. 160	**50.** −2						

Test 1 page 342

1. −16	**2.** 64	**3.** −15	**4.** −2	**5.** 15	**6.** 18	**7.** 3	**8.** −6
9. 11	**10.** −48	**11.** −7	**12.** 9	**13.** 6	**14.** −18	**15.** −10	**16.** 8
17. −6	**18.** −30	**19.** 4	**20.** −1				

Test 2 page 343

1. −16	**2.** 6	**3.** −13	**4.** 42	**5.** −4	**6.** −4	**7.** −12	**8.** −20
9. 6	**10.** 0	**11.** 36	**12.** −10	**13.** −7	**14.** 10	**15.** 6	**16.** −18
17. −9	**18.** 15	**19.** 1	**20.** 0				

Test 3 page 343

1. 100	**2.** −20	**3.** −8	**4.** −7	**5.** −4	**6.** 10	**7.** 9	**8.** −10
9. 7	**10.** 35	**11.** −20	**12.** −24	**13.** −10	**14.** −7	**15.** −19	**16.** −1
17. −5	**18.** −13	**19.** 0	**20.** 8				

Exercise 13 page 344

1. 36	**2.** 29	**3.** 8	**4.** 18	**5.** 84
6. 9×10^{12}	**7.** 165	**8.** $\sqrt{181}$	**9.** 1.62	**10.** 650

Exercise 14 page 345

1. −5	**2.** 8	**3.** −17	**4.** 8	**5.** −2	**6.** −27	**7.** 1	**8.** −22
9. −22	**10.** −22	**11.** −10	**12.** −2	**13.** 23	**14.** −44	**15.** 26	**16.** 25
17. −4	**18.** 0	**19.** −16	**20.** 22	**21.** −5	**22.** 30	**23.** 13	**24.** 25
25. 40	**26.** 3	**27.** −5	**28.** −12	**29.** −34	**30.** 2	**31.** 12	**32.** 39
33. 40	**34.** 7	**35.** 3	**36.** 10	**37.** 51	**38.** −2	**39.** 1	**40.** 11

Exercise 15 page 345

1. 4	**2.** 4	**3.** 9	**4.** 16	**5.** 8	**6.** −8	**7.** −27	**8.** 64
9. 8	**10.** 16	**11.** 8	**12.** 16	**13.** 18	**14.** 36	**15.** 48	**16.** 16
17. 20	**18.** 54	**19.** 144	**20.** 24	**21.** 13	**22.** 10	**23.** 1	**24.** 18
25. 13	**26.** 19	**27.** 10	**28.** 32	**29.** 16	**30.** 144	**31.** 36	**32.** 36
33. 4	**34.** 1	**35.** 2	**36.** −14	**37.** −5	**38.** −5	**39.** −10	**40.** 10
41. 0	**42.** 4	**43.** 50	**44.** 4	**45.** −10	**46.** −4	**47.** −6	**48.** −16
49. 28	**50.** 44						

Exercise 16 page 346

1. 2 2. $\frac{1}{2}$ 3. 0 4. 18 5. 3 6. 8
7. 26 8. −24 9. 2 10. 0 11. $\frac{1}{4}$ 12. $-\frac{2}{3}$
13. 17 14. $\frac{1}{3}$ 15. −3 16. $\frac{3}{4}$ 17. $\frac{4}{3}$ 18. $-\frac{5}{36}$

Exercise 17 page 346

1. 20 2. 200 g 3. 6 4. 400 5. $5 \times 7 \times 13 \times 71$
6. 225 mm 7. 1 8. a) 66 666 b) 82
9. a) 323 g b) 23 c) 67c d) 29

Exercise 18 page 347

1. \$10 485.76 2. a) 1 b) 15 3. $a = 100, b = 1$
4. 50 5. E 7. a) $\frac{1}{66}$ b) 16
8. 1105 9. 13 10. 10

Revision exercise 10A page 348

1. iii) $\frac{a}{b}$ 2. a) 8 b) 140 c) 29 d) 42
3. a) −11 b) 23 c) −10 d) −20 e) 6 f) −14
4. a) 3 b) 5 c) −6 d) −7
5. a) 14 b) 18 c) 28 6. 2.3×10^9 7. a) $z = x - 5y$ b) $k = \frac{11 - 3m}{m}$
8. a) 4^5 b) 1^7 c) $2^3 \times 5^2$
9. a) 6^5 b) 7^8 c) 3^7 d) 10^3 e) 5^4 f) 2^{-1}
10. a) 2 b) 2 c) 4 11. a) x^8 b) n^9 c) $12a^3$
12. a) 5×10^4 b) 6.1×10^5 c) 3×10^{-4} d) 1.5×10^{-3} e) 1×10^7
13. a) 3×10^{10} b) 4×10^4 c) 8×10^6 d) 4.5×10^7
14. a) $\frac{14}{15}$ b) $\frac{1}{4}$ c) $\frac{1}{10}$ d) $2\frac{2}{3}$ e) $1\frac{1}{10}$ f) $1\frac{11}{16}$
15. $\frac{5}{24}$ 16. $5\% = \frac{1}{20}$ is true

Examination-style exercise 10B page 349

1. a) 3 b) −4 2. a) 10 b) 3 c) −2
3. a) 1 b) y^8 c) $\frac{p^2}{25}$ 4. a) 1 b) q^{11} c) r^{-6}
5. a) $<$ b) $>$ 6. a) 1.13×10^6 b) 4.42×10^{-2}
7. 3.62×10^{-3} 8. a) 0.001 93… b) 7.63×10^{-2} 9. a) 12 b) $\frac{22}{18} - \frac{15}{18} = \frac{7}{18}$ 10. 12
11. 24 12. −27 °C 13. a) $x > y$ b) $x^2 < y^2$ c) $y - x < x - y$

Multiple choice tests

Test 1 page 371

1. C 2. D 3. D 4. B 5. C
6. C 7. A 8. D 9. B 10. B
11. C 12. A 13. D 14. C 15. C
16. D 17. A 18. C 19. B 20. D
21. A 22. B 23. C 24. B 25. C

Test 2 page 373

1. B 2. C 3. B 4. A 5. D
6. C 7. A 8. D 9. B 10. C
11. B 12. D 13. A 14. C 15. C
16. D 17. B 18. A 19. B 20. B
21. C 22. D 23. A 24. A 25. B

Test 3 page 375

1. D	**2.** D	**3.** D	**4.** B	**5.** A
6. C	**7.** A	**8.** D	**9.** D	**10.** B
11. C	**12.** D	**13.** D	**14.** B	**15.** A
16. B	**17.** C	**18.** A	**19.** D	**20.** D
21. C	**22.** C	**23.** B	**24.** B	**25.** D

Test 4 page 377

1. B	**2.** B	**3.** A	**4.** C	**5.** C
6. B	**7.** D	**8.** A	**9.** B	**10.** B
11. D	**12.** B	**13.** B	**14.** C	**15.** D
16. A	**17.** C	**18.** B	**19.** B	**20.** D
21. B	**22.** C	**23.** C	**24.** C	**25.** A

Examination-style Paper 1 *page 379*

1. 1024 **2.** 51 **3.** 5 **4.** 26 **5.** 25.231 325 22…

6. Any number in $10.58 \leqslant x \leqslant 10.63$ **7.** 19.7 cm^3 **8. a)** $\frac{2}{15}$ **b)** $\frac{10}{27}$

9. $2 \times 3^2 \times 5$ **10. a)** $3x + 7$ **b)** $5p(q+2)$ **11.** 50, 60 and 90 tonnes

12. b) i) 120° **ii)** 225° **13. a)** $6 \times (5+3) = 48$ **b)** $(28 - 12) \div 4 = 4$ **c)** $(9-3)^2 = 36$

14. $12x - 4$

15. a) 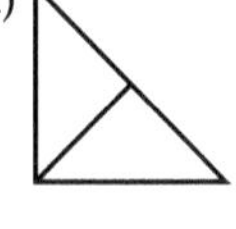 **b)**

16. a) \$3.49 **b)** \$1.31 **c)** \$1.82

17. a) $62\frac{1}{2}\%$ **b)** $\frac{1}{8}$

18. a) $\frac{3}{4}$ **b)** 14 **19. a)** Rhombus **b)** 2 **c)** 110°, 70°, 70°

20. a) 38 **b)** $12\frac{1}{2}$ °C **c)** $t = \frac{1}{4}(n+50)$ **21. b)** 03:00 **c)** 22:00 on Tuesday

22. 23 000 **23. a)** $A' \cap B$ **b)** $A' \cup B$

Examination-style Paper 3 *page 381*

1. a) i) 45° **ii)** 5 cm **iii)** 7.07 cm **b) i)** 30° **ii)** 6.93 cm **iii)** 8 cm **c)** Triangle DEF by 1.36 cm^2

2. a) 88, 888, 8888, 88 888

b) $98\,765 \times 9 + 3 = 888\,888$, $987\,654 \times 9 + 2 = 8\,888\,888$, $9\,876\,543 \times 9 + 1 = 88\,888\,8888$

c) 8 888 888 889

3. a) i) 11 °C (or −11 °C) **ii)** 34 °C (or −34 °C) **b)** $\frac{5}{12}$

c) i) −12 °C **ii)** −2 °C **iii)** −2.5 °C

4. a) i) 6.80 metres **ii)** \$57 **b) i)** 36.9° **ii)** 3.30 metres

5. a) −1, (−1.2), −1.5, −2, −3, (−4), (−6), (6), 4, 3, 2, 1.5, 1.2, 1

c) ii) order 2 **d) i)** −4, −1, 2, 5 **e)** (1.6, 3.8), (−1.25, −4.8)

6. a) X 12, 9, $13\frac{1}{2}$; Y 14, $10\frac{1}{2}$, $15\frac{3}{4}$; Z 16, 12, 18 **b)** 383 cm^3

7. a) i) Octagon **b) ii)** 11.1 cm **iv)** 11° **8.** Angles 180°, 60°, 40°, 80°

9. a) 157 cm **b)** 91 cm **c) i)** 9.42 m^3 **ii)** 7.07 tonnes

10. a)

Stem	Leaf
1	2 5 9
2	1 3 5 8
3	4 4 6 9
4	3

b) i) 26.5 years **ii)** 34 years **iii)** 15 years

11. a) 1.44 m^3 **b)** 2 hours 24 minutes **12.** Volume = 267 m^3, surface area = 289 m^2

Index